FUNDAMENTAL MARRIAGE COUNSELING

SPECIAL CHAPTERS BY:

Alphonse H. Clemens, Ph.D.
ASSOCIATE PROFESSOR OF SOCIOLOGY AND DIRECTOR OF MARRIAGE COUNSELING CENTER, CATHOLIC UNIVERSITY OF AMERICA.

Very Reverend Francis J. Connell, C.SS.R., S.T.D., LL.D.
PROFESSOR OF MORAL THEOLOGY AND DEAN OF THE SCHOOL OF SACRED THEOLOGY, CATHOLIC UNIVERSITY OF AMERICA.

Joseph A. Hardy, A.B., M.D.
ASSOCIATE PROFESSOR AND DIRECTOR OF DEPARTMENT OF GYNECOLOGY AND OBSTETRICS, ST. LOUIS UNIVERSITY.

Oscar B. Hunter, Jr., M.D., F.A.C.P.
INSTRUCTOR IN HEMATOLOGY, GEORGETOWN UNIVERSITY SCHOOL OF MEDICINE; ADJUNCT PROFESSOR OF CLINICAL PATHOLOGY, AMERICAN UNIVERSITY, WASHINGTON, D. C.

John J. Kuhn, A.B., M.D.
DIPLOMATE OF THE AMERICAN BOARD OF OBSTETRICS AND GYNECOLOGY.

The Honorable Matthew F. McGuire, A.B., LL.B. (LL.D. Hon.)
JUDGE, UNITED STATES DISTRICT COURT FOR THE DISTRICT OF COLUMBIA.

Reverend William E. McVeagh, M.S.SS.T., S.T.L.
PROFESSOR OF DOGMATIC THEOLOGY, HOLY TRINITY MISSION SEMINARY, WINCHESTER, VIRGINIA.

Reverend Romaeus O'Brien, O.Carm., M.A., J.C.D.
CATHOLIC UNIVERSITY OF AMERICA.

Reverend John J. O'Sullivan, S.T.D.
CHAPLAIN, CATHOLIC UNIVERSITY OF AMERICA.

FUNDAMENTAL MARRIAGE COUNSELING

A CATHOLIC VIEWPOINT

JOHN R. CAVANAGH, M.D.

FELLOW OF THE AMERICAN COLLEGE OF PHYSICIANS; FELLOW OF THE AMERICAN PSYCHIATRIC ASSOCIATION; KNIGHT OF ST. GREGORY; DIPLOMATE OF THE AMERICAN BOARD OF NEUROLOGY AND PSYCHIATRY; SPECIAL LECTURER IN THE SCHOOL OF SACRED THEOLOGY, CATHOLIC UNIVERSITY OF AMERICA; MEMBER OF THE COMMISSION ON MENTAL HEALTH, DISTRICT OF COLUMBIA; LECTURER IN MENTAL HEALTH, TRINITY COLLEGE; FORMER LECTURER IN PSYCHIATRY, NATIONAL CATHOLIC SCHOOL OF SOCIAL SERVICE; FORMER COMMANDER, MEDICAL CORPS, UNITED STATES NAVY.

THE BRUCE PUBLISHING COMPANY
MILWAUKEE

NIHIL OBSTAT:

Eugene B. Gallagher, S.J.
Censor deputatus

IMPRIMATUR:

✝ Patrick A. O'Boyle
Archbishop of Washington

June 19, 1956

Rosary College Dewey Classification Number: 392

Library of Congress Catalog Card Number: 56-11149

© 1957 by The Bruce Publishing Company
MADE IN THE UNITED STATES OF AMERICA

TO MY WIFE AND THE THREE GRACES

Preface

This book is not one which you are likely to sit down and read from cover to cover. It contains, however, information which you will need if you counsel married people. It assembles for your use a large mass of material which would require prolonged research if you went to the original sources. It is not a book to which a physician would refer for anatomical facts or other information that is strictly medical. However, it does supply all of the medical information that specialists in other fields would need. The moral theologian would not find here a complete treatise, but all other specialists will find a complete discussion of the moral problems relating to marriage.

It should appeal to all specialties, not because it is complete within their own specialty, but because we attempt to supply them with adequate information on related subjects. It is a handbook on marriage which should be on every marriage counselor's shelf, to supply the answers to questions which arise.

Those non-Catholics who are interested in the Catholic viewpoint on marriage may find it necessary to read only the sections of each chapter which are devoted to moral considerations. The index will help them to find answers to their specific questions.

A glossary is provided to help overcome the difficulty occasioned by the necessary use of technical terms. Most words which are not defined in the text will be found here. In addition, we have included for ready reference many common words used in the field, although they are defined in the text.

Foreword

It is with special delight that I write these few words to be added to this newest contribution to Catholic thinking. This book should favorably affect the lives of innumerable families in our country. It fills a desperate need.

FUNDAMENTAL MARRIAGE COUNSELING represents a balanced, whole, integrated volume. It reflects the unusual training of its author. It is this particular phase of the book which I will stress.

Analysis we know is the scientific tool of our age, but it always runs the risk of distorting reality. Everyone knows how easy it is to take a watch apart; the real problem is to get it back together again without any of the pieces left over. A human being is much more complicated than a watch. This is especially true when we try to study him in the complex, multiple relationships of marriage and the family. No longer do we examine an isolated individual (if there be such) but a whole constellation of persons whose lives are intimately bound to one another in a pattern of constant action and interaction.

There are so many important and significant aspects of human marriage that it is easy to fall victim to the temptation to overstress one factor at the expense of the others. Even a legitimate emphasis on one factor in marriage often runs the risk of appearing to deny another which is equally important: an integral, balanced approach is absolutely necessary.

Experienced marriage counselors insist that even intelligent, educated couples know pitifully little about the theological, psychological, cultural, and psychophysical aspects of marriage. This knowledge is not infused; it is not instinctive; it is not obtained by osmosis. The tragedy is that ignorance here sometimes results in heartbreaking moral and social consequences for the couple, for their children, and for society at large.

Knowledge of no one aspect of marriage is so essential that it can *make* a union successful; but ignorance of any one of a number of areas of married life can *break* a particular marriage. For instance, although sexual naïveté may exist in a successful marriage, lack of basic information about sex can and often does place unnecessary stress upon a family; on the other hand, sex instruction is no panacea

ix

—although understanding of every facet of sexual life is of itself
no guarantee of a happy marriage. It is unfortunate that so many
people identify premarital preparation with sexual education. In fact,
some even narrow sex instruction down to the merely physiological.

Premarital instruction must prepare the whole man: social as well
as individual, emotional as well as intellectual, moral and religious
as well as physical. It must be rooted in the facts of economics as
well as built up to high ideals. I feel that this book is an adventurous
take-off in that direction.

Not only must preparation for marriage be integral. It must be
balanced. First things must come first. For instance, the practical
solution of many questions in marriage depends upon the theological
appreciation of the destiny of a human being. To ignore or to deny
the relevance of theology here is to unconsciously and implicitly take
a theological position.

Premarital instruction must be balanced not only in maintaining a
priority of values, but also in presenting as total a picture as possible
of individual points. For example, it is easy to distort the nature of
Christian marriage, if consecrated virginity is left out of the context. It
is possible to propose the use of Rhythm in such a way as to encourage
couples to enter an occasion of sin without reason. A laudable effort
to counteract Jansenistic attitudes toward the use of sex can fail to
keep an eye on the need for Christian temperance and moderation
and lead to that sensualistic hedonism which is fatal to the spiritual
life. None of these dangers are merely theoretical as Pope Pius XII
constantly warns us.

The stability of a marriage is often the result of the determination
of the partners to stick it out at all costs. There is much more chance
of this type of motivation being present and operative if husband
and wife have a thorough and balanced insight into the meaning
of marriage. This is the task Dr. Cavanagh has set out to do. This
volume is a heroic, even daring, undertaking, but the Doctor and his
collaborators realize that creating and saving a Christian pattern of
family life today demand adventurous study and thinking under the
teaching authority of the Church. This they have done with many
master strokes.

RT. REV. MSGR. IRVING A. DEBLANC
Director, Family Life Bureau,
National Catholic Welfare Conference,
Washington, D. C.

Introduction

Marriage is the only vocation for which no previous training is usually considered necessary. This attitude is incomprehensible when we see that the nature of marriage demands it remain intact as long as both parties are alive. A profound and a permanent change affects those who take up the conjugal life. Such a step ought therefore to be undertaken only after long thought; yet we find this more often the exception than the rule.

Marriage is here to stay. Let us not doubt this in spite of predictions that it is on its way out.[1]

We would agree, however, that the external aspects of marriage do not always remain the same. There have been changes in many of these external aspects during the past thirty years. These changes have not been necessarily for the worse. Actually, they have prompted a much greater interest in marital affairs on the part of those who are interested in promoting human health, welfare, and happiness. The need for instruction in marriage as a vocation is again recognized. It is one of the reasons why this book was written.

As Doctor Alphonse Clemens of The Catholic University of America remarks:

> Even were marriage counseling not needed in a saner and simpler age, the complexities of life render it imperative today. Rearing a wholesome family amid the welter, confusion and chaos of urban centers or even along the paved highway which affords easy access to urban centers, is a vastly more complicated problem than that confronting the pioneer family in its wilderness isolation. The neurotic pressures of the age — from the screeching yells of the blood-besprinkled radio murder to the conflicting principles and ideals of the home and of the social milieu; the free intermingling of various social and cultural classes, the increasing mobility of the family with correspondingly lessened social and emotional security — these and similar social pressures in our modern environment require an expert attention and assistance to the family not as urgently needed before . . . apart from pathological

---

[1] *Chicago Tribune,* March 6, 1927, p. 1. P. A. Sorokin, *Social and Cultural Dynamics* (New York: Harper and Brothers, 1937), p. 776. Carle C. Zimmerman, *The Family and Civilization* (New York: Harper and Brothers, 1947), p. 796.

phenomena in familial living, expert study and guidance is indicated by the basic Christian principle of the need for striving for perfection. . . . It should be noted that during the Ages of Faith marriage and the family were accorded a degree of scrutiny and attention not given them since. The society of the Church has had its canonists and theologians; the State has been studied and guided by political science and jurisprudence; the economists have constituted a brain trust for harassed statesmen and business leaders in economic society; the professional educator has attended the fortunes and misfortunes of educational society; even recreational life has its experts. The family alone — the admitted cornerstone of civilization and culture — has been unaccorded any specific and professional expertness, with the result that it has been studied and guided . . . segmentally instead of integrally. The theologian, the lawyer, the medical practitioner, the home economist, the psychologist — each has treated some one or other aspect of marital living largely from the viewpoint of a distinct specialty. . . . It would seem that the emergence of marriage and family experts with the total point of view, far from being a faddish phenomena, indicates the belated fulfillment of a basic need. There is need of a profession to synthesize the scattered skeins of knowledge relating to marriage and family life.[2]

In this book we do not attempt to cover all aspects of the family relationship. We seek rather to provide the marriage counselor with information he will need either for giving premarital instruction or for aiding postmarital adjustments. We hope to review other relationships in a later volume. In this introduction we shall be content with a mere sketch of influences effecting changes in the family relationship.

The **changes affecting society are complex** but may be summarized under the following titles:

1. Greater ease of human contacts;
2. Change in the status of marriage;
3. Greater population trend toward urban areas;
4. Emancipation of women;
5. Increased ease of divorce;
6. Military service.

1. Greater Ease of Human Contacts

Greater ease of contact between people of all ages is due partly to the availability of a great variety of instruments and partly to the

---

[2] Alphonse H. Clemens, *Catholics and Marriage Counseling* (Washington, D. C.: Workshop on Marriage and Family Relationships, The Catholic University of America).

number of such instruments available. The number of such instruments of communication available in the United States today is almost unbelievable.

a) **Telephones.** Seventy per cent of homes have a phone. In 1954 there were 31.3 phones for each 100 of the population, a total of 52,000,000 telephones in use.

b) **Automobiles.** In 1953 the last year for which figures are available there were 46,000,000 registered motor vehicles. In 1954 6,601,000 new cars were sold. ·

c) **Radio sets.** As of January 1, 1955, there were 127,000,000 radio sets in 50,000,000 homes. In 37,000,000 of these homes there were at least two sets.

d) **Phonographs.** On January 1, 1954, there were 29,200,000 phonographs of all types in use.

e) **Television sets.** In 1954 there were 33,000,000 television sets in use. In that year there were 415 television stations as compared with five such stations in 1946.

f) **Newspapers.** In 1954, the latest year for which complete figures are available there were 1765 newspapers with a daily circulation of 55,072,400. On Sunday there were 544 papers with a circulation of 46,176,450.

g) **Magazines.** Circulation figures are not easily available for magazines but their monthly circulation runs well over 150,000,000. Of these there is a weekly circulation of approximately 37,407,403 comic books.[3]

During the past 50 years, movement and communication have shown tremendous increase. Few people 50 to 100 years ago traveled any great distance. If a person took a trip of 40 miles he made as much preparation as his modern counterpart would make for a trip to Europe. This ease of movement has resulted from speedier and cheaper modes of travel. These modes of travel today are such that they are available even to children. These children become acquainted with friends in areas which would have been unknown to them in the past. In the United States alone 1712 million passenger miles were flown on scheduled airlines; 29,300 million passenger miles traveled on railroads; and 17,700 million passenger miles on buslines in 1954. Children and adults have found themselves embracing a far wider

---

[3] These figures were gathered from a number of reliable sources and reported in the *Information Please Almanac for 1956*, Washington Star Edition, published by The Macmillan Co., New York.

field of action and a far larger number of acquaintances. This leads, of course, to more and keener competition.

Distances have shrunk to such a degree that relatives may be separated by 50 to 3000 miles and yet keep in regular contact either by telephone or by airplane.

Radio and television have brought the world into the living room, and have wrought important changes in family life. Despite lengthy and heated debates about the possible harmfulness of television to children, it is, in fact, extensively viewed by children of all ages. Whatever it may have contributed to their delinquency, it has undoubtedly added very much to their education and sophistication. An important by-product of television is a loss of reading interest and ability on the part of children.

Newspapers are also available to children and have added to their range of knowledge. So, too, with magazines. There is even a large number of magazines which are printed for child readers. It is, of course, almost too obvious to say that parents should check on what papers and magazines their children read. But the right use of all these means of communication gives all the members of a family an increasing awareness of what is happening in the world. This increase of knowledge could not fail to bring about some change in family relations — frequently for the better.

Comic books. The effect of the comic books on family life has aroused much acrimonious debate, and much concern on the part of parents. As I have written elsewhere:

> Pity the poor parents perturbed by the profound proclamations of psychiatrists and psychologists (and many others) concerning the menace to their children from reading the "Comics"![4]

The parents may read conflicting comments such, for example, as the following comment of Agatha Shea:

> Every now and then, when tragedy enters into the life of some boy or girl, investigation leads back to the youth's reading of the comic books and their incitement to crime and the community is, for the time being, alerted to the daily menace to our children. Sometimes our cities are moved to take legal action against the publisher and purveyors of this unfit reading matter for children, but at its best such action is

---

[4] John R. Cavanagh, "The Comics War," *The Journal of Criminal Law and Criminology of Northwestern University,* Vol. 40, No. 1, May-June, 1949.

necessarily slow and not always immediately effective. In the mean-time children continue to buy and read these crime and sex ridden booklets, and the home too often pays little heed until one of its own boys or girls becomes the victim or perpetrator of a crime. I have talked with hundreds of Chicago parents on this subject and find them all gravely concerned. They point out, and rightly, that banning unsuit-able comic magazines from the home only means outside reading and borrowing with perhaps a little added excitement in the circumventing of authority. What then can be done about this ever present problem? Must parents sit with folded hands while their children's morals and ideals are broken and a perverted view of life is left on impressionable minds?[5]

Such statements are doubly disturbing to parents who may have recently read a well-thought-out article in **Child Study,** a journal which they have always considered authoritative in its field, which stated unequivocally: "There is no competent evidence that reading about crime makes criminals. The motivation towards unsocial acts lies much deeper than any casual contact with ideas printed on a page."

Again may I repeat, pity the poor parent!

There is no need to prove that the comics are popular. This fact is already known. How popular they are is little short of amazing. There is no question but that they are big business today. It is difficult at first to grasp the fact that a reliable source indicates that in 1946 the monthly circulation was 40,000,000. This is especially remarkable when we realize that the first of the modern comic books was published in 1933. It is further estimated that each comic book is read by several people and that 75 per cent of all comic books are purchased by children out of their own funds — an outlay of $300,000 a month or $3,600,000 per year.

While we are on the statistical angle of the subject I should like to present just a few more figures, derived from Waugh's book entitled **The Comics,** an excellent history of the comic book from its beginning to the present day:[6]

(1) Between the ages of 6 and 11, 95 per cent of boys and 91 per cent of girls buy comics as a steady diet.

(2) Between the ages of 12 and 17, 87 per cent of boys and 81 per cent of girls use comics regularly.

---

[5] Agatha Shea, *What Are Your Children Reading?* Book Bulletin of the Chicago Public Library; November, 1948, 163–164.

[6] Colton Waugh, *The Comics* (New York: The Macmillan Co., 1947).

(3) Between the ages of 18 and 30, 41 per cent of men and 28 per cent of women retain their interest.

(4) After the age of 30, 16 per cent of men and 12 per cent of women read them.

(5) During World War II, the combined sales of *Life, Readers Digest,* and *The Saturday Evening Post* were exceeded by the comic books by a ratio of 10–1.

In a recent book Bejerot, in speaking of the impact of comic books on the children in his own country, stated that in the course of a single year Swedish children are subjected to the following fantastic numbers of pictures of crime and violence:

War-like activities	5 billion
Murder and killing	4 billion
Attempted murder and threat of murder	13 billion
Physical violence	7 billion
Cruelty and sadism	3 billion
Other acts of personal violence . . .	17 billion
Other crimes	26 billion
Threat with weapons	7 billion
Shooting incidents	6 billion[7]

What effect the comics have had or will have on family life is not yet determined. It will eventually prove to lie someplace between the extremes which are so violently discussed today. There are certainly many comics which are objectionable but this can hardly be said of all comics.

The group of comics known collectively as "jungle adventure comics" typify this class. Within this group all of the features are displayed which have been considered objectionable. Here are found the scantily clad females, the chained females, and the sexually suggestive situations which are the comics' most objectionable feature. However, such pictures and situations seem to arouse little anxiety in the well-adjusted reader.

Although much has been said pro and con in relation to comic books, studies such as those of Dr. Frederic Wertham[8] and that of Dr. Bejerot[9] mentioned above deserve serious consideration and

---

[7] Nils Bejerot, *Barn, Serien, Samhaelle* (Children, Comics, Society) (Stockholm: F.I.B. Publishers, 1954), p. 95.

[8] Frederic Wertham, *Seduction of the Innocent* (New York: Rinehart & Co., Inc., 1954).

[9] Bejerot, *op. cit.*

until equally serious studies prove that these authors are wrong, it will be well to accept them as guides.

2. Change in the Status of Marriage

Marriage is a relationship which results in a status (see chapter on the civil law). A **status** is defined as that condition of a person by which the nature of his legal personality and his legal capacities are determined. So reads the legal definition of **status**. Sociologists define this term differently, for example, Hiller defines status thus:

> The structure or organization of a society consists of statuses, such as occupations, offices, classes, age and sex distinctions, and other circumstances-occasioned reciprocities and rules of conduct. Each status is a place or position in the scheme of social relations and consists not only of norm-prescribed privileges and obligations but also of the comparative esteem and disesteem in which these social places are held. Each status consists of both implicit . . . and explicit rights and duties, and expected personal bearing of the members concerned.[10]

Christian marriage is a sacrament which joins a man and woman in an indissoluble union. The sacramental nature of marriage has been long under attack. The absurd effects of this attack are now realized in the view of some that marriage is not a change of status but merely an arrangement for companionship.

Some of those individuals who reviewed this manuscript felt that this change in marriage as a status was not really meant by some of those who have written about it. That while they seem to say this, they really do not mean it. Perhaps this is so, but such statements as this of Landis would be hard to interpret otherwise:

> Marriage was once considered a state. The roles of husband and wife had long been defined by custom and most young people went into marriage with a clear picture of what marriage was like, how each was expected to act, and what the rights and duties of each were.
>
> The female role was that of an obedient helpmate. The wife recognized her husband's right to decide things for the family. She expected and was expected to confine her thinking to matters of home and children. No doubt there were many marriages in which the relationship between husbands and wives was different, but this was general.
>
> Today marriage is considered not as a state, but as an *adjustment*.

---

[10] E. T. Hiller, *Social Relations and Structures* (New York: Harper and Brothers, 1947), p. 330.

This change has resulted as the emphasis in marriage has shifted from economic interest to that of companionship. The particular relationships established between husband and wife today while influenced by custom, are primarily a matter of the personal needs and desires of each mate.[11]

This new concept has numerous repercussions. Since it considers marriage as merely an arrangement for companionship, it puts the wife and husband on terms of equality as heads of the family. The husband is no longer the head of the family — and this denies the traditional and biological fact that the father is the head of the home. It also leads, too frequently, to the mother assuming matriarchal jurisdiction in the home. The tendency toward matriarchy has already gone too far in this country. We have only to realize that in recent years the majority of high school teachers have been women. This places the boy under the domination of women through high school. Even into college the young man may be supervised by women; and when he gets a job his boss may again be a woman. Because of this domination of women in both family and school life, a boy has no opportunity to learn independence of female domination. He accepts control and automatically obeys his female preceptor. As pointed out elsewhere (see chapter on psychological differences) the male should be the leader in a family, not only because of his physiological and psychological make-up, but also by divine injunction. Any change in the order of nature leads only to unhappiness. Any arrangement, except that which leaves the man as head of the home, in fact as well as in name, is bound to weaken the family unity and consequently the nation.

3. Greater Population Trend Toward Urban Areas

Since the days of the American Revolution there has been a trend toward urbanization. At the end of the war in 1790 only about 5 per cent of the population of the Colonies lived in communities of 2500 or more. With improved sanitation, mechanization, and industrial development, most of the population now live in urban areas. In 1950 about 64 per cent of the total population of the United States lived in towns of more than 2500 population.

There are significant differences between family life in rural and in urban areas. In cities most people remain more or less anonymous.

---

[11] Paul H. Landis, *Making the Most of Marriage* (New York: Appleton-Century-Crofts, Inc., 1955), p. 269.

They lose the friendship and emotional support which is so common between neighbors in rural areas. In the country the family was more likely to function as a unit and to work together and to play together. Most of the time which the children spent at home was engaged somehow in a family activity. In urban areas the family is much more likely to have diverse interests, and because of the fact that most household commodities are purchased rather than made, there is less need for family unity in work. For this reason the children find interests outside of the family. They may find interests in school activities, and their parents are quite likely to belong to various organizations which would take them away from home in the evening. Even in attendance at church, there is a difference, for in rural areas the family is quite likely to attend as a unit, while in urban areas each member may go to a different service, or even to a different church. Such a diversity of interests as occurs in the family unit in an urban area does not necessarily indicate a breakdown in the family unity. It merely indicates a diversity of interests which in the long run may make for better family spirit because each member has a new and interesting contribution to make.

4. Emancipation of Women

The emancipation of women, long sought by militant suffragettes, has also made its contribution to changes in the family relationships. The freedom which was sought so long has not always brought the happiness and the sense of well-being which was anticipated by its advocates. Perhaps one of its most easily observable results is the working wife. This brings her equality of income but is very likely to have a detrimental effect upon the upbringing of the children. It once was thought that equality of women in politics would bring about greater honesty there. This has not yet been noticeable. Women have gained the right to wear pants, but have lost much of their romantic appeal, and the competition between the sexes has greatly reduced their feeling of security in their intersex relationships, including marriage. Not many years ago almost every girl assumed that she would get married, and that sooner or later her husband-to-be would come along. At the present time this assumption has changed so that most girls seem to feel that they will probably not get married unless they do something to attract and hold the attention of men. This has resulted in a greater exhibitionist tendency, absurd fashions, and lax morality. Virginity which was once held in high esteem is now sacrificed, too frequently, in payment for an evening's pleasure. The so-called emancipation of women has brought more advantages to men than it has to women. As equals, women often are not treated with the honor and respect which once was theirs.

5. Increased Ease of Divorce

It has become increasingly easy through the years to obtain a civil divorce. In certain parts of the country the facility with which a divorce may be granted makes a mockery of marriage. This subject is discussed more thoroughly in the section on the Social Aspects of Divorce and will not be covered here. The most distressing effect of divorce is on the children. These children from broken homes constitute a tremendous pool from which arise the neurotic and delinquent adolescents of our times.

6. Military Service

Never in the history of the world have so many of a country's nationals found their way to foreign soil as did American citizens during World War II. Most of these individuals were males and they were not only exposed to foreign cultures and customs, but to both benign and malignant influences from their companions. Young men, and to a lesser extent young women, were taken from their homes and close contact with their families and were exposed in many cases to a training and experience which would not have been theirs in less turbulent times. The experience of national unrest brought on by war, restlessness arising from uncertainty, bitterness resulting from real or imagined loss, a feeling of urgency, all contribute to a sense of excitement associated with ease of sexual activity, alcoholism, and early marriage.

After such a period of national unrest it takes many years for the disturbed and uprooted millions to settle down and resume a normal life tempo.

Each of these influences and many others have contributed to a change in family relations. Many of these changes have been in the way of improvement. On the whole, families are happier and have more interests, and the children are better educated, better clothed, better fed, and more ambitious. The element of family unity is the one which has suffered most by the change. Present efforts to promote greater unity of action on the part of the family may overcome this loss of cohesiveness. More frequently we hear the statement, "A family which prays together stays together."

For the marriage counselor there are matters of more immediate practical concern than these remote causes of disturbed family relationships. The marriage counselor is more immediately concerned with helping premarital couples to understand better the responsibilities and duties of their expected state of life. Every contribution which a marriage counselor can make to prepare a boy or girl for better marital adjustment is a direct contribution to their future happiness. There are differences of opinion as to how such instruction should be given, but little disagreement as to the fact that it should be given.[12]

In the following pages we shall attempt to discuss those facts concerning the marriage relationship which are important to preserve its integrity.

Section I deals with the biological aspects of marriage.
Section II discusses the sexual aspects of marriage.
Section III is concerned with fertility and marriage.
Section IV presents the social aspects of marriage.
Section V deals with the religious aspects of the marital relationship.

Although we have attempted to document the material thoroughly, there are many statements which may appear to be too dogmatic. It must be realized, however, that the opinions expressed are based on long experience, although each one may not be backed up by statistical evidence. Statistics are necessary, but when we are dealing with the individual patient, it is experience which counts, because although statistically only 4 per cent of women develop an involutional depression, it is only clinical experience which may be used to pick out the women so affected. If statistical studies were the whole answer, then the statistician would always have the last word.

We have not attempted to discuss all aspects of marriage. The information contained in this book is that which seems to us most important. Some may believe that other matters should have been discussed. With many of these we will agree. There are, however, limitations of time and space. Any such work is perpetually perfectable. We must rest for the time being with this material. Other subjects will be covered in future publications.

---

[12] For a more complete discussion of these subjects see: Ernest W. Burgess and Paul Wallin, *Engagement and Marriage* (Chicago: J. B. Lippincott Co., 1953), Chapter 1.

In addition to Catholics who counsel regarding marriage, this book is highly recommended to those non-Catholic marriage counselors who must give advice to Catholics. Here they may find the Catholic teaching. To attempt to give counsel contrary to his religious principles can only create a more difficult situation for the client.

Some of those who have read the manuscript feel that it is overweighted with medical and philosophical material. My only answer to this is that I am a medical man who specializes in psychiatry. It is therefore natural that medicine should be so emphasized. I have attempted to overcome this difficulty by asking various specialists to contribute chapters. I hope that this alleviates any possible overemphasis on medicine and psychiatry. Goldstein's comment is very pertinent in this regard:

> For if we come from the field of medicine, we shall probably want to speak first of the medical aspects of marriage; if we come from the field of psychology or psychiatry, we shall want to discuss the psychological factors in marriage; if we come from the field of home economics, we shall want to emphasize the importance of housekeeping and homemaking; if we come from the field of law and are legally trained, we shall want to stress the legal implication of the marriage contract; if we come from the field of religion and the ministry, we shall probably want to impress upon them the sacredness of marriage and the sanctity of family life; if we have become members of the new profession of marriage and family counselors, we shall want to discuss with the young people all the aspects of marriage and specific problems that we discover in the course of our interview.[13]

I wish to thank at this time those individuals without whom this book would not have been possible. Particular thanks are due to my co-authors who, besides writing the particular chapter on which their names appear, contributed greatly to the other chapters by their helpful criticism. Special mention should be made of Dr. Paul Nolan who labored sincerely and earnestly in the research upon which the book is based. Miss Bernice Wyman, Miss Dolores Hanan, and Miss Lorraine Bennett rendered invaluable editorial assistance.

I also wish to thank those editors who have permitted us to quote from their various works.

JOHN R. CAVANAGH

---

[13] By permission from *Marriage and Family Counseling*, by Sidney E. Goldstein, p. 35. Copyright, 1945. McGraw-Hill Book Company, Inc., New York.

Contents

SECTION IV

SOCIAL ASPECTS OF MARRIAGE

SECTION V

RELIGIOUS ASPECTS OF MARRIAGE

SECTION I

BIOLOGICAL
ASPECTS
OF
MARRIAGE

God created man in His image; in the image of God He created him; male and female He created them. Gen. 1:27.

CHAPTER I

Principles of Counseling

COUNSELING IN GENERAL

We see many new books describing counseling and research in methods of counseling. Most of these contain material which is not new but merely repeats in different terms that which has been previously recorded. For example, the following quotations from St. Thomas Aquinas are as applicable today as they were 700 years ago when he wrote them. First, as to its **desirability,** St. Thomas says: ". . . it is proper to the rational creature to be moved through the research of reason to perform any particular action, and this research is called counsel."[1]

To the question **what is counseling** he says: "Counsel properly implies a conference held between several; the very word (concilium) denotes this, for it means a sitting together from the fact that many sit together to confer with one another."[2]

Is counseling sufficient or **should there be a follow-up?** St. Thomas says: "Counsel is not only about what is done but also about whatever has relation to what is done."[3]

The **distinction between counsel and direction** is described by St. Thomas in these terms: "Counsel is distinguished in two ways: namely, investigation concerning things to be done and friendly persuasion. A counsel is distinguished from a precept in the second manner (i.e., by gentle persuasion), it is not (distinguished) however according to the first way."[4]

We have in these quotations the background of modern counseling, including the thought that the counselor should **not be too authoritative but, as St. Thomas says, "persuasive."** The effort is to make the individual develop an insight into his own problems. **Counseling,**

[1] *Summa,* IIa–IIae, Q. 52, Art. I, Corpus. [3] *Ibid.*
[2] *Ibid.* [4] *De Veritate,* Q. 17, Art. 3, ad 2.

therefore, comes about **when one individual seeks out another** to assist him in his **"research of reason"** in an attempt **to find the means** to the **solution of a problem.** Counseling attempts to seek out only the means for the solution of a problem.

Mudd offers this definition:

> Counseling before and after marriage consists of confidential interviews which provide an opportunity to talk over questions or problems with a well-trained and understanding person. Primarily, people gain perspective on whatever situations they are facing and counseling aims to help people deal with these situations in the manner best fitting their particular needs.[5]

In our approach to counseling, we must consider carefully the method we intend to use. Any form of counseling which attempts to make each individual completely responsible for his own adjustment may become erroneous if, for example, it attempts to make each person set up his own set of values. This could easily bring about a denial of any objective code of morality.[6]

---

[5] Emily Hartshorne Mudd, *The Practice of Marriage Counseling* (New York: Association Press, 1951), p. 178.

[6] Such a comment was made by Odenwald and VanderVeldt in regard to Roger's nondirective counseling. They commented as follows:

"In the first place, client-centered therapy, as set forth by Rogers, is based on the belief that man is basically good. Catholics, too, hold that some positive, constructive elements may be found in every man, but they also hold that, as a result of original sin, man is inclined toward evil and that man, left to himself, is only too prone to follow his evil tendencies because his intellect is darkened and his will is weakened.

"Secondly, client-centered therapy, again as advanced by Rogers, is an antiauthoritarian system, i.e., it is based on the assumption that the source of valuing things lies exclusively in man himself. Man does not admit any authority outside himself, as he is the shaper of his own destiny. If we push this principle to its logical conclusions, it would follow that man is a law unto himself, both in moral and religious matters. In other words, client-centered therapy refuses to admit an objective norm of morality and disposes of the authority of God. In the final analysis, it makes man his own God. It should be emphasized that these principles and implications are inherent in the system itself. Obviously no Catholic can accept such implications" (By permission from *Psychiatry and Catholicism,* by James H. VanderVeldt, O.F.M., and Robert P. Odenwald, M.D., pp. 100–101. Copyright, 1952. McGraw-Hill Book Co., Inc., New York).

There are some Catholic authors who apparently do not agree with Father VanderVeldt. Father Charles A. Curran of St. Charles College-Seminary in Columbus, Ohio, has written extensively on the subject. In his text, *Personality Factors in Counseling,* he has an introduction written by Dr. Carl R. Rogers and a preface by the Bishop of Columbus, Ohio, Michael J. Ready. This would certainly seem to indicate Father Curran's approval of the method.

Father Albert F. Grau, S.J., writing in the *A.C.P.A. Newsletter,* states that he finds nothing morally objectionable in the Rogerian method of counseling. See: Rev. Charles A. Curran, *Personality Factors in Counseling* (New York: Grune and Stratton, 1945);

The **essential ingredients** of the counseling problem are, therefore:
1. The counselor
2. The counselee
3. The interview situation

THE COUNSELOR

It is obvious that **one essential quality of the counselor** is that he have **greater knowledge** of the subject than the **one seeking his advice.** Otherwise, all that he has to offer are understanding and sympathy. Although understanding is also an essential characteristic of the counselor, it is not enough. Sympathy is out of place in the counseling situation because, if, as the word implies, the counselor begins to "suffer with" the client, then they are both in the same emotional situation and are "brothers of the storm." There is little then that they can do for each other.

Obviously, **the counselor will like some persons more than others.** This is inevitable. He should, however, attempt to control this feeling. He should be **empathic. Empathy may be defined as the projection of one's own personality into the personality of another in order to understand him better.** In this sense the counselor attempts to understand the suffering of his client so that he may better help him to solve his problems. If in gaining this understanding the counselor develops too strong a positive identification with him

---

Counseling in Catholic Life and Education (New York: The Macmillan Company, 1952); and Albert F. Grau, S.J., "Acceptance in Non-Directive Counseling," *A.C.P.A. Newsletter,* Supp. 17 (September, 1955).

To this author it would seem that there is no single answer to this question. One cannot help but feel that some of these who use the method have not sufficient experience in counseling to evaluate it. They adopt it because it seems so simple. In this they are mistaken. It is not merely a matter of listening; one must know to what one is listening. It must be recognized that the method is not suitable for those seriously ill such as the psychotic individual and the seriously neurotic patient. I cannot agree with Father Grau that it may be used for the depressed suicidal patient. I am sure that Dr. Rogers, himself, would feel a need for intervention if his patient were standing with a gun to his temple. Father Grau does not feel that there is danger of scandal but under less than ideal circumstances this would certainly seem possible. Suppose for example that Sister X is counseling a not too moral young lady. Suppose further that this young lady tells Sister X of some immoral act which she intends to perform and Sister X expresses neither approval nor disapproval. The young lady then accepts her lack of comment as approval and tells her companions in immorality that she has told Sister X what she intends to do and that Sister X has not disapproved.

Even Father Curran recognizes that there must be restraints: "It would be a mistake, therefore, to assume that the freedom of non-directive counseling implies no restraints and no limitations" (*Personality Factors in Counseling,* p. 224).

(a high empathic index) or if, on the contrary, he develops too strong a negative identification (a low empathic index), it would be well to consider suggesting to the client that he consult someone else. Fortunately, all problems do not affect all people in the same way, so that a problem or personality which would arouse hostility in one person may not create similar feelings in another.

Ideally, the counselor **should be free of prejudices, inhibitions,** and **other resistances,** but such perfection is seldom found. The next best thing is to be **aware of these difficulties** so that they will not interfere with his work. The more conscious the counselor can be of these resistances the more he can use them helpfully. Otherwise, they may act as obstructions which prevent him from utilizing his capabilities to full advantage.

His **powers of observation** are one of the most important instruments which the counselor has in his work of counseling. What the client does, how he acts, his mannerisms, his silences, may have a significance much greater than what he says. These characteristics should be observed and recorded because their significance may not be readily apparent.

An interest in people, a desire to be of help, and the **ability to listen** are essential qualities of good counseling.

Above all other characteristics the counselor must be able to **understand** and to **accept.**

Understanding implies a great deal. It means knowledge, training, and awareness of the possibilities. With particular reference to the interview it means "a knowledge of what is meant by what happens" during its course. It means also that this understanding should not be too readily communicated to the subject. The fact that the client is seeking consultation means that he has **overcome certain resistances** in the process of which he has built up certain defenses. These defenses are constructed not only against the counselor but against the patient's own understanding of himself. If the counselor shows too quickly that he understands and has penetrated these defenses it may leave the client feeling helpless and naked. He may then need to escape, either literally, by terminating the interview, or into superficialities. The **primary understanding** should be of the **mental processes of the individual** rather than of **his behavior as such.** The counselor must develop the ability to communicate his feelings and understanding to the client.

Acceptance of people, a firm conviction of their basic worth, is another essential characteristic of the counselor. It implies an ability to accept people as they are, with interest and without annoyance, the ability to accept the sinner but not his sin, the ability to allow people to differ, and the ability to accept the realization that behavior is a complex pattern of thinking, willing, and feeling.

In his acceptance of the client, the counselor must avoid bringing personal experiences into the interview. The **interview should center on the client and his experiences.** Too frequently, a personal experience related by the counselor may be misinterpreted by the subject, and by touching upon sensitive areas may create a further resistance. For the same reason, it may be unwise to discuss other patients as examples, even though they are not identified. Two cases are seldom exactly alike, and in addition it may lead the patient to suspect a possible breach of confidence.

The counselor **must avoid:** (1) arousing defensive attitudes in the client by poorly timed interpretations which may be taken as criticism; (2) any attitude of intolerance; (3) any appearance of boredom; (4) anxiety which may manifest itself in frequent interruptions or premature interpretations; (5) promises of secrecy before the situation is understood.

Mudd summarizes the counselor's attitude in this manner:

> It takes time for people to change, to grow, to make adjustments. Therefore, the counselor should offer patience rather than haste, sympathy, not indulgence, tolerance, not criticism, and should support an individual's efforts to adjust, even though success is not immediate. Above all, the professional counselor should show a warm, human responsiveness that denotes keen understanding of human differences. The goal of counseling is to help people over the rough spots, and to make this a strengthening process so that they can better help themselves and each other and pull their own weight in the community.[7]

SECRETS

All information conveyed to the counselor should be regarded as confidential and there is an implied but seldom expressed agreement that the matter shall be kept secret. This would come under the head of an **entrusted secret.** The more serious the secret, the greater is the obligation to secrecy.

Under **certain circumstances,** in order to avert great harm, con-

---

[7] Emily Hartshorne Mudd, *The Practice of Marriage Counseling* (New York: Association Press, 1951), p. 179.

fidential material may be communicated to others. This may be done when it is necessary to **avert great harm** from: (1) the state or community; (2) a third, innocent party who would suffer from an **unjust** act intended by the client; and (3) either the client or the counselor. (See chapter on the Moral Aspects of Marriage, page 527 ff.)

THE COUNSELEE

The subject himself may vary infinitely in his personal characteristics, but the one thing which he has in common with others is his need of help, either because he feels the necessity or some other person feels that he does. The individual who does not come with complete voluntariness must be given special handling and the counselor should attempt to **desensitize him** to any threat, real or implied, which exists in the interview situation.

The mere presence of the patient indicates that he expects help from the counselor. What his needs are, however, he may find difficult to define and express. These needs can usually be subsumed under the following headings:

1. **Relief of pressure.** Emotional pressures may have accumulated to the point that the patient feels like "he was going to explode." The counselor, under these circumstances, may serve as a safety valve.

2. **Need for understanding.** Feelings of inadequacy and inferiority, a feeling of being misunderstood or not fully appreciated may lead the patient to the feeling that it is necessary to present his side of the problem to an understanding person.

3. **A need to share a guilty secret.** The need to unburden one's self is a common human characteristic. Such feelings can best be shared by a person bound to secrecy and by one of sufficient depth of understanding. The counselor represents to the patient such a person.

4. **A need for acceptance.** All of us have a need to be accepted by those around us. In times of personal trouble and conflict this need increases.

5. **A loss of perspective.** The client may be confused and unable to see any way out of his problems. He needs advice and clarification either because he has become so involved in his problem that "he cannot see the forest for the trees" or because he cannot choose between means to a given end.

6. **A need to clarify his responsibility in regard to certain matters which trouble him.** "Has this just happened, or did I bring it about?"

7. **It may not be readily apparent** either to the patient or to the

counselor why the interview was sought. "I just felt I had to talk to someone."

THE INTERVIEW SITUATION

CIRCUMSTANCES

The prime requisite of the interview from the standpoint of its setting is **privacy.** The place it is held should be out of the reach of the listening ear of others and it should be as comfortable as circumstances permit. **Enough time should be allowed** so that the discussion can be adequately carried out and so that the subject will not feel hurried. On the other hand, an **unlimited period of time may be a serious handicap** because the patient may not feel any necessity for coming to the point. The length of the interview should tactfully be brought to the client's attention early in the interview. In practice, a session of fifty to sixty minutes seems to work out best.

In setting the tone for the interview the counselor should create a **permissive atmosphere** with the indication that for this interview there is no limitation on expression, but only on conduct. The subject should understand that the counselor is prepared to listen to his whole story as he wishes to express it and that he will **not be criticized or judged.**

THE INTERVIEW PROPER

Once the setting is arranged, the patient should be encouraged to talk freely and to tell his story in the way which best suits him. **Direction has no place,** under ordinary circumstances, in the initial interview. The counselor should interrupt as infrequently as possible and then only to clarify an important point. Give the patient a chance to talk — the counselor's turn will come later.

If the patient has difficulty in expressing himself the **counselor should be helpful.** This might be done:

1. By talking about neutral subjects until he has gained his composure and feels at ease.

2. By speaking to him in familiar terms; do not attempt to display your own erudition.

3. By not appearing in a hurry. "Take your time, the hour is yours."

4. By being considerate; every possible effort should be made to avoid any evidence of contempt (the opposite of acceptance) or desire to humiliate.

5. If the patient begins to get upset, move to a neutral subject or wait with patience and understanding until he regains his composure.

6. By accepting periods of silence without anxiety. Silence may mean only that the patient has completed one line of thought and is waiting to resume another. He may be struggling to compose himself or may be attempting to overcome hostility. **In the case of hostility** which arises because the interview has been forced upon him, it may be desirable to attempt its resolution by discussing it. In the case of an enforced interview the silence may lead to a refusal to discuss anything. In this case some explanation of its nature may help to clarify the situation. In general, if the silence does not seem to be disturbing to the patient, it is best to merely wait.

7. **Don't probe too soon** — let the patient retain his defenses until his initial resistance to the interview is abated.

Taking Notes

A question which frequently arises is whether it is desirable for the counselor to **take notes** in the presence of the subject. There are many opinions on this subject. Many believe that note-taking inhibits the free expression of the patient. It should certainly not be done if the patient objects or becomes preoccupied with what is being written. On the contrary, many patients get concerned over the fact that no notes are being taken. "How can you remember everything that everyone tells you?" There is probably no single answer to this question except that some record of the interview should be kept. Experience indicates that most patients appreciate rather than object to note-taking during the interview.

The First Interview

No attempt need or should be made to structure the first interview. It should be allowed to take its own direction. The **counselor should attempt three things.** He should first **attempt to establish rapport,** i.e., to establish a relationship in which the patient feels accepted, free to express himself, understood, and wanted. He **should attempt an appraisal of the situation** and **reinforce the patient** in his desire for understanding and help.

Termination of the Interview

The interview should be terminated at the expiration of the stated time of the interview. If another interview is indicated, some definite time should be set. If this one interview seems enough, the patient should be encouraged to return if new problems arise. **Avoid letting the client feel that the door is being closed permanently.**

MARRIAGE COUNSELING

Marriage counseling is a specialized form of counseling. In terms of our previous definition of counseling, marriage counseling would result when an individual sought out another more skilled than himself in an effort to work out the means to a successful and happy marriage.

Training and education for the marriage counselor are of prime importance. Interest in the subject and a desire to help are not enough. A knowledge of law, of medicine, or of theology does not equip an individual as a marriage counselor. Members of these professions have special interests in marriage problems but each only in a limited area. The marriage counselor must have legal, medical, and theological information but he needs more. **The interest of the counselor is primarily in the prevention of marital problems rather than in their cure.**

Who is best equipped to be a marriage counselor and what should his education be? Father John Stafford made these very pertinent comments which are quoted at length with his consent.

I think the same solution might be applied to the question of who should do marriage counseling. The Report of the Joint Subcommittee on Standards for Marriage Counselors of the National Council on Family Relations obviously takes this view that no one of the existing professions should have exclusive right in Marriage Counseling when it states that the appropriate graduate or professional degree for a marriage counselor shall be in one of the following fields: education, home economics, law, medicine, nursing, psychology, religion, social anthropology, social work and sociology. That takes in about everybody who would want to get into the act.

The title of my paper is "The Equipment of the Marriage Counselor." My first point, just made, is a negative one: membership in no one of the traditional professions is to be set up as an essential condition for doing marriage counseling. Anyone can do it who is equipped. We will now proceed to examine what that equipment should be.

It is worthwhile to examine the qualifications set up by the Subcommittee on Standards for Marriage Counselors of the National Council on Family Relations. The first qualifications given are academic. The Subcommittee states: "Every marriage counselor shall have a graduate or professional degree from an approved institution as a minimum qualification. This degree shall be in one of the following fields: education, home economics, law, medicine, nursing, psychology, religion, social anthropology, social work and sociology." I certainly think some kind of advanced training with a degree beyond the bachelor's degree is essential for professional work as a marriage counselor. I do not see that it is wise at this time to require that the degree be in a specific field, as indicated above. I can think of two other graduate degrees, at least, that might be held by a marriage counselor, in philosophy and in economics other than "home" economics. It is difficult to see how a degree as such in one of the enumerated fields qualifies one for work as a marriage counselor. And since the Subcommittee itself goes on to specify areas of specialized training, it seems more prudent not to require that the advanced degree be obtained in a specified field. Once again, what is important is the actual equipment of the counselor, not the field of his graduate specialty.

The Subcommittee states: "Whatever the field of major emphasis, there shall be included accredited training in: psychology of personality development; elements of psychiatry; human biology, including the fundamentals of sex anatomy, physiology and genetics; sociology of marriage and the family; legal aspects of marriage and the family; and counseling techniques." I think we can agree without question that all of these areas of training are important for marriage counseling. But as Catholics, we must add more: *there must be training in the theology of marriage,* since the marriage state is more than a human relationship; there must also be a proper philosophical concept of the nature of man and of human powers. Scientific training in the areas indicated above is important; but our Catholic synthesis is a philosophical and theological synthesis as well: hence, in addition to training in the modern areas of scientific specialization there must be that deeper knowledge of man as a personality that comes from philosophical and theological insights into reality. In addition to theological and philosophical training I would add that the blueprint given above by the Subcommittee omits something else, training in the purely economic aspects of marriage and family life. It is wrong to say that all marriage difficulties are economically caused; it is also wrong to omit from the training of a marriage counselor equipment to handle problems of budgeting and of meeting financial obligations that often are at the root of marriage difficulties. In the area of psychological training I do not think it is sufficient to list the psychology of personality development and techniques of counseling. As we shall see shortly, the counselor is called upon to make diagnostic judgments. For this purpose he should have some knowledge of modern psychological testing techniques.

The Subcommittee lists next the professional experience that is to be required of a marriage counselor: at least three years of recognized professional experience subsequent to obtaining his degree, and some actual experience as a clinical assistant in marriage counseling under approved supervision. These requirements are indeed the ideal for the certifying of marriage counselors, and I think should be regarded as a goal toward which we should work. If marriage counseling is to be accepted as a serious profession and not the playground of quacks, then serious requirements must be set up for practitioners. Certainly these requirements will not be strictly enforced at the beginning; if so, there just wouldn't be much marriage counseling done. But experience is really the best teacher here as in about everything else. Hence I think we would do well to set our sights high and aim at the training of counselors who have not only book learning and fancy degrees, but the know-how that is acquired through actual work in a professional setting. This idea has long been accepted in medicine, where an internship is required, and in social work, where supervised experience is required. The latest profession to require such supervised training is clinical psychology, in which a full year's internship is required as essential to a doctorate program, and in which additional years of experience are required before full diplomate status as a clinical psychologist is given.

The Subcommittee continues: "A candidate's qualifications shall include diagnostic skill in differentiating between the superficial and the deeper levels of maladjustment, and the ability to recognize when the latter type requires referral to other specialists." That is really a large order. For such skill much more than a course or two in personality theory and the elements of psychiatry is needed. Real professional skill in making such diagnoses is hard to find even in experienced clinical psychologists, and if the problem requires differential diagnosis between psychological and physical maladjustments, then the professional training of the physician is required. To demand all of this of the marriage counselor is to demand the impossible. It is true that the marriage counselor can, through his graduate training and his experience, become sensitized to the recognition of the more serious forms of personality maladjustment; but it does not seem likely that he will be much of a diagnostician unless he is highly trained as a clinical psychologist or as a psychiatrist. I recall one little controversy between a sociologist and a psychiatrist, both interested in marriage counseling. The sociologist stated that in his experience relatively few marriages had psychological or psychiatric problems as their cause. The psychiatrist replied that the sociologist could say that because he was unable to recognize psychological or psychiatric problems when he saw them. The sociologist retorted that psychiatrists see personality disorders everywhere, and refuse to recognize other causes of marriage difficulties. So there we are! Most marriage counselors would not possess sufficient diagnostic skill unless long and detailed training were added to what has already been suggested. And, moreover, training in diagnostic skills *alone* will make the counselor so sensitive to psychological maladjustments that he may exaggerate their importance.

The Subcommittee is a bit over-excited about the importance of a scientific attitude in marriage counseling. It states that one of the qualifications of a marriage counselor must be "A scientific attitude toward individual variation and deviation, especially in the field of human sex behavior, and the ability to discuss sexual problems objectively." All this is of course obvious. The marriage counselor should be able to discuss all questions objectively, and not become emotionally involved himself in the problems of those he is trying to help. The counselor, too, should have a scientific attitude toward variation and deviation, as well as toward everything else. By scientific attitude here seems to be meant that the counselor will not let his own biases and prejudices determine his handling of a case, but will handle it against the background of all the facts obtainable. All this seems obvious in counseling as well as elsewhere.

Last to be listed by the Subcommittee are the personal qualifications for the marriage counselor. They are: "A. The candidate shall possess personal and professional integrity in accordance with accepted ethical standards. B. The candidate shall have an attitude of interest, warmth, and kindness toward people, combined with a high degree of integration and emotional maturity. C. The personal experience of marriage and parenthood is a decided asset." I don't think we can disagree with any of these recommendations. There might be added, however, certain precisions and developments of the points given above.

Whether the counselor goes all out for the client-centered, nondirective techniques, or attempts to use other techniques as well in his counseling, he must remember that the basic aim of all counseling must not be "doing something for the married couple," but "helping them to help themselves." Hence the authoritarian, didactic, domineering approach we find too often everywhere is impossible for good marriage counseling. Even on ethical and religious matters, the aim of the counselor should not be coercion, but clarification. In addition, the counselor must have considerable flexibility in his techniques. Rigidity is not a virtue in a counselor. A-1 perfectionist attitudes such as "my way is the only way" ruin the counseling relationship. Respect for the dignity of the persons being counseled carries along with it a very deep humility with regard to one's own involvement in the counseling situation. Above all for the Catholic counselor, there must be a deep appreciation of the sacramental character of the marriage relationship. The counselor must approach his task equipped not only with the scientific techniques of modern counseling but with the spirit of Christ and with the grace of Christ. The successful Catholic counselor will continue his work for his clients by praying for them: he must consider himself one of the ministers of God's grace, and must recognize that what he does is like the watering of Apollo: it is God Who will give the increase.

It is interesting that the Subcommittee of The National Council on Family Relations states that marriage and parenthood is a "decided asset" rather than an essential prerequisite for marriage counseling. I know nothing of the deliberations of the Subcommittee; but it does not seem fantastic to suppose that one of the reasons for this guarded wording is that the Subcommittee did not want to imply that the Catholic clergy, or other unmarried persons, were for that reason incapable of doing marriage counseling. I think we must admit, however, that marriage and parenthood *are* decided assets in marriage counseling. In a plan I shall propose shortly it will be seen how the skills of the clergymen can be combined with the additional insights of the laity who have had themselves the experience of marriage and parenthood. In this connection it is of extreme interest to note that the National Marriage Guidance Council of Great Britain has also declared that marriage and parenthood are assets to marriage counseling, but has made the added precision that the married counselor should have been *happily* married, and that divorced persons should be *ipso facto* disqualified as marriage counselors.[8]

THE AIM OF MARRIAGE COUNSELING

The primary aim of the marriage counselor should be preventive. He should endeavor to prevent those difficulties in which he is prepared to counsel. He should endeavor, therefore, to reach the couple before marriage, to help them lay the groundwork for happiness, to solve by anticipation problems which may arise in their future relationship. He must always remember that "an ounce of prevention is worth a pound of cure."

The need of therapeutic consultation with the marriage counselor after marriage is usually an indication of the failure of counseling. This is not necessarily an evidence of failure on the part of the counselor, because the decision to marry was undoubtedly made

---

[8] John W. Stafford, C.S.V., Ph.D., "The Equipment of the Marriage Counselor," *Marriage Counseling* (Family Life Bureau, N.C.W.C., Washington 5, D. C.), pp. 39–43.

before he was consulted. If the counselor was consulted before the couple had committed themselves to marriage, a greater responsibility for the success of the marriage would be his.

The aim of the marriage counselor should be prophylactic rather than curative. Young people should, therefore, be encouraged to seek help before marriage and preferably before any formal engagement.

What is to be done when no adequate counseling service is available? In the absence of such a counseling service, there are correspondence courses which could be used as substitutes. There are probably others not known to this writer but one such correspondence course is offered by the Marriage Preparation Service, The Catholic Centre, 1 Stewart Street, Ottawa, Canada. The course may be obtained by writing to this address. The subject matter of this course is quite adequate and well presented. With permission, the content of this course is reprinted for the benefit of the reader:

1. **The present situation with regard to marriage.** What young people think of it. The Christian ideal of marriage. How to prepare for it.

2. **The ideal husband — the ideal wife.** The qualities to look for in your partner. Defects to be avoided. The correction of faults.

3. **Love and happiness in marriage.** Its elements. True love and false love. True happiness in marriage.

4. **Courtship and engagement.** The purpose, duration, place of courtship. The dangers of flirting. Faithfulness. Christian engagement.

5. **Masculine and feminine psychology.** For men: how to understand women. For women: how to understand men.

6. **Economic preparation.** Economy. The trousseau. The budget. Insurance.

7. **The spirituality of marriage.** The vocation. The sacrament. The purposes and qualities of marriage. The sacramental grace. The spirituality of marriage. The child, etc.

8. **Civil law concerning marriage.** Legal formalities. Impediments. Nuptial agreement. Annulment, separation, and divorce. Last will and testament.

9. **Canon law concerning marriage.** Prenuptial inquiry. Impediments to marriage. Publication of banns. Conditions required for validity, etc.

10. **The marriage ceremony.** Liturgical explanation. Events before and after the marriage ceremony: showers, wedding outfit; confession; Communion; reception, honeymoon, etc.

11. **Masculine and feminine anatomy and physiology.** The plan of God. The personal and social role of purity.

12. **Relations between husband and wife, pregnancy, nursing, birth.** The mystery of the transmission of life. The beauty and grandeur of God's plan.

13. **Hygiene — venereal diseases.** General and sexual hygiene. Diagnosis and therapeutics of venereal diseases. Social consequences.

14. **What is allowed and what is forbidden in marriage. The moral aspect.** Continence. The Rhythm System.

15. **The first months of marriage.** The first relations. Physical, intellectual, and moral adaptations. The child.

JOINT INTERVIEWS

The joint interview with both husband and wife present may have definite value in certain cases. This method of counseling has not been used to any large extent and there is very little in the literature concerning it.[9] The mere fact that both parties are willing to seek counsel is a hopeful prognostic sign. It is an indication of their willingness to correct the problem, and for this reason, if no other, the opportunity of discussing their problem jointly should be afforded them. Such an interview requires special skill, tact, and adaptability on the part of the counselor.

If joint interviews are to be conducted, there should be an opportunity either in advance of such joint interviews, or afterward, for individual discussions with the counselor. It is a matter of common knowledge that witnesses to the same event may give different reports. It must therefore be recognized that in the presence of a marriage problem the husband and wife are quite likely to have divergent subjective views of the situation. One must also recognize that there may be aspects of the problem which, for one reason or another, they may wish to conceal, or which one is afraid to mention in the presence of the other. An opportunity for the discussion of these problems is afforded by the individual interviews, and the counselor may then go to the joint interview better equipped to understand the emotional attitude of each of the partners. In the presence of each other, and with the counselor as a stabilizing influence, they may be able to discuss their problems with greater objectivity and calmness.

Where only one partner seeks advice, great care should be exercised

---

[9] Mudd, *op. cit.,* p. 189.

in suggesting a joint session. This does not mean that the partner who has not sought advice should not be requested to come in for an individual interview, but it is likely that great harm might result if two individuals hostile toward each other are forced into a joint interview situation before they are prepared for it. There is no rule as to when the partners are ready. The counselor must decide on the basis of his experience in similar situations.

It is very difficult for the counselor, in most situations, to retain a completely objective attitude. He must therefore exercise great care not to take sides and to avoid identification with one or the other partner. Too strong an empathy for either client will negate the counselor's value.

COUNSELING AND PSYCHIATRY

Marriage counseling presumes that the individuals seeking advice are well integrated. Even if they are not, it may be that the problem concerning which they seek advice is not related to a psychiatric problem. In these cases the marriage counselor will probably be adequate in reaching whatever solution is possible. It is only in those cases in which the marital difficulty arises because of the psychiatric disability that a professional psychotherapist is necessary.

Confusion as to the relationship between counseling and psychiatry has arisen because the psychiatrist has been pre-eminently the member of the medical profession best equipped to handle marriage problems. In the average marital situation, however, he is not functioning as a psychiatrist as much as he is as a counselor. There is serious doubt as to whether the psychiatrist is the most suitable one to give marital advice because he is recognized as the member of the medical profession who deals with mental aberrations and, in the mind of too many, his handling of the situation implies that marital problems arise out of mental aberrations, which is not always true. It is equally true that, although the psychiatrist is the one who is best equipped to give advice on sex, there is again the implication that there is something mentally abnormal about those who have sexual difficulties, and this is not always true. There is, however, no other specialist in medicine as well equipped to give sexual instruction as is the psychiatrist. Individual members of other specialties have been interested, especially the gynecologists, but even in this group there are many who do not wish to take the time necessary for such instruction. If marriage counseling is to be done by a member of the medical profession, it is probably best done by the psychiatrist. It is well to remember, however, that psychiatry and counseling are not the same. A small percentage of marital problems do arise as a result of psychiatric abnormalities. In these cases there is no doubt that they are best handled by a psychiatrically trained physician.

More physicians should be trained as marriage counselors. It is traditional for the lay person to feel that the physician is the one best equipped to give advice in sexual matters. Medical schools should include in their curricula a more adequate and better instruction in regard to sex and marriage problems. No medical school gives such instruction.

CHAPTER II

The Anatomical Aspects of Marriage

THE BODY AS A WHOLE

Before proceeding to the discussion of the male and female sexual anatomy a brief discussion of the body as a whole seems appropriate.

In spite of individual variations in size and appearance, the human body is constructed according to a very definite pattern. It is only when an individual varies markedly from the usual pattern that we note this fact as unusual. It is interesting to note that, despite this uniformity of structure, no two people look exactly alike. Extremes of structure are occasionally noted.

DWARFISM

There are very few true dwarfs. Most individuals of small stature get that way because of disease, which causes a delay in development. The true dwarf is born that way and as a rule is well formed, robust, and intelligent. True dwarfism is hereditary and children of dwarfs married to dwarfs are always dwarfs. There have been numerous dwarfs celebrated in history, of whom one of the best known was Vladislas Cubitas who was King of Poland in 1305. He was noted for his intelligence, courage, and military genius. Geoffrey Hudson, most celebrated English dwarf, was born in 1699. At the age of eight he was not over a foot high; until thirty he was said to be not more than 18 inches high, when he suddenly increased to about forty-five inches. Another well-known English dwarf was Wibrand Lokes who measured 25½ inches in height. Many dwarfs live to a great age. Richeborg, a dwarf only 23 inches in height, died in Paris in 1858 at the age of ninety. These are but a few examples of better-known dwarfs, the best known at the present time being General Tom Thumb, who for a long time was with the Barnum and Bailey Circus.

GIGANTISM

There are many stories in the older literature regarding giants, most of which are undoubtedly exaggerations, the tallest authenticated giant scientifically recorded being 108½ inches tall (9 feet). In most of the instances reported in which bones of giants were discovered, subsequent investigation has shown that these were the bones of animals. Some of the better-known giants were above average but not of tremendous size. For example: Goliath, who was slain by David stood 6 cubits and a span tall — about 11 feet. Hercules, a man of incredible strength, was said to have been not even 7 feet high. There have been fabulous stories told of the Emperor Maximilian; some accounts say he was between 8½ and 9 feet high and used his wife's bracelet for a finger ring. It is only in the latter part of the present century that we have begun to have authentic heights of giants. The men being shown through the country today as measuring 8 feet generally exaggerate their height several inches, and exact measurements would show that few men commonly called giants are over 7½ feet tall or weigh over 350 pounds. Dana says that the number of giants figuring as public characters since 1700 is not more than 100, and of these, about 20 were advertised as being over 8 feet. If we confine ourselves to those accurately and scientifically measured, the list is surprisingly small. The tallest man in the Austrian Army was 8 feet 4½ inches tall. A giant called Winckelmeyer measured 8 feet 4 inches in height. Marianne Wehde, who was shown in Germany in the present century, measured 8 feet 3¾ inches when only eighteen years old. The most common cause of gigantism is a disturbance in the pituitary gland. As a rule, these giants are morose, sullen, and very irritable.

OBESITY

Obesity is not necessarily a disease of adults. There is reported, for instance, a girl of four who weighs 256 pounds. There is another instance of a girl of five who weighed 150 pounds and had the strength of a man. There was also described a girl of eleven who weighed 200 pounds, another young girl in Russia who weighed 200 pounds when she was twelve. The most obese individual of whom there is an accurate record was Edward Bright, sometimes called "The Fat Man of Essex"; he weighed 616 pounds. Probably the most famous of all fat men was Daniel Lambert, born March 13,

1770. He was apparently normal until the age of fourteen; at about nineteen he began to believe he would be very heavy and he began to develop great strength. He could lift 500 pounds with ease and could kick 7 feet high while standing on one leg. In 1793 he weighed 448 pounds; in June 1809 he weighed 739 pounds. At this time he measured 3 yards around the body and over 1 yard around the leg.

LEANNESS

There are the so-called living skeletons. One of the best-known examples of excessive leanness was Calvin Edson. At the age of 42 he weighed 42 pounds, although he was 5 feet 4 inches tall. It is said that he could chop a cord of wood without fatigue. He had four children. In most instances of the so-called living skeletons, the trouble is due to extreme muscular atrophy.

LONGEVITY

Longevity is the prolongation of life to, or beyond, the standard duration for the species. For the human species this is a little more than 100 years. Longevity should be carefully distinguished from the average length of life, also referred to as the expectation of life at birth. This term is an average taken from a large group of individuals. Preventive medicine during the past 50 years has added greatly to the average duration of life. For example, in the United States in 1901 the average length of life was 48.23 years for males and 51.08 for females. In 1944 this had increased to 63.55 years and 68.95 years respectively.

There are no reliable figures on longevity and because of a tendency for centenarians to exaggerate their ages there will probably be none. The list prepared by James Easton covering the years A.D. 66 to 1799 contains many exaggerated figures. For example, he cites Henry Jenkins as dying at age 169 years, Thomas Parr at 152, and Katherine, Countess of Desmond, at age 140.

The United States Census figures list the greatest age group as 75 or over so that no approximation can be made of those persons living over the age of 100. According to the 1950 figures there were 1,636,000 white males 75 years of age or more, 1,986,000 white females, 101,000 nonwhite males, 114,000 nonwhite females. These figures are based on a total population of 150,697,000 persons.

SIZE OF THE SEXUAL ORGANS
IN RELATION TO FUNCTION

This may all seem a rather long preliminary discussion to a very important point which must be made. It has been pointed out that marked variations in human size and shape occur, but many fail to recognize that a **similar variation exists in the sexual anatomy.** One could not even approximately estimate how much misery has been suffered by men who were excessively conscious of the size of their penis because it was smaller than that of another man. How many women have added artificial aids to enlarge their breasts because nature had not provided breasts as large as those of a neighbor.

A disproportion in size between the penis and the vagina may occur, but will be very rare. A very large penis may at first interfere with the consummation of the marriage. But with patience the vagina will dilate to permit its entry. Forceful attempts to insert a disproportionately large penis may result in serious injury to the woman. Gentle and gradual dilatation should be advised in such cases. Small size of the penis does not interfere in the achievement of orgasm by either party so that unwarranted fears that it may interfere with sexual adjustment should be discouraged. Although the penis varies considerably in size it should be remembered that size is not related to function, and from the standpoint of serving its purpose, size is not the important quality. The purpose of the breast is to provide nourishment for the offspring and its value for this function is not in proportion to its size. These points are mentioned because so many persons having feelings of inadequacy in relation to the size of the genitals that an effort should be made by the counselor to overcome these feelings.

THE GENERATIVE SYSTEM

The male organs of generation consist of:

1. Testes (2)
2. Vasa deferentia (2)
3. Seminal vesicles (2)
4. Penis
5. Prostate

The **testicles** (testes) are two oval glandular bodies suspended in the scrotum by the spermatic cords. These structures, which secrete the spermatic fluid, are about 4 to 5 centimeters in length and

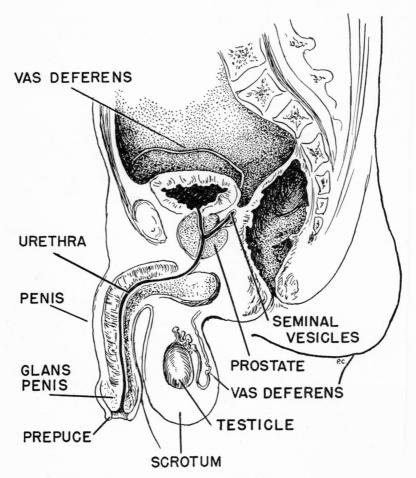

VAS DEFERENS

URETHRA

PENIS

GLANS
PENIS

PREPUCE

SEMINAL
VESICLES

PROSTATE

VAS DEFERENS

TESTICLE

SCROTUM

SAGITTAL SECTION OF THE MALE PELVIS

2.5 centimeters in breadth and 3 centimeters in their anteroposterior diameters. They each weigh about 15 grams. Each testicle consists of a body and an epididymis. The latter structure forms the outlet for the secretion of the testicle.

The **scrotum** is composed of skin which forms a sac for the testicles. Its surface is wrinkled due to the presence in its structure of the dartos muscle which may contract or relax due to a variety of stimuli.

The spermatic cord which supports the testicle on each side is derived from the connective tissues of the abdominal wall. Its only function is to hold the testes in place; through it passes the blood supply to the testes and the vasa deferentia.

Each **testicle** is composed of glandular tissue. This tissue is of two different types, one of which forms the spermatic fluid which contains the spermatozoa, and the other forms the male sex hormone. It is the presence of this latter secretion which produces the secondary sexual characteristics in the male. Removal or damage to the testicles before full development will, as a rule, result in imperfect development. The individual so affected does not develop the distinctive male characteristics. The principal secondary sexual characteristics of the male are:

1. Deep voice.

2. Growth of hair on the face, chest, inner side of the thighs, across the shoulders, and the calves of the legs. The pubic escutcheon (hair) is triangular with the apex toward the umbilicus.

3. Narrow pelvis.

The male sex hormone is liberated directly into the blood stream and is, therefore, called the endocrine secretion of the testicle (see Chapter III).

The **spermatic fluid** which is formed in the testes is liberated through a series of ducts which start on the testicle as the epididymis. This fluid (semen) is a viscid, whitish liquid composed of a colorless portion (the liquor seminis), the spermatozoa, and the seminal granules. These seminal granules are about 1/4000 of an inch in diameter and impart to the colorless liquor seminis its milky appearance. The spermatozoa are the essential element. These consist of an oval head, a body or middle piece, and a long incessantly moving tail. It is the tail which gives the organism its motility. The generative elements are contained in the head. The fully developed sperm cell contains only one half the number of chromosomes present in a somatic cell. This is to allow for the presence of the full complement of chromosomes in the fertilized ovum. Other information of interest in regard to the spermatic fluid is:

1. **Amount of fluid:** This varies ordinarily between 4 to 5 cubic centimeters (a teaspoonful) at each ejaculation. The frequency of ejaculation naturally influences this amount. The more frequent the ejaculation, the smaller the amount.

2. The **speed of travel** of spermatozoa varies. On a glass slide it

was measured at 1/7 inch a minute (Dickinson). In the more viscid seminal fluid before it liquifies it would probably be less.

3. The spermatozoa are **quickly destroyed** by acids, weak anti-septics, and heat.

4. The **number of sperms** in a single ejaculation usually varies between 300 to 500 million. The average number is probably 350,-000,000 (Dickinson). The frequency of ejaculation also affects the number of spermatozoa.

5. The sperm cell, under proper conditions, **retains its ability to fertilize** the female ovum for approximately 72 hours.

The **vasa deferentia** are tubules about 30 centimeters in length not considering convolutions. These serve to convey the secretion from the testicles to the seminal vesicles.

The **seminal vesicles** are two pouches which adhere closely to the undersurface of the urinary bladder. They vary in size but usually measure 6.5 centimeters in length and 1.25 centimeters in breadth. Each vesicle consists of a tube about 15 centimeters in length and closed at one end. It has the diameter of the inside of a lead pencil and is convoluted into a mass.

The **ejaculatory ducts** are formed by the union of the vasa deferentia and the ducts of the seminal vesicles. Each of these ducts is about 1 inch in length and passes through the prostate to open into the prostatic portion of the urethra.

The **penis** is composed of a peculiar, vascular spongelike structure which is arranged in three columnar bodies, the two corpora cavernosa and the corpus spongiosum. It is covered by skin which is loosely adherent and reduplicated at the distal end of the organ to form a fold called the prepuce. The distal end of the organ is capped by the glans, which is a blunt, cone-shaped body somewhat more expanded at its base than the shaft of the penis (corona). The urethra traverses the entire length of the penis, opening on the summit of the glans in a slitlike aperture called the urinary meatus. Erection of the penis results from the engorgement of the spongy structure with blood. The average length of the flaccid organ is usually given as 10 centimeters; when erect, as 15 centimeters.

The **male urethra** serves as a common passageway for the urine and semen. It extends from the neck of the bladder, where it is surrounded by the prostate gland, through the entire length of the penis. It is about 20 to 22.5 centimeters in length.

The **prostate** is a glandular body resembling a chestnut in size and shape. It surrounds the first portion of the urethra and is consequently closely attached to the floor of the bladder. Its undersurface can be felt just inside the anus. It consists of two lateral lobes and a middle portion through which the urethra passes. It contains many glands, the ducts of which open into the urethra.

The female generative organs:

1. Ovaries (2)
2. Fallopian tubes (2)
3. Uterus
4. Vagina
5. Vulva (external genitalia)
   a) Mons veneris
   b) Labia majora
   c) Labia minora
   d) Clitoris
   e) Urinary meatus
   f) Vaginal orifice

The **ovaries** serve the equivalent purpose in the female that the testes serve in the male. They liberate the female sex hormone and also the ova which are the female contribution to the generative process. They measure about 3.75 centimeters in length, 1 centimeter in width, and about 1.8 centimeters in thickness. They lie on either side of the pelvis on the posterior surface of the broad ligament and near the fimbriated end of the Fallopian tubes. The ovaries contain many thousands of ova, only one of which is liberated each month. The ovum which is to be liberated each month must first undergo a process of ripening. It is first surrounded by a ring of specialized cells (granulosa cells), from which it is soon separated by a collection of fluid (liquor folliculi) except for a small island of cells (discus proligerus) on which it rests. The completed structure is called the Graafian follicle (see pp. 65–66). As the Graafian follicle becomes mature, it gradually approaches the surface of the ovary. At the appropriate time, the follicle ruptures and liberates its contained ovum into the peritoneal cavity in the vicinity of the fimbriated extremity of the Fallopian tube (ovulation). Only one such rupture occurs each month, usually between the twelfth and sixteenth days after the first day of the last menstrual period. Such an ovum is capable of fertilization for only 24 hours. After the evacuation of the ovum, the follicle undergoes a rapid series of changes as a result of which it is converted into

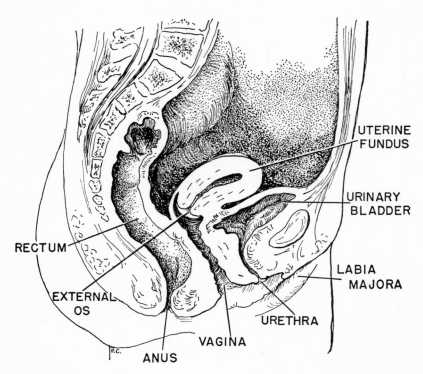

UTERINE
FUNDUS

URINARY
BLADDER

RECTUM

LABIA
MAJORA

EXTERNAL
OS

URETHRA

VAGINA

ANUS

SAGITTAL SECTION OF THE FEMALE PELVIS

a solid yellow body, the corpus luteum, which produces a hormone. This hormone is responsible for the changes occurring in the lining of the uterus designed to prepare it for pregnancy. If pregnancy does not take place, the corpus luteum undergoes degeneration. If pregnancy does occur, it becomes greatly increased in size (corpus luteum of pregnancy) and produces a correspondingly increased amount of hormone (progestin) (see Chap. III).

The **Fallopian tubes,** or **oviducts,** are ductlike structures which serve as passageways for the ova from the ovaries to the uterus. They are somewhat trumpet-shaped, the narrow end being attached to the uterus and the wide end directed outward. This end has numerous tentaclelike processes (fimbria) which reach out toward the ovary and attract the ova into the lumen of the tube. From the time the ovum is liberated until it is picked up by one of the fimbria, it is free in the abdominal cavity.

The **uterus**, or **womb**, is a hollow, muscular, pear-shaped organ designed for the reception of the fertilized ovum and for the development and expulsion of the product of conception. It is flattened in its anteroposterior diameter and measures 7.5 centimeters in length, 5 in breadth, and 2.5 in thickness. It is divided into two parts, a body or fundus, and the cervix or neck. The cervix of the uterus in the adult forms about one third of the structure and comprises the passageway from the cavity of the uterus into the vagina. The opening of the cervical canal into the cavity of the uterus is called the internal os, that into the vagina is called the external os. In the pelvis, the uterus lies behind the urinary bladder and in front of the rectum. It is held in this position by a firm fold of tissue called the broad ligament. This is fastened on each side to the pelvic bones and supports, besides the uterus, the Fallopian tubes which lie on its upper margin and the ovaries which lie on its posterior surface.

The cavity of the uterus is triangular from side to side with the base upward, but its anterior and posterior walls are almost in apposition. The openings of the Fallopian tubes are into its two upper angles, while the internal os of the cervix forms its lower angle. This cavity is lined by a glandular mucous membrane called the endometrium. Each month this membrane undergoes a change known as menstruation (q.v.).

The **vagina** is a collapsible membranous tube which connects the uterus to the vulva. It is approximately 10 centimeters in length and is capable of great distention, sufficient, in fact, to permit the passage of the baby's head during delivery. Normally its walls are in contact. At the upper end the uterine cervix projects into its cavity for about 1.25 centimeters. This projection makes an important pocket behind the cervix called the posterior cul de sac, where the seminal fluid collects following intercourse, forming the so-called seminal pool.

The **vulva** (external genitalia) is composed of:

a) The **mons veneris** is a prominence of skin over the pubis which is covered by hair. The female escutcheon is triangular like the male, but the apex of the triangle is directed downward toward the anus. The base forms a straight line just above the pubis.

b) The **labia majora** are two folds of skin which bound the vertical fissure of the vulva. They are covered on their outer surface with hair. They correspond to the scrotum in the male.

c) The **clitoris** corresponds to the penis in the male. It is also composed of erectile tissue, but is much smaller in the female. It measures about 3 centimeters in length and is located at the anterior extremity of the vulva just under the pubis, between the anterior ends of the labia minora which separate and form a prepuce for it. The clitoris is also capped by a glans. The clitoris differs from the penis inasmuch as it is not penetrated by the urethra.

d) The **labia minora** (nymphae) are two folds of mucous membrane which lie just inside the labia majora and extend from the clitoris,

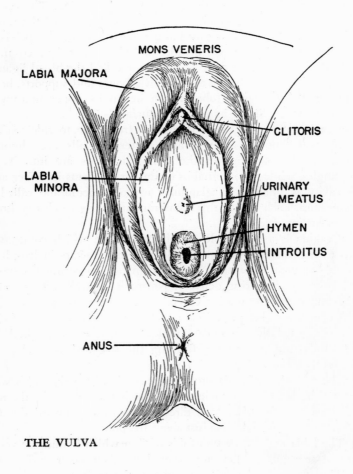

THE VULVA

which their anterior ends separate to enclose, to behind the vagina, where their lower ends usually merge with the skin surface.

e) Between the labia minora is a triangular area called the **vestibule** which contains the openings of the urethra (urinary meatus) anteriorly, and the vaginal orifice posteriorly. The vaginal orifice in the virgin is usually partially closed by a fold of mucous membrane called the hymen. The hymen may be ruptured in many ways so that its destruction is not necessarily evidence of sexual intercourse.

THE URINARY SYSTEM

The urinary organs consist of:
1. Kidneys
2. Ureters
3. Bladder
4. Urethra

THE KIDNEYS (RENES)

The kidneys are situated deeply in the lumbar region opposite the last thoracic and first and second lumbar vertebrae; the right is normally a little lower than the left. Each kidney weighs from 4½ to 6 ounces in the male, and 4 to 5½ ounces in the female. Their shape is characteristic. The notch on their inner margin is called the hilus. It is here that the blood vessels and nerves enter and leave and the ureter emerges as a continuation of the pelvis. On cross section, it is seen that the kidney consists of a cortex and medulla. The latter contains conical masses known as renal pyramids. These have their bases in the cortical area, and their apices, the renal papillae, projecting into the calices of the pelvis within the sinus of the kidney.

Microscopically, the substance of the kidney is made up of uriniferous tubules (nephrons). There are about 1,200,000 such units. Each nephron, which is the functional unit of the kidney, is composed of three parts:
1. The glomerulus
2. The secretory tubule
3. The collecting or excretory tubule

Each tubule is about 2 inches long but is so fine it is a microscopic structure. Each tubule is closely surrounded by blood vessels. The glomerulus consists of two parts, one a tuft of blood vessels which is invaginated into the ball-like upper end of the uriniferous tubule, so that it forms a capsule for it (capsule of Bowman). The secretory tubule, which forms the largest part of the nephron, is lined with a specialized epithelium. The collecting tubule, as its name implies, merely collects the urine and carries it to the pelvis for excretion.

Broadly speaking, the function of the kidney is to keep the composition of the blood constant by excreting in the urine any excess of substances normally present in the blood, such as water, salt, or glucose, or other substances which are not normal constituents of the blood. How this function is carried out is still a subject of dispute among physiologists. The consensus, at the present time, is that the urine is formed by filtration through the glomeruli of a fluid identical in composition with the blood plasma minus its protein (Menzies). The protein does not filter through the capsule of Bowman and is never a normal constituent of the urine. This filtrate, having been formed, passes through the secreting portion of the uriniferous tubule where certain substances are reabsorbed. These are known as **threshold substances.** These substances are normally present in the blood in a certain quantity (threshold value) and are reabsorbed up to their normal blood concentration. The threshold substances are water, glucose, and sodium chloride. The principal nonthreshold substances, none of which are reabsorbed, are urea, uric acid, ammonia, phosphates, and sulphates. It can readily be seen from this brief description that disease affecting any part of the nephron may cause serious interference with its function.

The urine is formed at the rate of about 30 drops per minute. The total amount of urine formed in 24 hours is approximately 1500 cubic centimeters. Of this amount, one liter is eliminated during the waking hours, and about 500 cubic centimeters at night while sleeping. From this, it may be deduced that if the bladder is emptied at bedtime, it should be unnecessary to awake from sleep for that purpose. A continuing increase of night urine over day urine is pathological. **Nocturia** is the term used to describe the need for emptying the bladder during sleeping hours.

Each kidney is surmounted by a suprarenal gland which forms part of the endocrine system of glands.

The Ureter

The ureter arises from a pouch, the renal pelvis. This pelvis is so arranged that, by a number of funnel-like divisions, called calices, it collects the urine excreted from all the renal papillae. This urine is carried from the calices into the renal pelvis proper. The ureter is a tube about 16 to 18 inches in length and with the diameter of a goose quill. It extends from the renal pelvis to the urinary bladder, which it enters by passing obliquely through its walls.

The Bladder

The urinary bladder is a somewhat distensible sac normally capable of holding about one pint. It is located in the front part of the pelvis just behind the pubis. Leakage from the bladder is guarded against by two sphincters. The internal sphincter is composed by involuntary muscle. This muscle has a tendency to relax when the pressure within the bladder reaches a certain height.

The bladder would then empty itself, due to the natural elasticity of the bladder walls. To prevent this from happening, there is a second sphincter, the external sphincter, which surrounds the urethra. This sphincter is under voluntary control and may be kept contracted or relaxed as desired. In the male, this muscle is located just beyond the prostate, and in the female, near the outer opening of the urethra. The desire to urinate arises by reflex nervous action when the bladder becomes distended.

The Urethra

The urethra is a tube which extends from the bladder to the surface of the body, so that urine may be eliminated. In the male, this structure traverses the penis and is about 20 centimeters in length. In the female, the urethra opens on the vulva just anterior to the vaginal orifice. It is about 3.75 centimeters in length.

CHAPTER III

Endocrinology of Marriage

JOSEPH A. HARDY

Until relatively recent years, the author who wrote on "hormones" and "endocrine glands" for a nonmedical public would have felt compelled to add a footnote in which he provided definitions of these unfamiliar terms. Today many a physician has the experience of being consulted by patients who literally request that they be given hormones for the relief of their real or fancied illness. It is, however, an apt commentary on the misinformation and confused conclusions which result from the barrage of pseudo-scientific articles appearing in a large number of circulation-seeking magazines that most of the people who use the terms so glibly have no real concept of their true significance and implications.

Endocrinology is one of the youngest of the fields of medical science. Its origins go back to the late nineteenth century when the French physiologist, Claude Bernard, expressed the thought that, in addition to the "external secretions" of the ordinary glands, there are also "internal secretions" which help to maintain the normal composition of the body. Another French physician, Brown-Sequard, in 1889, reported on his personal experience of rejuvenation following injection of a testicular extract. Even though we know today that the crudely prepared extract of Brown-Sequard could hardly have been biologically potent, the stimulus which he gave to investigating the physiology of the glands of internal secretion must be recognized as the foundation on which has been erected our present-day knowledge of the ever expanding field of endocrinology.

DEFINITION

It is probably an oversimplification to say that an **endocrine gland is a gland whose purpose is to produce one or more hormones which may either be secreted immediately into the blood stream or tempo-**

rarily stored within the gland for release at a later instant. Yet even such an incomplete definition will require clarification in order to establish what is meant by a hormone. This term derives from the Greek verb "hormao," meaning "I agitate" or "I stimulate." It is properly applied to certain physiological, organic (as opposed, for example, to mineral) substances which are produced within the body for the purpose of influencing the function and behavior of distant parts of the same body.

ENDOCRINE GLANDS AND SEX

With this understanding of the underlying principles and the terminology of the subject, we are prepared to consider to what extent sex, the sexual cycle, and the marital state are influenced by the endocrine glands and their hormones. We shall find that our considerations will revolve naturally around two of the endocrine glands, the so-called gonads or sex glands, the ovary and the testis. Each of these glands produces hormones which are characteristic of the sex of the individual. In the male the testis produces a hormone which is called testosterone; in the female the ovary produces a group of related hormones which are referred to as estrogens, and an additional hormone which is called progesterone. The specific activities and functions of these several hormones will be discussed below.

The type of gonad, and hence the sex of the individual, is determined by the sex chromosomes at the actual moment of conjugation of the maternal and paternal germ cells, the ovum and the spermatozoon. However, this genetic determination of the nature of the infantile sex organs cannot alone bring the individual to full physiological and anatomical development as a mature male or female. Such development requires the activity of the specific sex hormones. It is important also to understand clearly that there is no direct relationship between the germ cells produced by the respective male and female gonads and the specific sex hormones elaborated by these same anatomical structures. The ovary, for example, produces the ovum or egg which unites with the spermatozoon produced by the testis to bring about the conception of a new life. But the ovarian hormone (estrogen) and the testicular hormone (testosterone) have no direct and immediate connection with this process of conception. It is only in the further maturing of the newly conceived individual that their influence will be felt.

It is not within the scope of this discussion to consider in its entirety the various stages in the growth and maturation of the sex glands. Yet a certain understanding of the anatomy and the physiology of the ovary and the testis is essential if one is to explain the relation of their hormones to the sex cycle. Although the anatomy of these glands is discussed elsewhere (see chapter on anatomy), the structures themselves will be discussed again briefly.

THE OVARY

The ovaries in the adult female are paired organs, roughly almond-shaped and of the approximate size of a brazil nut. They lie in the pelvis at either side of the uterus, suspended by ligamentous attachments in a position adjacent to the Fallopian tubes. The surface of the ovary may be smooth or corrugated and it usually has a pearly white color. Microscopic examination of the cut section of an ovary discloses it to contain, among other structures, a very large number (as many as 500,000) of tiny, pealike vesicles. These are called follicles and they may be seen in varying stages of maturation. In each follicle is stored an egg or ovum. At more or less regularly recurring intervals one of these follicles, approaching the periphery of the ovary, reaches full maturity and its contained ovum is extruded. This happening is referred to as **ovulation** and with its occurrence the stage has been set for fertilization. If the subsequent behavior of the follicle from which the egg has escaped is observed it will be seen that it undergoes certain modifications in its size and appearance. It becomes larger and gradually takes on a yellowish color. In this phase of its existence the follicle is referred to as a **corpus luteum** (or yellow body). If the egg is fertilized and pregnancy begins, this yellow body, the corpus luteum, persists and becomes progressively larger during the first several months of the pregnancy. If, on the other hand, there is failure of fertilization, then the corpus luteum regresses and after a few weeks is represented only by a small, white scar on the surface of the ovary. Over and over, during the reproductive life of the female, this cycle of ovarian changes is repeated.

And over and over, during these cycles, there is being repeated concurrently the ebb and the flow of the tide of ovarian hormone secretion. From the maturing follicles come the several related hormones which we call estrogens — the sex hormone of the female. From the corpus luteum comes the hormone which prepares the way for gestation, the progestational hormone, progesterone.

THE TESTIS

Turning for a moment to the testis we find it to be also a paired organ. The two testes are small egg-shaped bodies lying side by side, suspended in the scrotum. Beneath, a fibrous capsular covering the testis is subdivided by tissue septa into some 300 to 400 tiny compartments. Within these compartments are found the minute, coiled tubules in which are produced the male germ cells, the spermatozoa. It is these germ cells which are destined to unite with the female ova to bring about conception. Also within these manifold compartments we find a great many highly specialized cells (the so-called Leydig cells) whose function is to produce the hormone characteristic of the male sex, testosterone.

One further concept must be established before we proceed with our discussion. We have thus far seen that the so-called sex hormones are secreted by certain structures contained within the sex glands. On the one hand, estrogen is produced in the ovary by the maturing follicle and progesterone by the corpus luteum. And on the other hand, testosterone is produced in the testicle by the Leydig cells. But this hormone production is not automatic. A stimulus is necessary before either ovary or testis will secrete its characteristic hormone. Here again endocrinology provides the key. Within the skull, lying at the base of the brain, is another endocrine gland, the pituitary body. It, too, produces hormones and among them are certain ones which are called gonadotrophins (i.e., gonad-nourishing or gonad-stimulating hormones). Here, then, we have a chain of endocrine relationships in which gonadotrophins secreted by the pituitary gland are carried by the blood stream to the ovary or to the testis where they stimulate the secretion of the respectively characteristic sex hormones. And, finally, by a further complexity of the endocrine system these sex hormones, entering the blood stream may react in turn by stimulating (or sometimes depressing) the activity of the pituitary gland.

THE SEXUAL CYCLE

One of the most interesting facets of endocrine function is its relationship to what has been called the sexual cycle. By this term we denote the more or less regular cyclic appearance and regression of fertility. Such cycles are observed in all animals, including man, though there is considerable species variation in the duration of the cycles and the manifestations of their recurrence. In the human male there is really no true cycle since he is continuously fertile throughout the reproductive period of life. The same is not, however, true of the human female whose periods of fertility follow a definite pattern and occur at more or less regular intervals, dependent upon the normal functioning of her endocrine glands. A parallel is seen in certain of the higher animals in which fertility is present only during the time of so-called estrus (or "heat"). It should be pointed out that estrus has no direct relationship to menstruation. Each of these phenomena is simply a separate manifestation of the sexual cycle. Estrus, in the human female, implies that ovulation, the expulsion of an egg from the ovary, has occurred. Without ovulation there can be no fertility. Menstruation, on the other hand, is simply the shedding of the membranous lining of the uterus, a process which is accompanied by more or less bleeding. Menstruation implies that the lining of the uterus (the endometrium) has been stimulated to growth by the ovarian follicular hormone, estrogen, and then transformed by the corpus luteum hormone, progesterone. When further secretion of estrogen fails (as a result of failure of fertilization of the egg) this progestational membrane is shed and the cycle is begun again. Actually, then, in the mature woman, both estrus, the condition of fertility, and menstruation are brought about by an interrelated sequence of endocrine-controlled events which may be summarized as follows:

Immediately following a menstrual period there is a gradual, progressive rise in the level of estrogen secretion as the ovarian follicle which is to ripen during this cycle becomes mature. Stimulated by this increasing supply of estrogen the endometrial lining of the uterus experiences a period of growth. Eventually, the estrogen concentration becomes sufficiently high to stimulate the production in the pituitary gland of gonadotrophin which then reacts upon the follicle to bring about ovulation. The egg is extruded and the state of fertility (or estrus) has been achieved. Conception may now occur if a potent spermatozoon is at hand. The ruptured follicle, still under the influence of the pituitary gonadotrophins, begins its conversion into a corpus luteum secreting increasing amounts of progesterone. The membranous lining of the uterus is transformed into a progestational endometrium so that a proper "bed" may be ready for the impregnated ovum when it reaches the site of its further development into an embryo.

But if, for any reason, fertilization has not been accomplished, then the corpus luteum regresses, the level of estrogen and progesterone secretion decreases, and when there is no longer sufficient hormonal stimulation to sustain the progestational endometrium, it crumbles, menstruation ensues, and the process is repeated during the succeeding cycle (see p. 216).

SEXUAL DEVELOPMENT

It should by now be fairly clear that the development of an individual as belonging to one or the other sex is dependent, first, upon the type of gonads with which he or she is born and, second, but perhaps equally importantly, upon the character, the amount, the proportions, and the potency of the secretions of his or her endocrine glandular system.

The female infant, for example, is born with ovaries which establish her sex. But she will never develop into a physiologically mature, complete woman capable of reproduction and with all the secondary characteristics of her sex unless there is proper timing and balance of the secretion of estrogen, pituitary gonadotrophins, and the other hormone products of her endocrine glands. From the third or fourth month of life until the eighth to the tenth year sexual development is largely absent. With the beginning of the second decade, we observe a new growth surge which is probably initiated by some sort of neurological or neurohormonal mechanism which stimulates the pituitary gland to produce increasing amounts of its gonad-stimulating hormones. As a result we find sporadic and incomplete attempts of the adolescent ovary to develop follicles and so the ovary begins to function tentatively as a gland of internal secretion. Once ovarian follicular formation has advanced to the point where estrogen is being secreted by the follicles there occurs marked and rapid growth of the uterus, the Fallopian tubes, and the vagina. At the same time there are visible indications of sexual development in the appearance of the so-called secondary sex characteristics. The development of the breasts, the reshaping of the bony pelvis, the appearance of pubic hair — all of these hormonally induced alterations herald the fact that the girl is becoming a young woman. At this stage the young ovary is producing estrogen in ever increasing amounts and with a definite cyclic variation. Ultimately, the rising peaks of estrogen secretion become sufficient to stimulate significant production of the specific pituitary hormone responsible for bringing about rupture of a mature follicle. Ovulation occurs and with it begins the second or progestational phase of the menstrual cycle. The lining membrane of the uterus, the endometrium, which underwent growth under the influence of estrogen, is now subjected to the qualitative changes induced in it by the action of progesterone. Conception has become possible; puberty has been attained; the girl has become a sexually mature woman.

On the male side the progress of sexual development proceeds with equal order if somewhat less spectacularly. Most boys begin to mature between the ages of twelve and sixteen. As described in connection with the female, sexual maturation is initiated through the function of the pituitary gland and its hormones, the gonadotrophins. In the male these gonadotrophins act upon the testes to evoke, on the one hand, development of the sperm-producing cells, and on the other, secretion of testosterone by the Leydig cells. These two functions proceed side by side as the boy approaches young manhood as evidenced externally by the changes in his body contours, the appearance of facial and body hair, the deepening of the voice, and the growth of the external genital organs. By the time he is seventeen years old the average boy will have reached the point in his sexual development when functionally mature spermatozoa are being produced in his testicular tubules; his endocrine glandular system is secreting sufficient amounts of testosterone to establish his bodily appearance; and his emotional reactions are characteristically masculine. He has, in other words, become a man.

And so we see that every individual, male or female, is what he or she is physically largely through the influence of the endocrine system. The development of the primary sex organs, the appearance of the secondary sex characteristics, the periodicity of the sexual cycle, the very fact of reproductive capacity — all of these are more or less directly controlled by the ebb and the flow of the tide of hormones.

CHAPTER IV

Menstruation and the Climacteric

Menstruation is the periodic, physiological discharge of blood, mucous and cellular debris from the uterus which recurs at more or less regular intervals from the age of puberty to the menopause. It results from a sequence of events which includes ovulation, failure of fertilization, and certain hormonal interaction which induces structural changes in the mucous membrane lining of the uterine cavity. Although it is a normal function of the female, it is frequently referred to as "monthly sickness," "the curse," or "off period." Aristotle compared menstrual blood to the matter; the sperm to the sculptor; and the fetus to the work of art.[1] As pointed out previously, an ovum is liberated from the ovary each month usually about midway between two menstrual periods. The Graafian follicle from which this ovum is liberated develops into the corpus luteum which liberates a hormone, progestin. The function of progestin is to prepare the lining of the uterine cavity for pregnancy. It does this by causing a proliferation of the mucous membrane which becomes greatly thickened and congested with blood. If pregnancy does not result, as it usually does not, this thickened endometrium sloughs off, giving rise to the menstrual flow. In the normal female this process takes place once a month from puberty until the menopause. (See Chapter III.)

In the female **the age of puberty,** which is indicated by the onset of the menses, varies somewhat according to climate. In tropical countries the onset of the menses may be as early as the eighth or ninth year; in cold countries as late as the sixteenth or seventeenth

---

[1] Aristotle, *Degeneratione Animalium,* 729a, 9–11; 729a, 22; 738b, 23–25; Vol. 5, trans. Arthur Platt, *The Basic Works of Aristotle,* ed. J. A. Smith and W. D. Ross (Oxford: The Clarendon Press, 1912).

729a, 9–11 states that the male furnishes the form and efficient cause; the female, the material cause.

729a, 22 states that the female contributes the menses.

738b, 23–25 states that the female provides body and matter. It is not necessary for the male to do so because the tools of the artist do not exist in the work of art.

year. In temperate zones, however, puberty usually begins at the ages of twelve to fourteen. In some unusual instances, the monthly flow may start much earlier.

Once initiated, the monthly flow usually occurs quite regularly — about once a month in most women. This regularity is not, however, as constant as was once thought. Only about 80 per cent of all women menstruate with any degree of regularity and not more than 60 per cent menstruate every twenty-eight days, which is the figure usually given for the intermenstrual interval. The duration of this interval and its regularity is of utmost importance in using the Rhythm Method of conception control. Many factors, however, may interfere with the regular rhythm of the menses. Among these factors are pregnancy, either full term or resulting in a miscarriage, febrile diseases, emotional upsets, severe fatigue or strenuous exercise, and occasionally cold baths such as ocean bathing.

The **duration of the menstrual flow** is usually fairly constant for each individual. It ordinarily lasts from three to six days, the greatest flow taking place during the first 48 hours. The same factors which may interfere with the regularity of the menses may also influence their duration. They may either shorten or prolong the period of flow. The most common cause for failure of the menstrual periods to occur is pregnancy.

Although menstruation is a normal function, it is frequently accompanied by certain unpleasant symptoms, the most common of which are low sacral backache, sensation of heaviness in the pelvis, and lower abdominal cramps. These symptoms usually appear slightly before the onset of the menses and may continue for 24 hours after it is established. These symptoms are so frequently present that they should not be regarded as abnormal unless they are severe. Disturbances which accompany menstruation when severe are spoken of as **dysmenorrhea.** Dysmenorrhea may at times be associated with symptoms of extreme severity, even by unconsciousness. Other terms commonly used in reference to menstruation are:

1. **Menorrhagia** — excessive menstrual flow, either in duration or amount, during the time of the period.

2. **Metrorrhagia** — bleeding between the menstrual periods.

3. **Amenorrhea** — failure to menstruate.

4. **Menarche** — onset of the menses.

5. **Menopause** — permanent cessation of the menses.

6. **Oligomenorrhea** — scanty flow during the menstrual period.

ANTHROPOLOGICAL DATA

Misconceptions concerning menstruation should not be blamed entirely on recent generations, since anthropological studies reveal that taboos connected with the menstrual period have been present from antiquity. The following examples will indicate only a few of the distorted attitudes toward this normal function.

On the Marshall Islands the girl who is menstruating for the first time withdraws to a hut which has been built especially for her by a group of young girls who have not yet reached puberty. The girl is dressed with two loincloths and wears a wadding which absorbs the menstrual discharge. She remains in her hut for 15 days and eats neither meat nor fish. No cooking is done inside the hut. She is instructed by an older woman of the village who teaches her songs and tells her stories containing points of moral value. Each morning the girl bathes in the sea and puts on a new set of loin mats. She is then purified and perfumed by the old woman who burns sweet-smelling leaves and passes them between her legs. Finally a ceremony is held on the fifteenth day of the period. From that time on she is considered a full-grown woman.

Natives of Queensland and of the Belgian Congo also perform elaborate rituals when a girl first begins her menses. Natives of the Pennefather River area in Queensland dig a pit of sufficient depth to allow the girl to stand in it up to her thighs. The pit is then compassed with stakes. The girl stands in the pit with her arms crossed and with the palms of her hands touching the sand. Only her mother is permitted to speak to her. The girl must go into this pit each time for her first three menstrual periods. After that time she indicates her menstrual periods by wearing across her shoulders a small basket full of empty shells.

In the Congo, the Bavili confine their girls in special huts for the first three months after menstruation begins. Their hair is shaven, and every day their heads are anointed with a reddish liquid concocted from the dust of a special kind of wood which has been dissolved in water. At the end of their term they bathe themselves and are then adorned by the married women with flowers and bracelets and are led back into the home of their families. All these ceremonies must be carried out, they believe, since otherwise the girls will be sterile or give birth to monstrous beings. Moreover, evil would befall the entire tribe, since rain would cease or all the cattle would die.

Usually among primitive peoples, the girl who is menstruating for the first time is taken away from the rest of the community and is kept in an isolated place until the period is over. Among the Maidu Indians of Southern California girls are confined in small huts which are built for this purpose. For five days they are allowed neither meat nor fish, nor any other thing which might contain blood. Neither are they permitted to touch food with their hands. They are fed by their own mothers or by some elderly woman of the village who puts the food into their mouths. At the end of this five-day period the young girls are allowed to take hot baths and may eat with their hands. Five days later they bathe in the river and are brought back to their families. At this time the fathers of the girls give a banquet in their honor, and they are presented with gifts. During the period of confinement the girls are allowed to visit their parents at night. They are serenaded by the men of the tribe who stand outside the door of the parents' house.

In many tribes this period of confinement is imperative not only for those women who are menstruating for the first time, but for all women who are menstruating. Usually the restrictions on the older women are not so heavy as those imposed on the younger ones. In some African tribes young women are forbidden to visit their families even at night, whereas the older women may do so, provided they return to their area of confinement before the sun rises.

A large number of tribes prohibit menstruating women from walking in sunlight or from putting their feet on the ground while the sun is shining. Among the Yaricanas of Queensland the women remain in huts specially constructed to keep them in a supine position. They also keep their eyes closed so that they will not see the rays of the sun.

The notion of the occult is frequently associated with menstruating women. Menstruation is frequently explained as the result of a prick by some animal or evil spirit. In Berlin and in Munich museums may be seen statues from New Guinea which depict a woman being punctured in the center of her body by a snake or a crocodile. Some groups attribute the menstrual flow to a puncture by a bird or a lizard.

It is common to find tribes that connect menstruation with the notion of evil. Menstruation is considered by these groups to be either the work of an evil spirit or of the women themselves, who are endowed with maleficent powers during this period. In Kola the girls flee from the sisi, spirits of evil who make stones grow in the uterus and cause all kinds of sickness, the most notable manifestation of this sickness being an emission of blood. The Zoroastrians of Persia attributed menstruation to the work of Ahura Mainyu, the demon of evil.

An example of the alleged maleficent powers of a woman at the time of her menses is seen in the story told by Tibori, an ancient Arabian historian. When Sapor, King of Persia, was besieging the city of Atrea, he met a daughter of one of the elders of the city outside the city walls. She had been sent out of the city because she was approaching puberty. The king fell in love with her, and she returned his love. One day she asked him, "What will you give me if I destroy the walls and kill my father?" Sapor promised to make her the first of his wives. The girl then commanded him to find a gray dove wearing a collar around its neck. The king was to write on the feet of this bird any message whatever. The message was to be written with the menstrual blood of a girl with blue eyes. Once this was done, the bird was to be released. The king did as commanded. When the bird was released it flew directly to the city wall where it perched. No sooner had it done this when the whole wall crumbled, and the city was destroyed and the father of the girl killed.

The notion of contamination connected with menstruation is found in a great number of tribes. Among some of the natives of the Torres Islands group, women are not allowed to enter any house in which there is to be found tortoise meat. Neither are they to approach a fire in which it is cooking, nor can they walk on any part of the seashore where it is abundant.

Sometimes the restrictions on contamination extend to the husbands of menstruating women. In the case of the natives of the Torres Islands, the husband of a menstruating woman is not allowed to hunt for turtles nor is he allowed even to participate in an expedition formed for this purpose.

Various evils were thought to attend those who failed to conform to the rites and regulations of menstruation. If a woman of the Yaricaras looked at the sun or ate an animal which lives in the salt water, it was thought that she would be devoured by serpents. Among the Reindeer Cherokee, it was thought that a woman who had coitus during this period would become sterile. In a great many instances the evil was thought to affect not only the woman but the male as well. If a male had intercourse with a menstruating woman, the Matacos believed, he would have an ache in his loins and in his head. Some African tribes believe that a man who has intercourse with a menstruating woman will develop a virulent sickness; other tribes believe that a man who has intercourse during the menses will lose his courage in battle.

It has been noted by Ford and Beach that the attitudes which different societies take toward women during these periods arise not so much from any change in the women themselves as in the attitude of others toward them.[2]

Since the misconceptions regarding menstrual activity are so widespread, it may be of advantage to describe some of the psychological problems which accompany it.

FIRST INFORMATION

Too frequently, the first knowledge which a girl receives concerning the menstrual flow is derived from her mother's disgusted remark, "Has that thing started?" when she comes to her with the first evidence of her menstrual flow. Having little knowledge of the physiology of the function, the mother is naturally unable to tell her daughter very much about it.

The concept that the time of the menstrual period is one of illness is transmitted to the daughter by parental oversolicitude. These parents often insist that "the poor dear child" stay in bed for all or part of the period. In a recent freshman college class, seven out of eighty girls stated that they spent the first day of the menstrual period in bed. When asked why, their only answer was that their mothers thought it was a good idea. It is from such maternal concern that taboos against taking baths, washing hair, swimming, getting chilled, and taking exercise have arisen. Actually there is no reason why any of these events should be harmful if performed during the menstrual period.

INSTRUCTION OF THE YOUNG GIRL

There is no doubt that menstruation is the most important event of puberty. Before it occurs the young girl usually knows something about it, although the information she possesses may not be at all

---

[2] Clelland S. Ford and Frank A. Beach, *Patterns of Sexual Behaviour* (London: Eyre and Spottiswoode, 1952), p. 212. Cf. also: Herman Heinrich Ploss, *et al., Woman — An Historical Gynaecological and Anthropological Compendium* (London: William Heinemann [Medical Books], Ltd., 1935), Vol. 1.

complete. She has heard of it either from her mother or from the girls with whom she associates. It is desirable that her mother give her instruction on the subject, but in too many cases the mother herself either knows nothing about the physiological process or has a distorted and unhealthy point of view. Even if the mother has not been forthcoming with instructions, the child, unless she is excessively shy, will usually have learned something about menstruation from her playmates. It is well known that smaller girls will often observe their older sisters with curiosity. The first menstruation may frequently be somewhat of a trauma. The reaction of the girl will depend upon how well she is prepared for it.

Many young girls think of the menstrual flow as unclean. They consider the flow as a discharge of waste material. The concept is not a recent one. In the sixteenth century, Moretaurus in his commentary on Hippocrates said, "The uterus is the sewer of all the excrements existing in the body for all decrements flow to the uterus."[3]

Misconceptions about menstruation can be dangerous to the healthy sexual development of a young woman, because she may become disgusted with her condition and renounce her feminine role. If she has been led to believe that woman is the weaker sex, she may intensify her tomboyish activity in order to assert herself more fully, or she may withdraw from association with what she considers to be an unclean group. Deutsch says that even in normal women there is a tendency to associate blood with conception, birth, and death.[4]

Menstruation may bring with it an increase in sexual excitability in a young woman. Apart from the physiological cause, there is a concentration of attention upon her genitals. How she will handle this situation depends a great deal upon her past sexual activity and her previous instruction in matters of sex.

THE HYGIENE OF MENSTRUATION

For a normal young girl the fact of menstruation is probably nothing new. She has heard of it, talked about it, and some of her own friends probably have experienced it. But with the arrival of her first menstrual period, that which was previously hearsay

---

[3] Bapt. Moretaurus, "De uterin. affectionibus," p. 221, quoted by Kreiger, *Die Menstruation* (1869), p. 5.

[4] Helene Deutsch, *Psychology of Women*, Vol. 1 (New York: Grune and Stratton, 1944), p. 179.

becomes a fact, presenting a much different experience and a much different problem. It is now her *own* experience and her *own* problem. It is advisable, therefore, at this crucial time that the individual, whether it is her mother, an advisor, teacher, or physician to whom the young girl goes for advice, should feel a responsibility, inasmuch as what is said at this time will formulate the mental attitude of the young girl toward the menstrual flow for years to come. To the young girl experiencing her first menstrual flow, it is the beginning of a new period of her life. It is also for the mother the factual realization that her child is now an adult who will progressively look forward to marriage and motherhood. It is important, therefore, that the attitude of the mother or other advisor be sensible and practical. The attitude that menstruation is a time of sickness should be carefully avoided. It is a period of normality, just as any other bodily function is normal, and should not be associated in the child's mind with disability or suffering. The principal obligation at this time would be to treat the occurrence calmly and to explain clearly the process of menstruation, using whatever illustrative material is available and desirable. Emphasis should be placed upon the fact that menstruation is a normal and important part of the female procreative function, and as such should not be related to any feeling of shame or uncleanliness. Any taboos or irrational ideas concerning the function should be explained away and reality emphasized. It should be emphasized that it is not dangerous to go swimming, to take a hot bath, or to indulge in any normal exercise during the menstrual period. It should be emphasized that it is not dangerous to follow a normal diet during menstruation, including cold drinks and cold dishes. There is no evidence that the menstrual period requires any change in the normal way of life for the average woman. Writing in 1876, on the question of the need of extra rest during the menstrual period, Mary Putnam Jacobi commented: "There is nothing in the nature of menstruation to imply the necessity, or even the desirability, of rest for women whose nutrition is really normal."[5]

TAMPONS

Menstrual protection may be provided by either an external vulval pad made of absorbent material or by a tampon which is inserted

---

[5] Mary P. Jacobi, *The Question of Rest for Women During Menstruation,* Harvard University (The Boylston Prize, 1876) (New York: G. P. Putnam's Sons, 1877), p. 227.

into the vagina. It should be noted that tampons alone will not always give adequate protection. They may not be adequate for the first few days. Their greatest usefulness will be found at the beginning and end of the menstrual period, when the flow is not heavy. This fact is usually not pointed out in the literature, but rather extensive surveys under actual use conditions indicate that this is true regardless of what brand tampon is used. To a large extent, it results from normal body activity during which such motions as sitting down will exert pressure on the tampon and tend to squeeze out the exudate which the tampon has already absorbed, thus causing leakage. Whether a tampon will give complete and adequate protection is largely an individual matter and depends upon such things as frequency of change, amount of flow, and capacity of the tampon to absorb.

The use of the vaginal tampon is usually thought of as a recent innovation. Because it has been mentioned so frequently in current literature as a possible source of immorality, a little of its history may be mentioned.

HISTORY

Hippocrates described an internal menstrual protection made of lint rolled into a solid shape, and also one made of a round piece of light wood with or without absorbent material covering it. The Egyptians, Assyrians, and Babylonians seemed to have had a preference for an internal roll made of soft papyrus for the wealthy, and of softened water reeds for the poor. The Roman women favored an internal roll of soft wool, greased or slightly waxed. In Parthia and in Bithynia an external vulval pad was the fashion in the court of Mithridates. At the height of Byzantine civilization, the aristocrats and the wealthy would use only the finest wool imported from the Caucasus, which was specially carded, combed, and rolled as a tampon in the Greek colony of Cherson in Crimea. During the Middle Ages, the Renaissance, and the period immediately following, internal tampons and external pads were both employed.

The little information available would lead us to the belief that in the past the vaginal tampon was favored where and when women had to lead an active form of life, and the external pad when a more sedate, leisurely, and domestic form of life was predominant. Such a life permitted a more elaborate dressing and an easier concealment of the more cumbersome external attachments. This choice seems to have been fairly constant in all groups of society. This thought seems to be borne out in equatorial Africa, where the scantily dressed and hard-working women use an inserted tampon made of vegetable material, such as grass or light reeds, sometimes softened through maceration in tepid water. The pastoral Peuls or Foulba who live in the French Sudan, and who are probably of Egyptian ancestry, favor a wooden plug covered with fine raw wool. In Timbuktu, the Afro-Arab women, whose life is more sedentary and whose clothing is more voluminous, are said to use a heavy external pad. In Mongolia, women of the nomadic tribes of the Balkash region use a woolen tampon built up around a body of horsehair. The sedentary Turkoman women of the rich oases of the Ferghana prefer external protection.[6]

THE MORALITY OF THE VAGINAL TAMPON

Whether or not the vaginal tampon serves as a source of erotic stimulation has been a matter of considerable discussion. Father Gerald Kelly has treated this question several times,[7] and Good and Kelly have commented as follows:

> We do not at all approve the use of devices for wear during menstruation which are made to be inserted into the vagina for the widely advertised purpose of avoiding "embarrassment" when wearing bathing suits, evening gowns, and the like. Such devices destroy the physical evidences of virginity by their insertion and may, like anything inserted into the vagina, furnish a stimulus to masturbation.[8]

There is no doubt that a vaginal tampon could be used for the purpose of masturbation, just as any other similarly shaped material could also be used. This has little to do with the practical question as to whether or not its routine use to retain the menstrual flow would induce or lead to such practices. The opinion that it does so is erroneous. The internal tampon, when inserted in the vagina,

---

[6] This material was abstracted from the following works: *Hippocratic Aphorisms*, Alexandrian compilation, second and third centuries B.C. (Oxford: Blackwell Scientific Publications); Aetius of Armida (royal physician of Justinian I), Byzantium: sixth century A.D.; works of Soranus of Ephesus (Tetrabilion), Philumenos, second century A.D.: E. Reinhard, *Ebers Papyrus* (Leipzig: Arch. f. Gesch. d. Med., 1915–1916); *Herodati Historiae,* ed. Abicht (Leipzig, 1869).

[7] Gerald Kelly, S.J., various publications, particularly the *Linacre Quarterly* in the past few years, e.g., Vol. 17, no. 1 (February, 1950), p. 5; Vol. 17, no. 4 (November, 1950), p. 15.

[8] Frederick L. Good and Father Otis F. Kelly, *Marriage, Morals and Medical Ethics* (New York: P. J. Kenedy and Sons, 1951), p. 42.

does not ordinarily lead to any erotic excitation. The vagina is a relatively insensitive area. Robert Latou Dickinson, for example, describes the vagina as a hollow organ endowed with sensory fibers of the mucous membrane which are so little sensitive in its deeper portion that one can operate there without anesthesia.[9] Goodall calls this cervical vaginal part "the great silent area of the pelvis."[10] The vaginal sexual response belongs, if anywhere, to the vaginal orifice. The erotic stimulus of the stationary internal protection is therefore negligible compared to the moving pressure of any external protection on the outer erotic area.

The selection of the type of menstrual protection is therefore a matter of choice as to what is more convenient for the woman, and has no moral implications.

A second problem which has been raised in regard to vaginal tampons is whether or not the tampon is harmful to the health. Father Gerald Kelly[11] quotes Father John McCarthy from the **Irish Ecclesiastical Record** of June, 1949, page 548, as follows:

> We have read in the *Catholic Medical Guardian,* January, 1941, and in the *Catholic Medical Quarterly,* July, 1948, statements which very definitely give the contrary opinion (that is, that tampons are not harmful). The statements record the considered opinion of a well-known gynecologist who makes a statement against any general use of tampons. They are useless for many patients; for others, especially for the young, they are harmful, physically harmful that is, and very frequently by the manner of their use they prove unhygienic. Another authority, in an address to the Westminster Branch of the Guild of St. Luke, SS. Cosmas and Damian, stated that: "one of the tragedies of school life today is that young girls of fifteen and sixteen years of age are allowed to use the so-called internal tampons." Apparently when such appliances are used organisms and infection are oftentimes introduced into the cervical canal and damage or alterations to the mucous membrane of the cervix uteri may result. This in turn would involve a grave risk of subsequent sterility. A large undenominational committee of women at a meeting in London in 1940 "strongly objected to the use of internal tampons and especially protested against such things being foisted by shops on young girls."

---

[9] R. L. Dickinson, "Tampons as Menstrual Guards," *J.A.M.A.,* Vol. 128 (June 16, 1945), pp. 490–494, quoting Poirier and Clarpy, *Anatomie* (1907), p. 572.

[10] J. R. Goodall, *Puerperal Infection* (Montreal, 1932), p. 75, quoted by Dickinson, *op. cit.*

[11] Kelly, *op. cit.,* Vol. 17, no. 1 (February, 1950), p. 5.

Father McCarthy also referred to an official statement of the hierarchy of England and Wales to the effect that they disapproved of the use of internal tampons instead of sanitary towels, and asked the Union of Catholic Women to make their decisions known to all Catholic Women's societies. Father Henry Davis, S.J., refers to a similar statement condemning the use of tampons because of moral and physical danger.[12] The objection of the hierarchy was raised because as a result of the development of State medicine in England, an attempt was made by the State to require the various dispensaries to dispense only tampons. From the strictly medical standpoint there seems to be a good deal of evidence that their use does not lead to the difficulties which were predicted.

There is clinical evidence based on the practical fact that more than two billion menstrual tampons have been sold and used without any proof of harm or impairment to the health of women. It is also true that in most medical centers, the internal vaginal tampons are commonly used either as a menstrual protection or as a useful and a beneficial appliance, medicated or not, between menses.

An absorbent menstrual tampon cannot block the flow and be a cause of an inflammation of the pelvis. In tests conducted at the New York Medical College in October, 1944, by Doctor I. S. Kleiner, it was shown that the menstrual tampon made of absorbent cotton let the menstrual fluid drip along the external cord for removal, when filled to 75 per cent of capacity. No damming of the flow can exist before the full capacity of absorbency has been reached.

K. J. Karnaky[13] in a test of 2000 women, including 110 nurses, after concluding in favor of the internal menstrual protection, resorted to a tight vaginal packing lasting from one to six days, with six women whose profuse bleeding called for abdominal surgery. After opening the abdomen, no evidence of backing up of the flow into the peritoneal cavity was found.

Clinical evidence over a number of years exists here and abroad regarding the usefulness of the internal protection and of its beneficial effects on the health of the vagina.[14]

---

[12] Henry Davis, S.J., *Moral and Pastoral Theology*, Vol. 2 (New York: Sheed and Ward, Inc., 1943), p. 254.

[13] K. J. Karnaky, "Vaginal Tampons for Menstrual Hygiene," *West. J. Surg. Obst. and Gynec.*, Vol. 51 (April, 1943), pp. 150–152.

[14] Further reports on the use of the tampon are to be found in the following articles:

Mary Barton, "Review of the Sanitary Appliances with Discussion on Intravaginal Pads," *Brit. Med. J.*, Vol. 1 (April 25, 1942), p. 524.

All findings and conclusions of the above references were confirmed by George Baba, M.D., at Loyola University, Mercy Hospital Clinic, under the supervision of Dr. Herbert Schmitz.[15]

Studies made in Germany by a group of gynecologists, Dr. Hildegard Kuhler Linke, Dr. Judith Jacobs-Esser, Dr. Gerd Romer, Dr. Adrienne Haeussler, and by Dr. K. Walker of the American Forces, bear out these facts.[16]

The case for and against the use of vaginal tampons is well presented by Dickinson:

> Among more than 6,500 women reporting on menstrual tampons as recorded in nineteen sources on the literature, medical and commercial, there are series that voice satisfaction ranging around the 90 per cents, especially with younger women, educated groups and better incomes. This includes much reliance on interior protection alone, but with some supplement by the external guard at the beginning of the period. One fifteenth of the bulk of material thus suffices to absorb the average flow of 2 to 4 ounces and avoids the harness and chafing and also minimizes odor. In another group of reports there is acceptance by one fourth to one third, discard being based on discomfort in about the same proportion, and on incompleteness of first day protection in about one fourth. Cramps and inflammation appear in

---

A. W. Diddle and L. J. Boulware, "Vaginal Tampons for Menstrual Hygiene," *Iowa Med. Soc.,* Vol. 32 (June, 1942), p. 256.

Morris Ferresten, "The Treatment of Trichomonas Vaginatis with Acetarsone Medicated Tampons," *Medical Record*, Vol. 155, No. 4 (February 18, 1942), pp. 130–132.

R. Greenblatt, "Trichomoniasis," *West. J. Surg. Obst. and Gynec.* (May, 1945).

H. C. Hesseltine, "Evolution by Controlled Series of Vaginal Trichomoniasis Therapies," *J.A.M.A.,* Vol. 109 (September 4, 1937), p. 768.

K. J. Karnaky, "Original Gynecological and Obstetrical Research — Sterility, Endocrine and Vaginal Operations," *Med. Records and Annals,* Vol. 35 (1941), p. 851.

Maurice O. Magid and Jacob Geiger, "The Intravaginal Tampon in Menstrual Hygiene," *Medical Record,* Vol. 155 (May, 1942), p. 316.

A. E. Rakoff, "Discussion of Hesseltine Paper," *J.A.M.A.,* Vol. 109 (September 4, 1937), p. 768.

Harry S. Sackren, "Vaginal Tampons for Menstrual Absorption," *Clinical Medicine and Surgery,* Vol. 46 (August, 1939), p. 327.

Madeline J. Thornton, "The Use of Vaginal Tampons for the Absorption of Menstrual Discharges," *Am. J. Obst. and Gynec.,* Vol. 46 (1943), pp. 259–265.

P. Titus, *Management of Obstetrics Difficulties,* 3 ed., 1945.

Elizabeth F. Widenius, "A Study of Commercially Manufactured Catamenial Tampons," *Am. J. Obst. and Gynec.,* Vol. 48, pp. 510–522.

[15] George Baba, *The Use of Tampax in Menstrual Protection and in the Treatment of Vaginal Discharge,* Loyola University, presented before the Obstetrical and Gynecological Conference, February 21, 1946, Chicago, Ill.

[16] *Die Medizinische Stuttgart,* February 16, 1952; October 4, 1952; November 24, 1952; October 4, 1942.

under 1 per cent of users; apprehension about damming back through the uterus finds scant support; salpingitis and serious complications are rare, appearing in two American and one foreign report.[17]

THE EFFECT OF A TAMPON ON THE HYMEN

Vaginal tampons are made in various sizes designed for the married and the unmarried and for those with a light or heavy flow. The smallest size is designed primarily for unmarried girls. In practically all cases there is an opening in the hymen through which the menstrual flow occurs. In an occasional individual the hymen will be imperforate. In this case it must be incised surgically to allow the menses to occur. The flow would otherwise dam up in the genital system and cause serious damage. In general the hymenal orifice varies between ¾ inch and ⅞ inch in diameter. The small tampon of one brand is ⁷⁄₁₆ inch. There should be no difficulty in the insertion of a tampon of this size especially if a small amount of vaseline is used as a lubricant. If the orifice is too small the insertion will be painful and cause the girl to stop its insertion. In either case, therefore, of its use or the discontinuance of its use the hymenal tissues will remain intact and unharmed. If any difficulty is encountered during the insertion the girl should desist and seek advice as to its further use. The assertion of Good and Kelly that the use of tampons necessarily destroys the physical evidence of virginity is a clearly erroneous statement for which they produce no factual evidence.[18]

The discussion of tampons has been somewhat lengthy because of the prolonged discussions in the literature concerning them. This discussion is not intended to imply that one method is better than another. What we wish to emphasize is that there is no basis for some of the assertions which have been made concerning tampons.

THE FEMALE CLIMACTERIC

Although the terms "climacteric" and "menopause" are often used interchangeably, they are not synonyms. **The term "menopause" merely means cessation of the menses, whereas the term "climacteric" refers to the whole series of changes which accompany or follow this event.** The cessation of the menses usually occurs around the age of fifty years. It may be earlier. A woman averages about thirty-five years of productivity. The age of the menopause will therefore be

---

[17] Dickinson, *op. cit.,* p. 494.   [18] Good and Kelly, *op. cit.,* p. 42.

related to the age of the menarche. In most cases, the regularity of the flow is disturbed and the periods occur at gradually decreasing intervals until they finally cease.

In a great number of women no unusual symptoms accompany the menopause. In a smaller number, however, moderately severe symptoms are present, and in a few, grave psychic upsets may occur. These disturbances probably have no causal relationship to the menopause but occur during the involutional period.

In the average individual the symptoms occurring during the climacteric are:

1. **Hot flushes** — these may vary from a few a day to several an hour. During the attack the patient usually flushes and experiences a sensation of warmth. This may be followed by a profuse sweat.

2. **Hot flashes** — these may also occur only occasionally or many times a day. They are less frequent than hot flushes but more disturbing because of their greater intensity. These are usually described as a sensation such as might be produced by a hot knife passing through the body. They are of short duration.

3. **Obesity** — the increased fat is most frequently deposited on the hips and abdomen.

4. **Headaches**

5. **Increased nervous irritability** — this is chiefly characterized by emotional instability.

The Counselor and the Female Menopause

There is a tendency to blame every disagreeable thing which happens during the menopausal period on "change of life"; this is hardly justified by the facts and is usually not warranted. A large number of emotional upsets may accompany the climacteric. These may vary from slight changes in disposition to actual insanity, the most common form of which is involutional melancholia. Although these disturbances occur during this period, there is no proof that they are associated with endocrine deficiency.

Since the cause of the climacteric symptoms is the failure of the body to adjust to the gradual decrease in the gonadal secretion, their treatment is obvious. We need only to replace artificially the deficient hormone and the symptoms will be relieved. The unpleasant vasomotor phenomena can, in practically all instances, be relieved by the administration of adequate dosage of the estrogenic hormones. These preparations are usually best given orally and may be given at gradually decreasing intervals as the body adjusts itself to their lack. Even after almost complete adjustment occasional doses may be necessary during periods of stress. During these times there is apparently an increased demand for the estrogenic hormone. Hormones for parenteral administration are becoming less popular.

Some unpleasant symptoms connected with this period may be removed through psychotherapy. Many of these patients are greatly disturbed mentally because they feel that the menopause is evidence of advancing years. They have noted other evidences of this in graying hair, increased weight, decreased physical attractiveness. They are afraid that they will lose their sexual desire and appeal. Much relief may be afforded them by explaining that sexual desire is not dependent on the presence of the menses and that the changes accompanying age are not necessarily unattractive.

If the counselor will keep in mind the following important facts he will save the menopausal patient much unnecessary distress. He should direct his therapy along these lines:

1. The menopause is a normal life epoch.

2. It is usually associated with a minimum of symptoms.

3. One does not "go crazy" as a result of the menopause.

4. Those symptoms actually due to ovarian deficiency can be relieved by oral medication.

5. The menopause does not mean old age but the beginning of a new epoch which can be rewarding.

6. Teach his client to grow old gracefully.

THE MALE CLIMACTERIC

While it is true that there arises in the middle-aged male a series of symptoms which are called the male climacteric, there is a question as to whether it occurs in the life of every male. In 1944 Heller and Meyers asserted that the symptoms should not be considered as normal.[19] But in 1946 Werner asserted that it can now be established as a fact that males do pass through a climacteric.[20] Dunn says that by far the largest number of complaints come from middle-aged men who are under a heavy load of responsibility and who might be expected to suffer a heavy strain.[21]

---

[19] C. G. Heller and G. B. Meyers, *J.A.M.A.*, Vol. 126 (1944), p. 472.

[20] A. A. Werner, *J.A.M.A.*, Vol. 132 (1946), p. 188. Cf. also: *J.A.M.A.*, Vol. 112 (1939), p. 1441; *ibid.*, Vol. 127 (1945), p. 705.

[21] C. W. Dunn, *Penn. Med. J.*, Vol. 45 (1942), p. 362. Cf. also: *Dela. State Med. J.*, Vol. 11 (1939), p. 46.

The change varies in different men. With some there is very little difficulty, whereas others are disturbed for months and perhaps at intervals for as long as five years. These climacteric symptoms come at a time in the life of a man when he is at his acme of production. The business or profession in which he is engaged is coming to fruition at that time. His family is at a stage of development in which the children are attending college, and he is making plans for his old age. In the midst of all this he finds that he has suddenly lost all the ambition and quick adaptability which formerly characterized him. The age of these climacteric changes in the male is about ten years later than in the female. They occur most frequently between the ages of fifty and sixty years.

The symptoms of which these men complain are numerous. The physical symptoms are few, since there is no definite sign of this change in the male as in the female. The psychic symptoms, however, are legion.

The usual physical symptoms are: (1) a more than ordinary fatigue; (2) difficulties in the circulatory system which include pains in the chest like those of angina; (3) vasomotor symptoms similar to those of the female climacteric. Douglas lists other physical symptoms:

> A loss of force to the urinary stream, a diminution of bladder neck function which extends to partial incompetence, vague pains over bladder and inguinal regions, a lowered metabolic rate, nocturnal sweating, increase in weight, a change in the size, shape, consistency and secretion of the prostate and seminal vesicles.[22]

The usual psychic complaints are: (1) a general feeling of uncertainty; (2) increasing "nervousness"; (3) dissatisfaction with libido or potency; (4) inability to make decisions; (5) a fear that mental powers are declining — especially memory and concentration. These men are usually hard to please, beset with worries, and they sometimes entertain thoughts of suicide. In severe cases these individuals approach involutional melancholia.

Werner gives a list of the relative frequency of symptoms which he found to occur in a group of 273 males who were diagnosed and treated as possessing symptoms of the male climacteric (see table, p. 58).[23]

Since a number of these complaints may be attributed to other ailments, a therapeutic test with male sex hormone over a period of

---

[22] R. J. Douglas, *J. Urol.*, Vol. 45 (1941), p. 404.   [23] A. A. Werner, *op. cit.*

	Per Cent		Per Cent
Nervousness, subjective	90.5	Vague pains	32.9
Potency decreased or absent	90.1	Headache	31.8
Libido decreased or absent	80.5	Itching	31.8
Irritability	80.2	Hot flushes	29.3
Fatigability and lassitude	80.2	Loss of confidence	27.1
Depression	77.2	Futility	27.1
Memory and concentration		Scotomas	26.0
decreased	75.8	Constipation	24.9
Sleep disturbed	59.3	Unsociability	23.8
Loss of interest	58.5	Obesity	21.5
Ill at ease	56.4	Aching in the vertex	17.5
Tachycardia, palpitation,		Sweating	17.9
dyspnea	51.2	Crying	15.3
Excitability	49.0	Tinnitus	10.6
Vertigo	46.5	Thoughts of self-destruction	7.4
Numbness and tingling	43.9	Chilly sensation	6.2
Occipitocervical aching	41.9	Self-accusation	2.4
Fear	40.6	Psychoses	2.4
Worry, unnecessary	33.7	Suicide attempted	.7
Cold hands and feet	32.9		

several weeks may be desirable. If the difficulty is due to climacteric changes in the body, the test will be at the same time a cure. This procedure will readily distinguish climacteric from psychoneurosis, psychogenic impotence, and anxiety-tension states.

THE COUNSELOR AND THE MALE MENOPAUSE

Once it has been determined that the patient suffers from symptoms of the climacteric, treatment is begun with dosages of testosterone. Once the symptoms have been relieved, smaller dosages of hormone may be administered.

It should be noted, however, that this treatment may make the patient temporarily sterile, that is to say, up to a period of several months after treatment has been discontinued. Also, a patient who has undergone treatment may feel a return of vitality. He should therefore be cautioned against exerting himself too strenuously.

Psychotherapeutically the advice previously given for the female menopause applies equally to the male. Men in general are less ready to accept the concept of menopausal changes and therefore may need more reassurance than women.

CHAPTER V

Heredity

Man begins life as a single microscopic cell. This cell is the product of fusion of two cells, one from the mother and one from the father. The ovum of the mother and the sperm of the father combine to form a single fertilized cell. Both parents contribute to the biological potential of the new individual. Each parent contributes equally a set of hereditary determiners which will, during the development of the infant, operate progressively under the influence of both internal and external environment to produce the physical characteristics of the child. The child inherits from his parents both the ability to become one of his own kind and the ability to be different from other members of his species.

THE CELL

The cell is an organized structure made up of both complex and simple chemical substances which are combined and integrated in such a way as to form living material known as protoplasm (see p. 60). The protoplasm forms cellular membranes, cytoplasm, and nucleus. The external limiting membrane of the cell is the thin delicate plasma membrane. This membrane encloses the cytoplasm, a transparent mass of living material which surrounds the nucleus. The nucleus is delimited from the cytoplasm by another delicate membrane, the nuclear membrane. This protoplasmic membrane encloses the nuclear sap. Embedded in the nuclear sap are nuclear bodies, the chromosomes. The chromosomes are the most interesting of nuclear structures in terms of heredity for they carry the genes, or hereditary determiners. Chromosomes are individual structures whose number normally never varies in any given cell. In fact, in a given animal the chromosome number is constant in all the cells of the body. Furthermore, the chromosome number is constant per

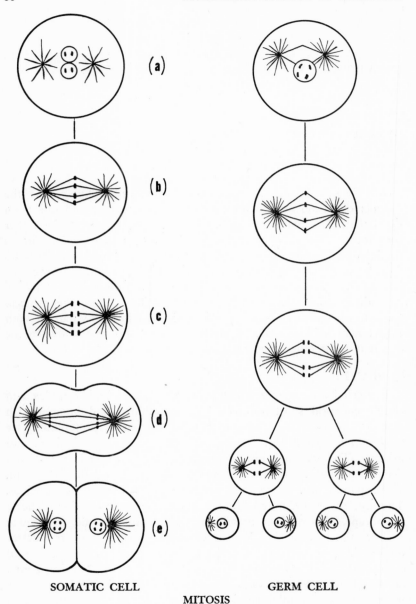

SOMATIC CELL   GERM CELL

MITOSIS

Mitosis in a somatic and a germ cell. Note that in the somatic cell each new cell contains the same number of chromosomes as in the parent cell, whereas in the germ cell each new cell has only one half the number.

species. **Thus in the human species each man has 48 chromosomes in each cell of the body.** The genes are chemical structures which are arranged in a linear series along the length of the chromosome. Like the chromosomes, of which they are a part, they are functionally, structurally, and numerically constant.

CELL DIVISION

Though life begins as a single cell, growth follows very shortly after fertilization and proceeds all through life. Growth occurs by increase in cell numbers and by an increase in the size of cells due to the uptake of food materials which are assimilated by protoplasm. Even in an adult growth occurs, for new cells must replace those that are degenerate. Within the lifetime of a single human being, many generations of cells may appear and disappear. Each of these cells in man must contain 48 chromosomes. Obviously, there must be some mechanism in operation by which the chromosome number is maintained at a constant value. One of the properties of chromosomes is their capacity to reproduce themselves. They are capable of manufacturing complex chemical materials like those of which they are already composed and of adding to their own structure. After growing by addition, each chromosome divides into two equal halves in a nuclear division process known as **mitosis** (see p. 60).

During mitosis the chromosomes within the nucleus shorten. As a chromosome shortens, it duplicates itself by splitting along its entire length into two equal longitudinal halves. During the progressive shortening of the chromosomes, the nuclear membrane breaks down and disappears. "Fiberlike" structures develop in the region of the old nucleus. These fibers arrange themselves in spindle-shape fashion and hence are known as spindle fibers. The double chromosomes line up in the center, or in the equatorial plane of this spindle. Then the halves of each chromosome begin to separate and migrate along the spindle fibers to the opposite poles of the spindle. Half chromosome separates from half chromosome, one half of the chromosome going to one pole while the other half goes to the opposite pole. On separation each longitudinal half chromosome becomes a chromosome in its own right. When separation and migration are complete, the cell contains two complete sets of chromosomes lying at opposite poles of the spindle. Each set reconstitutes itself as a nucleus.

Nuclear division is generally followed by cytoplasmic division. The cytoplasm constricts between the two new nuclei. The constriction gradually becomes deeper and eventually completely cuts through the cytoplasmic mass. As a result each new nucleus becomes enclosed in its own cytoplasmic envelope.

Mitosis is an equational division both qualitatively and quantitatively. Each of the 48 chromosomes is doubled in order that each new cell may receive 48 chromosomes. The half members of a doubled chromosome are essentially similar in character. The genes in each half of the duplicated chromosome are exactly alike in kind. At the end of the division process, both of the new nuclei are equal to the parent nucleus in kind and in number of chromosomes.

REPRODUCTIVE STRUCTURES

The general cell type described above is a **somatic cell.** There is, however, another cell type, the **reproductive** or **germ cell.** The somatic cells make up the large majority of all the cells in the body. Their function is vegetative; that is, their collective activity is responsible for all bodily functions except the reproduction of the species. The function of the reproductive cells, on the other hand, is to give rise to a new member of the species resembling the parents in kind. These cells are localized in the body of man in the reproductive structures, or gonads.

The **primary reproductive organ of the female is the ovary.** It is in the ovary that the germ cells, the eggs or ova, are found. In the human female the ovaries are small ovoid bodies located in the pelvic region where they are attached to the back of the body cavity by a broad ligament. Each ovary is enclosed in a connective tissue capsule. Internal to the capsule the ovarian tissues are the germinal epithelium, follicles in all stages of development, corpora lutea, and connective tissue. The germinal epithelium is a single layer of cells just inside the capsule. This layer of cells is the source of future egg cells. Internal to the germinal epithelium are the follicles loosely bound together by the supporting framework of connective tissue. Most of the follicles are immature or primary follicles. A primary follicle is composed of a large central cell, the cogonium, or future egg cell, and several surrounding layers of very small cells, the follicular cells. Primary follicles do not mature until the onset of puberty. After this time and all through active reproductive life, several follicles approach maturity on an average of every 28 days. In most cases, however, only one follicle attains full maturity in each 28-day cycle. The mature follicle is large and vascular and occupies about one fourth of the entire volume of the ovary. It has a large fluid-filled cavity enclosed by follicular cells several layers in thickness. Projecting into the cavity from the follicular wall is a small hillock of cells. Located in this hillock is the large egg or ovum. The entire follicle is enclosed by investing coats derived from the surrounding connective tissue. The follicle eventually pushes against the ovarian wall causing the wall at that point to become stretched and thin. In the meantime the cells of the hillock loosen and the egg, surrounded by adhering follicular cells, floats free in the follicular cavity. Follicle and ovarian wall rupture, and the egg is discharged into the body cavity. The discharge of the egg from the ovary is known as ovulation (see p. 216).

The collapsed follicle undergoes a transformation to become the corpus luteum (see Chapter III). Some of its cells increase in size by the manufacture and deposition of fatty substances in the cytoplasm. The entire structure becomes highly vascular by the invasion of blood vessels. The corpus luteum secretes hormones or chemical regulatory substances which cause those changes in the uterus necessary for the reception and retention of the egg in case of pregnancy. If the egg is not fertilized by a spermatozoon, it degenerates and disappears before reaching the uterus, and the corpus luteum begins to undergo degenerative processes. If the egg is fertilized, it passes down the oviduct into the uterus where it becomes implanted in the uterine wall. The corpus luteum of pregnancy persists from five to six months in order to maintain the uterus in a state conducive to pregnancy. In human females active reproductive life ceases after the menopause. After this period the ovary contains only degenerating follicles.

The primary reproductive organ of the male is the testis. The gonads are paired and each is located in an external pouch, the scrotum. The testis has a connective tissue capsule which is continuous with a fibrous band by means of which the testis is attached to the scrotal sac. Connective tissue passes into the testis incompletely dividing it into lobules. Each lobule contains a supporting framework of loose connective tissue and long thin coiled tubules, the seminiferous tubules. The outermost layer of cells in each tubule is a germinal epithelium. This epithelium is composed of two kinds of cells, spermatogonia and supporting cells. The spermatogonia are the source of sperm, or spermatozoa. They proliferate inward and give rise to four or five layers of cells encroaching on the lumen of the tubule. Each layer of cells more or less represents a different stage in the development of the sperm. The most immature cells in the series lie next to the germinal epithelium. They become increasingly more mature in each successive layer until finally fully mature sperm attached in clusters to the supporting cells line the lumen of the tubule. Most of the cells of the maturation series are present at birth. None of these mature as functional sperm, however, until puberty. After puberty, sperm are formed in large numbers at all times.

DIVISION OF THE REPRODUCTIVE CELL

The immature sex cells are the oogonia in the female and the spermatogonia in the male. In the human being both kinds of cells have 48 chromosomes in their nuclei. Obviously, if a 48-chromosome female cell were to fuse with a 48-chromosome male cell, the new individual would have 96 chromosomes in each cell. The chromosome number would be doubled every time a new individual was produced. But the species specific chromosome number is 48. Therefore, when the oogonia and the spermatogonia divide to produce sperm and ova the chromosome number must be reduced by half. This means that each ovum and each sperm will have half the species specific chromosome number, or 24 chromosomes. Then, when a 24-chromosome ovum fuses with a 24-chromosome sperm the new cell will have 48 chromosomes. In other words, the chromosome number must be halved in the sex cells in order that the 48-chromosome number may be restored when the sperm and the ovum fuse with each other. Spermatogonia and oogonia do not divide by mitosis, therefore, for mitosis maintains the 48-chromosome number from one cell generation to the next. The primary sex cells undergo a different type of cell division that will reduce the chromosome number. This type of cell division is known as meiosis.

Meiotic division involves the primary sex cells or the oogonia and spermatogonia. It has been indicated that these primary cells have the 48-chromosome number, a number made up of two 24-chromosome sets, one set of maternal origin and one set of paternal origin. A cell with a pair of chromosome sets is said to be a diploid cell. In a diploid cell each pair of corresponding chromosomes in the two complementary sets is homologous. Thus, chromosome A of maternal

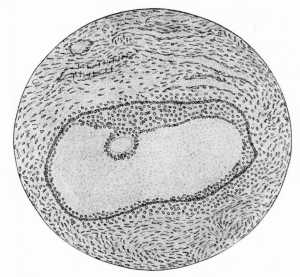

GRAAFIAN FOLLICLE

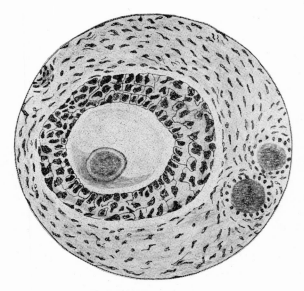

PRIMORDIAL FOLLICLES SHOWING
DEVELOPING OVA

origin is the homologue of chromosome A of paternal origin. **And each pair of homologous chromosomes corresponds gene for gene.**

Two nuclear divisions are involved in meiosis. Both resemble mitosis in the disappearance of the nuclear membrane, in the formation of the spindle, and in the shortening of chromosomes. The first meiotic division occurs in a diploid oogonium or spermatogonium, each of which carries 24 homologous pairs of chromosomes. During the first division the chromosomes line up in the equatorial plane of the spindle in homologous pairs. When the chromosomes migrate to opposite poles of the spindle, homologue separates from homologue. At the end of the division there are 24 chromosomes at one pole of the spindle and 24 at the other pole. **The first meiotic division is therefore reductional.** The primary cell has divided once to produce two cells each with one half the diploid chromosome number. **A cell with one complete chromosome complement is a haploid cell.**

The second meiotic division involves the two haploid cells. In the haploid cell each of the 24 chromosomes is split longitudinally into two equal halves. The chromosomes come to lie in the equatorial

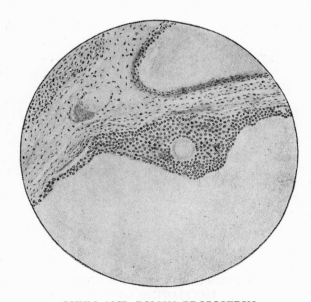

OVUM AND DISCUS PROLIGERUS

plane. At migration half chromosome separates from half, 24 going to one pole of the spindle and 24 to the other. Each of the two new cells developing from the haploid cell is in turn haploid. **The second meiotic division is therefore equational.**

Since the second meiotic division began with two cells, and since both of these divide each giving two new cells, the final result of meiosis is four haploid cells from each spermatogonium or oogonium. In the male every dividing spermatogonium gives rise to four haploid cells or spermatozoa, all of which are functional. In the female every dividing oogonium gives rise to four haploid cells, but only one of these is functional since the other three degenerate.

At copulation the sperm are injected into the female reproductive tract. They migrate through the uterine cavity and into the oviducts. If ovulation has occurred and if there is an egg in the oviduct, one haploid sperm may come in contact with and fuse with the haploid egg. The fusion is known as **fertilization. Fertilization restores the diploid chromosome number of 48.** In the fertilized egg, therefore, there is one complete 24-chromosome set of maternal origin and one complete 24-chromosome set of paternal origin.

MECHANISM OF INHERITANCE

The mechanism of inheritance can most easily be demonstrated by an example. Consider the inheritance of straight or curly hair.

Homologous chromosome pairs correspond exactly gene for gene. The homologous pair $A^m A^p$ (m = maternal chromosome; p = paternal chromosome) may carry genes for the expression of hair type. If the gene for hair type is for straight hair on both A^m and A^p, the genes are homozygous; that is, the genes in the pair are alike. If A^m carries a gene for straight hair and A^p carries a gene for curly hair, the individual will have curly hair because the gene for curly hair is **dominant** over the gene for straight hair. **The gene for straight hair is present but recessive; that is, it is not capable of expression in the presence of the dominant gene.** The individual carrying the contrasting genes for hair type is **heterozygous since the genes in the pair are unlike. Heterozygous pairs are also known as alleles.**

In a marriage the man may have straight hair and the woman curly hair. Both individuals may be homozygous for hair type. The man will carry two recessive genes for straight hair (ss); the woman, two dominant genes for curly hair (SS). The chromosome number and therefore the gene number will be halved during the meiotic divisions which lead toward the formation of sperm and egg. All the ova of the woman will carry only one S; all the sperm of the man will carry only one s. When the sperm and egg fuse the original number of genes is restored. An S-ovum combines with an s-sperm. The offspring will have a pair of allelic genes (Ss) for hair type. The offspring will resemble the mother in having curly hair. The gene contributed by the father (s) is carried by the offspring but is recessive. **When two individuals are alike in the visible expression of a character they are said to have the same phenotype.** The mother and child are phenotypes in the example given since the visible expression of hair type is curly hair. But the genes carried by the two are quite different. The mother carries the genes SS while the child carries the genes Ss. Therefore, **they are different genotypes because they possess different gene combinations.**

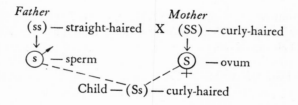

If the child (Ss) grows to adulthood and marries someone with the same genotype (Ss), both will produce the same kind of germ cell. The genes will separate at meiosis so that half the sperm (or ova) will carry an S and half the sperm (or ova) will carry an s. An S-sperm may fuse with an S-ovum giving a curly-haired offspring (SS); or an S-sperm may fuse with an s-ovum giving a curly-haired offspring (Ss). Both of these offspring will be curly-haired because they carry at least one dominant factor for curly hair. An s-sperm may fuse with an s-ovum giving an offspring with straight hair since this individual (ss) carries only the recessive factor.

Parents, homozygous for a characteristic, can produce only one kind of offspring, whereas parents, heterozygous for a characteristic, produce two kinds of offspring. In the example, if the parents are both heterozygous, the offspring may be either curly-haired or straight-haired in a phenotypic ratio of 3:1 and in a genotypic ratio of 1:2:1. At birth there will be a three to one possibility that the child will be curly-haired. The same possibility will occur again at

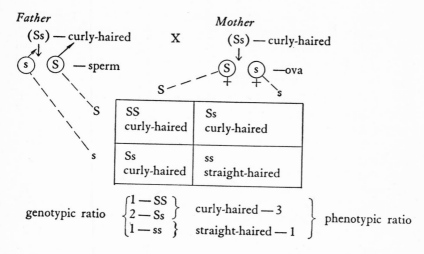

genotypic ratio $\begin{cases} 1 - SS \\ 2 - Ss \\ 1 - ss \end{cases}$ $\left.\begin{array}{l} \text{curly-haired} - 3 \\ \text{straight-haired} - 1 \end{array}\right\}$ phenotypic ratio

the next birth. None of the hereditary potential is lost by the parents at the birth of a child. Both father and mother still produce the same kinds of germ cells, with the same kind of genes, and in the same proportions as before the birth of a child. This is possible since the genes occur in pairs on homologous chromosomes. The paired chromosomes segregate or separate in the germ cells. They recombine at fertilization. **Which gene of the male will combine with which gene of the female is governed by laws which are as yet unknown.**

The genes for hair type are only two genes in a whole set of multiple alleles which are sets of contrasting characters. For hair type there is a gene for kinky hair, one for curly hair, one for wavy hair, and one for straight hair. This is a series of contrasting characters arranged in the order of decreasing dominance. All of these genes have arisen by a genetic mechanism known as mutation which is a change within the chemical structure of the gene.

MUTATION

The chemical change, or mutation, alters the gene in such a way that it causes the expression of some other characteristic. For instance, a mutation may occur in a gene for straight hair so that its locus becomes a determiner for curly hair. The new gene has the same chemical stability as the gene from which it was derived. Furthermore, a mutation need only occur once in a single cell of some one individual in order to cause the appearance of a new characteristic in the race. If the mutated gene determines a recessive characteristic, the characteristic will not appear in the offspring of the individual transmitting the mutated gene for he will have married an individual who is homozygous dominant for the characteristic. Conversely, if the mutated gene determines a dominant characteristic, it may appear in the offspring of the individual transmitting the mutation without skipping a generation.

THE Rh FACTOR

As was stated previously, multiple alleles, sets of contrasting characteristics, are the result of different mutations within a single gene. The Rh factor, like hair type, is also believed to be inherited on the basis of multiple allelism. The locus for this factor influences the production of antigens in the red blood cell. An antigen is a complex chemical substance which when injected into the blood of an individual lacking the antigen will cause the production in the injected individual of another chemical substance known as an antibody. The newly formed antibody will react with the antigen to neutralize the effect of the antigen. The production of antibodies against the antigen results in immunity to the antigen in question. When immune blood is injected into an individual with the antigen, the antibodies present in the immune blood will cause hemolysis (disruption) of the red blood cells. This result is obviously dangerous to the individual and therefore necessitates blood typing prior to transfusions.

Several genes are known for the Rh factor and all of these genes are dominant to the recessive condition or to the complete absence of any Rh factor. Regardless of how many genes are involved in the series of multiple alleles, only two will be found in any one person. Thus, an Rh negative person is a homozygous recessive (rh rh) and carries a gene on both homologous chromosomes for the absence of the Rh antigens while the Rh positive individual is either homozygous dominant (Rh Rh) or heterozygous (Rh rh).

If an Rh negative (rh rh) woman and an Rh positive man have a child, the child may be Rh negative if the father carries the gene. If, however, the father contributes an Rh positive gene to the offspring, this gene will cause the formation of Rh antigens in the embryo. The Rh antigens may pass from the blood stream of the developing infant into that of the mother. The mother develops antibodies against this antigen. The antibodies pass in the reverse direction from the blood stream of the mother to that of the child. There, the antibodies react with the antigen causing hemolysis of red blood cells. The child suffers from an anemia which may be so severe as to cause death.

MULTIPLE-FACTOR INHERITANCE

In the Rh-negative and Rh-positive example and in the curly-haired and straight-haired example only a single pair of factors was discussed. But two pairs of factors may sometimes be involved. These two factors may be on different chromosomes or on the same chromosome. If they are on different chromosomes, two homologous pairs will be involved in the two-factor cross. The two factors may, for example, be for hair type and for right- and left-handedness. Right-handedness is dominant over its recessive allele. A homozygous straight-haired, right-handed person will have the genes RR for right-handedness and ss for straight hair. His genotype will be RRss. This man may marry a woman who is also homozygous but for left-handedness and curly hair. Her genotype will be rrSS. Only one kind of sperm can be produced by the man, and all of these will carry one of each kind of chromosome, one R and one s. The ova, also, can only be of one kind, each ovum carrying one r and one S. When an ovum and a sperm fuse at fertilization, the child will be heterozygous (RrSs).

The child (RrSs) of this marriage on reaching adulthood will produce germ cells of four kinds (RS, Rs, rS, rs), each with one of each kind of gene. There is no tendency, therefore, for genes which are inherited together to remain together. Genes on different chromosomes segregate independently of each other and assort at random. Thus, when the chromosome number is reduced at meiosis R and r separate independently of S and s. There is an equal chance for R to remain together with S as with s.

If two heterozygous individuals (RrSs) were to marry, the sperm of the one and the ova of the other would be of the four kinds described above. There are sixteen possible combinations of the four different kinds of sperm with the four different kinds of ova. All offspring carrying an R will be right-handed, while all those carrying an S will be curly-haired. They will be left-handed and/or straight-haired when they are homozygous for the recessive characteristics, rr and/or ss. Within the scope of the sixteen possibilities, there will be one chance that the child will be both left-handed and straight-haired, three chances that the child will be straight-haired and right-handed, three chances that the child will be curly-haired and left-handed, nine chances that the child will be curly-haired and right-handed. At each birth the child will be one of the sixteen genotypes. This one genotype is not then eliminated. It has the same chance of occurring again at the second birth as it did at the first.

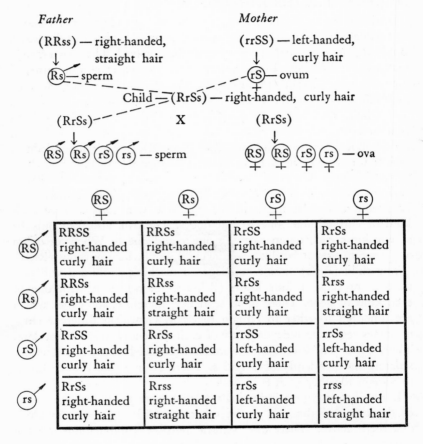

	(RS) ♀	(Rs) ♀	(rS) ♀	(rs) ♀
(RS)	RRSS right-handed curly hair	RRSs right-handed curly hair	RrSS right-handed curly hair	RrSs right-handed curly hair
(Rs)	RRSs right-handed curly hair	RRss right-handed straight hair	RrSs right-handed curly hair	Rrss right-handed straight hair
(rS)	RrSS right-handed curly hair	RrSs right-handed curly hair	rrSS left-handed curly hair	rrSs left-handed curly hair
(rs)	RrSs right-handed curly hair	Rrss right-handed straight hair	rrSs left-handed curly hair	rrss left-handed straight hair

If the two genes defined above are on the same chromosome they are said to be linked. Linked genes usually are transmitted together. If the genes **RS** are on the same chromosome their alleles **rs** are on the homologous chromosome. A heterozygote will have the genotype **(RS rs)**. When the germ cells undergo reduction division, the chromosomes will segregate so that half of the sperm (or ova) carry the **RS**-chromosome and half carry the **rs**-chromosome. Genes located on the same chromosome tend to remain together and do not separate independently or assort at random unless a new phenomenon known as **crossing over** occurs. **In crossing over, chromosomes exchange parts.** The noncrossover chromosomes are **RS** and **rs**. Crossing over results in an exchange of genes so that crossover chromosomes carry **Rs** and **rS**. If crossing over occurs, the individual will produce four kinds of gametes (**RS, rs, Rs, rS**). Wherever linkage groups are concerned, independent assortment is possible only when crossing over occurs. New linkage groups are formed by this method and they are inherited in the same way as any other linkage group.

DETERMINATION OF SEX

Of the 24 pairs of homologous chromosomes, one pair are the sex chromosomes. In the female the sex chromosomes are known as the XX-chromosomes, while in the male they are known as the XY-chromosomes. Sex is determined by the number of X-chromosomes possessed by the individual and by the kind of hormones secreted by testis or ovary. The female can produce only one kind of germ cell in relation to the determination of sex. All of the ova will carry an X-chromosome. The male, however, produces two kinds of germ cells. Half the sperm will carry the X-chromosome and half the Y-chromosome. If the X-sperm fertilizes the ovum the offspring will be female since the genotype is XX. If the Y-sperm fuses with the ovum, the child will be male since the genotype is XY. There is an equal chance at each birth that the child will be either a boy or a girl. If the first child is a boy, the chances remain equal as to whether the second child will be a boy or a girl.

SEX-LINKED CHARACTERISTICS

Genes located on the sex chromosomes are said to be sex-linked. The X- and Y-chromosomes are not completely homologous part for part. Some genes on the X-chromosome have no homologue on the Y. For example, **the gene for red-green color blindness,** located on the X-chromosome, has no homologue on the Y-chromosome. Red-green color blindness is recessive to the normal condition. If a homozygous normal-visioned woman (CC) marries a color-blind man (cY), all the ova of the female will carry a gene for normal vision (C), while half the sperm of the male will carry the recessive gene for color blindness (c), and half the sperm will carry the Y-chromosome on which there is no gene for the characteristic. When a C-ovum fuses with a c-sperm, the child will be a normal-visioned girl (Cc); when the C-ovum combines with the Y-sperm the child will be a normal-visioned boy (CY). A color-blind father, therefore, cannot transmit the character to any of his sons.

If the mother is a color-blind carrier (Cc) and the father has normal vision (CY), half the sons may be color blind. Sons will be color blind only when the mother is a carrier (Cc) or color blind herself (cc). If she is color blind herself all of her sons will be color blind. A daughter will be color blind only when her father is color blind and when her mother is a carrier or color blind herself.

The disease known as **hemophilia** is determined by a sex-linked recessive gene on the X-chromosome. Hemophilics are known as bleeders since the blood of hemophilics will not coagulate. Only hemophilic men are known (hY). Women are either homozygous normals (HH) or heterozygous normals (Hh). A woman would have to be a homozygous recessive (hh) to be a hemophilic. Since no hemophilic women are known, it is sometimes assumed that the recessive gene in the homozygous state is lethal. **Lethal genes** are those which cause the death of the infant before birth, shortly after birth, or some time before reproductive life begins. Rare cases may survive into early adulthood. Not all lethal genes are sex-linked. They are found on the other chromosomes as well. Death results only when they occur in the homozygous state. The heterozygous state may result in no visible effect, as in the female hemophilic carrier. Or it may result in a visible but nonlethal effect. For example, xeroderma pigmentosum is a skin disease determined by a recessive gene. In the homozygous state death generally results in early childhood. In the heterozygous state the individual is heavily freckled. In this case the normal condition is not completely dominant over the recessive gene. In the heterozygous condition there is an intermediate effect rather than complete suppression of the recessive by the dominant. Complete dominance, therefore, is not always the rule.

Some genes, not necessarily sex-linked, are dominant in one sex and not in another. The gene for baldness is dominant in men but recessive in females. A heterozygous male (Bb) will be bald since this gene is dominant over the nonbald condition in man. In females the heterozygote (Bb) is nonbald since this condition is dominant over baldness in females. Dominance here is influenced by the presence of different sex hormones in men and in women.

Not all factors are as sharply distinctive as those that have been described. There are characteristics that show minute differences in grade or degree. Between two extremes there may be a whole series of differences. Between one grade of the series and another the variation may be so slight as to be almost unrecognizable. Differences in size, complexion, head form, and mental ability are examples of characteristics which show all degrees of intergrading. Such characteristics are determined by a whole series of independent genes which segregate independently. Such genes show no dominance. Homozygous individuals of the genotypes AABBCC and aabbcc may be at the two extremes of darkness and lightness of complexion. The offspring of such individuals will be heterozygotes (AaBbCc) and will be intermediate in complexion between the two extremes. The factors for darkness and lightness are equal in their effect. The dark parent is darker than the heterozygous offspring because he has more dark genes. The effect is additive. The more dark genes carried by the individual the darker the complexion. Conversely, the more light genes carried by the individual the lighter the complexion. If two heterozygotes marry, the offspring can be as dark or as light as the two extremes or all grades in between dark and light. If a child of this marriage has the genotype AABBCC, he will be as dark as the grandparent (AABBCC). If he has the genotype AABbcc, he will be as dark as the parent (AaBbCc) since he carries three dark and three light genes. If he has the genotype AaBbcc, he will not be as light as the light grandparent (aabbcc) but he will be lighter than the heterozygous parent (AaBbCc). **This type of inheritance is known as multiple-factor inheritance.**

THE EFFECT OF ENVIRONMENT

Heredity, however, does not act in a vacuum, for environment acts as a co-operating factor influencing some inherited characteristics. While certain characteristics, such as blood types, are not affected by the environment, others are sensitive to environmental effects. Malnutrition may alter body form and size; education or lack of it has its effect on mental ability. The degree of sensitivity to environment may be difficult to determine. It may be even more difficult to determine just what is inherited and what is due to environmental conditions. For example, mental ability would seem to be the result of heredity, but there is as yet no valid way of determining how much environment has prevented us from measuring the inherited characteristic.

Despite the apparent difficulties involved in measuring intelligence, however, it can be inferred that mental ability is inherited on the basis of multiple factors. Furthermore, some types of mental deficiency, such as juvenile amaurotic idiocy, are definitely known to be hereditable. Others are known to have no hereditary basis at all. One of the symptoms of cretinism, for example, is mental deficiency. This disease is not heritable, but is due to underactivity of the thyroid gland through lack of sufficient iodine in the diet. Most heritable mental deficiencies are due to recessive factors. A homozygous recessive is generally recognized as a diseased individual. If an individual is heterozygous he will be normal, but a carrier for the disease. Most heterozygous persons marry normal homozygous dominants so that occurrence of diseased individuals is rare even when there is a history of the disease in a family.

Another example of the interplay of heredity and environment is provided by the case in which a man inherits a tendency to smallpox. If the virus which causes this disease never occurs within the environment of this individual he will never acquire the disease in spite of the hereditary tendency. Here is an instance in which both hereditary and environmental factors must be contributive before the gene can find expression. Only when the environmental factor is present can the presence of the gene be recognized. In addition, the individual may be rendered immune to smallpox by vaccination so that he will not acquire the disease in the presence of the virus. Or the person may have hereditary diabetes. Here the effect of the hereditary factor may be alleviated by the use of insulin. But the acquired immunity in the one case and the relief of the diabetic symptoms in the other does not have any effect on the genotype. **An acquired characteristic cannot impress itself on the gene.** For instance, a man who is blind through disease or injury carries genes for normal vision and transmits genes for normal vision to his children. The acquired defect does not alter the nature of the gene for acquired characteristics are not hereditary. It is for this reason that neurotic disorders are not hereditary, because being acquired after birth they do not alter the nature of the genes.

The mold within which a human being develops is determined by those factors which are inherited equally from mother and father. The rigidity of the mold is, in one sense, extreme, for it first of all determines that the human being will become one of his own kind. Once the basic form is established numerous accidental characteristics may be added to the mold. It is the accidental characteristics that show plasticity, and therefore, ability to vary. Any interference with the basic form through a mechanism like genic mutation would most certainly result in the death of a new individual, or in the degeneration of sperm and ova before fertilization, or in the inability of individuals carrying the mutated gene to produce sperm and ova. Alteration of a gene determining an accidental characteristic may also cause death depending on the closeness of its relationship to the fundamental plan. If a new individual carrying mutated genes survives it is because the altered characteristic has some degree of adaptability to the conditions of life. Once a new accidental characteristic appears it may or may not be influenced and altered further by environmental factors. The final cast of the mold, however, is certainly the product of heredity and environment.

Laboratory Methods of Interest to the Marriage Counselor

OSCAR B. HUNTER, JR.

Laboratory procedures during the past twenty-five years have contributed greatly to the accurate diagnosis of disease. They have also become useful in the diagnosis of conditions relative to medical problems that exist before and during the marital state. During the past fifteen years, laboratory examinations have been advised in many areas for those individuals entering the marriage state. In many instances local and state governments have required these tests to be performed as a prerequisite for the issuance of a license to marry. The test usually required is a serologic test for syphilis, together with a physical examination to rule out any obvious case of syphilis prior to the performance of the marriage ceremony.

SEROLOGIC TEST FOR SYPHILIS

There is no completely accurate diagnostic test for the presence of syphilis other than the identification of the typical **Treponema pallidum** in a syphilitic sore. However, with proper interpretation with reference to the patient's clinical condition, one is able to draw relatively accurate conclusions from the reactions of serologic tests. The following is a list of serologic tests for syphilis now used by different laboratories throughout the United States:

1. Wassermann test
2. Kolmer test
3. Kahn test
4. Presumptive Kahn test
5. Kline test
6. Hinton test

7. Eagle Flocculation test

8. Mazzini test

9. VDRL test (Venereal Disease Research Laboratory)

These tests vary greatly in their sensitivity, roughly the most sensitive test being the last mentioned. The more sensitive the test is, the less specific it is, constitutes the general rule in this type of work. The highly sensitive tests are so put together that their reactions will be demonstrable even with small quantities of reagins (antibodies). Because of this high sensitivity other antibodies developed as a result of exposure to other diseases will sometimes produce positive reactions in these serology tests. Noteworthy among the group are the following:

1. Malaria

2. Virus pneumonia

3. Infectious mononucleosis

4. Typhus fever

5. Rocky Mountain spotted fever

6. Smallpox

7. Vaccinia (smallpox vaccination)

Many other diseases allied to the above will also produce similar reactions in the syphilitic tests.

The difference between the true serologic reaction for syphilis and the biologic false positive reaction for syphilis in these serology tests lies in one main feature. The serologic test for syphilis is one which becomes present in from two to four weeks following the development of the initial lesion of syphilis (the chancre). Following the development of the antibody, a phase of two to three months transpires during which time the antibody develops to a relatively strong level. If not treated, and in some treated cases, the antibody will persist for years. With the other infections these antibodies disappear relatively rapidly after the patient has been healed of their infection.

Differentiation is frequently made evident by the fact that the more sensitive tests, such as the VDRL, showing a four plus or positive reaction, will be accompanied by a negative Wassermann reaction and perhaps a one plus or two plus Kahn reaction. This would be indicative of a relatively weak reagin and therefore would leave some question as to whether or not this was a true reaction for syphilis. This type of reaction could be present in a patient who had been previously treated for syphilis, it could be present in one who had never had syphilis and had suffered from a virus pneumonia, or from a recent vaccination with the vaccinia virus. A recheck of this test in one month's time in the biologic false positive will usually show decline in the strength of the reaction, whereas a true syphilitic reaction will not diminish in strength at all.

It is to be remembered that patients who have had syphilis and have been treated for syphilis with adequate therapy may still have a weakly positive syphilitic reaction. Nevertheless, these patients are not infective and therefore although they may have a positive reaction in the serologic test for syphilis, they nevertheless are without possibility of transmitting the syphilis infection and therefore there is no objection to their marriage from this cause. To be able to transmit the infection of syphilis one must have an active infection which usually consists of the presence of primary, secondary, or tertiary lesions. The primary lesion is the chancre, which is an open, hard, indurated painless ulcer usually on the genitalia, but may be in the mouth or other extragenital areas. The secondary lesion consists of a red eruption similar to measles. It is also demonstrable by the presence of ulcerating areas in the mucous membrane of the body, mainly of the throat, where the patient frequently has symptoms of a "sore throat." Where the patient has a positive serologic test and there is some question as to whether syphilis is or is not present after a period of observation, a spinal puncture and examination of the spinal fluid is of considerable help in distinguishing between the true luetic and nonluetic patient. In the nonluetic patient the spinal fluid is completely negative. In syphilis, in the late stages, the spinal fluid will show evidence of degeneration of the spinal cord from the protein and cell components of the fluid. The patient who is in the early stage of syphilis will show no spinal-cord changes (see Chapter IX).

LABORATORY TESTS USED IN THE MARITAL STATE

PREGNANCY TESTS

Pregnancy tests are numerous but all follow one basic principle. Their main objective is the demonstration of follicle-stimulating hormones produced by the placenta (afterbirth) and excreted in the urine of the mother. These hormones when injected into animals produce stimuli in the genital organ of the animal, and in most tests are made evident by the presence of a corpus luteum and a corpus hemorrhagicum in the ovary of the animal tested. Other tests utilize the excretion of these hormones in the mother's urine and quantitate the amount of the hormone excreted.

Biological Tests

THE ASCHHEIM-ZONDEK TEST

This test consists of injecting five immature virgin female mice with urine of the patient. After five days the mice are killed and their ovaries examined. A positive test shows the presence of corpora hemorrhagica and corpora lutea in the ovaries of these immature mice.

RAT TEST

This test takes six hours to run, and consists of injection of urine into the rat, which is autopsied after six hours. The positive test shows the presence of a hemorrhagic congestion of the Fallopian tubes and ovaries of the rat. This test is somewhat less accurate than the mouse test.

THE FRIEDMAN TEST

This test consists of injection of urine into the ear vein of a virgin female rabbit. After 36 hours the rabbit is autopsied and its ovaries examined. Changes similar to those seen in the mouse ovaries, i.e., of corpora hemorrhagica and corpora lutea constitute a positive reaction.

THE FROG TEST

This test consists of the injecting of urine of patients into the dorsal lymph sac of the frog. The frog is examined after one hour. The presence of spermatozoa in the cloaca of the frog constitutes a positive reaction. This test is subject to some error by virtue of the fact that the frogs, during the summer mating season, are susceptible to stimulation from seeing other frogs or by handling of the examiner. During this period toads can be used for this same purpose. This test is somewhat less accurate than the mouse test.

The above tests when positive are extremely accurate; however, they tend to err on the false negative side, the mouse test being the most accurate of the group. These tests may be positive approximately two weeks after conception, but may be negative for one month or more. In most instances, six weeks after conception all of the tests will be positive and close to 100 per cent accurate. This would mean, therefore, that after the second missed menstrual period, a pregnancy test can largely be relied on as quite accurate.

Chemical Test

PREGNANDIOL

This test consists of the estimation of pregnandiol in the urine excreted by the mother in a 24-hour period. Pregnandiol is the end product of progesterone metabolism which is produced by the placenta or afterbirth. This substance is excreted in small quantities by the corpus luteum, but after ovulation takes place there is a gradual fall in the progesterone excretion. If the patient becomes pregnant in this period, the pregnandiol level will rise gradually; otherwise it will diminish to a negligible level at the time of menstruation.

TESTS FOR THE VIABILITY OF THE FETUS

Laboratory tests for the viability of the fetus consist of estimation of hormone levels excreted by the mother. The pregnandiol test previously referred to is a helpful test to determine when the fetus is dead. The fetus may be shown to be dead when the pregnanediol level falls considerably over the period of one week's time. These levels are produced by the placenta, and when the placenta ceases to produce progesterone, further excretion of the hormone is halted.

BLOOD INCOMPATIBILITY

One complication of pregnancy is the presence of blood incompatibility. These incompatibilities exist in many of the blood factors found in the red cells of human beings. The most frequent incompatibility that exists is in the International Blood Grouping system, otherwise known as the O, A, B blood groups. In this situation where a mother and father are of different blood groups, the father is capable of transmitting his factor to the child. The child, existing within the mother's body, constitutes a foreign individual of different blood type that can set up antibody production in the mother by the process of extravasation of blood from the fetal into the maternal circulation. The most common occurrence in this situation is where the mother is blood group O and the father blood group A. The blood group A is transmitted to the child and is capable of producing an incompatibility. If the child's red cells are extravasated into the mother's circulation, the normal Anti-A antibody that is found in all group B people is stimulated and rises very considerably. This rise in antibody can be transmitted back into the fetal circulation where the antibody, under certain circumstances, can begin a destructive process on the fetal red cells. This results in anemia of the child, which if it continues over a long period will ultimately result in the deterioration of the fundamental life processes of the fetus. This is primarily compensated for by overproduction of red cells by the fetal circulation causing an enlargement of the red-cell elements in the bone marrow, liver, and spleen, as well as other tissues of the fetal body. When this type of child is born, it is found to have a very large liver and very large spleen, and because of the continued red-cell destruction, the baby would appear to be jaundiced. This jaundiced color results from the destruction of the red cells in the circulation and gives the skin a yellow pigmented appearance. In more severe situations, the child will become debilitated because of the extreme anemia, and fluid will extravasate into the tissues of the body causing edema or swelling. This edema or swelling produces a bloated appearance with an enlarged abdomen and an enlarged head and a mashed appearance to the face. On X ray the typical picture of a sitting Buddha is frequently found. These children when born may be alive but live only for a few minutes before they expire. Occasionally children of this type die in utero before delivery can be effected.

Incompatibility on the O-A-B basis is found once out of every fifty births. However, the majority of these cases are extremely mild and constitute no real clinical problem. In one out of every thousand births, the problem is sufficiently severe to require exchange transfusion of the infant at time of birth or shortly thereafter. Usually this is necessary because of severe jaundice developing.

Exchange transfusion constitutes one of the greatest advances in the therapy of this disease, since before exchange transfusion approximately 60 per cent of those with severe jaundice died. Fifteen per cent developed kernicterus which means pigmentation of the cells of the brain. This particular disorder results in poor locomotion and is noted in the spastic type of child. These spastic children are almost invariably the result of inadequate therapy at birth, and result from the destruction of brain cells because of the severe jaundice. Since exchange transfusion has been instituted these problems exist only in the cases which have not received adequate therapy in sufficient time to alleviate the problem.

Rh INCOMPATIBILITY

The Rh factor is another blood substance found only in the red cells of the body. In the Caucasian population, 85 per cent of the people are Rh positive, while 15 per cent are Rh negative. The percentage of Rh negative individuals in the Negro race is approximately 7 per cent, while in the Chinese race it is probably less than 1 per cent.

Incompatibilities in this blood group arise when a mother who is Rh negative has a child of a man who is Rh positive. The child, inheriting the Rh positive factor from the father, is able to exist within the mother and extravasation of blood occurs. This sets up an anti-body production against the Rh positive cells in the mother's body. This particular initiation of antibody production does not usually occur before the delivery of the first child. Consequently it is one of the subsequent pregnancies which usually suffers from erythroblastosis or hemolytic disease of the newborn.

Approximately 5 per cent of Rh negative mothers who have Rh positive children are sensitized from the first baby. In subsequent pregnancies there is an incidence of 9 per cent after the second, 11 per cent after the third, and 16 per cent after the fourth child. It is easy to see that as the number of pregnancies increases, the possibilities of sensitization to the Rh factor are also increased.

Diagnosis of the presence of these incompatibilities is usually a matter of routine in the ordinary prenatal studies given to mothers. When a mother goes to the doctor's office for her first visit, blood tests are usually done to determine whether the patient is Rh positive or Rh negative. If the mother is Rh negative, tests are done to determine whether or not she has any antibodies present. If there are no antibodies present, further examination of the mother's blood should be made at the twenty-eighth and thirty-sixth week of pregnancy. If no antibodies are found on these occasions, a prediction that no trouble will arise in the newborn child can be made. When the mother is found to be Rh negative, it is also wise to test the father to determine his Rh factor. If the father is Rh negative, no further studies would be necessary on the mother because it is only when the father is Rh positive that it is necessary to make antibody studies on the mother.

When antibodies are found in the mother, these antibodies should be followed during the pregnancy to determine how high they rise. If the antibodies remain below 1:8 in titer, very few children will suffer from a severe erythroblastosis. However, if the antibody titer rises over 1:8, the possibility for trouble is considerably increased. Approximately 17 per cent of babies born of Rh-negative mothers are stillborn, and of those that are born alive, approximately 10 per cent will die in spite of the fact that exchange transfusion is given.

From more recent work in this field, the prospects for improving the mortality rate of these children is considerably improved.

Rh TYPING OF THE FATHER

From the father's blood group, predictions can frequently be made that are helpful in establishing the expected problem in the child born of a particular couple. Of course, if the father is Rh negative no Rh incompatibility can exist except in extremely rare instances. On the other hand where the father is Rh positive, trouble may be predicted because of incompatibility in approximately 5 per cent of Rh-negative women. The blood group of the father may belong to the homozygous or heterozygous group; that is, the father may have an Rh-positive factor on both genes or he may have an Rh-positive factor only on one gene. In the instance where the father has an Rh-positive factor on both genes, 100 per cent of the children will have an Rh-positive factor, as all spermatozoa will carry the gene controlling this particular factor. On the other hand, where the father is heterozygous, one half of the genes will contain an Rh-positive factor and one half of the genes will contain an Rh-negative factor. Where the egg is fertilized by a spermatozoon containing a gene with the Rh-negative factor, the child will be Rh negative, and Rh positive in the other instance. Therefore, in such couples one may make a prediction that half of their children will be Rh positive and half will be Rh negative. This in most instances is a reasonable risk for even those sensitized very strongly with the Rh antibody.

OTHER BLOOD GROUPS

Erythroblastosis exists under other circumstances as a result of incompatibility with other blood factors. Of considerably less importance, but nevertheless occasionally seen, are incompatibilities due to the Kell factor, the P factor, the S factor, and the M and N blood factors. The instance of incompatibility of these groups is extremely rare. Kell being the more common; the others are seen only in very specialized laboratories.

BLOOD FACTORS IN PARENTAGE PROBLEMS

The use of the blood-typing method for establishing the possibility of parentage has been widely used for many years. At the present time in most jurisdictions the International Blood Groups are accepted without hesitation by the courts, since precedence has been established by the Court of Appeals.[1] In many jurisdictions at the present time other blood groups such as the M and N and the Rh blood groups are accepted by judges where the results are significant. The basis for the utilization of these blood groups is based on heredity and the use of the Mendelian law. With the blood groups O, A, and B, these factors are inherited according to the Mendelian law, and where the father contains certain blood groups his children must likewise contain one of the blood-group factors that his genes control. A typical instance would be as follows: If the child was blood group B, and the mother blood group O, the father then would have to belong to blood group B or blood group AB, in order to have fathered this particular child. Such a statement can be made without hesitation and unless the alleged father belongs to the blood group B or AB, he could be excluded as the father of this particular child. It is impossible, however, to make the statement that a particular man who is blood group B or blood group AB is this particular child's father, as it is obvious that this blood group B factor in the child could be inherited from literally thousands of other men. The M and N groups follow the same rule. If a child was blood group N and the mother blood group MN, then the father would have to belong to blood group N or MN. Since the child's blood contains only N factor, the father's blood must have this particular factor. Variations of the same problem exist with both of the factors.

In addition to the M and N factors, now the Rh factor is utilized in the same line. If the child has a blood factor that is not contained in the blood of the mother, then the father's blood must contain this blood factor in order to have it transferred to the child. With the Rh factor there are other possibilities of exclusion likewise, since there are six Rh blood factors, five of which can be tested. They are three in loci, which are occupied by the Rh-negative or Hr factors when the Rh factor is absent. Consequently where an individual lacks the major Rh factor (Rh_o) he must contain the reciprocal factor (Hr_o). However this Hr_o factor cannot be tested for because of the rarity of the serum available. The anti rh′ and anti hr′ serums, however, are much more readily available, and where an individual lacks the rh′ factor, he must therefore contain the hr′ factor on both

[1] Beach *vs.* Beach (1940) 114 F (2d) 479, 72 App. D.C. 318, 131 A.L.R. 804.

genes. Consequently both the mother and father must have an hr′ factor on both genes. Where the child lacks the hr′ factor, then both genes must contain the rh′ factor, and therefore both mother and father must have the rh′ factor in their blood. By these methods, therefore, exclusion is increased considerably and the possibilities of determining the actual father become increasingly more available.

TESTS FOR FERTILITY

As previously outlined, the pregnanediol test is an excellent test of female fertility, since at the time of ovulation the pregnanediol level rises appreciably. This test shows continued rise as the corpus luteum continues to produce progesterone with its maturation. The pregnanediol urine levels if followed daily from the time of ovulation should show a gradual increase until the time just before menstruation, at which point they will decline if the pregnancy does not occur. This test, therefore, constitutes an excellent way to determine the presence or absence of ovulation in the female. Other tests for fertility of the female are largely of a mechanical nature and require investigation by a competent gynecologist (see Chapter XXI).

Fertility Tests for the Male

In the male, the most common test for fertility is naturally an examination of the seminal fluid. The following is a list of the normal characteristics of a seminal ejaculation by a normal male:

Quantity: 5–7 cc.
Appearance: Cloudy
Total spermatozoa count: 100–150 million/cu. centimeter
Total number of active spermatozoa: 80%
Morphology: Normal appearing head and tail. Number of active spermatozoa more than 80%
Consistency of seminal fluid: Mucoid

These characteristics are those of a normal male, and if above the minimal level constitute a fertile seminal fluid. Where these normal characteristics are absent, further investigation of the metabolic processes is necessary to adequately arrive at a proper conclusion.

Obtaining specimens of spermatozoa presents a serious difficulty. As pointed out elsewhere (see Chapter XXII), according to Catholic moral principles the obtaining of spermatozoa by masturbation is contrary to the divine law.

POSSIBLE BLOOD-TYPE COMBINATIONS

If the child is	*and the mother is*	*the father must be*
O	O, A or B	O, A or B
A	O or B	A or AB
A	A or AB	O, A, B or AB
B	O or A	B or AB
B	B or AB	O, A, B or AB
AB	A	B or AB
AB	B	A or AB
M	M or MN	M or MN
N	N or MN	N or MN
MN	M	N or MN
MN	N	M or MN

Homozygous and Heterozygous gene components

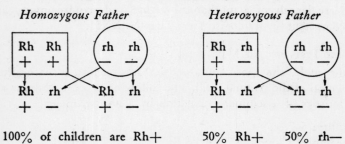

Homozygous Father   Heterozygous Father

100% of children are Rh+   50% Rh+   50% rh—

CHAPTER VII

Psychological and Physical Differences Between Men and Women

Mark Twain in **Huckleberry Finn**[1] wrote of two feminine characteristics in an instance which is probably well known to most readers. The hero was masquerading as a girl when put to a test by a suspicious woman. She threw a ball at him and in attempting to catch it Huckleberry put his knees together, a thing which no girl accustomed to skirts should do. She would throw her knees apart. The second test to which Huckleberry was subjected was that of threading a needle. The author observed that everyone knows that a girl pushes the thread through the eye of the needle, while a boy holds the thread steady and attempts to push the needle eye onto the thread.

Landis[2] points out some other characteristics which he feels distinguish male from female. He points out that a man, in attempting to remove a sweater, will pull it over his head whereas a woman reaches around her ribs and slips it off. A man pulls on his gloves from the front but a woman does so from the back; a man doubles his fingers into his palm to look at his nails whereas a woman will turn her palm down and look at the back of her hand. A man strikes a match toward himself but a woman will strike it away from herself.

Are these acquired or innate traits? We can all agree that, as far as these particular traits are concerned, it is relatively unimportant whether they are acquired or innate. They do serve however to empha-

---

[1] Mark Twain (Samuel Clemens), *Huckleberry Finn* (New York: Dodd, Mead).
[2] Paul H. Landis, *Making the Most of Marriage* (New York: Appleton-Century-Crofts, Inc., 1955), p. 38.

size the question as to whether there are any innate male or female characteristics or whether these are acquired from environmental influences. It seems quite clear that the traits mentioned above are acquired and when put to the test are far from universal.

Probably the best known study of the influence of culture on the development of male and female characteristics was that made by Margaret Mead.[3] Doctor Mead studied three tribes in New Guinea and found in these groups, which were geographically closely related, widely differing characteristics. Although this study is intensely interesting, it does not rule out certain basic natural characteristics of human beings. It serves to demonstrate that certain human characteristics are subject to change depending on circumstances. It does not, for example, demonstrate a change in the basic natural need for care of the mother during pregnancy and the puerperium. The dependent needs of the female created by these situations cannot be taken over by the male. As will be pointed out later, there seem to be certain personality characteristics in each sex which are natural and biological. These may, however, be modified by cultural factors, because it is obvious that no man or woman can grow up untouched by his environment. For example, however custom may change the methods of courtship there seems to be a biological basis for the pursuit of the female by the male (see p. 92). The male as the leader of the family group is also confirmed by nature. Any deviation from this established order has been only temporary or limited to small areas.

THE HUSBAND IS THE HEAD OF THE FAMILY

When a man and a woman marry they form a society. Soon after marriage children usually join the husband and wife, enlarging this society. Without a head in any society only anarchy would exist. Therefore nature has established a hierarchical order of authority which has been confirmed by divine injunction. The husband is the head of the family. Pope Leo XIII, in his encyclical letter on Christian marriage, so states:

> The husband is the chief of the family and the head of the wife. The woman, because she is flesh of his flesh, and bone of his bone, must be subject to her husband and obey him; not, indeed, as a servant, but as a companion, so that her obedience shall be wanting

---

[3] Margaret Mead, *Sex and Temperament in Three Primitive Societies* (New York: Morrow, 1939).

in neither honor nor dignity. Since the husband represents Christ, and since the wife represents the Church, let there always be, both in him who commands and in her who obeys, a heaven-born love guiding both in their respective duties. For *the husband is the head of the wife; as Christ is the head of the Church. . . . Therefore, as the Church is subject to Christ, so also let wives be to their husbands in all things.*[4]

Further emphasis was given this concept by Pope Pius XI in his encyclical **Casti Connubii.** After reaffirming the statement of his predecessor, quoted above, the Holy Father continued:

This subjection or obedience that the wife owes her husband does not mean slavery. It does not mean the surrender of that liberty which fully belongs to woman because of her dignity as a human person, as wife, mother and companion. It does not imply that woman is called upon to carry out her husband's request if it is unreasonable or contrary to her dignity as a woman. But it does forbid that false liberty advocated by feminists who claim that the wife should have the same liberty as her unmarried sister. "You lead your life and I will lead mine," means the ruin of husband, wife, and family. American divorce statistics prove that.[5]

This subordination of the wife to the husband is not absolute as indicated in this quotation. Father Vermeersch, S.J., describes this relationship in these terms:

This subordination is limited to the exterior acts of family life which may be reasonably demanded. The wife keeps the independence of a human person; she remains free in her personal conduct, in her practices of piety, in her goings and comings, with due consideration for the conjugal pact and the order of the house and family; she preserves the right to demand of the husband whatever her quality as wife and mother entitles her to, for she, too, has charge of the education of the children. Finally, as the husband and wife were equal in giving themselves each to the other, so they remain equal in regard to the right which flows from this mutual self-surrender. Besides, the subordination of the wife admits of a certain variation according to circumstances of time, place, and persons. Incapacity on the part of the husband confers upon the wife by a natural devolution the right to replace him in the government of the house. State laws, and the ante-nuptial agreement, if any, may modify the property rights of

---

[4] Pope Leo XIII, *Christian Marriage* (New York: The Paulist Press, 1942), p. 9.

[5] Gerald C. Treacy, S.J., *Love Undying:* Simplified Edition of the Encyclical *Casti Connubii,* on Christian Marriage, by Pope Pius XI (New York: The Paulist Press, 1944), p. 9.

the wife. There will, therefore, be, even as a regular thing, cases of independence and cases of equality; besides there are exceptional cases.[6]

Nature confirms this designation of the husband as the leader in the home by giving him greater strength, a natural ability in leadership and government, and in the fact that his fatherhood does not interfere with his duties in support of the family. The mother, on the other hand, is more frail, has a natural tendency to be dependent and is necessarily so at times because of motherhood. The husband is recognized by the wife as the natural leader because no woman would want to be married to a man whom she could not admire, upon whom she could not depend, and whom she would not desire to be the father of her children. These statements should not be interpreted to indicate "female inferiority." Men and women are different, not unequal. Each sex has been assigned by nature to perform a specialized role.

Biologically men and women differ in that their qualities tend to complement each other. Marriage is the completion of both the man and the woman. In marriage, the personalities merge and become one. Each aspect of the personality shows this relationship. Man's strength is complemented by woman's beauty, man's aggressiveness by woman's passivity. Even in their biological characteristics there is the same relationship — in the sex act the man gives, the woman receives, the spermatozoon is active, the ovum is passive.

MASCULINITY AND FEMININITY

The terms "masculine" and "feminine" when used as adjectives refer to personality traits which are predominantly male or female, i.e., those traits which are usually found in one sex or the other. These traits, may, however, be found in either sex and do not necessarily detract from the maleness or femaleness of the individual so affected. For example women are more sociable, more conforming, more co-operative, more submissive, exert greater effort to please, show greater domestic activity, are more given to aesthetic expression, and show greater verbal skills. Many of these characteristics may also be found in men. On the other hand men are usually physically stronger, more logical, more objective, more literal, more aggressive,

---

6 A. Vermeersch, S.J., *What is Marriage?* A Catechism Arranged According to the Encyclical *Casti Connubii* of Pope Pius XI, trans. T. Lincoln Bouscaren, S.J. (New York: The America Press, 1932), p. 21.

and less possessive, but these characteristics may also be found in women (see chart, p. 99).

Most males are predominantly masculine and most females predominantly feminine. The important thing for the couple about to get married is that they do not have too many similar traits. Their traits should complement each other, e.g., if one is aggressive, it would be better if the other is more passive, if one is not very self-assured, the other should be. These differences are principally psychological, but one may occasionally see that certain male anatomical features may be found in the female, and vice versa. This has no significance from the standpoint of marital adjustment.

ANATOMICAL DIFFERENCES

Men are stronger and more heavily built; they are more muscular, have more heavily built skeletons, and are taller as befits the more active part they are to play in life. The man must be the protector, the builder, and must consequently be the stronger and more stable.

Women are physically weaker, less heavily built, have a lighter skeletal structure, and are smaller as befits their less arduous tasks in life.

Men are stronger to pursue, women are more beautiful to attract.

Those anatomical structures in which the woman differs most from the man are those related primarily to her reproductive functions. In the male the breasts are atrophic because they have no function; in the female they are larger because they are functional. The female pelvis is designed to facilitate the passage of the baby through the birth canal. The pelvis of the woman is therefore lighter, lower, more graceful, less conical, and less heavily muscled. The pubic arch in the female is 90 to 100 degrees whereas the male pubic arch, better called a pubic angle, has an aperture of from 70 to 75 degrees. The male pelvis is heavier, higher, more funnel-shaped, and more heavily muscled. Because of the greater flare of the iliac bones the woman has a broader pelvis, evidenced externally by her more rounded hips.

The woman's sexual organs are constructed to receive and nurture, the man's sexual organs to give. The primary function of the woman is pregnancy. Louis I. Dublin expresses this well:

Childbearing always will remain the central fact of life for women. It is the basic reason why women save themselves from overwork,

protect their health, think subjectively, feel instinctively, react pro-
tectively and emotionally concerning their children; why they desire
peace and wish to preserve the existing social structure. It is the basic
reason why they are different.[7]

St. Thomas expressed this in a different but equivalent way:

> It was necessary for woman to be made, as the Scripture says, as
> a *helper* to man; not, indeed, as a helpmate in other works, as some
> say, since man can be more efficiently helped by another man in other
> works; but as a helper in the work of generation.[8]

INTELLECTUAL DIFFERENCES

There are here no clear-cut differences between the sexes. This is
true in spite of the opinion frequently held, even today, that women
are intellectually inferior to men. Louis I. Dublin, statistician of the
Metropolitan Life Insurance Company, after making a study of
the subject had this to say:

> Age for age, boys and girls average the same intelligence potential.
> However, test-makers have noted that in certain subjects girls excel,
> in others boys are ahead. The favored feminine areas, in preschool
> children, are color-matching, paper-folding, buttoning, tying bows; in
> grade school they are reading and language. Boys are better in sense
> of direction, in anything mechanical, in arithmetic, nature study; later,
> in history and the sciences. Though girls and boys come out about
> even in I.Q. tests, their skills and potentials are still not the same.
> Here, as elsewhere, the two sexes are not equal but equivalent; neither
> is superior or inferior; they are just different.[9]

Women excel in some areas, men in others. In most intelligence
tests men are somewhat superior. In tests of manual dexterity women
are superior. According to J. P. Guilford[10] these differences are as
follows:

Males excel in tests of:

1. Spatial aptitudes
2. Mechanical aptitudes

---

[7] Louis I. Dublin, "Women are Different," *The Reader's Digest* (December, 1950),
p. 60 ff. *Your Life* (December, 1950), copyrighted by the Kingsway Press, Inc., New
York, N. Y.

[8] St. Thomas, *Summa Theologica,* Ia, q. 92, art. 1 c, trans. Pegis.

[9] Louis I. Dublin, *op. cit.,* p. 58.

[10] J. P. Guilford, *Fields of Psychology* (New York: D. Van Nostrand Co., Inc.,
1950), p. 390.

3. Intelligence
4. Mechanical comprehension
5. Numerical reasoning
6. Arithmetic reasoning
7. Ingenuity

Females usually begin to talk earlier and mature socially and sexually at an earlier age.

In tests of the following they excel:

1. Dexterity
2. Speed and accuracy of computation
3. Clerical aptitude
4. Speed and accuracy of perceiving details
5. Verbal or linguistic ability
6. Speed of reading
7. Naming opposites
8. Analogies
9. Sentence completion
10. Disarranged sentences
11. Learning an artificial language
12. Code learning
13. Memory

Girls of preschool age have a larger vocabulary than boys. Speech disorders such as stuttering disabilities are less frequent in girls. Females also excel in scholastic achievement and have fewer behavior problems.

In the **area of the intellect** the following generalizations seem warranted:

Man is more reasonable (he figures things out), **woman is more intuitive.** "Intuition" is defined by Webster's **New International Dictionary** as:

2. Knowledge obtained, or the power of knowing, without recourse to inference or reasoning; innate or instinctive knowledge; insight; familiarly, a quick or ready insight or apprehension.

Women have been credited with intuition from time immemorial. Most of the credit has seemed to come from themselves. "I don't know how I know, I just know." There is no scientific basis for this belief.

Women usually have a greater grasp on the details of a problem, whereas men are better able to grasp the **entire** problem. Men reason from the general to the particular; women tend to go from the particular to the general. The male tends to be more factual in his approach to the whole problem, whereas the woman becomes lost in its minute details.

Women are more adaptable. They embark on an effort without a plan, and then adapt themselves to circumstances as they arise. Men, being more consistent, are less adaptable. They prefer to work according to a previously conceived plan. For this reason it is easier for the wife to adapt to her husband. He adapts less readily because he must constantly change preconceived plans.

Judgment is another aspect of the intellect in which men and women differ. Women tend to form quicker, almost instantaneous (intuitive) judgments whereas men are slower to come to a conclusion. For this reason **women are more changeable, men more stable.** For this reason, also, women are more frequently wrong, men more frequently right. Women are proud of their intuition, men of their logic.[11]

EMOTIONAL STATE

Men are more emotionally stable, women more emotionally labile. Women tend to be more suspicious because they are less secure. They are in constant need of reassurance in regard to their husband's love. The husband, on the other hand, takes his love for her for granted. He will state if asked that he proved his love by his marrige, that he continually proves it by his devotion to duty, by his support of his wife and children. This is not enough for the woman, however; she needs constant reassurance by words of endearment and demonstrations of affection that she is still her husband's only love.

In her insecurity the woman is likely to remain influenced by her first judgment, whether it was good or bad. It may be difficult to persuade her differently because logic has slight appeal for her. Her intuition is not subject to logic and although it is more frequently wrong than right, she maintains an unwarranted faith in its infallibility. It is here that a major problem frequently arises. The wife fails to recognize the logicalness and the literalness of what her husband says. He usually means literally what he says; she, however, judging him by herself, tries to read a hidden meaning into his words. It is usually not there. She should accept what he says literally.

---

[11] For a complete psychological study of this subject see Anne Anastasi and John P. Foley, *Differential Psychology* (New York: The Macmillan Co., 1949), pp. 612–688.

The husband, on the other hand, should not literally interpret his wife's words. She seldom means exactly what she says — he must read between the lines. A man should not, therefore, judge the comments of his wife or any other women as he would judge those of another man.

SEX LOVE

Traditionally the male is considered the aggressor. He is the one who takes the initiative. The male is the hunter, the female is the hunted. She sits at home and waits, he must seek her out. Traditionally she must not make the advances. She must be the charmer, but must not show her interest until he has first shown his. He seeks out his love, she waits to be loved. This is the traditional view, but it would seem to be more socially motivated than instinctually. Instinctually the woman is just as interested in seeking the male as he is in seeking her. In marriage the woman who is sexually interested should be just as free to suggest sexual relations as is the man. This does not deny the basic truth that woman seeks to be conquered, not to conquer. As it has been put by a wag, after attracting the attention of the male, the female runs away just fast enough to get caught. The woman is more possessive in her thinking. She is likely to pity a spinster, whereas the man is likely to envy his bachelor friends.

Too frequently the woman, by acting more as a *female* and less as a *woman,* drives men away. There is nothing more skittish than the male who sees a female approaching with the "mating look" in her eyes. Many girls make this mistake. They look at each man as a marriage prospect. As a consequence, she dates only once, and he is scared off by her urge to possess. Any girl who feels this possessive tendency should realize that her femaleness, her seeking of a mate, is too obvious. She should repress this tendency and treat her male friends just as she would other people. She should be less conscious of their *maleness* and think of them as *companions.* She must allow the skittish male a long tether.

The sex drive in the man and woman differs. The urge in the man is periodic, more subject to external stimuli, more sensual, more physical, less based on love. The sexual urge in the woman is cyclic, less subject to external stimuli, and is conditioned by her love for her sexual companion. The two principal tendencies of the sexual function, sexual gratification and reproduction, in the man are combined. Both are included in one act. In the woman on the other hand they are separated by a time interval. Sexual gratification is not as important to the woman. She participates in the act frequently to please her partner. Her reproductive function takes place without regard to her satisfaction.

LEGAL STATUS OF WOMEN

For many centuries and in many cultures women were considered socially inferior to men. It is only in quite recent times that they have been granted social and legal equality. It was not until the establishment of the Church that they were given equal status with men as human beings.

In most of the states in the United States the legal status of women formerly was that accorded by the Common Law of England. Under this law women were not allowed to vote or to hold any important public office. When a man and woman were married, the rights of the woman were merged and lost in those of her husband. The husband and wife became a unit and the wife had no independent legal existence. Up to 1938 a husband could get a decree of divorce on the grounds of his wife's infidelity, but the wife had no similar recourse. The right of a husband to physically chastise his wife remained on the statute books until quite recently. Since the turn of the century most of these legal restrictions have been lifted. The greatest single advance in this direction occurred when in 1920 the Nineteenth Amendment to the Constitution was enacted. This provided:

> The right of the citizens of the United States to vote shall not be denied or abridged by the United States or by any state on account of sex.

There is pending before Congress at the present time a so-called "Equal Rights Amendment" to the Federal Constitution. This proposed amendment reads as follows:

> Men and women shall have equal rights throughout the United States and every place subject to its jurisdiction.

If and when this amendment becomes part of the Constitution it is hoped that it will finally assure equal legal rights to both sexes.

TRAITS

Masculine	Feminine
Physically stronger	Physically weaker
Physically adapted to tasks of fatherhood	Physically adapted to tasks of motherhood
More realistic	More idealistic
More intellectual	More dexterous
Logical	Intuitive
More emotionally stable	More emotionally labile
Objective	Subjective
More factual	More fanciful
Slow judgment	Quick judgment
More likely to be right	More likely to be wrong
Literal	Tangential
Seeks love	Wants love
Aggressive	Passive
Sense of humor	Less sense of humor
Can take joke on self	Less able to take joke on self
Self-assured	Less self-assured
Holistic thinking	Grasps details
Less adaptable	More adaptable
More secure in love relationship	Less secure in love relationship
Less possessive	More possessive

This table is presented to show what might be called the "ideal" characteristics of each sex. It is not to be expected that all of these traits would be found in any one individual. Wide individual differences exist within each sex. As noted in the text (p. 92), these are to be considered masculine or feminine traits regardless of which sex they are found in.

CHAPTER VIII

Premarital Physical Examination

Health of mind and body are a natural requisite of happiness. This is true whether the individual is married or single. In approaching marriage with its greatly increased responsibilities, the question of health becomes immeasurably more important. Ill-health may cause serious disturbances which are a bar to happy married life. Many diseases are masked and fail to be recognized by the individual affected until they are so far advanced that invalidism cannot be avoided. Illness is expensive and may interfere seriously with the support of the family. For this reason those who are about to get married should have a physical examination to determine fully their physical ability to enter upon the responsibilities of their new state in life. An ounce of prevention is worth a pound of cure. Such an examination should not be resented on the grounds that it casts suspicion on the couple concerned. It is advised merely to detect and if possible to remove any physical barrier to happiness which may be present. A man or woman whose physical or mental health would prevent him from fulfilling the obligations of his married life should not get married. Father Edwin F. Healy, S.J., explains this:

> A person's right to marry is not an unlimited one. The licit exercise of this right is conditioned on one's ability to fulfill the duties which are involved in this state of life. Every husband has the grave duty to provide for the temporal needs of his dependents. This task could, however, be performed for the husband by another. Hence if his parents or some other relative or friend were to guarantee the adequate maintenance of himself, his wife, and his future family, even a helpless cripple could licitly marry.[1]

---

[1] Edwin F. Healy, S.J., *Marriage Guidance* (Chicago: Loyola University Press, 1948), p. 32.

For these reasons, as soon as is practical after their engagement the couple should be urged to have **a complete physical examination.** It might even be wise to arrange to have this examination before announcing their engagement because of the remote possibility that some matter might be discovered which would make the marriage inadvisable. This examination should preferably be made by a physician known to both parties and in whom they have confidence. On the part of the physician, he should be one who is willing to devote the necessary time and who has the requisite knowledge to make a proper study of the engaged couple. This examination should not be a quick routine asking of questions. It should be complete and thorough both in its historical and in its physical aspects.

The **premarital physical examination** should include:

1. A **complete medical history** of both parties. This should include not only general health but should be oriented to include any evidence of hereditary or communicable disease.

2. A **complete physical examination** of both parties.

3. A **mental examination** of sufficient extent to determine evidence of the presence of any serious mental or emotional disorder.

4. A **private discussion** with the boy and girl of the findings. This also gives the engaged couple an opportunity to discuss with the physician any fears or other concerns which they may have concerning the physical aspects of their marriage.

5. The engaged couple should also have a **joint meeting** with the physician to receive reassurance in regard to the physical status of their partner and to provide the opportunity for discussion of any mutual problems in regard to the physical aspects of marriage.

6. The **Rhythm** can be explained and discussed. For limitations on the use of the Rhythm see Chapter XIX.

7. A **discussion of the male and female genital anatomy** is desirable if the engaged couple has no previous systematized knowledge of this subject.

8. An appointment should be made for a **joint meeting** at least one month after marriage to discuss any new problems which have arisen during this time.

Such an examination is more complete than is usually given. But marriage is too important a step to be undertaken lightly. Although this more lengthy procedure may be somewhat more expensive it pays abundant dividends. The quicker routine might take only ten or fifteen minutes, but it usually accomplishes only one thing, that is, a blood test, and this under many circumstances can give a false reaction. Such an examination is not enough. Unfortunately, there are not many physicians who are prepared to handle this complete type of premarital examination. However, it is something for which we should strive, and if there is sufficient demand the medical profession will comply.

THE PHYSICAL EXAMINATION OF THE MAN

Aside from the usual clinical examination, the individual should be carefully examined for signs of communicable disease. A prostatic smear should be done, as well as a Wassermann and/or Kahn test.

Special inquiry should be made in taking the man's history to determine anything which might be a source of sterility, particularly a history of mumps and venereal disease. Inquiry should also be made in regard to masturbation to determine whether there remains any feeling of guilt which may interfere with his future sexual adjustment. There need not be much discussion of actual techniques of coitus but stress should be placed on the psychological importance of the first attempts at sexual relations. The need for gentleness and patience should be emphasized (see Chapter XII).

THE PHYSICAL EXAMINATION OF THE WOMAN

The history of the woman, in addition to the usual medical data, should make special inquiry into the menstrual history. Special attention should be given to irregularity or other difficulties which might interfere with the use of the Rhythm, if this marital practice becomes permissible or commendable in the course of marriage. She should also be encouraged to discuss any fears which she may have in regard to the physical aspects of sex, childbearing, or ignorance in respect to the sex act which she feels may be a handicap to her. An attempt should be made to elicit any feelings of guilt that she may have in regard to sex so that this can be discussed and, if possible, alleviated.

The physical examination should be complete. Very frequently the question arises as to whether or not a pelvic examination should be made in the virgin. There can be no reasonable objection to a bimanual rectal examination, and even though a complete pelvic examination is not done, vaginal and urethral smears can be made. Before pelvic examination the woman should be informed concerning its possible discomfort. Since venereal disease may be innocently acquired, false modesty on the part of the individual should not be allowed to interfere with the completeness of the examination. It is frequently advised that the hymen be ruptured during this pre-marital examination. There is no moral objection to this, but for sentimental reasons it should usually be advised that the hymen be left intact except in the presence of gross pathology. If natural spontaneous efforts on the part of the couple have not resulted in its obliteration upon the return visit one month after marriage, then some other procedure can be adopted. The function and nature of the hymen should be explained to the prospective bride and she should be desensitized to the painfulness of its rupture. Much undue fear is experienced by many brides in regard to this event. If it is decided to rupture the hymen before marriage the **consent of both the parties should be obtained.**

THE MENTAL EXAMINATION

There is no need that this should be a complete psychiatric examination, but the physician should attempt to determine the intellectual levels of the couple. He may also be able to determine in his conversation with them whether they present any evidence of a psychosis or severe neurosis. Their attitudes toward sex should be discussed not only to obtain information concerning their mental status, but also for the purpose of being helpful to them and providing necessary enlightenment. Any gross abnormalities noted in either should be brought to the attention of the other party during the last summing-up session. If it is felt that these abnormalities are of sufficient severity to warrant postponing the marriage, it would be advisable first to seek psychiatric consultation. It is probably best to withhold expressing any definite opinion until this examination is completed.

COMMUNICABLE DISEASE

If any evidence of communicable disease is found in either party, they should be strongly urged to desist from marriage at least as long as the disease remains communicable. In 36 states such a marriage is forbidden by the civil law.[2] What should be the attitude of the marriage counselor toward these so-called blood-test laws?

As Father O'Brien points out in his chapter on the *Canon Law of*

---

[2] Lovett Dewees, M.D., "Premarital Physical Examination," *Successful Marriage* (Garden City, N. Y.: Garden City Books, 1951), p. 57.

Marriage, the state is definitely restricted in its power to determine invalidating or prohibitive conditions for marriage.[3] Actually, there is only one instance in which the state is competent to so legislate, namely, a marriage between two unbaptized persons. The state may determine certain prohibitive and diriment impediments for such a marriage. Since these people are not subject to the laws of the Church because they have never been baptized, they do not fall within the scope of her legislation. As noted below:

> Her only right over such a marriage is the power to give authorita-tive interpretations and declarations regarding their rights and duties under the natural law. On the other hand, the state enjoys a peculiar authority in matters pertaining to them. Her authority is extended into the realm of a religious power over them, not as a purely secular authority to which the spiritual power is subordinated, but as the power of a God-given social superior. Thus the state can legislate in regard to the unbaptized even to the extent of creating invalidating impediments provided these are reasonable and do not derogate from the laws established over marriage by God Himself.[4]

With regard to the marriage of two baptized persons, the state does not enjoy the same competence. Christ elevated Christian matrimony to the sacramental order; and the administration of the sacraments has been entrusted solely to the care of the Church.[5] The Church alone may determine diriment and prohibitive impediments for the sacramental marriage of two baptized persons.

Regarding the marriage of a baptized person to one who is un-baptized, it can be said that such a marriage is governed exclusively by Church law. As Father O'Brien points out, some authors would maintain that the state laws must be observed "because the unbaptized person is subject to them. Nevertheless, since the contract (regardless of the subjection of the partners to different jurisdictions) is a unified entity, the superiority of the Church's jurisdiction is more commonly held to prevail."[6] Although such a contract is probably not sacramental, the state still lacks the power to determine conditions which might render such a marriage illicit or invalid. The marriage of a baptized person with an unbaptized person is very sacred and the Church has jurisdiction over all such sacred contracts entered into by any of her members. For any marriage, therefore, involving a baptized

---

3 See page 376.   5 See page 377.
4 See page 379.   6 See page 378.

person, it may be said that the right of the state to legislate is restricted solely to the civil effects of marriage, e.g., the right of inheritance of the wife and children.[7]

What, then, is the right of the state over the marriage of two un-baptized persons when one of them labors under an infectious and gravely injurious disease? The question reduces itself to whether or not such a marriage is forbidden by the natural law. The natural law demands that a person who is infected with a hidden infectious disease and who is about to marry make known his condition to the healthy party of the marriage. Not to do so would be an act of grave and gross injustice. Thus the state could forbid such a marriage for unbaptized persons under pain of nullity. However, if the healthy party were aware of the condition of the other party and were to consent to the marriage, the state could not permanently forbid the marriage because in this case there would be no violation of the natural law since no injustice would be perpetrated upon the inno-cent party. Therefore the state would be acting unjustly in refusing to grant a marriage license to such a couple.[8]

In those in whom it does not constitute a legal barrier venereal disease would certainly constitute a moral barrier, unless both are aware of the disease and nevertheless wish to go through with the marriage. For a person with a communicable disease to conceal his condition from the other party and yet enter marriage would be a serious act of injustice, and professional secrecy should not shield such a gross injustice.

HEREDITARY DEFECTS

The physician should fully inform both parties of any hereditary defects in either of the individuals or in their ancestors which might bring about defects in their offspring. This should not go beyond scientific facts, and should in general permit the individuals, who have been fully informed, to make up their own minds concerning marriage.

PROFESSIONAL SECRECY

In order to avoid any difficulty which might arise should a defect be discovered in one of the parties which he did not wish revealed to the other, a physician making such premarital examina-

[7] See page 378.   [8] Healy, *op. cit.,* p. 54.

tions should have an understanding with the engaged couple that he agrees to perform the examination only if he will be permitted to discuss his findings with both parties. In this case, should something be discoverd and the party concerned objects to revealing it to his partner, then the physician should immediately cancel his future appointments, and in this way the partner can readily understand that something has been discovered which the other partner does not wish revealed, and they should take warning from this fact.

A written mutual agreement to reveal the facts jointly may be desirable as a protection for the physician.[9]

---

[9] In reference to professional secrets see Chapter I, p. 7 f., and Chapter XXX, p. 527 f.

CHAPTER IX

Venereal Diseases

The venereal diseases continue to be one of the main problems of this age. In spite of recent advances in the understanding of the epidemiology and treatment of communicable diseases, including the venereal diseases, they continue to be an important medical problem. Being tied up with human passion, the venereal diseases are especially difficult to control.

HISTORY

The venereal diseases have a long and dishonorable history. The origin of syphilis is obscure. It is generally believed that this disease was introduced into Europe by the returning sailors of Columbus. There is little doubt that there were epidemics of the "Great Pox" as distinguished from "Smallpox" beginning after their return. Evidence of syphilis has been found in the bones of pre-Columban American Indians. Although the introduction of syphilis is comparatively recent into European culture, gonorrhea is of a much more ancient origin. Numerous diseases of the genito-urinary passages are mentioned in Assyrian tablets. Although there is no mention of syphilis, purulent urethral discharges suggestive of gonorrhea are mentioned.

> If a man's urine is like the urine of an ass, that man is sick of gonorrhea; if a man's urine is like beer-yeast, that man is sick of gonorrhea; if a man's urine is like wine-yeast, that man is sick of gonorrhea; if a man's urine is like gummy paint (varnish), that man is sick of gonorrhea.[1]

In spite of its earlier recognition the cause of syphilis was not discovered until 1905 when F. Schaudinn first described the **spirocheta**

---

[1] "Assyrian Prescriptions for Diseases of the Urine, etc.," Babylonia, 1934, 14: 108–109, quoted by Henry E. Sigerist, M.D., *A History of Medicine* (London: Oxford University Press, 1951), Vol. I, p. 482.

pallida. Before this in 1879 A. Neisser had described the bacterial cause of gonorrhea which has received his name. It is now called **Neisseria gonorrhoeae.** The first and still best known test for syphilis was described by August von Wassermann in 1906. It is a complement fixation test and bears his name. Another important advance in the diagnosis of gonorrhea was made when, in 1884, H. Gram first described his stain, which also bears his name, for the detection of gonococci in stained smears. The first effective treatment of syphilis by chemical methods was discovered by P. Ehrlich in 1910 when, in his now famous experiment "606," he discovered salvarsan. Since that time there have been rapid and numerous advances in effective treatment. At the present time penicillin and the sulpha drugs are extensively and effectively used in the treatment of all the venereal diseases.

CLASSIFICATION OF VENEREAL DISEASES

There are five diseases of a communicable nature which affect the genital apparatus. These are:

a) Syphilis
b) Gonorrhea
c) Chancroid or soft chancre
d) Granuloma inguinale
e) Lymphogranuloma venereum

These conditions have in common the fact that they are communicable from one infected person to another through genital contact, that their primary effect is on the genital apparatus although they may have metastatic effect on other organs, and that at least syphilis and gonorrhea may be transmitted to the offspring. Although it is possible for these conditions to be transmitted in other ways, their presence usually indicates that they have been acquired as a result of sexual contact with an infected person.

INCIDENCE

The seriousness of these disorders should not be minimized. Their significance can readily be understood when we realize that 10 to 20 per cent of all blindness, 30 per cent of sterility, and 75 per cent of pelvic infection in women result from gonorrheal infection.[2] There

---

[2] J. P. Greenhill, *Office Gynecology* (Chicago: The Year Book Publishers, Inc., 1940), p. 68.

are no statistics available for the incidence of gonorrhea. Such figures are difficult to obtain because of the high incidence of self-treatment and the failure of physicians to report cases. More is known about the incidence of syphilis because its presence may be discovered by a blood test (Wassermann or Kahn) even after active clinical symptoms may have disappeared. Of the first million men examined by the Selective Service during World War II, 45.2 per 1000 had evidence of syphilis.[3] It has been estimated therefore that 4.5 per cent of the inductees had syphilis. Other estimates indicate that at one time or another 10 per cent of the population will have the disease.[4]

The incidence of the other venereal diseases is unknown but they are undoubtedly less in frequency than is syphilis.

These diseases deserve the maximum attention of all workers, especially those in the field of marriage, because they are one of the most frequent causes of separation, divorce, broken homes, and morbidity. Their greatest tragedy is in their attack on children (see congenital syphilis).

SYPHILIS

Syphilis is a chronic, infectious, systemic disease due to the spirocheta pallida. It most frequently occurs as a result of infection introduced during sexual activity, but may be congenital.

Acquired Syphilis

Etiology

Syphilis is acquired as a result of the entry of the spirocheta pallida into the circulation through an abrasion of the skin or mucous membrane. The most common mode of infection is sexual intercourse with a person suffering from a communicable form of syphilis. **Many infections with syphilis are innocently acquired in marriage from a husband or wife who has the infection.**

The disease may be acquired from contact with any infected mucous membrane so that in addition to genital contact, oral mucous membrane contacts through kissing during the secondary stage is a frequent source of infection. This may lead to the appearance of the primary lesion (chancre) on the lips, tongue, or occasionally in a tonsillar fossa.

Another source of infection is transmission of the disease to the

---

[3] *Encyclopaedia Britannica*, Vol. 23, p. 43 (Chicago: University of Chicago, 1950).
[4] *Ibid.*, p. 43.

child by a syphilitic mother. It has been clearly demonstrated that if the child has congenital syphilis, the mother must also have it. The infection cannot be transmitted from the father to the child through an uninfected mother. Syphilis may also be acquired through infected surgical instruments and infected drinking glasses, but such sources are very infrequent. The lesions of primary and secondary syphilis are the most dangerous sources of infection.

Stages of Syphilis

Syphilis occurs in three stages: primary syphilis, secondary syphilis, and tertiary syphilis.

Primary Syphilis

Incubation Period: The initial lesion usually appears from fifteen to thirty days after the infective contact. The **chancre** is the characteristic lesion of this stage, and it usually occurs at the site of the infection. In the male this is most likely to be on the shaft or on the corona of the penis. In the female it usually occurs in the region of the introitus or on the labia minora. It may, however, occur in any other place where infectious material has been able to enter the body through an abrasion, e.g., on the lips or pharynx.

The chancre is small, seldom more than 2 centimeters in diameter, is painless, indurated, and superficially ulcerated. The secretion on the ulcerated area is richly supplied with spirochetes. Even without treatment the chancre will disappear in about thirty or forty days.

The diagnosis in this stage must usually be made by a dark field examination, because sufficient antibodies have not usually appeared in the blood to give a positive Wassermann or Kahn test. A dark field examination is performed by taking a small amount of secretion from the surface of the chancre and examining it under a specially equipped microscope which will reveal the presence or absence of the typical spirochete.

Secondary Syphilis

The secondary manifestations of syphilis occur from four to six weeks following the appearance of the primary lesion. The most characteristic lesion at this stage of syphilis is a cutaneous rash. Another feature is the appearance of slightly raised patches on the mucous membranes (mucous patches). This is most easily seen on the oral mucous membrane. These mucous membrane lesions are richly supplied with spirochetes. The individual who has such mucous patches has syphilis in a highly communicable form. There may be a slight fever during this stage, and the patient may complain of a sore throat, headache, backache, swollen glands, and generalized aches and pains. During this stage also the serological tests of the blood are quite regularly positive and may be depended upon to establish the diagnosis. Without treatment the secondary manifestations of syphilis will usually disappear in about three to four weeks (see Chapter VI).

Tertiary Syphilis

After the disappearance of the secondary lesions, the patient may have no symptoms for several months, and in fact none may appear for a period of many years, even up to fifty, after the initial lesion. Some manifestations are usually seen, however, after an average of five years. The characteristic lesion in the tertiary stage is the gumma. This is a granulomatous lesion, which may affect any of the bodily systems. These lesions have a tendency to heal, producing scar tissue, and in this way produce seriously deleterious effects on various bodily organs. The diagnosis of syphilis in this stage can usually be made from blood tests or the physical examination. The danger of communication of the disease to others is minimal during this stage.

SYPHILIS OF THE CENTRAL NERVOUS SYSTEM

This is usually a late manifestation of the disease in the form of tabes dorsalis and paresis. These are not likely to have much significance for the marriage counselor because of their age incidence.

Acute forms of involvement of the nervous system occur during the early stages of syphilis. These do not differ in their physical characteristics from central nervous system infections due to other causes. They differ only in their etiology, which can usually be detected from either the blood or spinal-fluid examination.

CONGENITAL SYPHILIS

Syphilis is not inherited, i.e., it is not transmitted from mother to child in the germ cells. It is acquired by the child from the mother after conception by transmission of the infection through the blood stream. The father cannot transmit syphilis to the child except indirectly by first infecting the mother. This means that if the child shows signs of syphilis the mother also has it. Maternal syphilis can usually be determined by means of a blood test which should be part of the examination of every pregnant woman. The detection of syphilis in the mother may be lifesaving to the child or save it from a life of invalidism. Premature stillbirths are four times as frequent in women with untreated syphilis. Infantile death will occur twice as frequently and 20 per cent of the surviving children will have congenital syphilis when the condition in the mother is untreated. Treatment very greatly reduces the incidence of all types of complications.

Of those children of syphilitic mothers who do not escape infection, some will show symptoms immediately after birth but some may escape until adolescence. In those cases which show symptoms immediately after birth they are quite likely to show cutaneous manifestations similar to those shown in adult cases of the disease. Where the condition is delayed until adolescence it is quite likely to manifest itself through the so-called stigmata of congenital syphilis. There are:

1. Saddle nose (due to loss of nasal cartilage)
2. Hutchinsonian teeth (notched, widely spaced, peg-shaped upper central incisors)
3. Deafness
4. Saber shins (anterior bowing of the tibia)

Other less well-known evidences of congenital syphilis are corneal scarring, mulberry-shaped first molars, a dish-shaped face, and radiating scars about the mouth (rhagades). In a small number of cases juvenile paresis is seen.

The prognosis in congenital syphilis, except for juvenile paresis, is good with modern treatment. Treatment in these cases should be left in the hands of the expert syphilologist.

TREATMENT OF SYPHILIS

The modern treatment of syphilis is safe and effective. Penicillin is used in large doses. Obviously, a book on marriage counseling is not the place that one would look for or expect to find the treatment of syphilis. Suffice it to say, therefore, that every case of syphilis should be referred to one qualified in its treatment. The earlier that treatment is started the more likely the individual is to avoid its late effects.

GONORRHEA

Gonorrhea is an infectious disease caused by the diplococcus (gonococcus) of Neisser. It is caused by the direct innoculation of the genital or urinary mucous membrane, usually as the result of a sexual contact.

Epidemiology

The gonococcus is rapidly destroyed on exposure to air, so that discharges from the body containing the gonococcus become innocuous within a few hours after excretion. For this reason, although it is popularly asserted that gonorrhea may be obtained from toilet seats, glasses, bedclothes, and bathtubs, these are probably a very rare source of infection. The dose of gonococci necessary to cause infection may be very small. The period of incubation averages about three to five days. Most cases develop within one week of infection. It is very rare for the infection to develop after ten days.

Types of Infection

The most common site of initial infection in both the male and female is the urethra. In the male this may proceed to the posterior portion of the urethra or prostate, and with the progression of the infection it may involve the epididymis and testicles. In the female its progression upward frequently leads to salpingitis (inflammation of Fallopian tubes), oophoritis (inflammation of ovaries), and peritonitis. In both sexes gonorrhea is a frequent cause of sterility, in the male by blocking off the vasa deferentia, and in the female by obliterating the lumen of the Fallopian tubes as a result of infection.

The gonococcus may be carried through the blood stream and set up metastatic lesions elsewhere in the body, the most common of which is gonorrheal arthritis.

Symptoms

Acute Gonorrheal Urethritis in the Male

The patient first notices a slight burning on urination. This is followed by a thin, milky secretion which may glue the lips of the meatus together, and the meatus may become red and swollen. The burning on urination usually becomes worse. The secretion gradually becomes thicker, and after several days is yellow or greenish, and may sometimes be bloodstained. These local symptoms are accompanied by constitutional symptoms, characterized by loss of appetite and generalized aches and pains. The acute stage of the disease usually lasts about one week, then gradually subsides until there may be a small drop at the meatus in the morning. This acute infection may become chronic and may ascend so as to cause an infection of the upper urethra or prostate (posterior urethritis).

Acute Gonorrheal Urethritis in the Female

The acute symptoms may involve the urethra, but more frequently the infection is limited to Skene's glands. There is a purulent discharge from the urethra. The entire vestibule may be tender and inflamed. These acute symptoms usually disappear in from two to four days, but the infection frequently spreads to the surrounding structures and glands, and may ascend and produce peritonitis or salpingitis. Any of these symptoms may become chronic.

Diagnosis

The diagnosis of gonorrhea in acute cases may usually be made by examining smears of the discharge by staining them by Gram's method. In the presence of gonococci the stain will show gram-negative **intracellular** diplococci. The diagnosis should never be made on the basis of **extracellular** diplococci because these are usually not gonococci. (For details of the Gram method of staining, reference should be made to standard texts on laboratory methods.)

In chronic cases and even in some acute cases it may be necessary to make cultures of the discharge to find the organisms.

CHANCROID

This condition, also called "soft chancre," is an acute localized lesion. It is most common in individuals whose contact with soap and water is minimal. It is **caused** by a bacterium, the Hemophilus ducreyi, which is a short gram negative organism. There are no accurate figures available in regard to its incidence, but it is a widespread infection.

It has an **incubation period** of from three to five days. The first lesion to appear is a pustule which soon breaks down to form a painful ulcer. In a few days to several weeks, enlarged inguinal glands (buboes) appear. These may suppurate and drain pus.

The disease is usually self-limited, but the continued presence of uncleanliness may prolong its course. The sulphonamides are specific in treatment.

The **diagnosis** can usually be made from the clinical picture. It is important to rule out syphilis. The Ito test, an intradermal test, made with a bacillary vaccine, is sometimes of value.

GRANULOMA INGUINALE

This disease usually appears in the inguinal region, although it may be found elsewhere. It is **due to the Donovan bodies.** These are small encapsulated bodies about one micron in diameter which are found on smear within the mononuclear cells. It is still undetermined whether they are protozoa or bacteria. Granuloma inguinale is the least common of the venereal diseases. The **incubation period** is unknown but is probably quite long. **Clinically,** it manifests itself as a deep, beefy red ulceration which spreads usually from the groin to the perineum. It is extremely chronic although therapeutically it usually responds to antimony compounds.

In addition to the clinical picture, the diagnosis may be established by finding the Donovan bodies in stained smears.

LYMPHOGRANULOMA VENEREUM

This venereal disease is due to a filterable virus. It is also known as Nicolas-Favre disease, climatic bubo, and lymphopathia venereum. The **incidence** of this disorder is also unknown. It is endemic in southern United States but is more frequent in the tropics. The **incubation period** is ten to thirty days after which the initial lesion appears. This is so slight that it may easily be missed, but shortly afterward swollen inguinal glands (buboes) appear. These glands are very tender and abscesses frequently form. In the female the primary lesion may be around the anus. In untreated cases, inflammation and ulceration frequently followed by stricture appear around the rectum. Other **sequels** may be elephantiasis (lymphedema) of the genitalia and polypoid growths around the anus.

The **diagnosis** may be suspected from the clinical picture. Once it is suspected, confirmation may be sought through the use of the Frei test (a skin test), a complement fixation test, or by biopsy. The sulpha drugs are those most effective in therapy.

PREVENTION

There is only one sure way to avoid venereal disease and that is to avoid all sexual contacts outside of marriage. People being what they are, there will be some who, as a result of premarital contacts, will bring venereal diseases into marriage and may thus bring about an infection in the innocent party. For this reason a complete physical examination, including a Wassermann or Kahn test and smears for gonorrhea, should be made on all candidates for marriage (see premarital physical examination). False modesty should not be allowed to interfere with the future health of the marriage partners or their offspring. Expectant mothers should also be examined (see hygiene of pregnancy).

There are certain other social measures which every one of us should encourage. Among these would be measures to repress prostitution, to decrease promiscuity, and case-finding studies to locate infected persons who do not voluntarily seek treatment.

SEXUAL
ASPECTS
OF
MARRIAGE

Love is swift, sincere, pious, pleasant, gentle, strong, patient, faithful, prudent, long-suffering, manly, and never seeking her own; for wheresoever a man seeketh his own, there he falleth from love.

— Thomas à Kempis: *Imitation of Christ*

CHAPTER X

Need and Desirability of Sex Education

SEX EDUCATION OF CHILDREN

While the causes of marital discord differ widely, there is little doubt that sexual maladjustment is a contributing factor in many cases. One remedy for this is sex education, which has been widely discussed during the first half of this century, not just in counseling circles, but in religious, medical, pedagogical, and in a growing number of popular books and periodicals. Most professional people realize the necessity for adequate sex instruction for children, but not all of them realize that sex instruction divorced from all thought of God does not teach the true nature of sex and in many cases is only instruction in ways of sinning.

Pope Pius XI, while realizing the need for sex instruction, stigmatized

> that exaggerated physiological education — laying much stress on these physiological matters in which is learned rather the art of sinning in a subtle way than the virtue of living chastely.[1]

It was formerly assumed that knowledge in sex was dangerous. We should not be too eager to discard this traditional view

> for it is fundamentally based on sound reasoning, viz., upon the fact that with the subject of sex, knowledge tends to be more operative and experimental.[2]

Recognizing these truths, instruction should be given to children, so that they will have the necessary guidance for maturity and common

[1] Pope Pius XI, *Casti Connubii,* December 31, 1930.
[2] James H. VanderVeldt, O.F.M., and Robert P. Odenwald, M.D., *Psychiatry and Catholicism* (New York: McGraw-Hill Book Co., Inc., 1952), p. 398.

sense in the matter of sex. Correct sex knowledge is needed as a positive safeguard to chastity. Temptations to purity will come and unless the child is fortified, he will succumb. Girls especially need correct information lest others take advantage of their innocence or lest they, by immodest dress or actions, become an occasion of sin to others.

The value of proper sex education for children and premarital instruction for young adults is inestimable. Both from the spiritual and physical points of view, these prerequisites for a healthy attitude toward the God-given powers of sex and a successful marriage are indispensable. From his first impressions of sex, the child often forms lasting attitudes which may help or hinder him in his later adjustment to marriage. Of great importance, then, is the necessity of teaching the child, through the proper individuals and in the proper manner, the Christian attitude toward sex and its use. For if the child does not obtain the information he desires from the proper channels, he is likely to seek it elsewhere and possibly acquire an altogether distorted view of the subject. Even the silence of parents or educators to normal questions conveys to the child's mind a disapproving or sinister attitude.

WHAT SHOULD BE TAUGHT?

Although there is accord as to the need of sexual education, there is not always agreement as to how it should be done. No program can be found which would be suitable for all. However, following Father VanderVeldt in his **Psychiatry and Catholicism,** we feel that sex education may be divided into four periods:

1. **From infancy to childhood** — Here the love, attention, and care of parents is all that is needed.

2. **From early childhood to late childhood** — Here positive training begins. The child discovers differences in sex. This period is most important because the child is so impressionable and can be easily formed to the proper attitudes. Instruction should be given naturally as occasion arises — when giving baths, teaching use of lavatory, choosing proper dress for the child, etc. In this period, too, the training in modesty and self-denial are continued. If the confidence of the child is won, later training will be made easier.

3. **Late childhood to pubescence** — Here arises the question of babies. This is best handled by the mother, in a truthful way — no stork myth — otherwise the information will come from the neighborhood

children, the radio, etc. The truth saves sensitive children from real hurt and lack of trust in the parent. This can easily be handled when another child is expected, by telling the story of Christmas, explaining the Hail Mary, or other ways the mother finds natural. Technical names are desirable, but the information should be given in a manner intelligible to the child. Character training should be stressed throughout the early education of the child. During this time and the next period, a love of purity should be developed by frequent reception of the sacraments and by inculcating a love of the Child Jesus and His Blessed Mother. The child should be protected against evil companions and evil reading. Hobbies and play should be encouraged as a healthful outlet for energy.

4. **Puberty to adolescence** — This period is characterized by radical physical and mental changes. According to the direction of the Holy Father[3] the father should instruct the boy, and the mother should instruct the girl. Explanations should candidly and gently be given about the powers of parenthood which are developing. The instruction should be given individually and according to the need and physical development of the child. A good rule to follow is to answer the questions asked. The psychology of sexual attraction and marital intercourse need not be explained until the time of serious dating or before marriage, depending upon the maturity of the child. Certainly a girl should be warned about the inflammable nature of the passions, especially in the male, so that she may protect herself and may not innocently tempt others. Information should be given in correct terminology to prevent the adolescent from descending to "gutter slang."

Sex instruction of children should ordinarily be given individually because each child has different needs. When there is group instruction, as in a religion class, it should be less detailed than sex instruction in the proper sense.

The adolescent should be told that sexual manifestations in all of their aspects are natural phenomena which have their proper use in marriage. The boy or girl approaching maturity should be informed that sexual continence is not harmful or impossible. The incorrect current attitudes toward sex so freely expressed in the movies and magazines about the desirability of free sexual expression should be explained to them in a way which they will understand and which will lead them to accept the correct concepts. In this way the attitudes

[3] Pope Pius XII, *Allocution to Catholic Mothers,* November 26, 1941.

necessary for a healthy childhood and adolescence, as well as for a happy marriage, will be fostered.

In general it may be said that questions should be answered when they are asked, truthfully and as completely as the child's age indicates. False information and ridiculous answers given to children in response to their legitimate questions often give rise to false concepts in regard to sex which are excellent cultures for the development of adult maladjustments. Children will usually find some answer to their questions. If they do not receive it from reliable sources, they will obtain it in a less satisfactory manner. It may be postulated that the less instruction there is in sex, the more likely is the growing child to develop the idea that even normal sexual relations are "unclean, animalistic, and something of which to be ashamed."

WHO SHOULD TEACH?

As the parents have the primary duty of directing the education of their children, the duty of sex instruction belongs to them. Pope Pius XII, in his allocution of October 26, 1941, says quite definitely that the responsibility for sex enlightenment is that of the parents. The parent will best note the stages of personality growth that call for increased knowledge and will give instruction in the family setting. The instruction thus is invested with its proper dignity and is placed on the high level of sacred and intimate things which belong to the family and are sparingly shared with outsiders. The Catholic bishops of the United States made this statement on November 15, 1950:

> Fathers and mothers have a natural competence to instruct their children with regard to sex. False modesty should not deter them from doing their duty in this regard. Sex is one of God's endowments. It should not be ignored or treated as something bad. If sex instruction is properly carried on in the homes, a deep reverence will be developed in the child, and he will be spared the shameful inferences which he often makes when he is left to himself to find out about sex.[4]

Should sex education be given in school? Many secular authors are advocating this and publishing pamphlets and movies to be used in these classes. We, as Catholics, are opposed to this education of a group. The Catholic bishops "protest in the strongest possible terms

---

[4] Statement of the Catholic bishops of the United States, *The Child: Citizen of Two Worlds,* November 15, 1950.

against the introduction of sex instruction into the schools. To be of benefit such instruction must be far broader than the imparting of information, and must be given individually."[5]

In an individual case, a teacher may in charity impart the "facts of life" to an individual child but it is advisable that the approval of the parents be always sought. It is the religious instructor's place to teach the human significance of, and moral principles of, rather than the physical facts of, sex.

The method commended by the Pope in the encyclical **The Christian Education of Youth** is clear.

> In this extremely delicate matter, if all things considered, some individual instruction is found necessary and opportune from those who hold from God the commission to educate and who have the grace of state, every precaution must be taken. Such precautions are well known in traditional Christian education.

These words, taken in conjunction with the decree of the Holy Office, leave no room to doubt that the Church is opposed to collective or public sex education with or without supposed "safeguards." She teaches that, in place of such methods of sex education, "care must be taken, in the first place, to give a full, firm, and uninterrupted religious instruction to youth of both sexes; that, an esteem and desire for and love of the angelic virtue be instilled into them; that they shall be urged, especially to be instant in prayer, assiduous in the reception of the sacraments of Penance and the Holy Eucharist; that they shall cultivate a filial devotion to the Blessed Virgin, Mother of holy purity, and place themselves under her protection; and that they shall carefully avoid dangerous reading, immodest shows, bad company, and all occasions of sin.[6]

Pope Pius further states in the encyclical letter **The Christian Education of Youth** that:

> . . . such precautions are well known in traditional Christian education, and are adequately described by Antoniano cited above, when he says:
>
> Such is our misery and inclination to sin, we find occasions for and inducements to sin itself. Hence it is of the highest importance that a good father, while discussing with his son a matter so delicate, should be well on his guard and not descend to details, nor refer to the various ways in which this infernal hydra destroys with its poison

---

[5] *Ibid.*

[6] "Joint Pastoral Letter of the Hierarchy of England and Wales on the Catholic Attitude to Sex Education," 1944.

so large a portion of the world; otherwise it may happen that instead of extinguishing this fire, he unwittingly stirs or kindles it in the simple and tender heart of the child. Speaking generally, during the period of childhood it suffices to employ those remedies which produce the double effect of opening the door to the virtue of purity and closing the door upon vice.[7]

More specifically, a pastoral letter of the German bishops states:

> The first natural and necessary element in this environment, as regards education, is the family, and this precisely because so ordained by the Creator Himself. Accordingly that education, as a rule, will be more effective and lasting which is received in a well-ordered and well-disciplined Christian family; and more efficacious in proportion to the clear and constant good example set, first by the parents, and then by the other members of the household.[8]

> If the need of instructions in sex matters proves necessary for children, the required information is to be imparted to girls by the mother, and to boys by the mother or father; or, in both cases, by the father confessor, all of them observing, however, the greatest possible caution. Spiritual directors of young men, sodalities or educational institutions, etc., may also occasionally exert good influence by discreet teaching and admonition given privately.[9]

It is thus obvious that the first duty of instructing children rests with the parents. Many parents, at the present time, however, are ill-equipped for this task or reluctant to undertake it. The duty then devolves upon those in a position to assist young people — pastors, teachers, counselors, etc. Pastors particularly have the duty of imparting to their young charges proper knowledge and attitudes. This may be done in several different ways. The priest in the confessional, for example, as well as in religion classes or through individual conferences, has a good opportunity of instructing and guiding young people. Teachers, social workers, and counselors also can find opportunity to instruct those young people whom parents have failed to guide. As a matter of fact there are not many teachers equipped to give such instruction dispassionately and without intruding their

---

[7] Pope Pius XI, "The Christian Education of Youth," *Acta Apostolicae Sedis*, Vol. 21 (1929), pp. 723–762.

[8] Pastoral Letter of the German bishops assembled in conference at Fulda in 1913, cited from Felix Kirsch, *Sex Education and Training in Chastity* (New York: Benziger Brothers, 1930).

[9] *Ibid.*

own conflicts. While the discussion of who should teach what goes on, the adolescent is not living in a vacuum. He too frequently learns by experimentation and occasional disaster what he might have learned without damage from a parent or teacher. In this area "experience is not the best teacher"; rather another proverb is more apropos, i.e., "a stitch in time saves nine."

Not only should these persons assist young people, however. They should also aid those parents who need assistance in giving instruction to their children.

In the case of those parents who do not know how to give the necessary information, the priest, counselor, or social worker can outline for them a talk with a young boy or girl in order to show them the correct approach to various problems.

Many pamphlets and books are available which the pastor is able to recommend to the parents to aid them in their task. Most of these contain the material to be given according to different age levels.[10] They also have the correct terms to be used in the presentation. Model talks between the father and his son or between the mother and her daughter put this material into a practical setting which can easily be adapted by the parents to their own individual circumstances.[11]

Question and answer books on the subject of sex are also easily

---

10 The following pamphlets are of this type:

a) A Catholic Woman Doctor, *Growing Up — A Book for Girls* (New York: Benziger Brothers), 59 pp., 50 cents.

b) Paul Edwards, *Sex and the Teen-Age* (New York: The Paulist Press), 24 pp., 10 cents.

c) Winfield Hall, M.D., *Steering the Boy to a Happy Marriage* (Huntington, Ind.: Our Sunday Visitor Press), 31 pp., 15 cents.

d) Felix Kirsch, O.F.M.Cap., *The Sex Problem* (New York: The Paulist Press), 32 pp., 5 cents.

e) Barclay Street Institute of Catholic Action, *The Toddler and Sex* (New York: The Paulist Press), 31 pp.

f) Rev. Dr. L. Rumble, M.S.C., *What Parents Should Tell Their Little Ones on Sex* (St. Paul, Minn.: Radio Replies Press), 46 pp., 15 cents.

g) The following pamphlets were prepared by Marion O. Lerrigo, Ph.D., and Helen Southard, M.A., and distributed by National Education Association, 1201 Sixteenth Street, N.W., Washington, D. C., and American Medical Association, 535 North Dearborn Street, Chicago 10, Ill.: *Parents' Privilege, A Story About You, Finding Yourself, Facts Aren't Enough, Learning About Love.*

11 A good example of a model talk is: *Christopher Dramatized Recordings on Sex Instruction:* Part 1. "How Babies Are Born" (for young children); Part 2. "Menstruation" (for girls 10–12); Part 3. "Problems of Growing Boys" (for boys 11–13); Part 4. "The Marriage Union" (for teen-agers) (The Christophers, 18 East 48th Street, New York 17, N. Y.).

available to the pastor and to the parents. In many instances the child's question parallels the question in the text.[12]

The pastor or other individual speaking to parents should emphasize to them that sex instruction alone is not enough. Training in chastity and the formation of the proper attitudes must accompany such knowledge to make it helpful to the young person. A distinction should be made between sex instruction, i.e., the imparting of information specifically related to the sexual organs and sexual education, which relates sex to the person as a whole, in its spiritual as well as its physical aspects. The good example of the parents is one of the best means of providing this basic foundation.

SEX FOR PARENTS

In the sophisticated United States in which we live today, it is difficult to believe that there would be need for sex instruction of parents. Having just lived through the latest Kinsey Report it would seem that there is little more to be learned. The fact is, however, that in regard to real understanding of sexual matters we as a nation are woefully ignorant. We look back with contempt to those days in the past when sex was discussed, if at all, behind locked doors, and point with pride to our present state of "enlightenment" when sex is discussed in all, not only in the best drawing rooms, and when the lurid details of sex crimes are described in banner type and when the intimate details of the sex life of the human female are published in a best-seller manner. But actually, is this education in sex? Accumulation of isolated facts is not education. These facts can only have value when they are used in a constructive way for the betterment of ourselves or others. Is the situation improved if, instead of the woman of fifty years ago who did not realize she was supposed to experience orgasm, we have the woman of today who wants a divorce because she doesn't experience orgasm at each act? Is it improved sexual knowledge when we try to separate morality and sex? For example, Doctor Kinsey suggests an experimental approach to marriage to see if a couple are sexually compatible.[13]

This is the tail wagging the dog. You cannot equate happiness in marriage with the number of orgasms experienced by the marital

---

[12] For example: Revs. Rumble and Carty, *Frank Youth Quizzes on Sex* (St. Paul, Minn.: Radio Replies Press), 24 pp., 15 cents.

[13] Alfred C. Kinsey, *et. al., Sexual Behavior in the Human Female* (Philadelphia: W. B. Saunders Co., 1953), p. 285.

partners. "A little knowledge is a dangerous thing" goes the old proverb. Just so, a little knowledge of sex is a dangerous thing and leads only to unhappiness and trouble.

Sex education should be a step-by-step process covering the whole educational spectrum from birth to maturity. When sex instruction is isolated from the rest of the teaching program it creates the impression of something secret and apart from the rest of life. The child's questions in regard to sex should be answered as readily and truthfully as his questions regarding other matters of fact. That parents so frequently cannot do this is clear evidence of their lack of knowledge concerning sex or their embarrassment about discussing it.

THE FACTS OF LIFE

What are these "facts of life" about which we hear so much? Many people, in answering this question, respond that the important facts concern the sex act itself. This popular belief, like so many other popular beliefs, is completely false. There is nothing which one would need to know concerning the actual sex act which cannot be learned in a few minutes. Concerning what is to be expected from the act cannot be told and must be learned. As Doctor Walsh said:

> Give a person who knows nothing about wine a complete treatise on the vine. Explain what is meant by fermentation, and other steps in the manufacture of wine. Describe its color, its bouquet, its varying qualities, as well as the principal vintages and their prices; and though you add fine detail of all these qualities, exact to the last degree, there will be no possibility of the person understanding what you are talking about, unless he actually tastes wine and even notes the effects produced upon him by the taking of it in any quantity. Just in the same way, it is impossible to give young folks by any system of instruction an idea of the essence of marriage. That must be left to personal experiences.[14]

I would, therefore, feel that a discussion of marital technics belongs rather to a premarital admonition rather than to a part of sexual instruction at any other time.

In a recent Broadway play "The Happy Time," by Samuel Taylor, sex education is summed up by the grandfather for his adolescent grandson: "To be truly a man one must know two things. One

---

[14] James J. Walsh, M.D., Ph.D., "Sex Instruction, II: Sex Information, When and How," *The Homiletic and Pastoral Review* (February, 1930), pp. 463–469.

must know love, one must know truth." These two statements form an excellent foundation for any educational system but are especially appropriate in regard to sex instruction. The whole teaching should hinge around the idea that love is the keystone of marital happiness and that truth is the **sine qua non** of good instruction. There is no place for the stork in sex education. Truth should, of course, be tempered to the age of the child. What the child needs to be told is dependent on the developmental phase in which he is.

What are the facts which should be taught? Of basic importance is a knowledge of anatomy; give the anatomical parts their proper names and, as the child gets older, teach him more about his internal structures. Avoid slang or so-called "baby names" for the parts to avoid embarrassment at a later date when the child will avoid proper references because he does not know what term to use. The physiology of the sex organs is important and this should include a discussion of menstruation with girls before the onset of the menses and with boys before marriage. The physiology of procreation geared to the child's understanding and illustrated by charts or diagrams may be important at an early age in answer to the perennial question of children: "Where do babies come from?" The part played by parents as co-operators with God in the formation of a new being should be stressed. As the child gets older, he should learn that sex impulses are normal and given by God for a specific purpose. It is up to the properly instructed individual whether these will be used for good or bad. The goodness of sex in its proper use should be stressed — not the evils involved in its improper use.

In adolescence, sexual attraction, the significance of petting and its limits, dating and its limits, and the problem of venereal disease should be discussed. Each of these subjects, I am sure, raises many puzzling questions to which the answers are not always clear. By the employment of proper principles, the solution of individual cases should not be difficult.

PREMARITAL INSTRUCTION

Of equal importance with sexual instruction for children and adolescents is premarital instruction for those about to be married. When sexual instruction of the young is properly organized and given, there will be no need for special premarital courses. Many young people, however, approach marriage without a proper knowledge of its physical or psychological aspects. How large a part ignorance plays in the divorce rate is impossible to determine, but it is a matter of common knowledge to those who deal daily with marriage problems that premarital instruction could have solved many of these situations before they arose. In spite of the often-repeated statement that the facts of marriage are of such a nature that everyone of a marriageable age should be aware of them, this is, unfortunately, not the case, and too many well-intentioned individuals enter marriage completely ignorant of what it will require of them. Numerous instances could be cited. Just to mention a few — there was a girl who, after eight years of marriage, came to inquire how to have a baby: "My mother told me that the doctor brought them and left them under a bush in the front yard. I know that is not true, but I really do not know how to go about having one." Another instance was that of a couple married ten years who came to inquire about her failure to become pregnant, and it was elicited that in their ten years of married life their marriage had never been consummated. The average layman usually considers that those connected with the medical profession are fully aware of the facts concerning sex. This is, unfortunately, not always true, as is exemplified by the case of a nurse who had not only been shocked after marriage, upon discovering the nature of its physical aspects, but who was also completely uninformed in regard to the menstrual functions.

Not only is ignorance a cause of divorce but it is also a hindrance to achieving that conjugal love which is one of the secondary aims of matrimony. Lack of proper prenuptial instruction is a serious handicap to a truly happy Christian married life. It is the duty of the pastor, or any person in charge of young people, to instruct them in the important phases of marriage. The Code of Canon Law (No. 1018), in fact, states that the pastor should not fail to instruct his people prudently about matrimony and the matrimonial impediments. The pastor or other counselor should realize that the young couple about to enter into marriage do have a right and an obligation to acquire all the information necessary for the intelligent performance of the duties and privileges of the married life. For without this knowledge they will be entering into a life for which they are not prepared. Such knowledge does not come to them naturally but through intelligent reading and competent guidance. It is the duty of the counselor to see that the couple is well prepared. The length of his instructions may vary according to the knowledge and ability of the couple. He should be careful to see, however, that all who come to him have a course sufficient to suit their individual needs. Such instruction may help to avoid situations such as this:

I went to a Catholic school for eleven years. The Sisters were always talking about being pure of heart. Being impure was the worst sin on earth and if one died who had a sin of impurity on his soul, he was condemned to hell fire. In school, if a boy would even grab a girl by the arm, he was immediately sent to the pastor. I was so afraid, in my teens, that I would commit a sin of impurity. If I happened to be with a group of girls and one would tell an off-colored story, I would try not to listen. If I could not put my thoughts elsewhere while the story was being told, I would make it a matter of confession. Once I was reading a book "The Captain of Castile," and I came across a paragraph where Pedro took Cantana Perez to bed with him. I knew I had committed a sin of impurity and could not sleep for my conscience bothering me. I ran to confession as fast as I could. The priest in the confessional explained to me that sometimes rather good books would have paragraphs in them of this sort. He said if I happened to read a paragraph not to contemplate on it and not take pleasure from it.

When I was sixteen I knew nothing of sex. I was coming home from the drug store with my girl friend and came across a group of teen-age boys standing around in front of my house. One of the fellows was telling the group how he was trying to kiss his girl friend goodnight. They were all laughing. I told the boys I thought they were silly always kissing girls and asked them why they liked to kiss girls. One of the boys said to me, "Kisses lead to something else." I asked him what kisses lead to. He said, "Jane, you had better go on in the house." I did go in. A few days later I went to visit my cousin, Susan, for a week. I asked her if she had heard the expression that "kisses lead to something else." She said she had but she did not know what it meant and she said she would ask her mother. My aunt told us that a man had a male organ called the penis. She said a woman had a hole called the vagina. When a man kisses a woman, he feels as if he wants to put his penis into her vagina. She also said that the result would be a baby born. I told my aunt I thought that was terrible and she told me that I did not know how terrible it was. I later told my cousin that I believed that was a sin. I asked her if it was a sin to have babies, but she did not know. I knew in my own mind that it was impure and told her I could not believe any woman would let a man have intercourse with her. But still everyone was having a baby. We came to the conclusion that the woman would have to be asleep during intercourse, thereby she would know nothing about it.

TEACHING THE PHYSICAL ASPECTS OF SEX

No one completely agrees as to how the physical aspects of sex should be taught. It is agreed in general that it is best done by a physician. In the Cana and Pre-Cana groups a woman physician is recommended for the women and a male physician for the men.

Keenan and Ryan[15] advise the separation of the sexes for a first series of talks on anatomy and physiology. In a second series of talks dealing with the reactions common to both sexes, they recommend mixed audiences. The necessity for such segregation is questionable. Experience has shown little difficulty in mixed groups and it helps further to desensitize those instructed to the "indecent" nature of the subject. More important than the separation of the sexes is the personality of the lecturer. The lectures on the physical aspects of sex are usually given by a physician. There is little doubt that education and training make the physician the one who would appear best qualified for this purpose. Unfortunately, most physicians are poorly equipped for this type of instruction. It is an area where scientific knowledge is not sufficient. Confidence in himself and respect for the subject matter are also important. The speaker must treat his subject dispassionately; even the tone of voice he uses is important. Humor is desirable but may easily be misinterpreted. Not all physicians are well informed in regard to Catholic sex morality. Most physicians are poorly equipped to discuss marital, or even sexual, maladjustments. A psychiatrist is better equipped if it is made clear that such difficulties are not always the result of mental or emotional illness. The psychological aspects of sex are equally as important as the physical. For this reason, a well-trained psychologist, sociologist, or other counselor may be better equipped to discuss certain aspects of marriage, beyond the anatomical, than is the physician. In regard to the problems of pregnancy, there is no one better prepared than the obstetrician.

The following is a suggested outline which might be followed by a physician in giving such talks.

TALK NUMBER ONE: KNOWLEDGE HELPFUL PRIOR TO MARRIAGE

1. It is evident that the doctor's talk will contain a discussion of some of the physical factors in the life of the girl. Under this heading, I would group the following:

---

[15] Alan Keenan, O.F.M., and John Ryan, M.D., *Marriage — A Medical and Sacramental Study* (New York: Sheed and Ward, 1955), p. 302.

  a) The changes experienced into womanhood — a brief explanation
     of the facts and the reasons attached to the menses.
  b) The naturalness of the sex attraction, its power, but the need
     of guidance and control, through the grace of God.
  c) Some elementary knowledge concerning the process of procrea-
     tion as planned by Almighty God.
  d) Practical reasons of a doctor for modesty and chastity.
     How much of the foregoing is to be treated is a matter of pru-
     dence, which the doctor will decide upon in consultation with
     a specified priest.
2. Some practical phases concerning the physical preparation for
   marriage:
  a) It might be recommended that consultation with a Catholic
     doctor both by the prospective bride and groom is of special
     value.
  b) A discussion of physical impediments to marriage and the dis-
     tinction between sterility and impotency.
  c) Explanation of the blood test required by the state law, its pur-
     pose, its value, and how it is conducted.

TALK NUMBER TWO: KNOWLEDGE WHICH MIGHT BE HELPFUL
SUBSEQUENT TO MARRIAGE

1. Normal married life. The psychological approach to married life, its
   lawfulness and its sacredness because it was established by God.
   Some practical reflections of the doctor on this point might be
   in order.

2. Motherhood:
  a) The naturalness of childbearing.
  b) Childbearing in women afflicted with different diseases, i.e.,
     tuberculosis, heart trouble, and the like.
  c) Care of the expectant mother by a physician during the period
     of pregnancy.
  d) Fears of childbearing which must be dispelled.
  e) The birth of the child — the labor pains.
  f) Unusual pregnancies are the exception to the rule.
  g) The life of the mother is always given full medical attention.
     It is never a question of sacrificing the mother to save the
     child. Medical science is committed to protect both lives (Chap-
     ter XVI).

h) Physical dangers attached to abortion — the malice of abortion. The position of the Catholic Church in forbidding the direct killing of the child has been a challenge to medical science and has helped medical science to discover ways and means of bringing pregnancies to term which ordinarily may have been terminated by abortions (see Chapter XXIII).

i) The care of the child.

j) The question of whether motherhood, that is, childbearing, is detrimental to the woman.

3. Contraception — It is explained that even from a medical point of view the practice of contraceptives has injurious effects (see Chapter XVIII).

4. Rhythm — The audience is usually interested in this point and it might be well to explain briefly and in passing the physical aspects of it, its nature, its certainty. The use of Rhythm is a moral question, requiring lawful reason and calling for advice of the confessor (see Chapter XIX).

CONCLUSION

The following are a few of the conclusions which may be drawn from this material:

1. Sex in itself is beautiful, sublime, and sacred.

2. Parents should consistently display affection to the children and to each other. A display of affection between the parents promotes a healthier attitude toward sex in the children.

3. The home atmosphere should be characterized by love, security, and tolerance.

4. Sex is only one part of an individual's personality and therefore sex education is best given as part of general education.

5. Children's questions about sex should always be answered as fully and truthfully as is consistent with the child's age. The child's attitude toward sex is likely to reflect that of the parent. The parent should therefore answer questions as frankly and dispassionately as possible.

6. Parents should remember that the sex impulse is a normal phenomenon and arouses a natural curiosity in a child.

7. Sex instruction is a part of every parent's educational mission which they hold directly from God. They should be prepared for it.

8. Unembarrassed explanations of the "facts of life" should be given to children of both sexes.

9. Parents should be careful not to allow their own faulty attitudes toward sex to color the instruction of their children.

10. Repeated warnings to girls that boys and men are nasty cruel beasts who constantly seek to take advantage of and ruin girls are a poor safeguard to chastity and likely to lead to a poor sexual adjustment later in life.

11. Parents should remember that severe indignation, punishment, and intimidation toward childhood sexual escapades is likely to do more harm than good.

12. Parents and older children should never influence a child toward behavior or feelings appropriate to the opposite sex.

13. Children should, if possible, have a room of their own. Children should not sleep in the same room as the parents if this can possibly be avoided. It is always harmful for the children to see or to hear parental intercourse.

14. Any pregnancy or birth difficulties experienced by the mother in giving birth to the child should never be mentioned to the child.

15. The parents should adopt a dispassionate, unembarrassed manner toward the child's sexual experimentation, toilet training, bathing, and exhibitionism so as to avoid developing in him a sense of prudery.

16. Children of both sexes may be allowed to play about naked and bathe together or before each other until they are four or five years of age.

CHAPTER XI

Courtship and Marriage

Courtship, according to Webster,[1] is (1) the act of wooing, (2) the relation of wooer and wooed prior to a formal betrothal, (3) figuratively, the endeavor to win or entice.

In turn, the word **woo**[2] means (1) to solicit in love, (2) to sue for the affection of and usually marriage with another, (3) to court.

Woo, according to the dictionary may be derived from the Latin word *vovere,* which means "to vow."

The third word in the group, **vow,**[3] means (1) to bind oneself to do, give, or the like by a solemn promise to God or some other deity, (2) to promise solemnly.

Thus, by a certain amount of circumlocution we could arrive at the definition of courtship as the relationship between a man and woman in which one sues for the affection of the other for the avowed purpose of marriage. This is, in fact, substantially the same definition as given in the Marriage Preparation Course: "By courtship is understood the regular and attentive visits of a young man with a young woman for the purpose of mutual understanding and with the idea of marriage in view."[4]

This does not mean, of course, that no boy-girl relationships should exist unless the intention of marriage is present. It simply means that regular, frequent, and attentive visits, i.e., what we usually mean by the phrase "going steady," should be only for the purpose of future marriage.

Strange as it may seem, courtship as we know it today in the

---

[1] Noah Webster, *New International Dictionary of the English Language,* 2 ed. (Springfield, Mass.: G. & C. Merriam Co., 1953).

[2] *Ibid.*

[3] *Ibid.*

[4] *Preparation for Marriage: Correspondence Course,* Marriage Preparation Service, 1 Stewart Street, Ottawa, Canada, Lesson 4, p. 2.

United States is not practiced among many peoples. As will be indicated below, certain aboriginal groups would consider our idea of dating preposterous. Also dating as practiced in the United States today is quite different from that practiced in previous years and from that practiced in other parts of the world today. It differs from these principally in its freedom from supervision and the degree of freedom of choice allowed to the young people, not only in their selection of companions, but also in their adoption of means of recreation.

ANTHROPOLOGICAL CONSIDERATIONS

Among primitive races courtship is far different from that practice as we know it in the United States. There is no need at this point for a prolonged discussion of courtship ideas in reference to aboriginal peoples; several examples will suffice to show contradictory ideas in this regard. One example, as given by Hagen, shows that the Papuans of New Guinea have a unique method of courtship. When a young man wishes to woo a girl, he rolls a cigarette in which he has entwined three hairs, one from his head, one from his shoulders, and one from his pubic region. Having smoked this cigarette halfway through, he then gives it to his mother, who takes it to the lady of the young man's choice. If this lady smokes it to the end, the suitor is accepted. Among the Hottentots the lover goes to the parents of his choice, sits down, and, without speaking, makes coffee. When the coffee is ready, he pours out a bowlful to hand to the prospective bride. If she drinks half of it and gives the bowl back to him so that he may drink the other half, he is accepted. This action means, "Yes, I will be your wife." If she leaves the drink standing, the lover does not grieve unduly, but rather wanders on to look for another girl to whom he may propose.

According to Steller:

> If one of the Kamchadale wants to marry, then he can get a wife in no other way than by winning her by serving her father. When he has seen a maiden whom he likes he goes and, without uttering a word, settles down as if he had long been known there. He begins to take part in all the work of the house and tries to make himself more pleasing than others, both to the parents-in-law and also to his intended bride, by strong labor and hard service. Now, although the bride and her parents become aware on the very first days of the object of his choice, because he works for her and takes trouble for

her all the time, and lies as near her as possible at night, nevertheless, nobody asks him until, after one, two, four years of service, he succeeds in getting so far as to please not only the parents-in-law, but the bride. If he does not please them, then all his service is lost and in vain, and he must go away without payment or revenge. If she gives him any sign of favor, then for the first time he speaks to the father about his daughter and declares the purpose of his service, or the parents themselves say to him, "Now you are a fine, industrious fellow; go on and see how soon you can overcome your bride."[5]

COURTSHIP IN THE UNITED STATES

It is generally considered that the instinct of race preservation or the so-called mating instinct is the prime mover in the attraction of the sexes for each other. Such a purely physical view lowers the dignity and detracts from the sacredness of the married state, the purpose of which is primarily to assist in the act of creation.

The existence of instincts in man as they exist in animals has been doubted. Even if they are present, instincts are certainly almost completely latent. Winston's **Encyclopedia** (1931) defines "instinct" as "the power by which, independently of instruction or experience, and without deliberation, animals are directed to do spontaneously whatever is necessary for the preservation of the individual, or the continuation of the kind."[6] Brennan states, "We may define instinct as an innate arrangement of animal powers which enables its possessor to recognize at once the usefulness and harmfulness of certain objects, to experience emotional excitement as a result of such knowledge, and to act or feel the urge to act in a particular way according to the biological value of the objects thus perceived."[7]

The Oxford English **Dictionary** gives this definition of "instinct," "An innate propensity in organized beings (especially in the lower animals) varying with the species, and manifesting itself in acts which appear to be rational, but are performed without conscious design or intentional adaptation of means to ends."

The definition of instinct has been stressed to show that these authors are in agreement that instincts, although providing the energy

---

[5] Hermann H. Ploss and Paul and Max Bartels, *Woman — An Historical Gynaecological and Anthropological Compendium* (London: William Heinemann [Medical Books], Ltd., 1935), Vol. I, p. 189.

[6] See also Thomas V. Moore, *The Driving Forces of Human Nature* (New York: Grune and Stratton, 1948), p. 231 ff.

[7] Robert E. Brennan, *General Psychology* (New York: The Macmillan Co., 1952), pp. 214–215.

to carry out an act, do not provide the animal thus driven with a knowledge of the end toward which he is striving or the purpose for which he is working. If interrupted in his task the animal is not likely to start over again but to continue from the point at which he was interrupted. This type of conduct is not evident in humans. Anyone who has listened to the laments and strivings of an adolescent trying to select a date for the junior prom would be sure that this conduct was not instinctual but learned (or learning) conduct. It takes very little experience with middle-aged unmarried girls who are in search of eligible males to realize that they are acting with a very definite end in view. We do not deny the **possibility** of a mating inclination in man similar to the instincts in animals. It does not, however, **compel** in the human being as it does in an animal but is **dependent on man's free will.** In man, moreover, it is ordained not merely to the production of a body but it is also an act of co-operation with God toward the creation of a spiritual, immortal soul.

Time does not permit an extended discussion of the topic of instincts, but enough has been said to indicate that although there is a force which urges a man to sexual activity, it is not a blind instinct in the sense described in animals. For want of a better term, we shall use the term **sexual drive** in place of the word "instinct."

THE SEXUAL DRIVE

The sexual drive is a biological urge which provides the energy for activity which is in some way beneficial to the individual or the race. Thus, there can be a drive to self-preservation or race preservation, of which the sex drive is the most important factor. The sex drive, therefore, is innate in man and provides the energy which brings the sexes together. There are certain important points which must be born in mind in regard to the sexual drive:

1. The sex drive is normal and natural.

2. The sex drive may cause trouble indirectly if the feelings to which it gives rise are not recognized for what they are and kept under control.

3. The sex drive is likely to produce certain disturbances of thought. These thoughts or imaginations may give rise to bodily sensations of venereal pleasure. These phantasies and sensations must not be entertained but rejected as soon as they are recognized for what they are since by God's law it is forbidden to unmarried persons to accept them deliberately.

4. The sex drive expresses itself in some way in ordinary life between men and women.

5. The sex drive was placed in mankind by God for a specific purpose.

This drive in human behavior, therefore, usually leads to marriage by a fairly definite course of action. This course of action can be itemized briefly as follows:

1. Dating
2. Going steady
3. A private understanding
4. An engagement

DATING

According to Webster's **Dictionary**[8] a date is an appointment or engagement for a specified time. It is obvious that a couple cannot become interested in each other unless they first become acquainted. Dating serves this purpose. **Dating, then, may be defined as the infrequent spending of time together for the purpose of companionship, getting acquainted, and the pleasure of the moment, usually without any present intention of marriage.** Burgess and Wallin give a similar definition. They define dating as "a social engagement of a man and woman which is for the enjoyment of each other's company and involves no matrimonial commitment."[9] Having fun and getting acquainted are the main purposes of dating. In our present state of society, parents make very little inquiry into their children's dating companions. This differs considerably from times in the not so distant past, when the young girl on her first date with any individual was required to have the young man first come to her home, where he was closely scrutinized by her father and mother. Also, the father more or less implicitly asked the young man, "What are your intentions?" Probably, some procedure halfway between these two extremes would be desirable. Parents should know with whom their children are dating, something of the frequency with which the dating is being done, and the type of entertainment sought by the young people.

According to Father O'Connor[10] there are four kinds of dating:

1. Social and recreational dating

---

[8] Webster, *op. cit.*

[9] Ernest W. Burgess and Paul Wallin, *Engagement and Marriage* (Chicago: J. B. Lippincott Co., 1953), p. 67.

[10] John J. O'Connor, S.J., *Preparation for Marriage and Family Life* (New York: The Paulist Press, 1947), p. 19.

2. More serious dating
3. Dating during courtship
4. Dating during the engagement period

Although this is a satisfactory classification of dating, it is much more inclusive than our use of the word. Father O'Connor's third and fourth types would not be dates in our classification. His Number 1 more nearly coincides with the ideas presented in the above discussion. Father O'Connor defines social dating as a prearranged meeting of a young man and woman for recreational and conversational purposes. Intellectual profit may also be obtained but there is little or no intention of marriage.[11] Father O'Connor defines dating of the second kind, "As a social meeting of male and female arranged beforehand for recreational, conversational, and intellectual purposes, with a view of courtship, engagement, and marriage."[12]

GOING STEADY

Going steady refers to a pairing off of a couple, usually to the exclusion of other dates, and frequently with the intention of marriage.

The couple may, however, go steady for other reasons than as a preparation for marriage. Some of these reasons might be:

1. No other dates are available at the time.
2. Being certain of having a date.
3. The couple feel safe with each other, and can thus avoid the necessity of making new acquaintances.
4. A certain prestige value of being "the steady" of a socially desirable individual.
5. The couple are "in love" but feel that the possibility of marriage is remote, and they merely wish to be with each other and to enjoy each other's company.

In general, "going steady" means to the individuals concerned the opportunity of exploring their likes and dislikes, their compatibilities and incompatibilities, in a relationship devoid of competition and with a view to determining their desire eventually to marry each other. For this reason, such couples do frequently become engaged.

Because of frequent meetings and the time spent together, certain dangers, particularly in the moral field, are associated with "going steady." One can agree with Father Lord when he says, "The high

---

[11] *Ibid.*
[12] *Ibid.*, p. 21.

school boys and girls who go steady deserve our unstinted pity. Seldom do they marry the youngsters with whom they go steady. Often they grow bored with one another, and yet they don't know how to break the bonds that bind them in boredom."[13] The danger of too much physical intimacy is lessened if such couples seek group activities, particularly out-of-door activities; if they double or triple date, or travel in groups; if they become interested in a mutual hobby; and if they are welcomed into each other's homes. They should be encouraged to utilize their initiative and originality in devising new and interesting activities.

The Marriage Preparation Course takes a dim view of dating for any purpose except eventual marriage, e.g.,

> The modern trend in "dates" is to be severely condemned, when, under the guise of company keeping, and with no serious intentions whatsoever, a person seeks only amusement with as many as possible of the opposite sex. It can be so interesting to compare different types, to break one heart after another, but it is at the same time exceedingly dangerous. It is a game that can lead only to disillusionment, so deep as to leave, almost inevitably, a permanent scar on other lives as well as on one's own.[14]

ENGAGEMENT

Engagement may be defined as the mutual understanding between a man and a woman of the intention to marry. Engagement or betrothal according to Canon Law may be of two types:

1. Informal
2. Formal

An **informal engagement** is a mutual, verbal agreement between the pair to test their love for each other, to become better acquainted, and to test their mutual compatibility for marriage. An informal engagement may be broken off merely through the desire of one or both parties.

A **formal engagement** is one which is made in writing and signed by both parties in the presence of the bishop or pastor, or in lieu of such a witness, in the presence of two other witnesses. It imposes a serious obligation, and should be broken for grave reasons only.

Having become acquainted during the period of "going steady,"

---

[13] Daniel A. Lord, S.J., *The Questions They Always Ask* (St. Louis: The Queen's Work, 1943), p. 16.

[14] *Preparation for Marriage: Correspondence Course,* Lesson 4, p. 4.

the couple should use the period of engagement as a final testing time to learn to understand each other and make their final plans before marriage. There are certain important discussions which should take place during this period and some very definite decisions made. In order to avoid future difficulties, the couple should discuss and settle during their engagement period the following questions:

1. The question of religion and, in the event of a mixed marriage, the future religion of the children;

2. The number of children and the matter of birth control, especially, again, if the marriage is a mixed marriage;

3. The family finances and how they are to be budgeted;

4. Social relations.

On the benefits to be gained during the period of the engagement, Professor L. M. Terman, quoted by Father O'Brien, says:

> This engagement period gives an opportunity for the couple to experiment with the experience of being devoted to each other, or belonging to each other exclusively in certain respects. They have an opportunity to find out whether this intensifying relationship will prove intellectually and emotionally satisfying, or irritating. They have an opportunity of trying out the social adjustments involved, introducing each other as their future husband and wife, seeing how their tentative partners get on with the other's friends, discovering whether the adjustments of emotional and social partnership really work out well, or begin to chafe. Often the period of betrothal is also a time when the couple are building up the economic resources and status necessary to start the kind of home towards which they aspire. The engagement might well be characterized, then, as the period during which the idea of marriage with this particular mate is being explored as a working hypothesis.[15]

LENGTH OF ENGAGEMENT

The question as to how long an engagement should last is frequently asked. It is difficult to answer such a question specifically. The couple should certainly know each other long enough to get acquainted, to understand each other, and to be sure that they are sufficiently compatible to live together in love and contentment. Experience and the consensus seem to indicate that an engagement should not be less than six months in duration. In less time than this

---

[15] John A. O'Brien, *Choosing a Partner for Marriage* (Notre Dame, Ind.: Ave Maria Press, 1948), p. 11.

the couple can hardly get sufficiently well acquainted to be sure of success in their future marriage. Hasty marriages are to be avoided. According to Father Doyle, "Circuit Judge M. D. Miller of Chattanooga, Tennessee, who has handled over 25,000 marriage failures in his career, unreservedly asserts that over 40% of the marital tragedies resulted from hasty marriages of the physically and mentally immature."[16]

This is a matter of common experience. Hasty marriages usually lead to trouble. There is no truer statement than the old proverb, "Marry in haste and repent at leisure." Burgess and Locke state, "The longer the acquaintance and engagement, the more stable and happy the marriage. Conversely, the hastier the marriage, the sooner the divorce."[17]

Although an engagement should not be too short, neither should it last too long. The maximum desirable period for an engagement should not exceed one year. In this opinion various authors agree. Father Lord, for example, has this to say in regard to the length of the engagement period:

"The couple should keep company long enough to know each other thoroughly, to have observed each other under various and varied circumstances, to have learned how many interests they have in common, and to have tested the durability of their affection. But the company keeping should be short enough so that they will not grow tired of each other, or become the occasion of dangerous temptation for each other.[18]"

Father Lovasik says:

While the church warns against courtships of undue brevity, she likewise counsels against those of excessive length. No hard and fast rule can be laid down to determine the length of courtship. It should be of sufficient duration to allow young people to learn the character and disposition of each other quite well. This can usually be done in a period ranging from six months to a year.[19]

---

[16] Rev. Charles H. Doyle, *Cana Is Forever* (Tarrytown, N. Y.: The Nugent Press, 1949), p. 12.

[17] Ernest Burgess and Harvey Locke, *The Family from Institution to Companionship* (New York: American Book Co., 1945), pp. 461–462.

[18] Daniel A. Lord, S.J., *Questions I'm Asked About Marriage* (St. Louis: The Queen's Work, 1938), p. 36.

[19] Lawrence G. Lovasik, S.V.D., *Clean Love in Courtship* (St. Paul: Radio Replies Press, 1948), p. 61.

LOVE

What is love? This question is one which will be asked frequently of the counselor and it is one which he may have trouble answering. The supernatural form of love is Christian charity, commanded by Jesus Christ when He said, "Thou shalt love thy neighbor as thyself."

The human form of love consists of three elements according to its type:

1. A warm affectionate feeling;
2. A sexual element;
3. An intellectual element which guides and controls.

Between parents and children and between friends, whether of the same or opposite sex, the warm, affectionate feeling with its intellectual control is all that should exist. When only these elements are present it would be proper to speak of **love.** Parents love their children and friends love each other. When the sexual element is added we might more properly speak of being **in love.** A husband is "in love" with his wife but he may also "love" her. The matter of "love" is more important because this will persist into old age whereas the sexual attraction is more transitory.

Love, which leads to marriage, may be defined as a deep, warm, personal, affectionate, permanent feeling between two persons of the opposite sex who are sexually attracted to each other, and which is under the guidance and control of the intellect.

Such love should also include a firm conviction of mutual marital faithfulness. No marriage can be firmly established which is not based on mutual trust. Jealousy before marriage should be considered a warning sign of future trouble. Marriage does not allay pathological jealousy.

It must be emphasized to the couple that physical attraction is not love; that a desire for sexual satisfaction with the person is no indication of real love. Love is of the head, as well as of the senses, and therefore, in the selection of a mate, it is better to be guided more by one's head and less by one's heart. Rev. J. J. O'Connor, S.J., quoted in **Cana Is Forever,** distinguishes between true love and its facsimile:

> Happiness and joy in each other's company, and anxiety for self-development to be more worthy of the partner, a consciousness of an intellectual, moral, and emotional advancement as a result of being together; a longing for each other when separated; a toleration of each other's foibles, and a willingness to make concessions; if these

are the sensations had by a courting couple, then they can be quite certain that between them true love exists.[20]

Other definitions of love are:
Father Scott:

> The result of sexual attraction between persons of the opposite sex who find in each other qualities of mind and heart which urge them to life-long and intimate companionship.[21]

Father Healy:

> Love is the deep, ardent and devoted affection for another which delights in, and seeks the other's presence, and constantly tries to further his good.[22]

Father Lord defines the love which should be found in marriage as:

> A deep and permanent emotion expressed by a man and a woman who are attracted to one another. This emotion springs from physical attraction; but the man and the woman, realizing that in each other's life-long company they are going to find peace, security, and the fulfillment of their destiny, elevate this physical attraction to a higher plane.
>
> Note that *though love is an emotion,* though it *has the element of physical attraction,* it has a *distinct intellectual content.* Love may be prompted by the powerful physical urge of a man toward a woman, but if it is really love, both the man and the woman are clear-eyed enough to foresee their suitability one for the other after the physical urge will have grown less urgent.
>
> The powerful physical urge is passion. The emotion of love is largely a thing of the senses. But the measured conviction of suitability one for the other is rooted in the intellect. And the determination to make that suitability permanent is in the will.[23]

These definitions of love have been given because they may serve as guides to young people who wonder if they are in love. They must be sure that real love is present. Sexual attraction is not love. As pointed out by Father Scott:

> Lust, although it may accompany love, is not love. One may be affected by sexual passion for a person and yet despise or hate that

---

[20] Doyle, *op. cit.,* p. 71.

[21] Martin J. Scott, S.J., *Marriage* (New York: The Paulist Press, 1940), p. 1.

[22] Edwin F. Healy, S.J., *Marriage Guidance* (Chicago: Loyola University Press, 1948), p. 41.

[23] Daniel A. Lord, S.J., *Questions I'm Asked About Marriage, op. cit.,* p. 12.

person. Sex passion, like any other passion, is violent while it lasts, but like all things violent, does not last. The passion of anger, for instance, no matter how violent, subsides after a furious outburst.[24]

PARENTAL ADVICE

In every case, the boy or girl becoming seriously interested in another should be urged to seek his parents' advice. He may feel that his parents are "too old," that they "won't understand," or give many other reasons for not seeking parental advice. An effort should be made, however, to convince him that no one has his interest more at heart than his parents, that no one understands him better than his parents, and that no one is more willing to offer helpful advice. Parents must remember that they have no right to dictate to their children regarding a state of life. The decision to marry, to remain celibate, or to enter religious life is an individual and personal decision. Parents are obliged to counsel and guide their children in these matters but beyond this they have no right. The same principles are to be applied in the choice of a life partner. In the presence of a refusal to consult with the parents, the individual should be referred to a pastor or another clergyman in whom he may have confidence. It must be emphasized that the function of the marriage counselor is not to make decisions for the individual, but to guide him in such a way that he will be able to make his own decisions.

The following advice of Pope Pius XI may be called to the attention of young couples:

> Let them not omit to ask the prudent advice of their parents with regard to the partner, and let them regard this advice in no light manner, in order that by their mature knowledge and experience of human affairs they may guard against a disastrous choice, and, on the threshold of matrimony, may receive more abundantly the divine blessing of the fourth commandment: "Honor thy father and thy mother (which is the first commandment with a promise) that it may be well with thee and thou mayest be long-lived upon the earth."[25]

SELECTION OF A MATE

His Holiness Pope Pius XI, in his encyclical letter "On Christian Marriage," has this advice for those who are thinking of marriage:

---

[24] Scott, *op. cit.*, p. 1.
[25] Pope Pius XI, *On Christian Marriage* (New York: The Paulist Press, n.d.), p. 38.

To the proximate preparation of a good married life belongs very specially the care in choosing a partner; on that depends a great deal whether the forthcoming marriage will be happy or not, since one may be to the other either a great help in leading a Christian life, or a great danger and hindrance. And so that they may not deplore for the rest of their lives the sorrows arising from an indiscreet marriage, those about to enter into wedlock should carefully deliberate in choosing the person with whom henceforward they must live continually: they should, in so deliberating, keep before their minds the thought first of God and of the true religion of Christ, then of themselves, of their partner, of the children to come, as also of human and civil society, for which wedlock is a fountainhead. Let them diligently pray for divine help, so that they make their choice in accordance with Christian prudence, not indeed led by the blind and unrestrained impulse of lust, nor by any desire of riches or other base influence, but by a true and noble love and by a sincere affection for the future partner; and then let them strive in their married life for those ends for which the State was constituted by God.[26]

Regarding the selection of a marriage partner, a number of questions are usually asked about which the marriage counselor should have definite information and opinions which he should express, without attempting, however, to force his own way of thinking on the client. The most frequent question asked concerns the type of person one should marry, "What should one look for in a husband or wife?" The answer to this question can best be given after one has become acquainted with the personality of the individual asking it. To outline the qualities which one should look for in a mate may create a feeling of discouragement, because of the natural tendency to draw the picture of the perfect person, few of whom are to be found on this earth. However, one must have some criteria by which to judge. For didactic purposes, these qualities may be divided into four general groups:

1. Physical qualities
2. Psychological qualities
3. Ethical qualities
4. Religious qualities

PHYSICAL QUALITIES

1. It is obvious that the marital partner should be in **good health.** There is a growing custom for each of the engaged couple to have

26 *Ibid.*

a physical examination. This is usually done, however, shortly before marriage when things are more or less settled and when any postponement or change in the marriage plans would be embarrassing. It would be wiser, therefore, if both parties would inquire into the physical health of their prospective mate before the engagement is announced. If there are any serious physical disturbances (e.g., the Rh factor), particularly those of an hereditary nature, or those likely to produce frequent or eventual disability, serious thought should be given before the engagement is considered final.

2. A **good family background** is essential, not only from the standpoint of freedom from hereditary disorders, but from the standpoint of social heredity, and it is not advisable for a couple to become engaged until they have had an opportunity of meeting their prospective in-laws in their home territory and under a variety of circumstances.

3. **Physical stature** should be considered to some extent.

4. **Age** is a very important consideration. Usually the man should be older than the woman, although a few years might not make too much difference. Careful consideration should be given to any marriage in which there is a difference of more than ten years in age between the partners. In general, ten years' difference should be considered a maximum difference in age consistent with a happy marriage. In regard to the best age at which to marry, Father Lord says that an individual is ready to marry when "he is an emotional and social adult."[27] That means when he is able sanely to meet life inside and outside of himself, to handle life with maturity and some measure of self-reliance. Father O'Connor says:

> The age element, too, should be considered because of its relationship to childbearing and compatibility. Age differences of three or four years generally need not cause great concern. A disparity of nine or ten years may, but does not necessarily, lead within a few years to important differences in views and interests. . . . According to many studies, the most suitable age for marriage is at 23 or 24 for the young man, and 21 or 22 for the young lady. These ages usually find the young people sufficiently mature emotionally, and at the same time, sufficiently young to be able to make adaptations and accommodations rather easily. Marriages of those under 20 are very frequently unsuccessful. There are exceptions, of course, and not infrequently young people under 20 who are planning marriage will point to

---

[27] Lord, *The Questions They Always Ask*, *op. cit.*, p. 6.

these exceptions to justify themselves. Nevertheless, because there is too great danger of emotional immaturity and of a lack of sense of responsibility, these marriages generally should be discouraged.[28]

The following authors who have determined the age at marriage which is most likely to result in a successful marriage arrive at very similar conclusions:

Age at marriage compatible with success in marriage:

1. Burgess and Cottrell —   Male: 22–30 years   Female: 19 years or over
2. Locke —   Male: 24–29 years   Female: 21–29 years
3. Terman —   Male: 22 and over   Female: 20 and over
4. Terman and Oden —   Male: 23 and over   Female: 23 to 28
5. King —   Male: 21–32 years   Female: 20–25 years[29]

As to the age difference between the couple, Terman and Oden feel that the man should be older than the woman except where the man is one to three years younger. Burgess and Cottrell and King feel that the man should be older by one to three years or the same age.

In regard to age difference Father Lord says:

It depends on who is 20 and who is 29 years old. A nine year difference between a normal man and a normal woman is not generally considered an obstacle to marriage if the man is the older, but it is not, as a general rule, wise for a woman to marry a man who is very much older than she is. If he is very much older than she is, let us say 15 years or more, their marriage will create complications. Let us say that when they marry she is 30 years old and he is 45 years old. Then when she is 45 and still comparatively a young woman, he is 60 years old and approaching old age. . . . Experience has shown that the woman's being nine years older than the man creates a natural barrier to the happiness and unity of the marriage; for when the man is 41 years old and still in his prime, the woman is 50 years old and in all probability will be past her prime, perhaps past her change of life. This complicates things considerably. A man matures and ages and loses his interest in the physical element of marriage much later than does a woman. For that reason, it is naturally more suitable for the man to be older than the woman. A man aged 50, and a woman aged 44 are of approximately the same physical age. But when the man is 44 and the woman 50, they are separated not by six, but by ten or even twelve years of development and maturity.[30]

[28] Quoted in Doyle, op. cit., pp. 30–31.
[29] Burgess and Wallin, op. cit., p. 521, Table 75.
[30] Lord, Questions I'm Asked About Marriage, op. cit., p. 34.

One can agree completely with Father Lord in regard to the importance of age in marriage, but one cannot agree that always, or even usually, sexual desire lasts longer in the man than in the woman.

PSYCHOLOGICAL QUALITIES

1. **The mate should have no serious neurotic traits.** This is an important consideration, because, as is well known, a neurotic individual is egocentric and seldom possesses the ability to project his love to others. His love is so tied up in himself that he is incapable, as long as he remains seriously neurotic, of having an unselfish love for another.

2. **A high level of intelligence.** Love occasionally blinds the individual to the lack of intelligence in his prospective partner. Little traits which may seem "cute" in a "date" can be catastrophic faults after marriage. Mental defectives and psychotic individuals are barred from marriage by law because of their lack of ability to give consent.

3. **A good sense of humor**
4. **Courtesy and good manners**
5. **Approximate equality of education.** If there is any inequality, the man should be the better educated.
6. **Industry**
7. **Pleasing personality**
8. **Good judgment**
9. **Equality of social status.** If there is any inequality, the man should have the higher social status.
10. **Neatness**
11. **Sincerity**
12. **Dependability**
13. **Genuine affection**
14. **The ability to understand mutual problems**
15. **Deep sympathy**
16. **Unselfishness**
17. **Congeniality**
18. **Thoughtfulness**
19. **Consideration of others**
20. **Love for children**
21. **Emotional maturity**
22. **Enthusiasm**
23. **Optimism**

24. Initiative
25. Self-possession

ETHICAL QUALITIES

The partner should be:
1. Truthful
2. Loyal
3. Pure in thought
4. Temperate, especially in regard to gambling and drinking
5. Economical
6. Modest
7. Honest

RELIGIOUS QUALITIES

The partner should be:
1. Of the same religious belief. Mixed marriages are seldom successful.
2. Faithful and regular in the fulfillment of his religious duties
3. Careful in his use of language, i.e, the avoidance of vulgar or profane language

A few of the above-named qualities need further discussion, particularly emotional maturity.

EMOTIONAL MATURITY

Many of the qualities referred to above under the heading "Psychological Qualities" could be subsumed under the title "Emotional Maturity." Such maturity, as it refers to adult humans, is a poorly understood concept, which like so many other concepts, is used freely by those who do not understand its significance. The Hinsie and Shatzky **Psychiatric Dictionary,** published in 1933, does not define either the term "maturity" or the term "immaturity." This dictionary defines "mature" in this manner: "The term describes the reproductive cells which have undergone the process of maturation or meiosis." Webster's **Dictionary** defines the term "mature" as "The state of, or quality of being mature; ripeness, full development." There may, therefore, be some excuse for a lack of understanding of the term by the average person.

Being mature emotionally means:
1. Being comfortable with one's self.

2. Being able to get along with others, both socially and professionally.

3. Being able to accept authority.

4. Being able to be independent in thought and action.

5. Being tolerant.

6. Being patient.

7. Being adaptable.

8. Being pliable.

9. Being self-understanding.

10. Being dependable.

11. Being able to see a job through.

12. Being able to express aggression in a socially acceptable manner.

13. Being able to love someone other than oneself.

14. Being able to accept others as they are with interest and without annoyance.[31]

Obviously, such perfect maturity is seldom attained, but one should seek for a matrimonial partner with a high degree of such maturity (see Chapter XXIV for a further discussion of emotional maturity).

MOST DESIRABLE QUALITIES IN A MATE

In an attempt to discover what degree of uniformity there would be as to the most desirable qualities in a mate, a questionnaire was prepared giving 160 qualities which might be desirable in a mate. The senior class of a Catholic girls' college was asked to check the ten traits which they considered most desirable. Very little uniformity was displayed in regard to any characteristic except religion. Ninety-nine out of the total class of 125 felt that both husband and wife should be of the same faith.

The ten most desirable traits in a mate, according to this class of 125 female college seniors, were:

1. Same religion	99	6. Faithful	29
2. Strong character	49	7. Good father	28
3. Fond of children	46	8. Sense of humor	27
4. High moral standards	43	9. Willingness to sacrifice	27
5. College graduate	29	10. Unselfish	27

The less desirable traits in a mate as far as this group was concerned (in that they each received only one vote each) were the following:

[31] John R. Cavanagh, "Problem Parents," *The Bulletin,* Georgetown University Medical Center, 1950–1951, 4:4, p. 88.

1. Stimulating conversationalist
2. Determination
3. Easy to get along with
4. Expresses emotion
5. Enthusiastic
6. Not jealous
7. Kind
8. Good leader
9. Older
10. Sensitive

PETTING DURING COURTSHIP

This is an important question for the engaged couple because, due to their frequent meetings and the amount of time spent together, time often spent inactively because of low finances, a tendency toward increased physical intimacy becomes evident. Very frequently, due to repression or ignorance, the couple does not recognize the effects of too much petting, and its undesirability on purely physical grounds, over and above the moral considerations. Frequently an explanation of the physiology of petting is in itself an effective deterrent.

It should be explained to the engaged couple that the normal preparation for the marriage act consists of stimulation of the erogenous zones in the body. This process consists of what is popularly known as "petting." The purpose of such stimulation is to prepare the sexual organs concerned with intercourse for the completion of the act. As the result of such stimulation, the glands in the genital organs begin to secrete lubricating fluid which will facilitate the sexual union. At the same time the erectile tissues become turgescent with blood. As the petting goes on, sexual desire increases, and if it is not satisfied by the completion of the act, the individuals are left unsatisfied and with the organs in a state of congestion. From this, it is obvious that if petting is frequent and prolonged, the pelvic organs will remain in a chronic state of congestion from which many symptoms may arise. Among these symptoms may be irritability, backache, low abdominal discomfort, chronic genital discharges due to prolonged secretion of the lubricating glands, insomnia, and many others. It is for this reason that science agrees with the frequently repeated statement of moralists that excessive petting is extremely undesirable.

There are other physical factors which should be indicated. Petting may limit an individual in his choice of companions often to his detriment because the more desirable marriage partners may refuse to pet. It often keeps the couple away from more healthful activities and gives rise to very uncomfortable feelings of guilt. It may lead the couple into unwanted and immoral premarital relations with their threat of pregnancy. The feelings of guilt associated with serious degrees of petting frequently render a successful sexual adjustment in marriage very difficult, if not impossible. Premarital relations frequently cast a cloud over an otherwise happy marriage.

How can we tell when our petting is getting out of hand? This often-asked question is one which is subject to marked individual variations, but the following thoughts may be offered to questioning couples as guides:

1. When there is a question in your mind as to whether what you are doing is right.
2. When you feel flushed and, especially, when there is increasing genital sensation.
3. When you feel an urge to continue, or find it difficult to stop.
4. When you become irritable and begin to spend restless nights.
5. When you feel guilty after petting.
6. When you would rather pet than follow your previous interests in sports and games.

What is permissible? It is generally agreed that a little more physical intimacy is permitted to the engaged couple. This should, however, be moderate, and not lead to sexual arousal. In regard to this matter, Father Gerald Kelly, S.J., says,

> It is clear that two people eligible for marriage and genuinely in love *do not sin* by manifesting their love in a modest and moderate fashion, with a reasonable assurance of controlling themselves should passion be unduly aroused. Again the kiss or embrace which is according to a recognized convention *of good people* is not sinful. Generally speaking, such things do not abuse passion, or if they do, it is slight and easily controlled.[32]

Father Healy says that the engaged couple, "are entitled to indulge in certain marks of affection. . . . sinful petting . . . means a hugging, embracing, or caressing of the body that is of such a kind as ordinarily to excite venereal pleasure."[33] As pointed out above, aside from the immorality of excessive petting, there are physical changes which take place as a result of it and these may interfere with the proper sexual adjustment in marriage. As Groves points out,

> The second consequence of courtship intimacy may be a fixation of

---

[32] Gerald Kelly, S.J., *Modern Youth and Chastity* (St. Louis: The Queen's Work, 1941), p. 68.

[33] Healy, *op. cit.*, p. 50.

sex hunger beyond the line of what is known as its secondary expression. In cases, not a few, as the specialists know, individuals who seem highly sexed in courtship have lost because of their habit of secondary sex expression their normal biological hunger, and are thus forced to find in marriage an anti-climax.

It is also found in some instances that by allowing sex intimacy to go to great lengths, the value the woman had for the man, or that the man had for the woman, and which had previously prophesied marriage, is lost and the association is aborted by having become so largely physical in character.[34]

Having in mind all of the above facts both from the moral and physical fields about the dangers inherent in petting the counselor should point out these dangers to those young people who consult him before marriage.

He should discuss with them the danger especially of spending too much idle time together. They should be encouraged to date with others and to engage in mutual hobbies. They should be encouraged to arrange their dates so that time on their hands, when there is nothing to do but pet, can be avoided.

GOING OUT WITH OTHERS WHILE ENGAGED

Circumstances alter cases, but in general it is unwise for engaged couples to date others. The purpose of the engagement is to prepare for marriage and there is no disagreement with the opinion that married persons should not date others. If either partner to the engagement insists on dating others, it should be regarded as a danger sign and should raise serious question of his or her readiness for marriage. These statements would certainly apply when the engaged couple are present and living in the same city. If, however, they are to be separated for long intervals due to unavoidable circumstances such as military service, it is not improper for either party to attend social functions. Even for this purpose a specific date is not desirable, but they may accompany friends to and from such affairs. Except under very unusual circumstances, engaged persons should not date even during a period of separation.

SECRETS FROM THE PAST

There is no need to reveal any secret from the past which is not seriously detrimental to the relationship between the engaged couple.

[34] Ernest R. Groves, *Marriage* (New York: Henry Holt and Co., 1933), pp. 114–115.

There is, however, a real obligation to reveal any previous matter or defect which would be actually injurious. It would be a matter of prudence whether fornication or adultery previous to the engagement should be revealed. The secret from the past may, or may not, be revealed when it consists of any circumstance which would not make the marriage intolerable, fraudulent, or harmful. On the contrary, there are certain matters which in conscience should be told:

1. Known sterility
2. Pregnancy by another man which is actually existent
3. A previous marriage
4. The presence of a communicable disease
5. Hereditary defects
6. A prison record
7. A serious mental breakdown
8. Financial obligations acquired before marriage

FUTURE IN-LAWS

Traditionally, mothers-in-law have received much of the blame for marital discord. Scientific studies seem to bear this out. For example, Dr. John L. Thomas, S.J.,[35] in a study of 7000 married couples, found that more marriages broke up in the first year because of mother-in-law trouble than from any other cause. He found further, however, that if the marriage survived through the first five years it was unlikely to break up for this reason. The husband's mother more frequently is the one causing the difficulty because she is more likely to be overly possessive and unwilling to relinquish her son. She is frequently willing to accept a new daughter, but only as long as this does not interfere too much between her and her son.

Because of the importance of in-laws the couple anticipating marriage should make as many visits to their prospective in-laws as possible. This is particularly true when the couple have not known each other long or have grown up in different cities and different

---

[35] John L. Thomas, S.J., *Some of the Factors Involved in the Breakdown of Marriage* (Chicago: University of Chicago Doctoral Dissertation, 1949). Father Thomas' study was based on cases referred to the Chancery Court of the Archdiocese of Chicago. This latter fact will suggest that the causes for divorce based on this study should not be taken as universally representative: first, because the parties, as conscientious Catholics, sought a solution in accordance with Catholic doctrines on marriage; second, the majority most probably applied to the court only after other solutions had failed. This material was later published under the title, *The American Catholic Family* (New York: Prentice-Hall, Inc., 1956).

cultures. They should ask themselves the question, "Would I want to introduce them to my friends?" and "If my husband (or wife) were to be away for a long time could I live with them in peace and contentment?" or "Do I want these people to be the grandparents of my children?" If these questions are answered in the affirmative, then thought should be given to the following points, all of which, if answered in the affirmative, help to promote good in-law relationships:

1. Do both sets of in-laws approve of the marriage?
2. Have both families of in-laws met and do they like each other?
3. Are the parents of the husband (and wife) happily married?
4. Are the in-laws of the same religious belief?

If these questions are also answered in the affirmative, then the couple may safely proceed to marriage provided that they intend to live by themselves. **Under only the most desperate circumstances should a married couple live with their in-laws.** It seldom works.

In cases of marital difficulty the best advice a counselor can usually give the in-law who inquires how he, or she, may help is to recommend a "hands-off" policy and to restrain himself at all costs from giving uncalled-for advice. It never pays to say, "I told you so." The married couple will get little help from interfering in-laws who, by the very nature of things, are prejudiced in favor of one partner or the other.

SUMMARY

In general, the marriage counselor should not be too dogmatic in giving specific advice in regard to the suitability of an individual as a marriage partner. There are, however, certain characteristics which, if found, are so destructive of the possibility of a happy marriage that they should be emphasized. Among these are:

1. Alcoholism. If an individual is unable to stop before marriage, he is most unlikely to stop afterward.
2. Extreme stubbornness
3. Jealousy. The Scripture truly says, "A jealous woman is the grief and mourning of the heart."[36]
4. Mental illness, especially prepsychotic or psychotic persons
5. Extreme penuriousness
6. Psychopathic personality
7. Immature personality.

---

[36] Ecclus. 26:8.

The lovers must be urged to be objective in their evaluations, because as Jessica told Lorenzo in **The Merchant of Venice** — "But love is blind, and lovers cannot see — the pretty follies that themselves commit." Or as Rosalind reminded Orlando in **As You Like It** — "Men are April when they woo, December when they wed: maids are May when they are maids, but the sky changes when they are wives."

CHAPTER XII

The Marriage Act

PURPOSE OF MARRIAGE

The primary purpose of marriage is the procreation of children. However, in matrimony, as well as in the use of matrimonial rights, there are secondary ends, such as mutual aid, the knowledge of mutual love, and the quieting of concupiscence, which are legitimate so long as they are subordinated to the primary end of marriage, and so long as the intrinsic purpose of the act is preserved. A great deal has been written during the past decade concerning the physical aspects of marriage. Much of this has tended to emphasize the physical aspects of the marital relationship and to minimize or ridicule its primary end. A de-emphasis of these false ideas should be available to every marriage counselor. The Holy Father, speaking to the Italian Catholic Union of Midwives, in October, 1951, spoke emphatically and clearly on this subject:

> The "values of the human person" and the need of respecting them is a subject which has occupied writers more and more for twenty years. In many of their writings even the specifically sexual act has its place assigned to it in the service of the married couple. The proper and more profound meaning of the conjugal right must consist in this — that the union of the bodies is the expression and the physical manifestation of personal and mutual affection.
>
> Articles, chapters, entire books, lectures, especially on the "technique of love," are written to diffuse these ideas, to illustrate them with advice to newly-married couples as a guide to matrimony in order that through stupidity, wrong notions of modesty, or baseless scruples, they do not miss that which God Who has created the natural inclinations also offers them. If from this complete mutual gift of the couple there arises a new life, it is a result that remains outside or, at the most, on the border of the "values of the human person," a result not denied but not desired as the center of conjugal relations.

159

According to these theories, your self-dedication for the good of
the life still hidden in the womb of the mother and its happy birth
would have no more than a secondary importance.

Ideas Opposed to Christianity

If this relative appreciation stressed merely the value of the persons
of the married couple rather than the offspring, one could, strictly
speaking, let this question pass. But we are faced with a serious
inversion of the order of values and ends established by the Creator
Himself. We are faced with the propagation of a host of ideas and
sentiments directly opposed to the clarity, depth and seriousness of
Christian teaching. Here, then, is another place where your apostolate
must enter. It may happen that you are confided in by a mother
and wife and questioned about the most secret desires and the
intimacies of conjugal life. How can you who are aware of your
mission make the truth and right order prevail in the appraisals and
actions of couples if you yourselves do not possess an exact knowledge
and are not armed with the strength of character necessary to uphold
that which you know to be true and just?

The truth is that matrimony as a natural institution, by virtue of
the will of the Creator, does not have as its primary, intimate end
the personal improvement of the couples concerned but the procreation and the education of new life. The other ends, though also
connected with nature, are not in the same rank as the first, still
less are they superior to it. They are subordinated to it. This holds
true for every marriage, even if it bears no fruit, just as it can be
said that every eye is made for seeing although in certain abnormal
cases, because of special internal and external conditions, it will never
be able to see.

The Primary Purpose of Marriage

Some years ago (10 March 1944) with the precise aim of putting
an end to all these uncertainties and errors that threatened to spread
mistakes about matrimony and the mutual relation of its ends, We
Ourselves made a statement on the order of these ends. We indicated
what the inner structure of the natural disposition reveals, what is
the heritage of Christian tradition, what the Sovereign Pontiffs have
frequently taught, and what is established in proper form by the Code
of Canon Law (Canon 1013, par. I). A few years later, to correct
conflicting opinions, the Holy See issued a public decree stating that
the opinion of certain recent authors could not be admitted, authors
who denied that the primary end of matrimony was the procreation
and rearing of children or taught that the secondary ends of marriage
are not subordinated to the primary end but of equal importance

and independent of it (S.C.C. Officii 1st April 1944 Acta Ap. Sedis Vol. 3, a 1944, p. 103).

Does this mean that we deny or diminish what there is of good and right in the personal values arising from marriage and its carrying out? Certainly not. In matrimony, for the procreation of life, the Creator has destined human beings made of flesh and blood, endowed with minds and hearts: they are called as men, not animals without reason, to be the makers of their descendants. For this end God wishes that couples be united. Holy Scripture says of God that He created man to His image and that He created the human being both male and female (Gen. 1, 27), that, as we find it so often in the sacred books, "man must abandon his father and his mother and unite himself with his wife forming one flesh" (Gen. 2, 24, Matt. 19, 5, Eph. 5, 31).

Perfect Married Life

All this, therefore, is true and so willed by God. But it must not be divorced from the primary function of marriage, which is service for new life. Not only the common work of external life but also intellectual and spiritual endowment, even the depths of spirituality in conjugal love as such, have been put by the will of nature and the Creator at the service of our descendants. By its nature, perfect married life means also the complete dedication of the parents for the benefit of their children, and in its strength and tenderness, conjugal love is itself a postulate of the most sincere care for the offspring and the guarantee of its being carried out. (St. Thomas 3 p. q. 29 a. 2 in c. Supplmt. q. 49 a. 2 ad I).[1]

MARRIAGE RIGHTS

It may seem unnecessary to make a special point of the rights which married people have in a physical way toward each other, but the question arises with sufficient frequency to make such a discussion worthwhile. It has been the constant teaching of the canon and civil law that neither partner may deprive the other of his marital rights without a grave reason. "Rendering the requested marriage debt is a grave obligation, especially when the petitioner is in danger of incontinence or would have to make a great sacrifice to overcome temptation."[2] The rendering of the marital due is an

---

[1] Pope Pius XII, "Moral Questions Affecting Married Life," address to Italian Catholic Union of Midwives, October 21, 1951, National Catholic Welfare Conference, Washington, D. C., par. 43–50.

[2] Heribert Jone, O.F.M.Cap., *Moral Theology* (Westminster, Md.: The Newman Book Shop, 1945), p. 557, par. 754 (I).

obligation of justice. Very frequently, however, one comes across a case, usually that of the wife who, either consciously or unconsciously, deprives her husband of his marital rights as a punishment for either real or imagined wrongs. In this same category belongs the wife or husband who takes unnecessary or prolonged vacations away from home in order to deprive the spouse of marital relations. Except by mutual consent and some exceptional cases mentioned below it is gravely wrong for either party to live apart. St. Paul made this point very clear when he said, "Let the husband render the debt to his wife and the wife also in like manner to the husband. The wife has not power of her own body: but the husband. And in like manner the husband also has not power of his own body: but his wife. Defraud not one another."[3]

For **clearly specified and grave reasons** it may be legitimate not to accede to the request of the partner. Among these reasons might be:

1. Adultery on the part of one's spouse. This must be certain and have been a voluntary act. However, the other party has no right to refuse the adulterer if he (or she) was guilty of the same sin or gave occasion for the other's sin (for example, by refusing him his rights, or gave consent to the act, or has forgiven the culprit [Canon 1129]).

2. Sickness. Ordinary kindness should dictate that intercourse should be interrupted during an acute illness. When the illness is prolonged and the discomfort is increased by sexual contacts, they should be avoided.

3. Too frequent requests. Since there is no normal frequency the term "too frequent" may seem indefinite but for each situation it is not difficult to determine. It would include, in addition to "too frequent," requests at unusual times, such as when the spouse was performing some necessary task, for example, preparing a meal or getting the children ready for school.

4. When the partner is grossly intoxicated or psychotic.

5. When offensive or perverse demands are made.

6. In the presence of venereal disease.

7. When there is imminent danger of a miscarriage of a fetus already conceived. The mere knowledge that abortion or miscarriage will occur if pregnancy results from the act is not sufficient grounds for refusal.

8. When the intercourse would be done immorally. For example, through the use of contraceptives.

---

[3] 1 Cor. 7:3 ff.

9. Nonsupport of wife and children.

10. Where great and immediate danger to the health or life of the partner will result.

It is naturally understood that the requests must be reasonable and compliance possible. Minor inconvenience would not be an adequate cause for refusing sexual relations. The use of the Rhythm Method of birth prevention unless mutually agreed upon may lead to an abridgment of the marital rights of the other party. But a married person who has the right to refuse intercourse because of any of the reasons listed above may, instead, limit the partner to the use of Rhythm.

The **keynote to sexual adjustment** should be **kindness, understanding,** and **mutual desire.**

RHYTHM OF SEXUAL DESIRE

Mutual desire will be fostered if the marital partners will remember that there is a rhythm of sexual desire and conform as nearly as they can to this pattern. This fluctuation of desire is most noticeable in the female. In spite of this, some authorities in the past have questioned the actual presence of erotic sensation in the female as noted in the following quotation from Stone and Stone, but there is now no doubt that such feelings are naturally present:

> The degree of woman's erotic sensibility has long been a matter of considerable dispute. For a time it was seriously maintained that sex desire was primarily or entirely a masculine attribute and that woman was devoid of sexual feelings. Acton, a well-known English physician who was considered an authority on sex maters some fifty years ago, wrote that "the majority of women, happily for society, are not much troubled with sexual feelings," and that the supposition that women possessed any erotic desires was a "vile aspersion." Other writers of that period maintained a similar point of view. . . . After a rather exhaustive survey of this subject, Havelock Ellis comes to the conclusion that the sexual impulse is fairly well balanced between the two sexes. It is rather generally assumed at present that the woman's erotic desires are just as strong as those of the male, although the manifestations of the sexual urge may vary considerably in the two sexes.[4]

In the male there is also a fluctuation of desire, but this is more conditioned by external environmental factors than by hormonal

---

[4] Hannah M. Stone and Abraham Stone, *A Marriage Manual* (New York: Simon and Schuster, 1935), pp. 165–167.

changes. In the female, however, it seems clear that there are certain internal changes which occur which promote a fairly definite rhythm of sexual desire. One of these periods occurs at the time of ovulation. This is understandable, inasmuch as it is nature's method of rendering more likely the propagation of the race. The woman's desire is therefore greatest at the time when conception is most likely. Stone, for example, says:

> Furthermore, in all animal life the days of ovulation coincide with the period of greatest sexual desire. In many species, in fact, the female will accept the male only during her fertile period. It is likely that in the human female, too, there is an increased sexual interest during her ovulation time, and the observance of the "safe period" which bars sexual relations at this time is a practice which is not always desirable or advisable from a psycho-sexual point of view.[5]

There is a second period of increased desire in the female which occurs just before and just after the menstrual period. This is probably due to the pelvic congestion resulting from the endocrine and vascular changes related to the menstrual flow. Most authorities are in accord with this belief. For example, Stone says:

> There is, however, some evidence of the existence of a monthly rhythm in the intensity of the sexual urge of woman. The studies of Havelock Ellis, Marie Stopes, Katherine Davis and others seem to indicate that there is a periodic rising and waning of sexual desire during the menstrual month. The erotic impulses are apparently increased either a few days before the onset of the menstrual flow or, more frequently and more definitely, toward the end of the menses and during the few subsequent days, although the latter rise may partly be due to the abstinence which is usually maintained during the menstrual week. Stopes claims to have observed also a second rise of sexual desire during the middle of the menstrual month. There are apparently individual differences in this cycle of desire and the woman can best determine for herself her own particular rhythm. It is advisable, however, to allow these periods of increased sexual interest on the part of the wife to regulate in some degree the time and frequency of the sexual relations in marriage.[6]

Kroger and Freed say:

> They found that in the days before ovulation there was heightened

---

[5] *Ibid.*, p. 107.
[6] *Ibid.*, p. 220.

sexual drive and a desire to be relieved of accompanying tension, reaching its peak at ovulation, when the level of estrogen is high.

Dickinson, Davis and Stopes all believe that women demonstrate increased sexual desire just before and after the menses. Greenblat has observed nymphomania during the premenstrual phase in some women. Daniels' observations are in support of the results obtained by Benedek and Rubenstein as to the change in sexual orientation after ovulation.[7]

In cases of frigidity this periodic rhythm of sexual desire should be borne in mind and utilized in efforts to improve the condition. Most women are able to detect it if they pay special attention to their feelings.

LOVE IS HUMAN

In spite of much that has been written, especially in recent years, it is important to remember that the love between a man and a woman is not merely an animal reaction. Love is human. One does not marry merely a body. One marries a human person, one who has a body and soul. Love, therefore, is the attraction between one person and another person. There are all sorts of love between humans, but even mother love is associated with certain external bodily manifestations. Thus, also, the sexual activity of lovers is simply a natural manifestation of their love for each other. The primary expression of this love is in the creation of a new human being. The beauty of the act of conception is too often overlooked. The co-operation of the parents with God in the formation of a new human being is not only a wonder of science, but is a tribute to the majesty and power of God. **When one realizes the purpose of the sex act and its naturalness, need more be said to those who feel guilty concerning the physical aspects of marriage?**

PHYSICAL RELATIONSHIP IN MARRIAGE

PROPER USE

Although physical relationship is proper for married persons, there will undoubtedly be times when its indulgence is not feasible or desirable. For example, in the case of individuals who are employing the Rhythm, they should be warned that outside of the times for intercourse it is inadvisable to excite each other to the verge of sexual satisfaction. Under these circumstances, such excitation may

[7] William S. Kroger and S. Charles Freed, *Psychosomatic Gynecology* (Philadelphia: W. B. Saunders Co., 1951), p. 250.

lead to immoral acts. Some married couples do not realize that thoughts and desires for sexual activity with their marital partner are in no sense immoral, inasmuch as the act itself is permissible. The state of marriage naturally does not confer upon the individual the right to have sexual fantasies concerning any other individual other than his legitimate spouse, and does not give him the right to masturbate. In answer to the frequently asked question in regard to how much love-making may be done outside of times of intercourse, the only answer that can be given is that this will depend upon the sensitiveness of the individuals to stimulation. The petting should not lead either party to serious danger of orgasm. Reasonable displays of affection usually do not lead to any difficulty.

PROPER TIME

As to the proper time for sexual relations, there is no definite answer. It will naturally depend upon both parties, the best time being when both are willing. If one is willing and the other is not, the individual having the desire should do everything in his power to stimulate the partner before insisting on the performance of the act.

THE PHYSICAL RELATIONSHIP

Much has been said in the current literature about the techniques of intercourse. Too many people have read these detailed descriptions and consequently have developed a mechanical concept of the relationship almost as it it were to be done by the count. This has resulted in many couples developing undue concern in regard to the method of performing the act, so that they cease to approach it in a natural, unhurried, and relaxed manner. They consequently develop tension and dissatisfaction. This is especially true when the woman remains frigid or the man suffers from premature ejaculation. It is recommended that the marriage counselor say very little to the couple before marriage concerning the actual technique of sexual relations. He should advise them, however, as has been indicated above, to remember:

1. That they are the same two people who were in love before they got married.

2. That they should engage in an extension of the signs of affection which they employed before marriage.

3. That they should not hurry.

4. That the act is proper and desirable for married couples.

5. That they should assume any position that they find comfortable and desirable.

6. That they should do "what comes natural."

NORMAL UNION

Position

The position assumed for sexual intercourse should be the one which occurs naturally to both parties. Actually, there are only a few positions which can be assumed:

1. **The classic position,** in which the man is on top. His thighs may both be placed inside of hers or both outside. This position permits the greatest freedom of motion, and usually brings about adequate contact with the clitoris and, unless there is marked discrepancy in the heights of the two parties, permits a face-to-face relationship so that there may be lip-to-lip contact. **In this position it is extremely important that the man not bear his full weight on his companion, but should support himself on his elbows.** This not only keeps his weight from being oppressive, but also permits a greater freedom of motion on the part of his spouse.

2. **The woman on top.** This is the best position for the initial relations because it allows the woman to control the pressure being made upon the hymen, but does not permit very much movement on the part of the male. It is a position, however, in which there is a good approximation of the clitoris to the shaft of the penis, and for that reason may be desirable where such contact is difficult to obtain otherwise.

3. **The side position** is found desirable by some couples, but, in general, is not as satisfactory as the first two.

4. **The standing position.** This position is adopted by some couples as a form of variety, but is not, in general, frequently employed or satisfactory.

5. **Seated position.** In this position, the man sits on a chair without arms, and his companion can sit astride of him so that the penis may enter the vagina. This position has the advantage of good contact between the clitoris and the shaft of the penis.

Numerous positions are described in works on the art of love, the number reaching astronomical proportions in some of them, but all of these are merely minor variations of the positions described and have no real advantage to offer except variety.

LOVE-MAKING

Benjamin Franklin is reported to have said that every man should seduce his own wife before each act of intercourse. This still holds true, in that the most satisfactory physical relationship is that which follows a preliminary period of love-making. This love-making should not be a hurried, dutiful procedure, but should ideally extend over a period of time, as, for example, if one of the partners is desirous of relations in the evening, the first approaches might well be made on the husband's return from work, so that the love-making may extend with gradually increasing physical contact for the whole evening, with the actual physical relationship coming as a climax. The question is frequently asked as to **what is the minimum amount of love-making that should be indulged in before intercourse is attempted.** The best answer to this question is that the petting should be continued until both parties are ready. This would be demonstrated physically by the presence of considerable secretion in the area of the vulva, which helps to lubricate the entrance of the penis. Many attempts have been made to set a time limit on this love-making. This is undesirable, but in general, it is agreed that it should not last less than twenty minutes. During this period of stimulation it should again be remembered that **any form of physical stimulus which is acceptable to both parties is morally permissible, provided the act ends with the deposition of the semen in the vault of the vagina.**

NUDITY

The question is frequently asked as to whether the clothing should be removed during sexual intercourse. Some women, because of a false modesty, have refused to do so through many years of marriage. Many women are seen who brag that their husbands have never seen them nude. One seldom hears this statement in a compatible marriage. A thirty-year-old female was recently seen who stated that her mother told her she should never let her husband see her in the nude, and that she had successfully carried this out during their twelve years of marriage. It is seldom that one hears a male making this statement, but a patient was recently treated for impotency who stated that during their eight years of marriage his wife had never seen him nude and he had not seen her.

The vast majority of educated people have sexual relations in the nude. It would appear to be the natural and freest method, and the refusal of either to do so at the request of the other could only be regarded as false modesty. Nudity is more important for the female than for the male because of the presence of erotic sensitivity in the skin of the female, which makes skin-to-skin contact very important to her. Here, again, the matter of mutual desire is important, and where there is any discussion of the propriety of nudity it should be settled to the mutual satisfaction of both partners. They should understand, however, that **there is no immodesty in performing the sexual act in the nude.**

CO-OPERATION

Should the woman make sexual advances to her husband? There is only one answer to this question, in spite of strong feelings to the contrary which are expressed by some people, and that is that she should if she has the desire to do so. It is an old-fashioned idea that only the male should make sexual advances in marriage. Marriage is a partnership, and both parties should feel equally free to express their sexual interest. There is something wrong with a marriage in which the woman will say, "We have relations only about once a week, but it never seems to be at times that I feel like it, and yet when I do feel like it my husband gets angry when I suggest it to him." As we have previously noted, the sexual desire in women normally shows a twice-monthly increase, at the time of ovulation and just before the menstrual period. Since her desire is greatest at this time, she should certainly be free to make the suggestion to her husband. Such co-operation with each other should be naturally a part of a happy married life, and it cannot help to promote a happier marital relationship when the women has relations only in accordance with her husband's wishes.

If, for any reason, the couple have agreed upon the use of the Rhythm as a method of controlling conception, co-operation is especially necessary, because if they have agreed mutually to employ it for a period of time, neither partner should become angry if he is refused an impulsive desire for a relationship during this time.

The passivity of the female in the sexual relationship has been overemphasized, and many women overlook the fact that during the sex act they should **actively** participate. She should not be motionless and should not act as a patient undergoing a physical examination. She should respond to her husband's advances; should return his kisses and reciprocally employ weaving motions of her hips in response to his coital movements. The act is for both parties and should be mutually enjoyable, and this can best be achieved by mutual participation.

ORGASM

Ideally, a simultaneous orgasm in both parties is desired. This will probably not be achieved in the beginning of any marriage. It is achieved only as a part of becoming experienced and understanding each other's needs. Because the climax is not simultaneous the parties should not be disappointed, should not be upset, and should not feel that their marital adjustment is a failure. In general, both parties should be able to achieve an orgasm. Where the woman is unable to do so, there is nothing morally wrong with digital stimulation to bring it about after his ejaculation in the vagina. This, of course, must be part of the act, and not occur at long intervals after the act has been completed. This may be brought about in a number of ways:

1. Before intromission and during the love play, the wife may prepare herself by gently stimulating her clitoris.

2. After the husband has completed his orgasm and the wife has not done so, she may stimulate herself and thus bring about her orgasm.

3. After the completion of the act, the husband may bring about her orgasm by stroking her genitals.

4. After the love-making, she may assume the position of the woman above and after his orgasm, by keeping the penis in place and moving her hips, she may bring about orgasm.

It is quite likely that the woman may not achieve an orgasm spontaneously each time. This does not mean that she does not experience pleasure in the bodily contacts and in the fact of giving pleasure to her husband. She should not feel cheated, but should continue in her efforts to bring about a satisfactory relationship, and enlist the co-operation of her husband in this attempt.

FREQUENCY

The number of times any given couple will wish to have sexual relations will vary inversely with the duration of their marriage. It is to be expected that they will have more frequent relations during the first months and years of their marriage than they would have at a later time. An important question is not how frequent the relationship should be, but what is the minimum frequency which would fulfill the individual's right to the marital relationship. "In ancient times law-givers set up minimum standards so that in disputes the courts would be able to decide whether the husband and wife had mutually fulfilled their marital duties. Solon set the interval between two copulations at ten days; Zoroaster at nine; Mohammed at eight, and Luther composed this maxim for married couples:

"Two times a week is 104 times a year,
Which harms neither you nor me."[8]

In this couplet, Luther expresses what is usually considered the average, which is about twice a week in couples who have been married for several years. The frequency varies, however, from the rather fantastic extreme of the Don Juan individual who claims to have relations twenty-five times a night, to the neurotic individuals whose relationships occur at very infrequent intervals. During the past week, for example, one couple was seen who had had no sexual relationships for twenty-four years, and another who had had none for twelve.

LOCATION OF THE ORGASM IN THE FEMALE

A great deal is known concerning the physiology of the male orgasm, but much less is known concerning the orgasm of the female. This is understandable, there being no ejaculation or easily observed phenomena. Even the subject of the orgasm may have difficulty describing her sensations. It is generally taught at the present time, in accordance with Freud's observations, that genital erogenicity in the normal female, although first centered in the clitoris, eventually becomes transferred to the vagina, and that sexual orgasm in the normal, healthy female should be in the vaginal, rather than in the clitoral, stimulation. Although this statement is generally accepted as true, there seems to be very little evidence to support it. This belief also has done considerable harm psychologically in the case of those women in whom sensation is fixed in the clitoral region. This belief has emphasized feelings of guilt, because it is frequently asserted that the individual who has masturbated tends to fix the sensation in the clitoral region, and thereby deprives herself of the greater pleasure of vaginal orgasm. There is no proof that this is true. Marmor, after a study of the subject, concludes:

> Some considerations have been presented which throw doubt on the popular assumption that genital erogenicity in the female becomes transferred from the clitoris to the vagina. There is evidence to indicate that clitoral sensitivity is a continuing factor in adult female sexuality,

[8] Fritz Kahn, *Our Sex Life* (New York: Alfred A. Knopf, 1946), pp. 120–121.

and that the chief difference between so-called clitoral and vaginal orgasm is explicable not in terms of the different origin or location of the orgastic response, but in the different intensity of it and in the degree to which cortical facilitation of the spinal reaction has taken place.[9]

FINALE

The natural conclusion of the sex act is for the partners to go to sleep in each other's arms. If the act is performed at night, all preparations for sleeping should have been made before the act started. The toilet should have been completed, the doors locked, the dog brought in and the cat put out, so that when the act is completed both parties are ready to go to sleep. A frequent source of discord is when one of the individuals is ready to sleep and the other one has to get up and perform household duties.

THE HONEYMOON

According to Webster's **New International Dictionary** "the honeymoon is the first month or so after marriage; now, usually the holiday spent by the couple after marriage before settling down." The purpose of the honeymoon is to allow the newly-married husband and wife to become accustomed to each other, both as persons and as sexual partners, away from their usual environment. Considered in this light, the honeymoon away from home has advantages and disadvantages. It would seem wiser to spend the money, frequently much more than the couple can afford, which would be spent on the honeymoon to help furnish the new home into which the couple intends to move after marriage. Instead of a honeymoon away from home they could then spend a much more comfortable and more relaxed immediate postmarital period in their own home among the things which by this time have become familiar to them.

Honeymoons are not only expensive but frequently a fatiguing, boring, and disappointing experience. It is better for the newlywed couple to go from the marriage ceremony to their own apartment and merely tell their friends when they will be at home to them. They are much more likely to find comfort and relaxation there than in some uncomfortable and expensive hotel. The problems of adjustment of the young couple are frequently great, and both of them are likely

---

[9] Judd Marmor, "Some Considerations Concerning Orgasm in the Female," *Journal of the American Psychosomatic Society,* XVI:3, pp. 240–246, May–June, 1954.

to have anxieties concerning their initial sexual contacts. With increasing sexual knowledge, this anxiety is not as great as it once was, but it does, nevertheless, persist.

For these reasons the best advice which can be given to most couples concerning the honeymoon is to spend it at home.

THE FIRST NIGHT

Traditionally, the completion of the marriage act is expected on the first night. Under some circumstances this may be most undesirable. This is especially true if there has been a large wedding with a great deal of preparation and many parties for weeks before. The bride has usually been subjected to long, strenuous social activities which may have reduced her endurance and left her far from her normal self. Instead, she may be tense, fatigued, and irritable. Her greatest need at this time may be for rest and sympathetic understanding. She is ill-prepared for sexual activity. Under these circumstances the thoughtful husband will see that she obtains the rest and understanding which she needs, and will avoid sexual overtures until she is physically and emotionally ready for them. Hurried and painful attempts at sexual relations under such circumstances may have an adverse effect on their future sexual acts. The husband, particularly, should respect his wife's modesty and her natural anxieties as to her new state in life. He should encourage her to realize that they are the same two people they were before marriage, when they found pleasure in the physical contacts which were permitted them at that time, and that as far as the honeymoon is concerned, their caresses need not go further than they did before marriage. Such an attitude will allay her anxieties, and it will not be long before the desire for a more intimate relationship is mutual. The keynote for the honeymoon should be kindness and consideration.

THE FIRST PHYSICAL RELATIONSHIP

Too many brides look forward to the first sexual relationship with fear. One reason for this is undoubtedly because of the frequent comment that the rupture of the hymen occasioned by the first sex act is painful and may be associated with bleeding. Undoubtedly this fear has been exaggerated. If both parties approach the act with intelligence and understanding of the anatomical factors involved, the pain and bleeding, if present at all, will be definitely minimized. In preparation for the first relationship, both parties should have informed themselves concerning the anatomy of the parts. They should both be informed, particularly in regard to the nature and structure of the hymen (see page 103). They should be aware that it is usually a thin, membranous structure with a small opening, which guards the lower end of the vagina at the introitus, and that when it is penetrated by the penis it will either stretch or tear. Stretching would be more desirable, and the first act should be so regulated that stretching is likely to be accomplished, rather than by forceful entry to produce a painful tear and possibly bleeding.

Some discussion of the part played by the hymen in sexual relations should be given by the counselor in every instance, because there are so many misconceptions concerning it, particularly in the minds of foreign-born individuals. According to tradition, if there is not a blood stain on the sheets from the first intercourse, the girl is not a virgin at the time of her marriage. This belief has led to much unhappiness and to much deceit. In my own practice, patients have told me of devices which they had used to produce the appearance of bleeding so that their husbands would believe that they were virgins. It should be made clear that there are many reasons why there would not be pain or bleeding at the first relationship. For example, the opening in the hymen might be of such a size that no rupture is required for penetration. It may have been ruptured accidentally. It may have been ruptured as the result of a physical examination. It may have been ruptured as a result of masturbation, or taking douches, or the use of vaginal tampons to retain the menstrual flow, or it may have been congenitally absent. It should be emphasized that the absence of an intact hymen is not necessarily an indication of a lack of virginity.

POSITION FOR THE FIRST PHYSICAL RELATIONSHIP

If the hymen is intact, the best position to assume for the initial sexual relationship would be with the husband on his back, and his wife seated or crouching in a position in which she or he can direct the penis into her vagina. Being in the top position, she can then lower herself upon the penis, exerting whatever pressure is indicated or she feels is desirable to allow a gradual stretching of the hymenal ring. Being in the top position, she is situated to control this pressure. It may be desirable to stretch the hymen gradually several times by intercourse in this position before complete penetration is accomplished. There is little doubt that there are certain robust women who would suffer no psychic trauma if the hymen were to be stretched suddenly and painfully, but on the other hand, there are so many sensitive, fearful, anxious wives that this more careful method of dilatation would seem more desirable. Sudden intromission, confirming the fear on the part of the woman that sex relations are painful, is so frequently a source of frigidity as to recommend only the slow method of approach.

GENERAL SUGGESTIONS

In view of the fact that so many women look forward to their first physical relationship with fear, both parties should be urged to overcome their natural reticence concerning discussion of such an intimate subject, and to discuss these fears frankly, so that everything possible may be done to ameliorate them. Most problems which arise during the early days of married life can be relieved by an intellectual approach. It should be emphasized that women can, and should, derive the same pleasure from sexual relationships that their husbands do and that in order to obtain this pleasure they must approach the act without fear and in as relaxed a state of mind as possible. They should be urged to be natural and uninhibited and to realize that the sex act is only an extension of the physical contacts which were permitted to them before marriage, and that if they will start the act in this same manner of demonstrating affection, and approach it leisurely and under suitable environmental conditions (see page 176 f.) they will be able to achieve, in regard to the physical aspects of their marriage, what they have been led to believe is possible.

A certain percentage of people will have difficulty in their initial attempts at sexual relations and all couples should, therefore, be advised to return for a discussion with the counselor about one month after marriage. At this time they will have had experience, and any difficulties concerning the physical relationship can be discussed more intelligently.

The difficulties most likely to arise in this area are usually the result of:

1. Failure on the part of the man to realize that the woman is slower to be sexually aroused, and that therefore a certain amount of lovemaking is not only desirable, but necessary, before she is prepared for intercourse. Any attempt at intromission before adequate arousal is likely to be uncomfortable or even painful.

2. Failure on the part of the woman to understand that it is de-

sirable that she co-operate with the man by engaging in coital movements. Although it is recognized that she has a more passive part to
play in the relationship, she should not act like a patient undergoing
a physical examination.

3. Fear of impotence. Early in marriage it is not unusual for the man
to have some doubts of his potency, and such fears may result in
psychic impotence, which is a form of stage fright. Very little more
needs to be done except to give him encouragement that everything
will be all right.

4. Fear that some of the acts are abnormal or immoral. This is a
frequent difficulty and one concerning which many married people,
particularly women, find difficulty in discussing. A great deal of
anxiety in this area may be avoided if the couple are assured that any
act which is desired or acceptable to both parties is permissible as part
of the sex play prior to intercourse as long as the act ends properly
with the deposition of the semen in the vault of the vagina in such a
way that there is no interference with the primary purpose of the act.

5. Lack of physical cleanliness. Difficulty frequently arises where
the sexual partner is not fastidious in the care of his person.

6. Fear concerning the size of the penis. There is frequent concern
as to whether the penis is either too large or too small. Very frequently
the man develops feelings of inadequacy because of the size of his
penis. In this connection, Kroger and Freed[10] mention the case of an
extremely promiscuous and almost totally frigid woman who told
them that the only time she had achieved an orgasm was with a man
who had the smallest penis she had ever seen. Since there may be a
disproportion between the size of the male and female organs, a
physical examination should be recommended in the presence of this
complaint.

7. Environmental factors. There are certain environmental factors
which adversely effect the success of sexual relations. Among these may
be mentioned:

a) Living with in-laws and a feeling on the part of the husband or
wife that they may overhear. This would include concern over open
windows and unlocked bedroom doors.

b) The question of light or darkness. One party may have a strong
desire to see the partner in the nude. The other partner, for a variety
of reasons, may like the room dark. This may give rise to discord.

---

[10] Kroger and Freed, op. cit., p. 308.

c) Too much drinking may create a feeling of distaste or repugnancy, and in some may produce impotence.

d) Pain, anxiety, fear of pregnancy may also play a part.

This list is probably far from complete, but at least indicates the type of difficulties which the counselor should bear in mind when he discusses problems concerning intercourse with the married couple.

SUMMARY

Each party to a marriage has the right to the proper use of his partner's body for the purpose of performing the sex act. Nothing may be done to frustrate the primary purpose of the act, but during petting preliminary to the act, any act is permissible provided the act ends with the deposition of the semen in the vagina. Honeymoons are best spent in the couple's new apartment because it is both more economical and more comfortable.

CHAPTER XIII

Impotence and Frigidity

IMPOTENCE

Impotence is the inability of the male or female to perform the sexual act completely. It should be clearly understood that while impotence in this sense may cause sterility, sterility in no way implies that the individual necessarily is impotent.

In the older literature some of the terms used are confusing to those who are acquainted only with present-day terms. **Impotentia coeundi** corresponds to the present medical use of the word **impotence** to mean "inability to perform sexual copulation." **Impotentia generandi** means the "inability to produce children" and has been largely displaced in the present terminology by the term "sterility." **Impotentia erigendi** is the most common type of impotency in the male and it implies "impotency due to the loss of the power of erection." The division of impotency into **absolute, relative, antecedent, perpetual,** and **temporal** although seldom used is of great practical importance from the Catholic standpoint, since the validity or nonvalidity of a marriage may depend upon it. For a complete understanding of this discussion a knowledge of the anatomy and physiology of the male and female genitalia is required (see Chapter II).

For the canonical consummation of marriage it is necessary that the vagina of the woman be penetrated even partially by the male organ and that the act be completed by the ejaculation at least partially of the male seed within the vagina (Decree of the Holy Office, February 12, 1941).

Physical potency of the male, therefore, requires:

1. The ability to have a penile erection with the ability to retain that erection for a sufficient length of time to permit entrance of the organ into the vaginal canal.

2. The ability to evacuate within the vagina the genital secretions.[1]

3. The presence of the testicles in a condition capable of producing the necessary hormones to bring about an erection.[2]

---

[1] Cf. *S. R. Rota Decision*, Vol. 35, p. 17, which states that the marriage act must be completed by the ejaculation, within the vagina, of the male semen elaborated in the testicles.

[2] A man lacking both testicles is canonically *ipso facto* impotent and not merely sterile. Cf. *Rota Decisions*, Vol. 32, p. 650.

The Constitution of Sixtus V concerning the marriage of eunuchs *Cum Frequenter* (1587) presents an authoritative and binding judgment on this subject:

"Because it frequently happens in your territory that there are certain eunuchs and castrated men, who lack both testicles, and who, therefore, certainly cannot ejaculate true semen . . . but only a certain fluid similar to semen which is in no way suited for generation and for the purpose of marriage . . . and since these presume to contract marriage, and even pertinaciously maintain their right to marry, you, Dear Brother, have asked us for a decision regarding marriages of this kind.

"Turning our attention to this problem, we observe that, in accordance with canonical decrees and the law of nature, those who are frigid and impotent are considered to be in no way suited to contract marriages; that the aforesaid eunuchs . . . do not wish to live with those, as sisters, with whom they cannot live as with wives, because experience teaches that these, while themselves capable of intercourse, as well as the women who marry them, are drawn to unseemly sexual activity so that they cannot live chastely but that they are joined to each other in the flesh by a base and sensual intention under the pretext and semblance of marriage . . . that such unions are to be ended forthwith.

"And considering, moreover, that from marriages of this kind no good proceeds, but rather there arise alluring temptations and incentives to impurity, we order that you prohibit marriages of the aforesaid parties lacking both testicles and that you declare, on our Authority, that these are fully incapable of contracting marriage; (we further command) that you see to it that those who have actually entered marriages in this condition be separated, and that you decree that such marriages are null, void and invalid."

"Cum frequenter in istis regionibus eunuchi quidam et spadones, qui utroque teste carent, et ideo certum ac manifestum est, eos *verum semen emittere non posse . . . et humorem forsan quemdam similem semini*, licet ad *generationem et ad matrimonii causam minime aptum* effundunt, matrimonia . . . contrahere praesumant, idque sibi licere pertinaciter contendant . . . requisivit a Nobis fraternitas tua, quid de huiusmodi connubiis sit statuendum.

"Nos igitur attendentes, quod secundum canonicas sanctiones *et naturae rationem*, qui frigidae naturae sunt et impotentes iidem minime apti ad contrahenda matrimonia reputantur; quod praedicti eunuchi . . . quas tamquam uxores habere non possunt, easdem habere ut sorores nolunt, quia experientia docet, tam ipsos, dum se potentes ad coeundum iactitant, quam mulieres, quae eis nubunt, non ut caste vivant, sed ut carnaliter invicem coniungantur prava et *libidinosa intentione sub praetextu* et *in figura matrimonii* turpes huiusmodi commixtiones affectare . . . sunt ab Ecclesia Dei prorsus exterminandae. Et insuper considerantes, quod ex . . . huiusmodi . . . coniugiis *nulla utilitas* provenit, sed potius *tentationes illecebrae et incentiva libidinis* oriuntur . . . mandamus, ut coniugia per dictos . . . utroque teste carentes . . . contrahi prohibeas. eosque ad matrimonia quomodocumque contrahenda inhabiles Auctoritate Nostra declares . . . eos etiam, qui sic de facto matrimonia contraxerint, separari cures et matrimonia ipsa . . . *nulla, irrita and et invalida* esse decernas."

The definition is worded as it is because in certain cases, e.g., after a vasectomy performed because of an unjust law, marriage may still be licit. This is so even though because of the operation the spermatozoa cannot actually get into the ejaculate. As long as there is the potentiality that a repair operation could be performed perpetual impotence is not present.

There is a difference of view among theologians as to whether a vasectomized man is potent or not, because they do not agree as to whether the male secretion must contain spermatozoa. In other words, some theologians would not accept the definition of the sex act as given in this chapter unless there was added to "male secretions" the words "containing spermatozoa." Father Francis Connell agrees with the definition given above.[3] The following quotation from Niedermeyer concerning a communication from the Holy Office lends strength to this definition:

> In most recent times the impotence of one who has been vasectomized has been indirectly emphasized by a decree of the Holy Office of the 16th of February, 1935 which grants the concession that those who have forcibly undergone the statutory sterilization imposed by an immoral law are not to be prevented from contracting marriage.
>
> The decree was issued in answer to a question of the Bishop of Aachen on December 17th, 1934. The question arose because a number of men had been subjected to a vasectomy as a result of a German law promulgated to prevent a rising generation which would be afflicted with hereditary diseases. Only by reason of this operation would they be permitted to enter a civil marriage, which by law had to precede the ecclesiastical ceremony unconditionally; without the operation there could be no marriage, for thereby the ecclesiastical marriage was also prohibited. According to Gasparri I, p. 467 and other authors in this case impotence is established. On the other hand some modern authors are of the opinion, that, in this case "it is not certain that there is an impediment and therefore according to C. 1068, par. 2, the marriage is not be to prohibited." These maintain that the act of natural intercourse can be performed at least according to its externals just as well (by those vasectomized) as by those who are not vasectomized, "and that nothing more is required for the natural act."
>
> The question is formulated as follows:
>
> May a man who has undergone a bilateral vasectomy, total and irreparable, or any other surgical operation having the same effect,

---

[3] Father Connell also agrees with Father Nowlan's view given on p. 185.

namely, that all communication with the testicles is irreparably cut off so that no sperm can be conducted and transferred in the natural way, (may such a man) be nevertheless safely permitted to enter marriage according to the norm established in C. 1068, par. 2?

The answer runs as follows:

From the Holy Office, February 16, 1935

Having received the letter of Your Most Reverend Excellency, dated December 17, 1934, the Most Eminent and Most Reverend Cardinals, giving the matter diligent examination decreed in a plenary session on Wednesday, February 6th, 1935: (that) "In the case of the afore-mentioned sterilization imposed by an immoral law, marriage is not to be prohibited, according to the meaning of C. 1068, par. 2."

D. Cardinal Sbaretti.[4]

---

[4] "In neuester Zeit wurde die Eheunfähigkeit des vasektomierten Mannes indirekt dadurch unterstrichen, daß eine Entscheidung des S. Officium vom 16. Februar 1935 die Erlaubnis erteilt, bei den zwangsweise der gesetzlichen Sterilisation (*'iniqua lege imposita'*) Unterzogenen 'matrimonium non esse impendiendum.'

"Die Entscheidung ist ergangen auf eine Anfrage des Bischofs von Aachen vom 17. Dezember 1934. Die Anfrage geht davon aus, daß nach dem deutschen Gesetz zur Verhütung erbkranken Nachwuchses vom 14. Juli 1933, zahlreiche Männer der Vasektomie unterworfen werden. Nur auf Grund dieser Operation werden sie zur zivilen Eheschließung, die gesetzlich unbedingt der kirchlichen vorauszugehen hat, zugelassen; ohne Operation nicht, wodurch auch die kirchliche Eheschließung verhindert wird. Nach Gasparri I. p. 467 u. a. Aa. ist in diesem Falle Impotenz begründet. Andrerseits behaupten einige moderne Autoren, in diesem Falle, 'non constare in casu de impedimento ideoque ad normam § 2 can. 1068 matrimonium non esse impediendum.' Sie behaupten, der Akt der natürlichen copula könne wenigstens secundum speciem externam ebenso ausgeführt werden wie von nicht vasektomierten Männern, 'neque plus ad actum naturalem requiri.'

"Das dubium wird formuliert wie folgt:

"An vir qui subiit vasectomiam bilateralem, totalem et irreparabilem vel aliam operationem chirurgicam eiusdem effectus qua scilicet omnis communicatio cum testiculis irreparabiliter ita intercluditur, ut nulla spermata ex illis traduci et transferri naturali via possint nihilominus ad matrimonium ineundum admitti tuto possit iuxta normam in § 2 can. 1068 statutam?

"Das Responsum lautet:

"Ex aedibus S. Officii,

"d. 16. Februarii 1935 (prot. 80/35)

"Acceptis litteris ab Excellentia Tua Revma die 17. Decembris 1934 datis, E. mi ac Rev. mi Cardinales, re diligenti examini subiecta, in plenario conventu feria IV diei 6. Februarii 1935 decreverunt: 'In casu sic dictae sterilizationis iniqua lege impositae, matrimonium, ad mentem p. 2, can. 1068, non esse impediendum.'

"D. Card. Sbaretti"

(Albert Niedermeyer, *Handbuch der Speziellen Pastoralmedizin,* Vol. 2 [Wien: Verlac Herder, 1952], pp. 327–329.)

Canon 1068:

"Par. 1. Impotence, antecedent and perpetual, whether on the part of the man or the woman, whether known to the other party or not, whether absolute or relative, invalidates marriage by the law of nature itself.

Physical potency of the female requires:

1. The presence of a vagina which is sufficiently large to permit the entrance of the male organ.

2. The absence of severe vaginismus (vaginismus of such a degree to prevent intromission).

The failure of any of the above requirements will produce impotence in the male or female partner of a marriage. The presence of these factors produces **potentia coeundi** but not necessarily **potentia generandi**. Even in a canonical sense they cause the potency which is required for a valid marriage.

DESIRE NOT ESSENTIAL FOR POTENCY

Desire before the act and pleasure during the act are not essential for potency inasmuch as priapism from aphrodisiac drugs may occur unaccompanied by desire, and in certain diseases of the spinal cord mentioned below there may be erection with ejaculation causing conception and the individual may be unaware as to when ejaculation occurs. (Priapism means a persistent erection of the penis, especially when due to disease or drugs and not provoked by sexual desire.)

CAUSES OF IMPOTENCE

More specifically, the causes of impotence in the **male** are as follows:

Permanent or Perpetual Impotence

1. Lesions of the external genital organs:

a) Absence of the penis

b) Extreme degrees of epispadias (a malformation of the penis in which the urethra opens on the dorsum) and hypospadias (a defect in the wall of the urethra so that the canal is open for a greater or lesser distance on the undersurface of the penis)

c) Exstrophy of the bladder (Due to arrest in development, the

---

"Par. 2. If the impediment of impotence is doubtful either in law or in fact the marriage is not to be hindered.

"Par. 3. Sterility neither invalidates marriage nor renders it illicit."

Bouscaren comments in regard to the question of impotence:

"A practical criterion . . . is this:

"Whatever hinders only the *natural process* of generation constitutes sterility only; whatever hinders the *human action* of generation, that is marital copula, constitutes impotence. Even this criterion will leave some cases doubtful. . . ."

(T. Lincoln Bouscaren, S.J., and Adam C. Ellis, S.J., *Canon Law, A Text and Commentary* [Milwaukee: The Bruce Publishing Co., 1953], pp. 524–525.)

lower part of the abdominal wall and the front wall of the bladder are absent. The pubic bones are separated. The penis is rudimentary and complete epispadias is present.)

d) Extreme degrees of imperfect, curved, or bent erections

e) Stricture (a circumscribed narrowing or stenosis) of the urethra of an extreme degree

f) Malignant neoplasms

2. Testicular deficiency:

a) Congenital (may be associated with female configurations)

b) Acquired (as a result of accident or disease)

c) Cryptorchidism (the failure of descent of the testicles)

3. Disease of the central nervous system:

This may be the result of infection, e.g., tabes dorsalis (a chronic progressive sclerosis of the posterior spinal ganglia and roots, the posterior columns of the spinal cord, and the peripheral nerves), or paresis; or unknown etiology, as in multiple sclerosis; or traumatic, e.g., accidental injury to the cord.

4. Hermaphroditism

Relative Impotence

Relative impotence means that the impotence is limited to a certain person. This is most likely the result of:

1. Disproportion between the size of the male and female organs

2. Psychic disturbances (which will be described later)

Temporary or Correctible Impotence

Temporary or correctible impotence may result from:

1. Lesions of the penis:

a) Phimosis (narrowness of the opening of the prepuce preventing its being drawn back over the glans)

b) Benign neoplasms of the penis

c) Elephantiasis (hypertrophy of the skin and subcutaneous tissue due to obstructed circulation in the blood or lymphatic vessels of the penis and scrotum)

d) Extreme redundance of the prepuce

2. Deformity of surrounding structures:

a) Extreme obesity

b) Bony deformities

3. Acute diseases in which the impotence is symptomatic of the disease.

4. Psychic causes (**impotentia erigendi**) (see below).

5. Physiological impotence may exist before age of puberty and in old age

Impotence in the **female** may result from:

1. Anatomical defect:

a) Absence of the vagina

b) Imperforate or otherwise impenetrable hymen

c) Atresia of the vagina. This term usually relates to complete closure of the vaginal canal, but stenosis may take place at any point from the cervix to the hymen.

d) Hypertrophy of the clitoris or neoplasms of the adjacent structures which would interfere with intromission

2. Psychic causes:

a) Severe vaginismus

b) Homosexuality

No absolute rule can be established with regard to the permanence of all cases. They vary in severity and suitability for operative correction; each case must be decided on its own merits. In a general way the above classification would be applicable.

EFFECTS OF CASTRATION

Most of the above classification is self-explanatory. However, discussion of a few points may clarify some difficulties. The effects of early human castration before the development of the secondary sexual characteristics are well known. These consist of a retention of a high-pitched voice, reduction of hair growth, particularly the beard and around the genitalia, a tall, slim figure with disproportionate length of the extremities. The external genitalia are poorly developed and libido is usually absent. Castration after puberty produces none of these changes and there is no change in the physical characteristics of the individual. Physical potency may be retained at least for some length of time, although naturally sterility is present. The loss of the endocrine function of the testicles eventually results in atrophic changes in the accessory structures and the loss of potency. The changes resulting from castration have nothing in common with the results of double vasectomy except that in both instances the spermatozoa are removed from the genital secretions.

The effect of prostatectomy on potency has been the subject of study. It apparently has no effect on libido or potentia coeundi, although some decrease of the potentia generandi has been claimed by Kneise.[5]

VASECTOMY

There has been considerable discussion in the ecclesiastical literature in regard to the potency of the doubly vasectomized man. From the medical standpoint, there is no question of the ability of such a person to perform the sex act. Erection and ejaculation are possible. The vasectomized man is, however, sterile. Father Nowlan's statement, "The question of the impotence of the vasectomized man in the view of the average physician is not worth discussion. Doctors in general can see no room for debate on the question, since they simply assume that a man who can achieve penetration and *insemination* with satisfaction is on the face of it capable of the marriage act,"[6] is in accord with my own feeling.[7]

The following facts in regard to double vasectomy are reported by capable observers:

1. Ligation of the vas deferens results in a degeneration of the seminiferous tubules while the interstitial cells are retained or even proliferated.[8] It is these interstitial cells which elaborate the endocrine secretion of the testicle and which are concerned with the development of the secondary sexual characteristics and potency. In spite of the degeneration of the seminiferous tubules a restoration of fertility five years after double vasectomy is reported by Cameron.[9]

2. The possibility of the reversal of the operation of vasectomy depends to a great extent on the type of operation which has been performed. The chance of success in surgical reconstruction of the vas varies from 50 to 25 per cent.[10]

3. Vasectomy does not produce any change in sexual desire or change the character of the sexual act in any degree. At least it does not change the character of the sex act as far as sense observation is

---

[5] *Forschr. d. Therap.,* Vol. 7 (1931), p. 101.

[6] Italics mine.

[7] E. H. Nowlan, S.J., "Double Vasectomy and Marital Impotence," *Theol. Stud.,* Vol. 6, no. 3 (September, 1945), p. 392. (It is obvious that Father Nowlan is here using the word "insemination" as synonymous with "ejaculation.")

[8] Carl J. Wiggers, *Physiology in Health and Disease,* 5 ed. (Philadelphia: Lea and Febiger, 1949), p. 1060.

[9] Cameron, "Anastamosis of Vas Deferens," *J.A.M.A.,* Vol. 77 (1945), pp. 1119–1120.

[10] Dickinson, "Sterilization Without Unsexing," *J.A.M.A.,* Vol. 42 (1939), p. 378.

concerned. It is changed considerably in that the ejaculate now contains no spermatozoa.

4. The material ejaculated by the vasectomized individual is similar in amount and consistency to the ejaculate of the unvasectomized individual. It differs, of course, in the absence of the testicular portion of the fluid which is, however, not noticeable on gross examination. At this point the ecclesiastical and medical terminology become confusing. Admittedly loose terminology is used by many medical men, but even so all would agree that semen in its integrity consists of the testicular fluid plus the secretions of the other glands. Etymologically semen means seed and in the ordinary medical usage it would be understood to be the secretion of the testicles containing the spermatozoa (seed). The definition given by Stedman is "Semen; seminal fluid, sperm; a thick yellowish white, viscid fluid containing **spermatozoa;** it is a mixture of the secretions of the testicles, vesiculae seminales, prostate, and Cowper's glands."[11] The fluid ejaculated following vasectomy cannot be considered semen in the strict sense although it is frequently referred to by that name. It consists only of the glandular secretions which are designed to lubricate the genital tract and provide a vehicle for the semen. It might be properly referred to as the seminal fluid for this reason. However, as was noted above, it is at least probable that this is all that is required by divine law for the essence of the marriage act.

5. The operation of double vasectomy does not interfere with the performance of the marriage act as it is defined above.

Cryptorchidism is not infrequently associated with impotence as well as sterility. Modern methods of treatment, both surgical and endocrine, are becoming increasingly effective and it would be necessary to decide each case on its own merits.

PSYCHIC IMPOTENCE AND FRIGIDITY

Psychic impotence in the male and frigidity in the female can be discussed together because one is the counterpart of the other and their etiology is similar. They differ, of course, in that impotence in the male renders the marriage act impossible, whereas frigidity in the female, because of the passive role played by her in sexual relations, still permits the completion of the act and even impregnation. There is one type of frigidity, namely **vaginismus,** in which there is active

---

[11] Thomas L. Stedman, *A Practical Medical Dictionary* (1926), 9 rev. ed.

interference with the marriage act to such an extent as to constitute true impotence on the part of the woman. **Vaginismus,** which in its primary form is considered psychic in origin, may be defined as an involuntary spasm of the vaginal muscles and other muscles·making up the pelvic floor, of psychic origin, arising upon attempts at sexual relations. This reaction is associated with a strong contraction of the adductor muscles of the thigh and a drawing away of the pelvis.

Psychic impotency in the male consists not only of the **inability to obtain an erection** (impotentia erigendi) but also **failure of ejaculation** (ejaculatio deficiens) or **premature ejaculation** (ejaculatio precox) of such a degree as not to constitute a proper marriage act.

Frigidity in woman (sexual anhedonia, anesthesia, anaphrodism, dyspareunia) consists of an absence of sexual pleasure, or even revulsion for sexual relations, which is psychic in origin. In many cases sexual desire may be present although satisfaction is lacking. It occurs in 60 to 80 per cent of women in marriage. To show that this is a conservative estimate, the following authors are quoted:

Kroger and Freed:[12]

> Gynecologists and psychiatrists, especially, are aware that *the majority of women derive little or no pleasure from the sex act.* Many not only fail to experience pleasure, but actually suffer pain and revulsion. This fact assumes added significance for the medical profession because it is one of the sources from which stem divorce, broken homes and neurotic children. Many psychogynecic conditions are often a façade for the deeper problem of frigidity which in itself stems from neurotic conflicts.

Brown and Kempton:[13]

> It is estimated that between forty and fifty per cent of the married women in America suffer from this condition to some extent although no authoritative figures are available.

Spurgeon English:[14]

> Conservative estimates report that less than half of the marriages show sexual compatibility. Less conservative ones indicate that not

---

[12] William S. Kroger and S. Charles Freed, *Psychosomatic Gynecology* (Philadelphia: W. B. Saunders Co., 1951), p. 294.

[13] By permission from *Sex: Questions and Answers,* by Fred Brown and Rudolph Kempton, p. 117. Copyright, 1950. McGraw-Hill Book Co., Inc., New York.

[14] O. Spurgeon English, "Sexual Adjustment in Marriage," from *Successful Marriage* by Morris Fishbein, M.D., and Ernest W. Burgess, Ph.D., p. 102. Copyright 1947 by Morris Fishbein, reprinted by permission of Doubleday & Co., Inc., New York.

one marriage in ten has a satisfactory sexual relationship. Today's woman is doubtless by reason both of biological endowment and sociological training less prone to physical response.

Kinsey:[15]

That something between 36 and 44 per cent of the females in the sample had responded to orgasm in a part but not in all of their coitus in marriage. About one-third of those females had responded only a small part of the time, another third had responded more or less half of the time, and the other third had responded a major portion of the time, even though it was not a hundred per cent of the time (Table 112).

Kinsey's figures, however, do not apply to the population as a whole but must be applied only to his "5000 talkative women."

Frigidity is such a common experience that for many years many women were unaware that they were supposed to experience the same pleasure in sexual relations that the man did. Knowing this has done little more than increase the unhappiness which many women have in regard to their sexual relations, because to their frigidity is added a feeling of being cheated which produces a feeling of frustration. In addition to feeling cheated, many women have felt that frigidity is a bar to pregnancy. This false belief has added to their unhappiness.

Frigidity may also manifest itself as revulsion in varying degrees to the sex act, by indifference to it, by an attitude of dutifulness or by the development of **"nerves." Nymphomania,** although not usually thought of as such, is a form of frigidity in which the woman desires sexual relations almost constantly. During coitus she is greatly excited, but can never attain orgasm. Such a woman sometimes masturbates frequently and is chronically dissatisfied with her sex life.

All psychic impotence is probably relative and the individuals so affected may be able to have satisfactory relations with other partners.

PSYCHOPHYSIOLOGY OF ERECTION

Physiologically, the dilatation of the arteries of the penis during erection is a reflex act. The reflex center is in the lumbar portion of the spinal cord and the efferent impulses are carried in the pelvic nerve (nervus erigens).[16] The afferent pathway for the reflex is through

---

[15] Alfred C. Kinsey, et al., Sexual Behavior in the Human Female (Philadelphia: W. B. Saunders Co., 1953), p. 375.

[16] William H. Howell, A Text-Book of Physiology, 12 ed. (Philadelphia: W. B. Saunders Co., 1933).

the pudendal nerves. Stimulation of the erogenous zones (glans penis, clitoris, breasts, etc.) may reflexly give rise to erection of the penis or clitoris, but this usually does not occur unless there is a corresponding erotic stimulation of the higher centers. Experimentally, erection of the penis with ejaculation may be produced in dogs following complete severance of the cord.

Erotic fantasy is an essential part of the mechanism for proper sexual relations and it is in this respect that those who are psychically impotent are at fault. The occasions for sexual stimulation in either sex, whether these be sights, contacts, odors, or words, give rise to erotic fantasies in which they appear as pleasurable and there is an associated preparation of the sexual organs for the completion of the act. If, on the other hand, such occasions give rise to unpleasant, fearsome, or repulsive fantasies, the reflex does not take place and there is no effect on the organs involved. Most psychic impotence and frigidity is explainable on this basis. One of the simplest cases of psychic impotency to understand is that of a seventeen-year-old boy who sought treatment for impotency. He was in great distress and stated that he had repeatedly tried to have sexual relations with his girl friend but had been unable to obtain an erection. Questioning elicited the history that his attempts were being made on the sofa in the living room of the girl friend, while her father paced around upstairs calling down at frequent intervals, "When is that young man going home?" It is not difficult to imagine that an image of the impatient father interfered with his erotic fantasies and broke the path of the reflex.

This same thing happens in most of the other cases although they are not as easy at times to visualize. The permanence of psychic factors depends to a large extent on how deeply rooted they are in the personality. As pointed out above, many of them may be relative but are probably permanent as far as the particular individual is concerned.

More specifically the causes of psychic impotence and frigidity may be listed under the following headings:[17]

1. Fear

Fear may in a variety of ways interpose an image which will eliminate the erotic feeling; fear of the consequences as in the case above, fear of disease, fear of pregnancy. Feelings of inferiority which give rise to a fear of the inability to complete the act are a frequent source

---

[17] See chapter on the marriage act (p. 176 f.) for additional environmental factors which contribute to impotence and frigidity.

of temporary impotence on the part of the male, but his roughness or inept attempts at intercourse may cause such pain and tension on the part of the woman that it gives rise to permanent frigidity. There is associated in her mind the relationship of pain to sexual relations. Incorrect ideas of how to perform the act, and attempting to proceed before the woman is properly prepared frequently make the husband the agent who produced frigidity in his wife.

2. Revulsion

Many women and some men are conditioned to a rejection of their role in regard to sex by faulty attitudes which they acquire from their parents. Frequently at a conscious level they recall remarks from their parents, usually their mother, that the sex act is "not nice," "a sin," "a filthy habit," "animalistic." Since this reaction is so frequently conscious it undoubtedly occurs frequently at an unconscious level. These early training inhibitions and faulty education are a common source of difficulty. Less common difficulties arise from some disfigurement of the sexual partner, such as skin disease, or some habit or other characteristics not discovered before marriage which give rise to a feeling of disgust, hate, or shame.

3. Guilt

Feeling of guilt on either a conscious or unconscious level is a frequent source of conflict. Guilt over masturbation, previous sexual relations, venereal disease, or even over imagined sexual irregularities is commonly expressed. It is not unusual for a man to express the idea that he has too much respect for his wife "to use her." If he really feels this way it is usually an expression of guilt over previous experience or over extramarital relations.

4. Lack of a Proper Stimulus

Under this term may be included such conditions as homosexuality, sexual perversions, and hermaphroditism. Some homosexuals are able to indulge in heterosexual relations by indulging in homosexual fanatasies preliminary to the act. Narcissistic individuals with their excessive self-love may be unable to transfer their love to another.

5. Fatigue

This is a common source of temporary impotence. Not only physical fatigue but mental fatigue may give rise to difficulty. Neurasthenia, excessive indulgence in sexual relations, or excessive stimulation as in prolonged engagements with much sexual play may also be factors.

6. **Less common causes are:** (a) narcissism; (b) obsessive fear of sexual relations; (c) fear of pregnancy; (d) the maternal type of

woman who regards her husband as a child and is satisfied that he desires the pleasure of the relationship; (e) mutilating operations on the genitals; (f) resentment at being a woman; (g) fear of being hurt; (h) hostility toward husband.

7. Drug Addictions

Although small amounts of alcohol increase libido, and by lowering of the level of inhibition may promote sexual promiscuity in predisposed individuals, excessive indulgence in alcohol is a frequent source of impotency, not only during the spells of overindulgence, but also later in the relatively sober periods. Drugs such as morphine, cocaine, and others are sometimes sources of impotency.

As mentioned above most of the psychic causes of impotence are probably relative. Many of those who are unable to perform the sex act in marriage properly are able to do so outside of marriage or are able to masturbate satisfactorily. From the list of factors enumerated it can easily be seen how this could come about. Many women who are frigid in their first marriage can have satisfactory relations in their second marriage. The treatment of psychic impotence by psychotherapeutic methods is frequently satisfactory, but there are many failures. The therapeutic result depends largely on the causative factor and the depth to which it is implanted in the personality. Hormones have no value in the treatment of frigidity. Perfection in sexual relations can frequently be attained with practice — complete satisfaction is not to be expected on the honeymoon. In the presence of frigidity, the couple should adopt an attitude of continuous courtship. The feeling of being loved and cherished is necessary before a woman can achieve sexual satisfaction. It should be remembered that the greatest sexual desire in the female is at the time of ovulation and just before and after the menses.

In conclusion it may be stated that the causes of impotency in the male and female, although numerous, are infrequent. Of the various causes psychic impotence (including vaginismus) is the most common and although it is difficult to demonstrate its antecedent character, it is frequently permanent, at least as far as the two individuals are concerned.

CHAPTER XIV

Marriage and the Homosexual

INTRODUCTION

It may seem somewhat incongruous to include a discussion of homosexuality in a book on marriage. Homosexuality is so little understood, however, that every marriage counselor should carefully study this area of human behavior. Many unhappy marriages can be forestalled if this sexual deviation is clearly understood.

Homosexuality as a sexual inversion may be defined as a **"perversion characterized by a desire for sexual relations with members of the same sex."**[1]

It is so important to get a proper understanding of this subject that individuals with homosexual tendencies have been asked to contribute their ideas for this chapter. These statements, which have been incorporated into the following, may seem somewhat startling and frank to ears unaccustomed to this approach but they will certainly be informative. They represent a consensus and are similar to those opinions expressed by numerous homosexual individuals who have also been interviewed. The facts contained in this chapter are in accord with present-day opinion.

MARRIAGE AND THE HOMOSEXUAL

There is a great deal of misunderstanding in the public mind on just what homosexuality is like. The majority of people seem to think of the homosexual as an abnormally lustful person of more or less insatiable and uncontrollable impulses who, because of some sinister reason, directs his lust to persons of his or her own sex. The homosexual who is the object of jokes in a burlesque theater is described usually as an individual with a high-pitched voice and mincing gait,

---

[1] John R. Cavanagh and James B. McGoldrick, S.J., *Fundamental Psychiatry* (Milwaukee: The Bruce Publishing Co., 1954), p. 521.

who regularly practices **fellatio,** and who confines his social life strictly to those of his own kind. If the homosexual is female, she is usually represented as a deep-voiced woman who regularly wears slacks, cuts her hair in a mannish clip, and smokes continuously.

These views are attributable to only a small number of homosexuals. This type of homosexuality is better known than any other because it is more overt and at one time or another runs up against the law. Actually, the homosexual who runs into conflict with the law is usually the more promiscuous type and is comparable to the prostitute or procurer of heterosexual love. In the minds of many responsible judges, lawyers, and even social workers, one may find the term "homosexuality" used as a catch-all for any and every kind of sexual deviation: pederasty, satyriasis, nymphomania, necrophilia, transvestism, voyeurism.

It is necessary, therefore, to give a more accurate definition of homosexuality in order to dispel some of the confusion on the subject. **A homosexual may be defined as an individual who, although apparently physically normal, is unsusceptible to any sexual or emotional attraction from members of the opposite sex, but who is susceptible to the sexual and emotional attraction of his or her own sex.**[2] One should note that this definition contains no reference to extreme lustfulness nor to insatiable desires or impulses. It also contains no reference to homosexual sexual activity because **homosexuality is a way of thinking and feeling** and not necessarily a way of acting. As pointed out by an author (himself a homosexual) who prefers to remain unidentified:

> . . . there are many inverts who, despite strong temptations, lead completely continent lives, and others who, like some perfectly normal men, suffer few temptations of the flesh.[3]

It should be pointed out, moreover, that performance of homosexual acts is no proof of homosexuality. It should also be pointed out that although the individual may have strong homosexual attractions this does not constitute a compulsion to act as a homosexual. To quote Anomaly again:

> Among the normal are saints and profligates. Between those who have achieved sanctity and those who have chosen vice will be found the larger number, struggling sinners whose faltering progress is

[2] Anomaly, *The Invert* (Baltimore: The Williams and Wilkins Co., 1948), p. 6.
[3] *Ibid.,* p. 80.

marked by many a pitiful tumble. Among inverts there are saints and profligates, and between the extremes many who are struggling in a more or less successful attempt to follow the dictates of conscience and the direction of authority.[4]

It requires a voluntary act on the part of the homosexual to perform a homosexual act. The homosexual has the same ability, and should be expected to abstain from sexual activity, in the same manner that the heterosexual person is expected to abstain from sexual activity outside of marriage. This may seem somewhat of a cross for the homosexual to know that he is deprived of the channels of expressing his love but he is not alone in this respect:

> Even if the invert has no hope of legitimate sexual expression he is, after all, not much worse off than the members of that huge army of women for whom there are no mates in this female-ridden world, and who are chaste and surprisingly happy. . . .
>
> It is true that unmarried women are spared many of the trials which the invert has to endure, and that some of them are sustained by religious rule. It is also true that many good works, whether performed in the name of Charity, Social Service or Civic Pride, would never be accomplished were the supply of mateless women to fail. Now the relation between the idea of mateless women doing so much of the world's most heroic work, and the idea of sublimation of the instincts of inversion, is not far to seek. It is based on the fact that these women find in their devotion to humanity at large that satisfaction, content and happiness which married women find in the service of their immediate families. Since the invert is shut out of the satisfactions and obligations of normal family life, he, too, must seek in works of life and service an outlet for his zeal and energy.[5]

There is no reason why a homosexual cannot lead a celibate life. But it often happens in practice that the homosexual considers himself so far removed from society as a whole that he is almost convinced that the laws of normal behavior do not apply to him. He may be so convinced of his isolation that he does not see how closely his sexual drive parallels that of his heterosexual companions and that the rules of chastity which apply to them will apply to him as well. This failure on the part of the homosexual to understand the closeness of his drive (except for the love-object) may leave him with the feeling that he is "doomed" to perform eventually some kind of overt activity.

[4] *Ibid.*, p. 84.
[5] *Ibid.*, pp. 118–119.

There may be nothing in his physical appearance which singles out a person as homosexual. In most cases a homosexual appears to be normal and lives like the rest of his fellow associates.[6]

TEST FOR HOMOSEXUALITY

The simplest methods of determining a homosexual attitude is by answering the following questions: Does the individual find himself sexually excited by thoughts about members of his own sex? Does the individual find himself sexually unmoved by thoughts about members of the opposite sex? If the answer to first question is "yes" and if the answer to the second question is "no," there is good reason to believe that the individual has a homosexual attitude. If the presence of homosexuality is suspected, a person should consult a competent psychiatrist for a further checkup.

INCIDENCE OF HOMOSEXUALITY

The number of individuals who suffer from this disorder is higher than one might think. Various estimates have been given, but there is no figure which has been universally accepted. The difficulty in obtaining statistics is due to the stigma which society at present places upon the homosexual, who is consequently reticent about giving out the information. It was estimated that in Germany prior to World War II the number was as high as 5 per cent of the total population. The Kinsey Report on the male population of the United States of America states that $6\frac{3}{10}$ per cent of the total number of male orgasms are derived from homosexual outlets; for the female he gives 19 per cent for unmarried females in their late thirties (p. 457). Havelock Ellis in 1936 estimated that 2 to 5 per cent of all males, and double that figure for females, were homosexual. Hirschfeld in 1903 estimated that $2\frac{3}{10}$ per cent of males were homosexual; Hamilton (1929) gave 17 per cent of males. Ramsey (1943) stated that 30 per cent of 291 junior high school boys were homosexuals; and Finger (1947) stated that 27 per cent of 111 college males were sexual deviates.

With these few facts established, we may go on to a clearer discussion of homosexuality.

In the rest of our discussion we shall concentrate upon homosexuals who have carried on some kind of overt activities. Most of what we say about overt homosexuals will apply also to those who have never

---

[6] Cf. *ibid.*, p. 29: "The struggling invert should be brought to realize that his difficulties are shared by men who have proven themselves to be admirable members of society in peace and war."

engaged in any overt activity but who may have been subjected to
the temptations of homosexual **desires** rather than acts.[7]

The homosexual who is most widely known is the promiscuous
type. In addition to the promiscuous homosexual there is another
large number of individuals who confine their activities to only one
person at a time, if they have any overt homosexual activities at all.
It is a well-known fact that many homosexuals never reveal the fact
that they are suffering under the difficulty, and they may pass their
entire lives unnoticed even by those who are living in close quarters
with them. For example, the brothers and sisters of a homosexual
may never even suspect, much less learn of, the presence of his
neurotic condition.

Broadly speaking, there are two types of individuals who engage in
homosexual activity: (1) those who have never had sexual attraction
toward any but members of their own sex (the true homosexual), and
(2) those who have had at least some degree of attraction toward
those of the opposite sex as well as toward those of their own sex. The
former are called "true" homosexuals whereas the latter group are
usually called "bisexuals" (also pseudohomosexuals or environmental
type).

TRUE HOMOSEXUALITY

The true homosexual is absolutely incapable (sic) of emotional involvement with a member of the opposite sex; and it is quite unlikely
that a true homosexual will ever enter the married state of his own
accord. The true homosexual will have had so little interest in the
other sex that he will not be intimately associated with any member
of the other sex so that marriage would ever be a natural consequence
of their acquaintance. The true homosexual will have such a horror
of the body of the other sex that it would be impossible for him or
her to feign sexual stimulation. In fact, it seems impossible to imagine
a true homosexual ever engaging with pleasure in any form of heterosexual petting or love activity of any kind whatever. The true homosexual would be so emotionally cold about the question of sex that
it is difficult to see how a member of the opposite sex would not sense
that something was wrong in the situation.

However, the distinct possibility remains that under some circumstances the true homosexual might be forced into marriage. An only

[7] Nevertheless we must repeat what we have already said before: there is no
need for a homosexual to engage in overt activity. He may lead a life as chaste as his
heterosexual neighbor, and he does so frequently.

son, for example, might yield to the social pressure of his parents and join in a marriage contract in order to perpetuate the family name. Other homosexuals have been led by misguided counselors into contracting marriage as a cure for their sexual difficulties. Advice of this kind is usually disastrous. Instead of one difficulty there are now two difficulties. Those who have suggested marriage as a cure for homosexuality have never really understood the unconscious reservoir of fear that the homosexual has in regard to the state itself, nor could such a counselor ever really appreciate the **horror feminae** that is in the mind of the homosexual. The true homosexual may have a clear realization in his mind of the differences between the male and female genitals, but when he comes to actually seeing them — as in a photograph — he associates the lack of a penis in a woman as a physical deformity — a castration — a mutilation. In other words, for the true homosexual the vaginal orifice is like an open wound; and the true homosexual has no more intention of inserting his penis into that opening than a heterosexual male would of inserting his penis into a wound located on any other part of the female body. But the vaginal orifice is more than a wound — it is a rather ugly wound, where the skin has not healed over smoothly but in raised lumps of flesh with hair growing out of it.

Consider these comments of a male sexual invert in regard to sexual attraction:

SEX WITH WOMEN

As far as women were concerned, I never felt attraction for them. When I was growing up, there were only two girls in the neighborhood whom I would even have considered having anything to do with. (When I say "having anything to do with" I mean merely, going to the movies or spending an hour in conversation). One of these was a cousin, the other was her friend. The rest of the women in the neighborhood were of only average intelligence, their family backgrounds were average, their fathers were policemen, street car operators or mechanics and the girls themselves expected to get married after two or three years out of high school. We, on the other hand, knew that we would go on to college.

Since already I was attracted toward men in college and since women had no attraction for me, I associated more with men. I made several attempts to get to know women better. I used to talk to them, I used to go to a few proms with them — but I never felt at ease, as I did with men. If you take a girl to the movies, you have to walk home with her. If you go to the movies with another man, you can leave him outside the theater and go your own way. If you invite a girl to dinner, you have to spend the whole evening with her. When a man is concerned, you can get up and leave when you want to. . . .

A woman was something delicate — a lovely creature — child-like in many respects, witty, intuitive, who could see the heart of a situation without giving a reason. For a man to violate a woman was the most heinous act possible next to violating a child. How did this view arise? It was partially because I saw women abused in the neighborhood where I lived as a child. Mrs. A——, a kindly, ambitious woman, was married to a man who was continuously drunk and who beat her and the children. Mrs. B—— was married to a man who went on drinking bouts. I can remember one cold February night when two of the B—— brothers who were around my age (9 or 10), were trying to bring their father home. They were trying to hold him up and he kept falling into snowbanks. Helen D—— had a brother whom she supported. He never worked. His clothes always smelled of sweat and urine. He is confined to a home for alcoholics. Helen is in an institution — she became senile. Alice E——'s husband left her. She brought the children up alone. One of Alice E——'s daughters died in childbirth. Mrs. F—— worked to keep her house together. Her husband refused to fulfill his role as a father. One of the sons is in prison for life. Another son became an alcoholic. And he had two sons and a daughter. The daughter has been married twice — has been brought up for passing bad checks. One of the sons became a dope addict — he even removed the copper lining out of his grandmother's washing machine to sell it for dope. He was killed a month ago in an automobile crash. Mrs. G—— was beaten by her husband. Margaret H——'s life with her husband was described as a crucifixion.

When women were not mistreated, they were the stronger of the pair in a married couple. This was the attitude I had toward my own mother, toward the mothers of several of my friends. It was true in my own mother's family that all of the men were weaklings and the women produced results.

Thus already I had drawn from these experiences the conclusion that women were to be respected. In reading poetry like Tennyson's "The Idylls of the King" which we studied in sophomore English class in high school, the notion of respect for women was coupled with the new one of courtesy toward women. This was increased in college in studying the history of courtly life.

But there was a problem. Women were to be respected. This I acknowledged. Women were supposed to be frail, to need protection.

But most of the women I met were not particularly frail, nor did they need protection. If anything, they were as aggressive as I was. Some were supporting themselves, some were putting themselves through school. There was nothing shy about them. And there was something else! Women who were supposedly delicate and frail were covered with hair on their bodies, although not as much as men were. And the touch of a woman's flesh was too soft. If you pressed on it at all you soon felt a bone. And immediately I would think of a skeleton. If you had sex relations with a woman, then, you would probably be aware of her skeletal structure, and you would have the feeling of sexual intercourse with a skeleton.

Moreover, if you had sexual intercourse with a woman, other than a prostitute, you would be married to her. And that marriage would probably turn out like those which I had seen in the early neighborhood. My mother had frequently said that "a marriage can easily make you or break you." From my experience it seemed that 98% of them broke.

Thus, it came to me as somewhat of a surprise when I realized in the last two or three years that friends of mine who had married found that marriage was more than an attraction by nature, that the biological interest was only a part of marriage. They have been married for seven, eight or nine years — and they are satisfied with it today as when they began.

The female homosexual feels a similar revulsion toward the male organs. It is rather significant that so many female homosexuals envision the male organ as erect, as a rather blunt instrument which is capable of inflicting a wound — of drawing blood — an awkward instrument which may rupture the inner lining of the female body.

Psychologically, the homosexual never envisages members of the opposite sex as members of the same race. There is an almost "conventional" racial barrier between homosexuals and the opposite sex as there seems to be a "conventional" racial barrier among the members of different racial groups. For the homosexual, the opposite sex comprises members who are either angels or devils. There are no intermediates; members of the group are either too idealized or looked down upon — that is one reason why the homosexual can never make contact with them — they scare him off — they do not correspond to the picture that he has of them. There may be a few members of the opposite sex who do not fit into either category; but he does not bother to investigate these cases since the problem seems to be of little interest.

BISEXUALITY

In the case of the bisexual type, matters are somewhat different. The bisexual type may be divided into two broad groups: those for whom bisexuality is a permanent condition, and those for whom it is a temporary expedient. This latter group may frequently include members of the same sex who are deprived of the company of the opposite sex for a long period of time, such as sailors, or prisoners, either male or female. In the case of these individuals the condition may clear up as soon as they are back in the company of the opposite sex. But there is another type of bisexual who may be called the "permanent" type. And in this group we may find degrees of bisexuality. Some bisexuals find their love interests permanently divided between males and females. Others are inclined toward their own sex only periodically. All they seem to need is a single night's experience every six or eight months and they return to their husband or wife and concentrate interest upon the spouse until the next episode. Others may find themselves even less frequently involved in the problem. Thus, one might say that there are degrees of homosexuality — varying from the "true" homosexual to those who exhibit the difficulty at spasmodic intervals.

The bisexual type may find his life highly complicated by marriage; and, depending upon his general outlook, a great deal of anxiety may arise. The bisexual is frequently married to a partner whose own love life is more normally oriented and who consequently would not understand the problem with which the bisexual partner is confronted. When the bisexual says that he or she really loves the marriage partner, it is true as far as the bisexual knows. But the bisexual member, while loving the marriage partner, may love a member of his or her own sex as well — somewhat as a man with a harem may love several wives.

The anxiety of the bisexual can be greater than that of the true homosexual. The true homosexual may be anxious over the fact that he is breaking the moral or civil law and he may be found out. But the bisexual will have all this to worry about and more besides: he may be more readily subject to blackmail; he has a wife to consider; he may have children to consider. His activity may be found out directly by his wife; or the first intimations may come through a neighborhood gossip.

THE HOMOSEXUAL ON HOMOSEXUALITY

When the homosexual views his sexuality he finds himself in a position similar to that of the man who was left a legacy of one million dollars with one proviso — he must not spend the money. The homosexual finds himself with the same drive to sexual satisfaction which his heterosexual neighbor feels. But in the case of the latter there is at least the chance that fulfillment can be realized, whereas in the case of the homosexual there is no outlet unless he chooses to break the moral and civil law, or goes even beyond this point by denying their reality altogether.

How far a homosexual will go will depend upon his general outlook on his environment. If he has any ethical sense whatever, or if he gives any recognition to the civil law, he will never entirely consider homosexual activity as an acceptable condition. On the other hand, the homosexual who has had little moral training and who has been allowed to give free rein to any impulses will not attempt to correct the condition and will muster up arguments to prove why homosexuality is a "natural" condition. He will attempt to get arguments from heredity which suggest that the condition is an inherited one, or arguments from some already-deluded literati who claim that the constant state of anxiety of a homosexual makes him more sensitive. This type usually do violence to their own intelligence and attempt to twist the scheme of reality around in such a way that they conclude by saying that the man who does not yield to his "natural" impulses has perverted himself and is therefore immoral.

Let us divide the discussion into two types: (1) those who have been in an atmosphere where they have never been allowed to give full rein to their homosexuality, and (2) those who have no intention of changing to heterosexuality.

It should be made plain at the outset that no homosexual is altogether to blame for his condition. That is to say, the homosexual developed in the way he did because of external influences: possibly a dominant parent of the opposite sex, or a lack of contact with members of the opposite sex during puberty, a weak parent of the same sex, or a fear of marriage itself. This is one of the reasons why the homosexual may himself subscribe to the heredity argument — he sees no place in his life where he ever made any choice in favor of homosexuality — it has always been there.

But it should be made clear to the homosexual that, while he is not responsible for the oncoming of his homosexuality, he is responsible for homosexual actions just as much as his heterosexual neighbor would be for performing heterosexual acts outside of marriage. The homosexual may plead that he has no normal outlet for his capacity to love, but the same argument is true for those heterosexual persons who have never been given the opportunity of marriage. There is a large number of the female population in the United States alone who will never be able to realize their capacities for motherhood.[8]

The homosexual who has been brought up in an atmosphere where behavior has been more or less in accordance with conventionality has a singular advantage over the homosexual who has been brought up without such restraints.

The homosexual who has lived with people who are more or less normal will necessarily encounter rules and attitudes of behavior which will put a check upon his giving free rein to his homosexuality. Two homosexuals in this group may be good friends and will never reveal their homosexuality to each other because of the possibility that the homosexuality of the other is only suspected but not known as a true fact. In addition to the strong opposition from his social group there will be other deterrents as well: a good religious atmosphere, respect for the civil code, fear of punishment, the feeling of "not belonging." In other words, these notions and unpleasant experiences will constantly bring before the mind of the homosexual the fact that his activity will not be tolerated in the scheme of things. A homosexual in this atmosphere will never be really "adjusted" to his homosexuality. This atmosphere may, however, become too strict . . . so strict that the homosexual never dares to bring up the subject even to an adult who seems to understand him otherwise. The homosexual of this kind is constantly spending his time concealing his difficulty from his friends — and this is accompanied by a great expenditure of anxiety. He feels isolated and helpless about it.

This is one of the reasons why a knowledge of homosexuality should be given to parents just as knowledge of communicable diseases is usually given to them. Nobody would benefit more than the homosexual if the general causes of the trouble were better known and if the possibility of a cure were better known. The day when homosexuality is recognized as a neurosis will be a better day for

---

[8] Cf. Anomaly, *op. cit.*, pp. 118–119.

society as a whole.[9] If consideration is given to the **medical** as well as to the **moral** aspects of the problem, the homosexual himself would obtain a great deal of relief and would have his psychological tension lowered sufficiently to enable him to realize that the problem is not as overpowering as he was previously led to believe. This fact alone would be a tremendous impetus for the homosexual to seek out help. It seems hardly necessary to add that if knowledge of homosexuality were disseminated more widely among the general public, it would undoubtedly enable confessors, teachers, and those engaged in guidance work to recognize the symptoms more quickly and to suggest earlier treatment. The sooner the treatment the less will homosexual trends become imbedded in the character of the individual.

Let us consider now the second type of homosexual. Here we are referring to those whom we described earlier as accepting the condition as "normal." This group is made up of these who refuse to control their homosexual impulses, just as there are heterosexuals who refuse to control their heterosexual impulses. Both the unrestrained homosexual and heterosexual attempt to justify their activities. The incontinent homosexual will muster a number of arguments but they can be reduced pretty much down to the following four: (1) he has not consciously brought it about, therefore it must be a bodily condition and he must have been born with it; (2) he may have adult relatives whom he suspects of suffering from the same difficulty, and he concludes that it is probably inherited; (3) homosexuals comprise a "third" sex, intermediary between male and female, and they can understand both sexes and are therefore privileged; and (4) the homosexual is more sensitive than other normally sexed individuals, and therefore homosexuality is more conducive to artistic excellence.

None of these arguments can be held in the face of the evidence now at hand. It is quite true that the homosexual has not consciously adopted his homosexuality. On the other hand, it does not necessarily follow that the homosexual syndrome did not develop during his early years as the result of some overwhelming emotional problems or other. Homosexuality is more probably the aftereffect of a series of painful emotional experiences. It is an unconscious secondary result rather than a consciously and directly willed effect. Moreover, it is a well-

---

[9] For example, among laymen the common opinion today is that homosexuality is a perversion of only the most diabolical of humans. The adolescent who is falling into a pattern of homosexuality does not consider himself as a homosexual because he does not see himself as a diabolical person. Therefore, he does not feel that his difficulty is homosexuality.

recognized fact today that homosexuality does not result from an endocrine imbalance. It has been found that when male homosexuals were given injections of androgen and when female homosexuals were given injections of estrogen there was no decrease in their homosexual libido. In fact, just the opposite resulted. Among both males and females there was an increase in homosexual libido.

The second argument from heredity has been neither proven nor disproven. But in any case, if homosexuality is transmitted at all in the genes, it would be better to say that parents may not only transmit the disposition toward homosexuality in the genes, but at the same time they may reproduce a psychological environment which favors the development of homosexual trends; i.e., a parent whose marriage is unsuccessful may transmit a fear of marriage to the children.

The third and fourth arguments ought to be answered together because they are both based upon the rationalization that homosexuality is a "privileged" state. Only the overt homosexual will attempt to prove this. He will frequently tell the undiscerning heterosexual that the latter is not sensitive enough to understand what the homosexual is talking about — that if he himself were homosexual, he would readily understand. This homosexual says that he has both male and female tendencies and consequently has a better vantage point from which to discuss the subject of love. This group may occasionally include highly talented individuals who may tend to disseminate their doctrines by developing strange theories of religion, morality, legal principles, and other subjects. In literature they incline to picture a strange immoral world where sexual love of one kind or another becomes the be-all and the end-all of human activity. This type, especially when found in a genius, may have a pernicious effect upon the whole of society.

Krausz describes homosexuality as a functional neurosis and, more specifically, as a compulsion neurosis, not so much a biological entity as a neurotic syndrome which has as good a chance of being cured as any other neurosis. According to Krausz' view, the homosexual "makes love to" another of his own sex not so much because he actually loves the other individual, but because he sees in this "love-making" a way of neutralizing an individual who would be otherwise a competitor. In other words, there is really no love in the homosexual, but rather a deep-seated hate which puts on a disguise of love. There may be something to Krausz' opinion. There is another explanation which would be derived from Krausz' theory but which would come to a different conclusion and seems to stay closer to the homosexual's feelings: the homosexual makes love to some individual who possesses a characteristic which the homosexual feels that he himself lacks. By mutual giving in an act of love, the homosexual vicariously acquires what he felt he had been previously lacking.

MARRIAGE ADVICE FOR HOMOSEXUALS

If a homosexual comes to a marriage counselor, what ought the latter to advise? There are a number of things which the counselor should tell him:

1. Keep away from **marriage itself** until the condition has been entirely cleared up.

2. This does not mean, however, that he or she should stay away from company with members of the opposite sex. However, the homosexual should avoid association with individuals of the opposite sex who are in need of psychiatric treatment.

3. Seek out psychiatric treatment.

4. Seek out the guidance of a **sound** spiritual counselor at the same time you are undergoing psychiatric treatment.

The homosexual should keep away from marriage itself until the difficulty is cleared up because he or she will not be able to fulfill his or her marriage obligations. This will only complicate matters. On the other hand, association with normal members of the opposite sex will help to give concrete evidence of their desirability.

Seek out psychiatric treatment. Seek the services of a sound psychiatrist. It is usually said that psychiatric treatment is expensive — and in some respects it is. Certainly as far as the patient is concerned it seems to be. But one should take into account the relief it can bring. Moreover, most psychiatrists will adjust their fees according to the financial condition of the patient, and most large cities have at least one center where some psychiatric treatment is given free of charge.

Finally, the homosexual should have the guidance of a sound spiritual advisor, and this requires a certain amount of training on the part of the advisor.[10] Direction is most important in the case of

---

[10] "I bear witness to the fact that, in spite of the limitation of certain confessors, I believe confession to be supernaturally efficacious and most helpful to self-discipline" (Anomaly, *op. cit.,* p. 86). "The priest must . . . be very understanding but discreet and considerate, in his first questions, awakening confidence before going on to speak of spiritual remedies" (R. Père Charles Larere, "Passage of the Angel through Sodom," *New Problems in Medical Ethics,* ed. Dom Peter Flood, O.S.B. [Westminster: The Newman Press, 1952], pp. 108–122).

the self-revealed homosexual. The priest must be prudent; he should show absolutely no sign of contempt — that is what the homosexual is afraid he might do, and if he finds it in the man to whom he has gone for help, he may never return. He might instead try to find a cure in books, and many of these only make matters worse when they say that there is no cure, etc. The very fact that the homosexual is turning to the priest and psychiatrist indicates that he is trying to find a cure.

In general, the marriage counselor should always take a positive approach toward the cure of homosexuality. Emphasize to the patient the fact that **he can only be cured if he wants to be cured.** Do not minimize the effort involved. Make him realize that much of his personality will be changed after the process. **But hold out that assurance for him.** Most homosexuals **want to be cured.**

We said earlier that the homosexual has the same feeling of frustration about sex as a man who inherits a million dollars provided he promises not to spend the money. The marriage counselor ought to point out that this is not exactly the situation. Rather, the homosexual ought to feel like a man who has been left a legacy in a foreign country provided he goes to the foreign country and takes up a permanent life there. Whether a man will pull up all his old roots and re-establish himself in the new country will depend largely upon the amount of the inheritance. If the legacy is fifty dollars he will hardly consider the change. But if the legacy has considerable value, he will take steps to leave the old country in order to live in the new. So, too, with the homosexual; whether he will uproot himself from the past will depend upon how great a value he puts upon heterosexuality and partly upon the disadvantages he finds in homosexuality.

Homosexuality was initially a compromise solution for a clash of sexual interests. In other words, the homosexual **unconsciously** adjusted himself to a sexual attitude which, at the time, seemed to be a comfortable position — just as poor posture originates as a comfortable, though inadequate, bodily position.

Nobody realizes more fully than the homosexual how fragile and unreal are the foundations of his love — how quickly the foundations may crumble, how much anxiety is spent in conflict with moral and social problems. Nobody realizes more than the homosexual how much he is separated from the main stream of life. Like Moses, he marches toward the Promised Land but dies on the borders and never enters its territory alive.

SECTION III

FERTILITY
AND
MARRIAGE

Then God blessed them and said to them, "Be fruitful and multiply."
Gen. 1:28.

CHAPTER XV

Hygiene of Pregnancy

JOHN J. KUHN

It is unlikely that a client would expect the marriage counselor to give prenatal care. It is an area, however, in which the counselor should be informed so that he may respond intelligently to whatever general questions the woman may ask. He should also be alert to the necessity of early prenatal care and its public health value.

The woman should be impressed from the beginning that pregnancy is a normal condition. It is not a sickness and should be a period of joyful expectancy. Pregnancy fulfills the purpose of marriage. Too frequently a young married couple are ashamed to tell their family and friends about a prospective pregnancy. They have a feeling that in some way "they were caught" and through their own fault. Such an attitude is naturally to be decried. As a result of this a very large number of women resent their pregnancy through the first trimester. Lull and Kimbrough estimate that this is true in 75 per cent of their patients.[1] This resentment tends to decrease as the patient approaches term and with the delivery very little is usually left. Pride in possession and pride in self overcomes the resentment of the discomforts and fears of pregnancy. This is especially true where the delivery and pregnancy were uneventful. When complications have developed the rejection, anxiety and aversion to pregnancy may persist. Most physicians at the present time believe that most of the symptoms of early pregnancy are related to the mother's rejection of her pregnancy. The severity of the symptoms, especially the nausea and vomiting, is usually in direct proportion to the degree of rejection.[2]

The factors behind the rejection of the pregnancy are sometimes difficult to determine. Shame "at being caught" is frequently present.

[1] Clifford B. Lull and Robert A. Kimbrough, *Clinical Obstetrics* (Philadelphia: J. B. Lippincott Co., 1953), p. 150.
[2] *Ibid.*, p. 170.

Fear, concern over finances, resentment of the child as a confirmation of the permanency of an unhappy marriage, and pre-existing neuroses are common factors. Failure of acceptance of the female role is probably a more basic reason. Whatever the factor, it is important to the proper conduct of the pregnancy that there be a close rapport between the patient and her obstetrician. An opportunity to discuss her psychological problems should be afforded. The "mystery" of pregnancy should be explained. Fear decreases as knowledge increases. The process of growth should be explained and labor described. Many women are burdened by fantastic tales regarding the pain and severity of the process to which they should be desensitized. This is an area in which the marriage counselor can be of value. Many of the individuals who consult him have problems arising in this area. A persistent fear or aversion to pregnancy needs careful exploration.

A complete history and physical examination should be made early in pregnancy. This examination should be complete because only in this way can future complications be avoided. Laboratory studies should include a study of the woman's Rh status as well as the blood count, Wassermann or Kahn test, and urinalysis. A chest X ray is usually desirable. The completion of this examination is a very good opportunity to reassure the woman if all is well. She will naturally be somewhat apprehensive, especially if this is her first pregnancy. A few words of reassurance at this early stage of pregnancy will be of immeasurable value.

The woman should be apprised of possible difficulties and told how to recognize them. The possibility of spontaneous abortion should be discussed and the significance of any vaginal bleeding, even of "spotting," should be explained. She should be instructed to report any abdominal cramping or unusual backache, either of which may be the precursor of an abortion. She should also be instructed to report persistent headaches and edema, which are danger signs of other difficulties. Any unusual manifestation should be called to the attention of the physician.

Nutrition is an important factor in prenatal care. It must be realized that the baby derives its nutrition from the mother throughout the pregnancy. One should not wait until the baby is born to give it a good nutritional start. From early in its conception, a diet high in proteins, minerals, and vitamins is essential for the growth and development of the child. The diet should be constructed around the following foods:

Proteins:
1. Lean meat or fish — at least 8 ounces daily
2. Eggs — at least two daily; more if desired
3. Cheese — about 1½ ounces daily
4. Milk — at least 1 quart a day. This may be taken between meals.

Carbohydrates:
1. Green vegetables
2. Fruit
3. Avoid potatoes, noodles, spaghetti, macaroni, and large quantities of bread. These may be taken occasionally.

Avoid too many sweets such as ice cream, candy, soft drinks, and sugar. These should be reserved for special occasions.

For dessert use jello, junket, custard, or puddings. Sugar substitutes such as saccharin and sucaryl may be used in the preparation of desserts.

Fats are best avoided but butter or oleomargarine may be used in small amounts.

Salt should be restricted. Sodium in other forms, such as sodium bicarbonate, should also be restricted.

Supplemental items. These should be added in the form of vitamins, calcium, and iron.

Calories. This depends on weight, but should average 2300 to 2700 for the normally weighted woman.

Diet is related to the toxemia of pregnancy and should be carefully watched.

Weight and blood pressure are important indications of impending difficulty and will usually be checked on each visit. Increasing weight may be an early sign of edema and a rising blood pressure is a frequent indication of toxemia. Other symptoms of toxemia are: (1) increase in nausea or vomiting; (2) visual disturbances, e.g., spots before the eyes; (3) swelling of the extremities; (4) albumen in the urine. Regulation of the diet and fluid intake will usually correct minor degrees of toxemia but hospitalization is occasionally necessary to bring it under control.

Boy or girl? This frequently asked question must be answered simply by telling the truth. There is no way to determine the sex of the child in advance.

Nausea and vomiting. As pointed out above, this usually arises because of an emotional problem. If the condition is mild the patient can usually be made more comfortable by eating a cracker or dry toast before arising in the morning. Eating small amounts frequently is also helpful. Although the condition occasionally becomes severe it is easily controlled by modern methods of treatment.

Exercise. The pregnant woman can do most of the things which the nonpregnant woman can do. The keynote is moderation. Excesses should be avoided. Housework, dancing, and walking can be beneficial. Most doctors restrict golf, tennis, horseback riding, and swimming, but even these may be permitted in some cases. Tub bathing is usually restricted in the last six weeks. Showers, hair washing, and permanent waves are permitted at any time.

Sexual relations. The sex act is permitted during all of pregnancy except for the last six weeks. It is restricted because of the danger of introducing infection into the genital tract. Sexual activity should not be resumed until six to eight weeks after delivery.

Travel. World War II demonstrated the ability of pregnant women to travel where and how and when they pleased. Since that time, obstetricians have not been as concerned about travel of pregnant women as they once were. If any complication is present, travel would be undesirable. There is no one mode of travel which has any particular ill effect.

Clothing should be comfortable. In spite of her changing shape, the pregnant woman who is content with her state radiates a special charm which is a reflection of pride in her motherhood. Constricting bands around the waist and extremities are likely to lead to discomfort and should be avoided. Tight garters are likely to lead to varicose veins. High heels are dangerous in that they may lead to falls and backaches.

Care of the breasts is important. Early in pregnancy the breasts begin to enlarge and during the course of pregnancy may each increase as much as a pound in weight. A secretion, colostrum, forms in the breast and may leak through the nipples. This secretion should be washed away gently with soap and water and thoroughly dried. Inverted and retracted nipples may require special care and the doctor should be consulted in such cases.

Dental care is essential and should be started early in pregnancy.

Moderation is the keynote in pregnancy. Moderation in diet, in exercise, in travel, in the use of alcohol and of tobacco is essential.

Post-partum exercises. After delivery there are certain exercises which will strengthen muscle tone and consequently restore the figure.

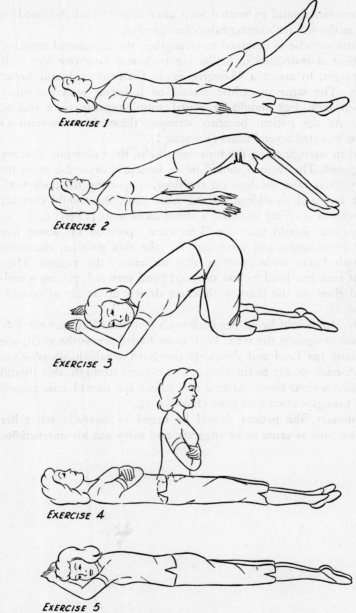

EXERCISE 1

EXERCISE 2

EXERCISE 3

EXERCISE 4

EXERCISE 5

POST-PARTUM EXERCISES

These exercises should be started soon after delivery and increased in number as the woman's strength becomes greater.

The first exercise is designed to strengthen the abdominal muscles. The patient is instructed to lie on her back and raise one leg, with knee straight, to about a 45-degree angle (halfway up) and lower it slowly. The same procedure should be followed with the other leg. Then both legs should be raised simultaneously to a similar position. As the patient becomes stronger these three movements should be repeated several times (Exercise 1).

To aid in strengthening the hips and thighs, the following exercises are suggested. The woman should lie on her back, draw the knees up part way, then raise the hips off the floor, supporting the body with only the feet and shoulders. At the same time, she should contract her muscles as if trying to check a bowel movement (Exercise 2).

The patient should take the "knee-chest" position for about five minutes every night and morning. To take this position, she must kneel with knees wide apart so that air enters the vagina. Then she must turn her head to one side and bend forward, placing shoulders and chest on the floor, with knees drawn up as far as possible (Exercise 3).

Finally, she should lie on her back with feet braced against the foot of the bed or against the wall. With arms folded across the chest, she should raise her head and shoulders slowly to a half-sitting position, then sink back slowly to the floor. As she gains strength, this should be repeated several times. After a few weeks she should raise herself to a full sitting position each time (Exercise 4).

In summary, the patient should be urged to carefully select her doctor, see him as often as he suggests, and carry out his instructions.

CHAPTER XVI

Pregnancy

Pregnancy results from the union of the mature spermatozoon and the mature ovum. This process, called impregnation, usually takes place in about the middle of the Fallopian tube. Following a single intercourse, such for example as that constituting rape, impregnation could not take place sooner than 35 minutes, probably longer, following the act. This estimate is based on the rate of speed of 1 inch in seven minutes for the spermatozoon over an estimated distance of 5 inches. From this it is apparent that every pregnancy is tubal in its inception. The fertilized ovum is then carried by a ciliary current in the Fallopian tube into the cavity of the uterus where the process of **nidation** takes place. The lining of the uterus (endometrium) which is prepared for pregnancy each month has been greatly thickened in preparation for the event which has now occurred (see chart on p. 216). The product of conception when it arrives in the uterine cavity becomes buried in the thickened mucous membrane (nidation) where the process of growth continues. As a result of the changes which have already occurred the corpus luteum has grown and become the corpus luteum of pregnancy (see Chapter III). This supplies the hormones necessary for the continuation of the gestation.

Soon after the union of the two elements their nuclei unite to form the segmentation nucleus. Mitosis quickly takes place within it and division of the ovum into two cells occurs. These two cells divide giving four. This process of cell division or segmentation goes on until the original ovum becomes converted into a mass of cells (morula or mulberry mass). Soon, thereafter, differentiation of cells for a particular body function takes place and the cell mass very early is recognizable as a fetus. The early cell growth starts in the oviduct immediately following fertilization. The transit through the

Fallopian tube is believed to take from 5 to 7 days. So that the uterine pregnancy does not usually start until about one week following conception.

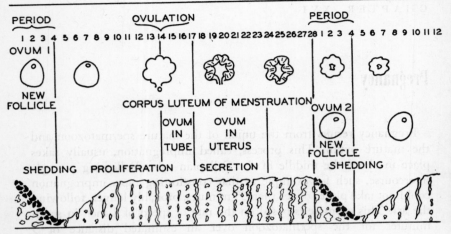

NORMAL MENSTRUAL CYCLE

Note changes in the Graafian follicle (top line) leading to ovulation and corpus luteum of menstruation. This is followed by the next menstrual period.

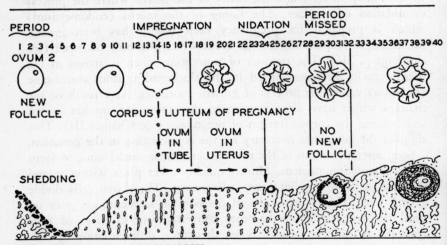

ENDOMETRIUM OF PREGNANCY

Note that when the ovum is fertilized the thickening of the endometrium continues, nidation takes place, the corpus luteum of pregnancy is formed, and the early development of the embryo begins.

DEVELOPMENT OF THE OVUM

FORMATION OF BLASTODERMIC VESICLE

About one week after fertilization fluid appears in the interior of the mulberry mass which had previously been a solid group of cells. This fluid forces the cells to the periphery and gives rise to a vesicular structure consisting of a single layer. This structure is called the blastodermic vesicle (Fig. 1, p. 218). Soon after, a thin collection of cells appears on the inner surface of the blastodermic vesicle called the internal cell mass. It is from this mass of cells that the fetus develops (Fig. 1). The outer layer of the blastodermic vesicle consists of nucleated protoplasm without definite cellular structure (syncytium). Its inner layer is composed of a layer of cuboidal cells known as the Langhans cells. Both of these layers are composed of ectoderm, whereas the inner portion of the internal cell mass consists of entoderm while its outer portion is made up of ectoderm.

FORMATION OF AMNION AND CHORION

After the blastodermic vesicle is formed a third type of primitive tissue develops, the mesoderm. This arises from a portion of the internal cell mass known as the embryonic shield. At this stage of development there are present for the first time all three types of primitive tissue. These are the cells from which all the others eventually develop. The **ectoderm** forms the epithelial tissues, the skin, the mucous membranes, the glands, and the nerves. The **mesoderm** forms the connective tissues principally the muscles and bones. The **entoderm** forms the gastrointestinal tract (Fig. 2).

The next step in development is the separation of the entoderm from the inner cell mass (Fig. 3). A small cavity then appears in the inner cell mass which is the primitive amniotic cavity (Fig. 4). Soon thereafter a portion of the mesoderm disappears and a new cavity is formed, the extraembryonic cavity (Fig. 5). Next the mesoderm pushes up and dissects around the primitive amniotic cavity and inversion of the entoderm and primitive amniotic cavity occurs (Fig. 6). The primitive amniotic cavity then increases in size in all directions and as it increases it pushes the mesoderm ahead of it until it finally surrounds the entodermic cavity (Fig. 7). In this manner are formed the amnion and chorion. From the drawing (Fig. 7) it may be seen that each is composed of ectoderm and mesoderm and at this stage of development they are separated by the

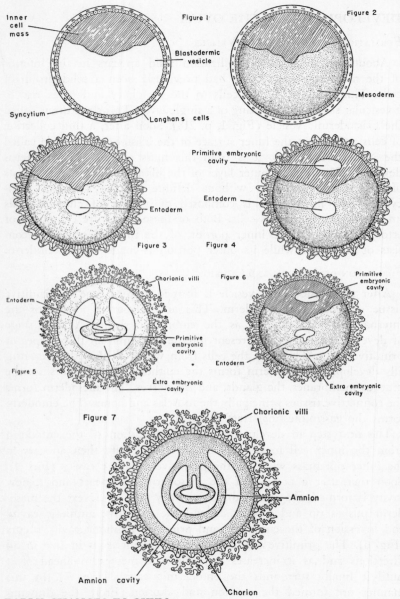

EARLY CHANGES IN OVUM
Diagrammatic representation of the early development of the ovum. (See text, p. 217.)

extraembryonic cavity. These two structures together form what are usually spoken of as the fetal membranes. As development proceeds, fluid appears in the amniotic cavity called the Water of Vater. The average amount is 600 cubic centimeters at the end of pregnancy. It has a specific gravity of 1.002 to 1.028 and contains albumin, urea, creatinin, and salts.

THE DECIDUA AND THE DEVELOPMENT OF THE PLACENTA

On the seventh to the tenth day following fertilization the ovum enters the uterine cavity. It stays on the surface only a short time during which it moves to an anterior or posterior position. It seldom goes to the fundus or to one of the angles. It is believed from good evidence that the syncytium surrounding the ovum secretes a proteolytic enzyme which digests the hypertrophied mucous membrane lining the uterus (decidua). As a result of this digestion the embryo descends into the endometrium for about two thirds of its thickness and the mucous membrane grows back over the opening. This process is called nidation. The embryo continues to develop in this location and as it increases in size it pushes the endometrium ahead of it into the cavity of the uterus. The endometrium of pregnancy is quite thick, usually about 1 centimeter. The decidua (endometrium of pregnancy) is divided into three parts depending on their location (Fig. 8). The decidua basalis or serotina is the portion between the fetus and the wall of the uterus. The decidua capsularis or reflexa is the portion which surrounds the embryo, while the decidua vera or parietalis is the portion lining the remainder of the uterine cavity.

While imbedded in the decidua the embryo liberates an enzyme which digests the walls of some of the maternal blood vessels as a result of which it becomes surrounded by blood. The digested blood vessels in the decidua are very small being capillary in nature; for this reason the amount of bleeding is seldom, if ever, severe or excessive. This lake of blood is known as the troposphere. The enzyme which digests the vessels has, also, the property of keeping the blood from clotting. This blood, which continues to circulate in the maternal blood stream supplies the embryo with nourishment. The decidua basalis behind the embryo is where the placenta will develop. The growth of the fetus is such that by the end of the fourth month the decidua capsularis meets the decidua vera and the cavity of the uterus is obliterated. The decidua capsularis then disappears and leaves a decidua about one to two centimeters in thickness. As the

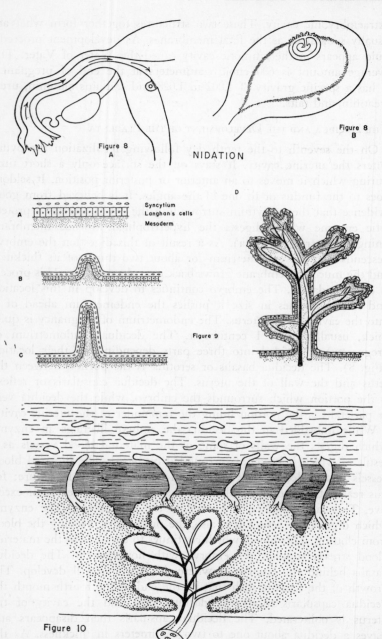

Figure 8
A

Figure 8
B

NIDATION

A — Syncytium — Langhan's cells — Mesoderm

B

C

D

Figure 9

Figure 10

NIDATION AND DEVELOPMENT OF PLACENTA

Diagrammatic representation of nidation (Fig. 8A), the development of the decidua (Fig. 8B), and the early development of the villi (Figs. 9 and 10). (See text, pp. 219–221.)

size of the embryo increases the blood lake is no longer adequate for its nourishment and villi develop.

DEVELOPMENT OF THE VILLI

Villi are protrusions from the surface of the embryo so that a greater surface area may be exposed to the maternal blood supply.

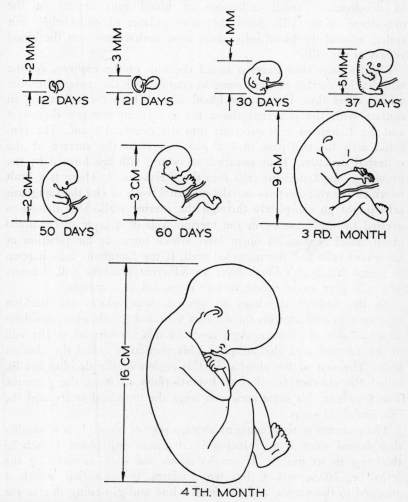

DEVELOPMENT OF FETUS

Size of fetus at various stages of development up to the fourth month.

In the development of the villi the first step is a projection of the
syncytium into which also goes the layer of Langhans cells and
mesoderm (Fig. 9). This protrusion continues until a complete main
villus is formed. As the demand for nutrition becomes greater these
main villi branch to form subbranches; these in turn develop branches
so that the final result resembles a tree. As early as the third week
of development small collections of blood cells appear in the
mesoderm of the villi. Soon thereafter a layer of endothelial cells
collect around the blood cells; these soon coalesce to form the blood
vessels of the villi.

Blood vessels thus develop in all the villi of the embryo. As the
villi develop certain of them come in contact with the maternal tissues
while others float free in the blood lake. Where the villi come in
contact with the maternal tissue the syncytium enzyme digests it
and the Langhans cells protrude into the maternal tissue. The syn-
cytial cells do not pass in but pass out onto the surface of the
maternal structure. Thus so-called anchoring villi are formed by the
growth of the Langhans cells into the uterine wall. There is a limit
to which the villi can pass into the maternal tissue or else the Langhans
cells might go completely through the uterine wall. This danger is
averted by the presence in the uterine wall of a layer of canalized
fibrin called Nitabuch's fibrin layer which forms at the junction of
Langhans cells and the maternal wall. If the Langhans cells happen
to pierce Nitabuch's fibrin layer an adherent placenta will develop.
The villi give an increased surface estimated at 6 meters.

As the embryo develops, its growth soon places the decidua
capsularis in contact with the decidua vera and the decidua capsularis
atrophies due to pressure. As a result of this pressure all of the villi
in the affected area also atrophy. This portion is called the chorion
levae. The rest of the chorion in this region of the decidua basalis,
called the chorion frondosum, hypertrophies to form the placenta.
The vessels in this same area soon form the umbilical artery and the
two umbilical veins.

The placenta at term contains about a pint of blood. It is a roughly
dish-shaped mass 6 to 9 inches in diameter and about 1 inch in
thickness in its middle. It weighs about one sixth as much as the
fetus, i.e., 500 grams. It has two surfaces, the maternal, which is
attached to the uterus, and the fetal, white and glistening due to the
amnion which covers it.

DURATION OF PREGNANCY

There is no accurate measure of the duration of pregnancy. As a rule labor starts 280 days (10 lunar months) after the first day of the last menstrual period. This rule is far from absolute, however, and apparently well-developed children have been born as early as 240 days or as late or 320 days after the last menstrual period. The duration of pregnancy is frequently important legally in determining

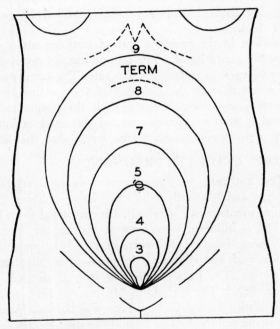

PREGNANCY

Size of the uterus at each month of pregnancy.

legitimacy. Consequently, the courts of all countries have ruled as to the legitimacy of certain periods of gestation. Thus in Scotland, France, and Italy up to 300 days from the cessation of the menses is allowed; in Germany a period of 302 days is permitted; in Austria, 307 days; in England the courts have declared a birth legitimate 331 days after the last coitus; in the United States pregnancies lasting 313 and 317 days respectively have been declared legitimate.

Webster[1] mentions the following cases reported in the literature: Acker reported a case lasting 305 days; Parkhauer, 316 days; Hames, 320 days; Taussig, 323 days; Murray, 330 days; Resnikow, 11 months; Schlichting, 334 days; Holland, 340 days; Miller, 12 months; and Wilson, 371 days.

The **estimation of the probable date of confinement** is difficult as indicated by the above figures. For routine use, however, the method proposed by Naegele is sufficiently accurate. The calculation is made by adding seven days to the first day of the last menstrual period **which occurred,** and then counting back three months. The date thus obtained is merely approximate and the onset of labor usually begins during the week before or the week after this date.

PRECOCIOUS AND LATE PREGNANCY

The earliest authentic pregnancy previously reported (Bodd) was a girl of 8 years and 10 months who had a baby weighing 7½ pounds. Williams[2] also mentions a girl who had menstruated from her second year, and had a full-term pregnancy at the age of 9 years. There has recently been reported, however, in the daily press the case of a child 5 years of age who was delivered of a full-term child by Caesarean section. The facts in this case were confirmed by Wilbur H. Ferguson, R.N.[3] The girl, Lina Medina, in 1939, at the age of 5 years gave birth to a 6½-lb. boy. Lina was born on September 23, 1933. She was the eighth child in a family of nine brothers and sisters. Her mother asserted that Lina showed evidence of sexual precocity at 7 months, when she first menstruated and continued to do so regularly thereafter. In regard to the paternity of the child Ferguson points out two beliefs held in certain portions of Peru which may be pertinent. One is the belief that coitus with little girls is considered

[1] Ralph W. Webster, *Legal Medicine and Toxicology* (Philadelphia: W. B. Saunders Co.), p. 215.

[2] J. Whitridge Williams, *Obstetrics* (New York: D. Appleton & Co., 1927), p. 85.

[3] Lina Medina, *The Bloodless Phlebotomist*, Vol. 8, no. 6, pp. 2–3, quoting from Wilbur H. Ferguson, *The Trained Nurse and Hospital Review* (August, 1940).

to be a cure for impotence and another is the belief that such a practice will stimulate the growth and development of a child.

The latest pregnancy on record, according to DeLee,[4] is one reported by Kennedy. This woman was sixty-two years old and it was her twenty-second labor. In some of the cases reported menstruation had been absent for years. In general, pregnancy is not likely to occur if the menses have been absent for three months or more. This is far from certain, however.

> The occurrence or absence of menstruation admittedly cannot be considered an indication of fertility. Pregnancy in apparently post-menopausal women under 50 is possible, as is irregular vaginal bleeding in the very elderly.
> From available vital statistics and from medical literature, it appears that parturition in a woman over 52 years of age . . . is rare, and that, therefore, were it surely to occur in a woman, say of 55, it must be considered a gross aberration of reproductive physiology.[5]

LABOR

Labor is the process by which the female organism expels the product of conception from the uterus and through the vagina into the outside world and to a separate existence apart from the mother. Synonyms for labor are: travail, confinement, delivery, parturition, accouchement, and childbirth. This process usually starts about 280 days after the first day of the last menstrual period. If the process occurs earlier than at term it is usually called an abortion, a miscarriage, or premature labor depending on the length of the gestation at the time it occurs.

An abortion may be spontaneous or induced. To the laity the term "miscarriage" is used to indicate a spontaneous interruption of pregnancy at any time before the child is viable. Although to most people the term "abortion" means an induced interruption of pregnancy before the period of viability, it means strictly any interruption of pregnancy before the twenty-eighth week of gestation (see Chapter XXIII). By viability is meant that the child is capable of a separate existence. It is evident, of course, that every viable child must be living, but every living child is not viable. It is generally believed

---

[4] Joseph B. DeLee, *The Principles and Practice of Obstetrics,* 2 ed. (Philadelphia: W. B. Saunders Co., 1915), p. 115.
[5] James W. Newell and John Rock, *Am. J. Obst. & Gynec.* (April, 1952).

that the fetus is not viable until the end of the seventh month of gestation. There are, however, exceptions to this general rule.

According to its character labor is called:

1. Eutocia, normal labor
2. Dystocia, difficult, or abnormal labor

Regardless of its character labor is usually divided into three stages:

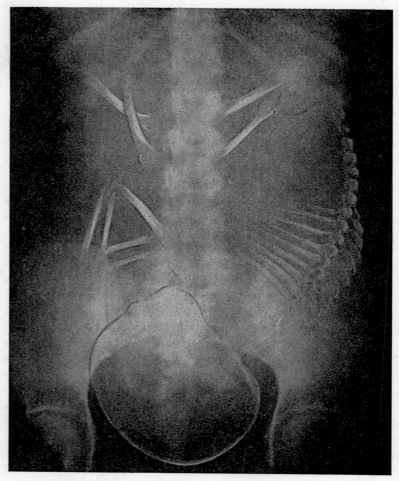

FULL-TERM PREGNANCY

X-ray picture of a normal full-term pregnancy. Note head in pelvis with the spine curving up left side of the mother's abdomen. (Courtesy of Dr. Alfred Den.)

1. **The first stage or stage of dilatation.** During this stage dilatation of the cervix of the uterus takes place. It lasts from 12 to 24 hours as a rule. The length of each stage depends on the parity of the patient. The first labor is usually the longest.

2. **The second stage or stage of expulsion.** During this portion of the labor which lasts from the time the cervix of the uterus is dilated until the child is completely expelled from the body of the mother the baby traverses the birth canal. This stage usually lasts from 1 to 2 hours.

3. **The third stage or placental stage.** The expulsion of the placenta or afterbirth usually occurs within 15 to 30 minutes after the birth of the baby.

Under normal circumstances the onset of labor seems to be quite sudden. There are frequently prodromal symptoms which, however, the patient does not usually recognize. The most common of these is "lightening" which is due to a dropping of the baby into the pelvis. It occurs usually about 2 or 3 days before the onset of labor. The uterine contractions, which are perceived by the patient as pain, recur regularly, once they are started, at about 15-minute intervals. As the labor progresses the pains usually get closer together so that before the onset of the second stage they usually are recurring at about 2-minute intervals. Each contraction lasts from 30 to 90 seconds. The intensity of the pain seems to vary in direct ratio with the degree of culture of the woman. The less culture, the less the pain and vice versa. There are, of course, hysterical individuals of all degrees of culture who seem to find the pains unbearable. The uterine contractions during this stage are entirely involuntary. They have for their purpose the dilatation of the uterine cervix to allow passage of the baby's head. The patient is usually quite comfortable and cheerful between pains. Very frequently the "bag of waters" or the membranes rupture during this stage but may not do so until during the second stage.

In the second stage besides the involuntary uterine contractions, the patient employs some of her voluntary muscles particularly those of the abdomen to aid in the expulsion of the baby. The pains during this stage are much more severe and in modern practice some form of anesthesia or analgesia is usually employed. The choice of anesthesia varies widely among different obstetricians but practically all modern methods are quite safe for both mother and child. After delivery the umbilical cord which connects the child to the maternal blood supply is cut and dressed. The afterbirth or placenta is usually expelled quite painlessly within 30 minutes after the birth of the baby.

OBSTETRICAL OPERATIONS

APPLICATION OF FORCEPS

The obstetrical forceps is an instrument designed for the extraction of the fetus by the head, under certain conditions, without injury to the mother or child. The use of forceps was first introduced into obstetrical practice in about 1580 by Peter Chamberlen, the Elder. It has not undergone any radical change since that time but its use and the indications for its employment are much better understood. It is also much more safely employed. The instrument is made of two blades which are curved to fit the shape of the baby's head and also to accommodate themselves to the curve of the birth canal. When properly used the application of forceps does not add materially to the risk of the mother or child.

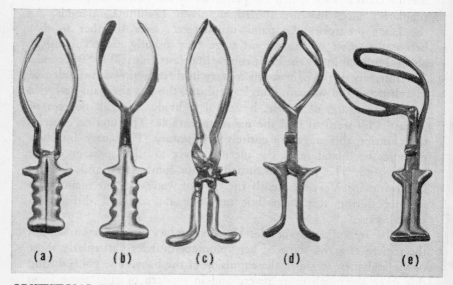

(a)   (b)   (c)   (d)   (e)

OBSTETRICAL FORCEPS

This photograph shows several varieties of forceps. Forceps are usually named after the obstetrician who devised them. In this photograph the forceps are thus devised by (a) Simpson, (b) Tucker-McLean, (c) Tarnier — axis traction forceps, (d) Kjelland, and (e) Barton — usually used in the case of a transverse arrest of the head.

EXTRACTION

The delivery of the child by traction when the feet protrude in breech presentations is probably the oldest obstetrical operation. The morbidity and mortality of breech presentations (a condition in which the baby comes feet first instead of head first) is considerably higher than in head presentations. The principal reason for this is the fact that the child will usually die within eight minutes after the delivery of the umbilicus if its mouth cannot be brought to the vulva so it can breathe. This occurs because the baby's blood supply is cut off due to pressure of the head against the pelvis. In these cases it is always best to baptize the baby if difficulty is experienced in delivering the head.[6] Death in these cases results most frequently from asphyxia which occurs when the umbilical cord is pressed between the head and the pelvic brim. Much difficulty may be avoided if studies are made in advance to rule out contracted pelvis.

VERSION

Version or "turning" is an operation by which the position of the fetus is altered. A less favorable presentation is usually changed to a more favorable one. It is called cephalic version when the head is brought down as the presenting part and podalic version if the feet are brought down. The procedure may be carried out by external manipulation alone or may be done by a combination of internal

---

[6] For the valid baptism of an unborn baby, it is imperative that the water make contact with the skin. If possible the water should be poured on the head. The membranes must therefore be ruptured before the child can be validly baptized. Any baptism performed prior to full birth of the child must be done under absolutely sterile conditions. The umbilical cord is not part of the baby but is an outgrowth from the mother. Therefore, baptism performed on the cord alone would not be sufficient. The proper rite for valid baptism is that, as the water flows, the minister of the sacrament pronounces these words: *"I baptize you in the name of the Father, and of the Son, and of the Holy Ghost."*

The child can be baptized in the uterus. If the membranes are not ruptured this may be done by locating the head of the fetus. Then a needle attached to a syringe containing sterile water can be inserted through the membranes. The water is then injected on the head as the obstetrician says the words of conditional baptism. If the membranes are ruptured the water may be applied directly to the head with a needle-less syringe. If there is doubt because of malformation or immaturity as to whether the product delivered is a child or a tumor, the whole mass of material is baptized conditionally by immersing it in water while repeating the formula of baptism. This second baptism is also conditional because one cannot be sure whether the first took effect, or whether under certain circumstances one is baptizing a living fetus. The formula for conditional baptism is: *"If you are capable, I now baptize you in the name of the Father, and of the Son, and of the Holy Ghost."*

and external manipulation. The prognosis of this procedure depends largely on the skill of the operator and the conditions which required the interference. It should never be lightly estimated. Modern practice has reduced version to a minimum.

MANUAL DILATATION OF THE CERVIX

As the term implies this refers to the dilatation of the cervix by hand. This is usually accompanied by lacerations and is usually used when speed of delivery is important. Since the procedure is associated with complicated cases, the prognosis for mother and child is not good.

INDUCTION OF LABOR

Premature induction of labor is indicated for a number of medical reasons, particularly in rare cases of toxemia, low-lying placenta and lesser degrees of separation of the placenta. Induction of labor as a matter of convenience to the patient or doctor should be discouraged because of the risk which it adds for both mother and child.

DESTRUCTIVE OPERATIONS

Under this heading are included those operations by which the child is destroyed so as to reduce its size. Such reduction in size is desired to facilitate delivery. The most common operation for this purpose is craniotomy. By this term is meant any operation which reduces the size of the head. It is usually performed by making a perforation in the skull and through it evacuating its contents. Another operation is embryotomy which includes such procedures as evisceration, decapitation, or amputations. Fortunately such operations are becoming rare as obstetrical skill increases. The immorality of such operations on the living child is evident.

THE PATHOLOGY OF PREGNANCY

Although pregnancy is usually regarded as a normal condition and labor a normal function of the female, there are many conditions which complicate it and may even endanger the life of the mother or child or both. By some physicians these conditions are regarded as indications for the termination of the pregnancy.

HYPEREMESIS GRAVIDARUM

Almost all women especially in the early months of pregnancy have some degree of nausea and vomiting. In some patients, the condition persists and becomes a serious complication. According to DeLee, Charlotte Bronte died of this condition. Most authors distinguish two varieties of vomiting in pregnancy — the neurotic type and the pernicious type, or hyperemesis gravidarum. In the former type the general condition of the patient suffers little in spite of persistent vomiting. Suggestive therapy usually gives a good result in treatment. The prognosis in this type is always favorable. In the more severe type the patient is severely ill and, if the condition persists, marked emaciation is likely to occur. The outlook for recovery in this type is favorable with good treatment and death rarely results.

PRE-ECLAMPTIC TOXEMIA

This condition usually occurs in the middle trimester of pregnancy and unless checked results in the more severe eclampsia or convulsions of pregnancy. The condition is easy to recognize, if it is looked for, and as a result responds readily to treatment. Occasionally, notwithstanding the most rational prophylactic treatment, it may terminate in eclampsia. In pre-eclamptic toxemia the patient becomes drowsy and irritable. She frequently complains of a severe headache, and edema, particularly of the ankles, is an almost invariable accompaniment of the condition. On examination, the blood pressure is usually elevated, the body weight is increased due to the edema, and the urine shows the presence of albumin. The condition, once recognized, usually responds readily to treatment. There is no tendency for this condition to recur in subsequent pregnancies, as there is in nephritic toxemia.

ECLAMPSIA

Eclampsia is an acute toxemia which may occur during pregnancy, labor, or the puerperium. It is usually accompanied by tonic or clonic convulsions, during which there is loss of consciousness, followed by more or less prolonged coma. The condition may terminate in death. The condition occurs about once in each five hundred pregnancies. In almost every instance, it is preceded by a pre-eclamptic toxemia. It occurs practically always in the second half of pregnancy and its incidence is increased as term is approached. About one fifth of all cases occur after delivery. The cause of eclampsia is unknown. At autopsy in practically all cases, extensive liver damage is found. The prognosis in this condition is always serious. The most important step in the treatment of eclampsia is its prevention by recognizing and treating pre-eclampsia (see Chapter XV).

RENAL TOXEMIA

As its name indicates, this condition results from kidney damage. In many instances the nephritis may have had its onset following a childhood attack of scarlet fever, although in some cases it undoubtedly arises during the pregnancy. This condition differs from pre-eclampsia and eclampsia in that it does not disappear following the puerperium. The condition is usually only aggravated by the pregnancy, not caused by it. Each pregnancy, however, makes the condition worse, the symptoms appearing at an earlier period in each successive gestation. The outlook for the child is also bad and becomes progressively poorer in each pregnancy. Future pregnancy is inadvisable when this condition has been diagnosed.

PLACENTA PREVIA

Placenta previa is the development of the placenta in an abnormal location. Under ordinary circumstances, the placenta is implanted high up on the uterine wall and ordinarily remains **in situ** until the delivery of the baby is complete. In this condition, the placenta is attached low down on the cervix in that portion which is affected by its dilatation. This produces a double danger — the danger of hemorrhage for the mother and the danger of asphyxia for the child, because the source of its blood supply may be cut off before its delivery is possible. This condition is always a serious and formidable complication to both the mother and the child. Mortality statistics vary from 7 per cent to 19 per cent for the mother to as high as 48 per cent for the child. In this condition Caesarean section is the treatment of choice.

ABRUPTIO PLACENTAE

Abruptio placentae or premature separation of the placenta from its normal site is a not uncommon complication of pregnancy. It occurs most frequently in connection with the toxemias described above, occasionally as a result of traumatism, and other unusual causes. The condition is always potentially serious for the mother and frequently fatal for the child. Lull and Kimbrough report a series of 170 cases treated in the Pennsylvania Hospital in which there was a maternal mortality of 1.2 per cent. The corrected infant mortality was 18.8 per cent.[7] Where the separation is not complete, the prognosis is somewhat better.

INCARCERATION OF THE RETROFLEXED UTERUS IN THE PELVIS

In this condition, the growing uterus which has been posteriorly displaced becomes firmly fixed below the promontory of the sacrum. The condition at the present time is exceedingly rare because women consult physicians earlier. When the retroversion is recognized before incarceration takes place the uterus is easily placed in a less dangerous position. This condition is of some interest in that it is the only instance in which Sanford[8] recognizes indirect abortion as morally permissible. In his opinion, the draining off of the amniotic fluid which would relieve the mother's condition immediately, is permissible. The abortion which would inevitably follow is an indirect effect which is permitted but not sought. This opinion is not held by all moralists. It is almost impossible under present conditions for circumstances requiring even a consideration of such a procedure to come about. It would be evidence of gross neglect or ignorance. If the uterus cannot be returned manually to a less dangerous position, it can usually be returned by laparotomy. It is only in those cases in which the condition has been neglected that the procedure mentioned by Sanford would be indicated. In connection with Sanford's opinion, it might be mentioned that Bumm drew off enough amniotic fluid to allow replacement of the uterus, and abortion did not follow.

NEOPLASMS

The three most common tumors complicating pregnancy are: (1) Fibromyomata; (2) Ovarian cysts; and (3) Carcinomata. **Fibromyomata** of the uterus are benign growths which cause trouble in pregnancy by placing an obstruction in the birth canal. Women with uterine fibroids are apt to be sterile and when pregnancy does occur abortions are more apt to occur than in normal women. The majority of pregnant women go to and through labor without difficulty. Excessive pain and repeated, profuse hemorrhages may require treatment. It is best when possible to postpone any operative procedures until near term. If the fibroids are producing obstruction to the pas-

---

[7] Clifford B. Lull and Robert A. Kimbrough, *Clinical Obstetrics* (Philadelphia: J. B. Lippincott Co., 1953), p. 274.

[8] Alexander E. Sanford, *Pastoral Medicine* (New York: Joseph F. Wagner, 1905), p. 244.

sage of the head, Caesarean section with hysterectomy or myomectomy is the treatment of choice.

Ovarian cysts vary greatly in size and in speed of growth. While most ovarian cysts are benign they are occasionally malignant. These cysts by their size and location produce obstruction just as a fibroid may do. If they are increasing rapidly in size surgical removal of the tumor may be indicated. While this may occasionally result in miscarriage, it does not always do so.

Carcinoma of the cervix in pregnancy is a rare condition. According to Lull and Kimbrough, the incidence of carcinoma of the cervix in 100,000 pregnancies was 0.017 per cent.[9] In the reported cases, there is a gross survival rate of 33 per cent which is comparable to the rate in the nonpregnant. Pregnancy as a rule increases the rate of growth of the carcinoma. The obstetrical indication, according to most authors, is early and complete removal of the cervix and uterus if the condition is discovered and in the early portion of pregnancy. If the condition is discovered late in gestation or is inoperable, when discovered, the patient is usually allowed to go to term and the child delivered by Caesarean section if the condition of the cervix is such that spontaneous delivery is unlikely. According to Williams[10] the action of radium, which is frequently employed in the treatment of this condition, inevitably results in the death of the child. This, however, is not always the case.

CAESAREAN SECTION

In Caesarean section the child is removed from the uterus through an incision made in the abdominal wall and the anterior surface of the uterus. Popularly the name is supposed to be derived from the method by which Julius Caesar was born. There is, however, frequent mention of the operation in the literature before him. As a rule, in the earlier days, the operation was performed on the dead or dying woman but since the advent of anesthesia and aseptic surgery its indications have been much broadened. Formerly, also, the operation was accompanied by an appalling mortality, more than 50 per cent of the mothers dying. Under modern surgical methods the mortality is, in properly selected cases, almost negligible. In Caesarean section, as in all surgical procedures, the outcome of the operation depends

9 Lull and Kimbrough, *op. cit.,* p. 347.
10 Williams, *op. cit.,* p. 639.

to a large extent on the skill of the surgeon and the preoperative condition of the mother.

The indications for the Caesarean section are divided into absolute and relative. The absolute indication is the presence of some obstruction in the birth canal such as a markedly contracted pelvis (conjugata vera 5 centimeters or less), the presence of a tumor, or a very rigid cervix due to scar tissue. Under these circumstances the child cannot be delivered alive or dead, even after craniotomy. With the improved technic of Caesarean section and its lowered mortality a conjugata vera of 7.5 centimeters or less is usually regarded as an absolute indication for section.

The relative indications are in part: myomata of the lower uterine segment or other tumors which produce obstruction; cicatricial contraction of the cervix or vagina; carcinoma of the cervix; uterine inertia; any condition in which a rapid delivery is desired with the least possible exertion for the mother, as, for example, abruptio placentae.

Porro Caesarean Section (Caesarean Hysterectomy)

In this operation after the removal of the child the uterus is amputated and removed. The tubes and ovaries are left in place. The operation was originally designed to avoid the danger of hemorrhage and infection when the operation of Caesarean section was decided on after the patient had been in labor for some time and was potentially or actually infected. This operation has somewhat wider indications at the present time and is usually performed when myomata are present, in cases of rupture of the uterus, or where the uterus has been torn in efforts at delivery. This is the operation of choice for those surgeons and obstetricians who believe that the patient should be sterilized at the time of the operation. The opinions on this score vary greatly, from one group which feels that every patient requiring Caesarean section should be sterilized, to another group which feels that the procedure should be carried out under the limited and real indications outlined above. Many obstetricians base their decision to sterilize the patient on the old dictum, "Once a Caesarean, always a Caesarean!" This statement is, of course, not true, and many women who have had one Caesarean section have had future spontaneous deliveries. Such a sterilization is not always licit.

Post-Mortem Caesarean Section

Caesarean section upon the dead or dying woman has been performed from ancient times. Except under the most unusual and extraordinary circumstances section of the dying woman should not be performed. This, in spite of the fact that, according to DeLee, such an operation is demanded by the Talmudists and the Catholic Law.[11] In the dead woman, however, such an operation should always be performed if she has reached or passed the twenty-sixth week of gestation. If the operation is performed quickly enough the chances of getting a live baby are very good. The operation can be performed by anyone who has the courage and sufficient anatomical knowledge. The only implement needed is a knife or other object which is sharp enough to cut through the tissues. This operation is one of the very few real emergencies which is likely to occur in medical practice and, yet, may not occur during a lifetime of practice. It is an emergency because the child will live for only a short time after the death of the mother. The length of time that the baby will live after the mother's death depends on the manner of her decease. If death is due to accidental causes the child may live for 10 to 20 minutes after the mother; if the mother's death is due to a prolonged constitutional disease, such as tuberculosis, the death of the baby will probably occur first.

Who should perform the operation? Anyone can perform the operation but naturally one with medical training would be the operator of choice. Preferably the operation should be performed by someone outside the immediate family because the mental strain of the unusual procedure would be less on an outsider. There has been considerable discussion as to the propriety of a priest performing the operation. Under ordinary circumstances I would agree with those who consider such an action improper. By ordinary circumstances I mean that others are present who could perform the operation and the duty of the priest would be ended when he instructed them in the right procedure. Theologians are not in agreement as to whether or not a priest should perform the operation.[12] Risky as the operation may be, this consideration should not outweigh the possible saving of a human life and soul. In speaking of post-mortem section Sanford says:

[11] DeLee, *op. cit.*, p. 1031.
[12] E. F. Regatillo, S.J., and M. Zalba, S.J., *Theologia Moralis Summa* (Madrid: Biblioteca Autores Cristianos, 1954), Vol. 3, no. 44.

The Cesarean section on the body, warm and fresh, of a woman just deceased, is even for experts a very exacting operation, especially because it mostly must be performed without expert assistance. The alarming case in itself, the excitement and suspense — whether or not the corpse will stir at the first incision — the constant gush of warm blood — all these things which would affect any one but an expert, who remains calm because familiar with the operation and used to bloody surgery. Who, then, can reasonably demand that it be made mandatory of the priest to perform the section in case of emergency, when he has but a vague idea of the operation, gleaned from an aphoristic description of the same? The little he knows of the operation, would it not become entirely useless in his natural trembling and hesitancy, and would not the success of the operation be thereby rendered improbable to the highest degree? I shall not allude to other evils in the wake of such a process. Who will protect him from slander, given rise to by the circumstances of a proceeding uncommon for a layman? Will not the people ask, "Why did he meddle? It was not his business."[13]

The operation must be performed soon after the death of the mother. Linzenmeir concluded that 20 minutes was the maximum length of time after death that a live baby could be obtained.[14] Bacon found no case on record in which the child lived more than 25 minutes after the mother's death.[15] The fetal prognosis is better when the mother's death has been sudden and rapid.

Once it has been ascertained that the patient is dead the operation is very simple. Once the fact of death is certain the patient should be placed on her back and the abdomen exposed. An incision is then made through the abdominal wall about 12 inches in length over the largest part of the uterus. This incision is quite deep because it must penetrate the skin, fat, fascia, and peritoneum. By pulling apart the edges of this incision the uterus will be exposed. When incising the uterus, care must be taken not to cut the baby because the uterine wall is quite thin. When the baby is removed, it should be immediately baptized and then the umbilical cord cut. It should be kept warm until it can be placed in proper care.

There has been much discussion about the legal aspects of postmortem Caesarean section. I find myself in complete agreement with this statement of Lattuada:

The obligation to save the human fetal life when it can be done

13 Sanford, op. cit., p. 261.
14 Linzenmeir, quoted by Lattuada.
15 Bacon, quoted by Lattuada.

without destroying or jeopardizing another life is absolute. It is generally believed that no court today would hold that a father has the right to choose death for an unborn viable child by withholding his consent for a postmortem section. Common sense, Christian morals, and natural justice force this conclusion and it is this opinion that any court of today would so hold.[16]

DETERMINATION OF SEX

Each germinal cell contains 24 chromosomes. This is one half of the number present in a somatic cell. The ovum provides 24 chromosomes and the spermatozoa the remaining 24 requisite for the complete complement of the somatic cell. About one half of the spermatozoa produced by an individual have an X-chromosome and the other half have a Y-chromosome. It is this odd chromosome which determines the sex of the child. For example:

X-Ovum plus X-Sperm equals XX (girl)
X-Ovum plus Y-Sperm equals XY (boy).

There is no known way that the sex of the child can be influenced. This is just as well as it would certainly be a source of continual argument between the parents (see Chapter V).

MULTIPLE BIRTHS

Twins occur about once in every 87 pregnancies.

Identical twins are formed from a single fertilized ovum. The break occurs very early. Since they come from a single ovum they are always of the same sex and have an identical hereditary endowment.

Fraternal twins result from fertilization of two ova by two spermatozoa. They may be of the same sex or one may be a boy and the other a girl. They do not have the same hereditary endowment and consequently may not closely resemble each other.

Births of triplets or larger numbers of babies occur not infrequently. For information relative to multiple births reference should be made to other texts.[17]

---

[16] H. P. Lattuada, "Postmortem Cesarean Section," *Am. J. Surg.* (August, 1952), quoted in *Medical News Letters,* Vol. 20, no. 4.

[17] John B. Nichols, "Multiple Births and Fecundity," *Med. Annals of the D. of C.,* Vol. 19 (1950), pp. 601–607, 659.

CHAPTER XVII

Natural Childbirth

Natural childbirth is a new approach to a technique as old as Adam and Eve. It is an approach to childbirth which attempts to eliminate the fear which most women have of the process. It is an approach which aims to indoctrinate the prospective mother to a total concept of her impending delivery. Natural childbirth is based on the concept that childbirth involves too much pain, and that relief from this pain may be obtained through the prevention of fear and its resultant tension. Its proponents claim that it makes the time of pregnancy the happiest and healthiest in a woman's life; that the birth of a baby becomes a thrilling and satisfying experience. As its name implies, this technique is the least complicated of all methods of delivery. The process is merely left to nature. The woman remains wide awake during her labor and delivery and receives no medication or anesthesia. The mother is aware at all times that the baby is being born, and is enabled to co-operate with those attending the birth.

Natural childbirth was popularized by Doctor Grantly Dick Read, an Englishman. His book, **Childbirth Without Fear,** was the first exposition of the natural-childbirth theory. He first wrote on this subject in 1933, but this book attracted little interest and no favor in medical circles, although it did receive much comment by nurses, midwives, and prospective mothers. He wrote again in 1944, for the general public, and at this time his volume was received with much greater interest.[1] In 1947, Doctor Read came to the United States under the auspices of the Maternity Center Association in New York. His lectures in this country stimulated a great deal of interest and won him a number of adherents, the best known of whom is Doctor Herbert Thomas, Professor of Obstetrics and Gynecology at Yale.

In the opening pages of his book, Doctor Read presents a very

---

[1] Grantly Dick Read, M.D., *Childbirth Without Fear* (New York: Harper & Brothers, 1944).

moving account of an experience which initiated his thinking along natural-childbirth lines. He was conducting a delivery in a slum area. The patient was co-operative and things went well. At no time during the delivery did the woman ask for an anesthetic, nor did she show any signs of great discomfort. When he was about to leave he asked her why she had not wanted an anesthetic. He states that he never forgot her reply: "It didn't hurt. It wasn't meant to, was it Doctor?"[2]

It was this experience, he states, that inspired him to the working out of the theory of natural childbirth. He reasoned that civilization and culture have brought influences to bear upon the minds of women which have introduced certain fears and anxieties concerning pregnancy and childbirth.

It has always been believed that women have pain during delivery. It is natural that they should be afraid of pain. The sequence then would be, fear of pain causes tension; tension may then cause pain. He reasoned, therefore, that if fear could be eradicated, then labor could become a pleasurable experience. He describes this theory in the following words:

> Civilization and culture have brought influence to bear upon the minds of women which have introduced justifiable fear and anxieties concerning labor. The more cultured the races of the earth have become, so much the more dogmatic have they been in pronouncing childbirth to be a painful and dangerous ordeal. This fear and anticipation have given rise to natural protective tensions in the body, and such tensions are not of the mind only, for the mechanism of protective action by the body includes muscle tension. Unfortunately the natural tension produced by fear inhibits; that is to say, gives rise to resistance at the outlet of the womb, when in the normal state those muscles should be relaxed and free from tension. Such resistance and tension give rise to real pain, because the uterus is supplied with organs which record pain set up by the excessive tension. Therefore, fear, pain and tension are the three evils which are not normal to the natural design, but which have been introduced in the course of civilization by the ignorance of those who have been concerned with attendance at childbirth. If pain, fear and tension go hand in hand, then it must be necessary to relieve tension and to overcome fear in order to eliminate pain.[3]

This passage gives the impression that without culture delivery is relatively painless, and that with culture it is definitely painful. This

[2] *Ibid.*, p. 2.
[3] *Ibid.*, p. 5 ff.

is in accord with the popular belief that primitive labor was a painless event and that labor is still painless in primitive areas. Such beliefs, however, do not harmonize with scientific data. It is not my intention to enter into this controversy, but it should be pointed out that anthropologic research seems to prove the facts to be otherwise than held by popular opinion.[4]

There are five factors stressed by Doctor Read in his system of natural childbirth:

1. Health;
2. An understanding of how babies are born;
3. Adequate physical preparation;
4. Support and encouragement during labor;
5. Post-partum restoration.

Health is naturally a first requirement, and in any pregnancy it is important that the mother be guided toward the best possible state of health. It is generally recognized that those women in a good state of health are those who are likely in any case to have the shorter and less complicated deliveries. Instruction of the individual in the process of labor is designed to overcome fear and in any case is a very desirable procedure. Anything which can be done to promote the concept of childbearing as a natural body function would bring with it comfort and security. Our greatest fear is the fear of the unknown, and a knowledge of what the process of labor is like will help the parents to work toward the best possible natural development of the mother's body. Such preparation would include exercise so that the mother's body may be prepared for the delivery. The expectant mother is taught techniques for relaxing tension and for proper breathing. Exercises are designed to improve the tone of the muscles that will be used during labor.

During the actual delivery the obstetrician should be present to give encouragement and support. Fear of the delivery is less if the patient feels that there is someone with knowledge to help present, should help be necessary.

Some proponents of natural childbirth feel that the father should be present during the delivery. Aileen Hogan makes this comment:

Now it is most necessary that on this day the parents be together. This is the day the mother most needs to know that her husband is by her side. There is no loneliness when she opens her eyes and sees

---

[4] Cf. Herbert Thomas, M.D., *Training for Childbirth* (New York: McGraw-Hill Book Co., 1951), p. 1 ff.

him sitting there by her bed. If under the stress of labor she forgets her past, there is no one who can help her back to her role better than her husband.[5]

A similar view is expressed by Doctor von Gagern:

In the case of the actual *birth,* many women object to the presence of the husband until all is over. They do not like to be seen in their weakest moments, or they have a feeling they would prefer to face the great event alone. But it may well be said, on the other hand, that it is a beautiful and significant thing if the husband can participate. It is, after all, his child as well as hers. Moreover, he can often cooperate, giving comfort and encouragement and possibly physical assistance. It is, in our view, right that the husband should stand by his wife in this difficult time, and it will do him no harm to experience exactly what goes on. It is important that he should remain, with all his affection, perfectly quiet, self-controlled and matter-of-fact. Anxiety and excitement can serve only to upset the wife. Most doctors and midwives object to the husband's presence because so many men lose their heads on this occasion. In a hospital ward, it is in any case hardly practicable. But where the birth is in the home, no husband should allow himself to be prevented from supporting his wife.[6]

After the delivery the restoration of the mother's organs is helped by exercises designed to restore the tone of muscles which have been stretched during the pregnancy and labor.

This, in brief, is the theory and method of Doctor Read. It appears simple but in practice, as will be pointed out, it is difficult to apply generally to pregnant women.

There is one point in what Doctor Read has written which seems to have been generally misunderstood. Doctor Read has implied that childbirth done "naturally" is entirely painless. Natural-childbirth literature seems to give rise to this impression. In his books many readers get the impression that he maintains that childbirth should be conducted without anesthesia, and that it can be made devoid of pain altogether. This is not altogether true.

Doctor Thomas states that Doctor Read and others

have never claimed that childbirth should be conducted without anesthesia, or that it can be devoid of pain. Under the regime of

---

[5] Aileen Hogan, "Natural Childbirth," *The Grail Magazine* (December, 1950).

[6] Baron Frederick von Gagern, M.D., *The Meaning of Life and Marriage,* trans. from the German by Meyrick Booth, Ph.D. (Westminster, Md.: The Newman Press, 1954), pp. 243–244.

natural childbirth most patients do experience pain to a greater or lesser degree, and analgesia and anesthesia are not withheld when they are indicated.[7]

It is certainly true that Doctor Read suggests that analgesia and anesthesia should always be at hand and should be used when necessary. On the contrary, there exists a genuine foundation for the belief that Doctor Read claims that childbirth can be made devoid of pain. He may not have intended to create that impression. Doctor Read's statements show too much enthusiasm, and in his attempt to "eliminate the pain," if he himself does not equate natural childbirth with painless childbirth, certainly many of his followers do. He is no philologist, but he might have chosen his words with greater care. He surely knows the difference between "eliminating" and "reducing" pain. Painless childbirth is not the same thing as childbirth with greater or lesser degrees of pain. There are some women who maintain that they have had painless labor, but these are definitely in the minority. It is difficult to conceive of a completely painless delivery. Doctor Thomas writes:

> Anyone who thinks that the preparation for labor that we follow in this birth clinic will abolish pain or discomfort in every case of childbirth is not thinking correctly. We would indeed be very foolish to make such a claim.[8]

Pain is too subjective and too related to the sensitivities of the individual to be completely eliminated in all women. Doctor Scadron comments as follows:

> Recent studies published in the AMERICAN JOURNAL OF OBSTETRICS AND GYNECOLOGY have shown that there is no definite relationship between the strength of a labor contraction and the actual pain experienced. Pain varies with different women, and most patients admit that it wasn't nearly as bad as they had anticipated. For this reason it is obviously beneficial for women to know what to expect, and this accounts for the popularity of so-called natural childbirth instruction. It does help in alleviating the anxiety (and therefore a good deal of subjective pain) during labor.[9]

Most of the professional writers have emphasized that not all

---

[7] Thomas, *op. cit.*, p. 3.

[8] *Ibid.*, p. 28.

[9] Eugene N. Scadron, M.D., "Myths About Pregnancy," *This Week Magazine* (February 6, 1955).

patients are suitable for this technique. Lull and Kimbrough make this comment:

> However, the application of these technics in a large clinic or private practice is rarely feasible. Several factors must be considered when deciding whether to use these technics in a particular case. The emotionally unstable patient is not receptive and the time necessary to stabilize her will probably consume most of the prenatal period. In addition, the time necessary to institute the Read technic will not be available for most clinic patients, and will be contraindicated on a financial basis for many private patients.[10]

Doctor Thomas makes this comment:

> Not all patients are equally suited for this technique. Some of my patients acquired an enthusiasm for natural childbirth' from their own reading. . . . Almost without exception these were outstanding successes and some refused all analgesia or anesthesia because they wished to be completely alert throughout the entire experience. . . . Another most favorable type of patient is the young primigravida intellectually alert and perhaps a trifle aggressive, who is very anxious to have a baby and has an immense curiosity about everything related to the pregnancy and delivery. Such a patient often resents the hiatus of unconsciousness and amnesia and also resents being delivered without her own active participation much more than she minds the slight discomfort of natural childbirth. These patients derive an emotional satisfaction from successful natural childbirth which no other method of delivery even remotely approximates.[11]

Doctor Thomas then concludes:

> In summary, I feel that natural childbirth technique is a valuable addition to obstetrical procedure and that the principles involved are of value in the conduct of any labor. Over half of my private patients are successfully delivered by this technique, in comfort, though conscious throughout. For the woman who is physically and psychologically suited to this method, no other technique for the conduct of labor is as rewarding to the patient or as safe for mother and child.[12]

Natural childbirth is relatively new, and is far from being completely accepted by the medical profession. Men of reputation in the field have lined up on both sides of the fence. Doctors Read and

[10] Clifford B. Lull, M.D., and Robert A. Kimbrough, M.D., *Clinical Obstetrics* (Philadelphia: J. B. Lippincott Co., 1953), p. 161.

[11] Thomas, *op. cit.*, p. 100.

[12] *Ibid.*, p. 101.

Cohen of Harvard Medical School suggest that it is related to previous obstetrical practices, and that the results await further evaluation.

Doctor Faison, attending physician in obstetrics in St. Vincent's Hospital in New York, says: "The results so far give reason to believe that the practice of natural childbirth should be continued and expanded." In an article entitled "The Middle of the Road in Obstetrics," Doctor Nicholas Eastman sums up the controversy and comes to this conclusion:

> If the notion is dismissed that natural childbirth is a competitor of medicinal analgesia and anesthesia, and if it is regarded as a broad, basic educational program in which the need of such drugs is minimized as the result of less apprehension and better understanding, but not eliminated, the controversy will disappear.[13]

Lull and Kimbrough offer these objections:

> The patient who is receptive to types of nonanalgesic and nonanesthetic deliveries is encouraged, but the time necessary to adapt these procedures to overall clinic or private practice has not been found available to the staff. The status of the baby under attempted Read type technics is in no way improved. In too high a percentage of patients the technic will fail, resulting in excessive excitement, irritability and unfavorable reaction to labor. This may require excessive doses of analgesia to accomplish rest or comfort for the patient. In most cases, this will prolong labor and increase the stress on the baby. Consequently, indiscriminate attempts to use these technics simply for their own sake are condemned. It requires specially trained and experienced personnel to handle these patients during labor, as well as special ability in instituting a properly receptive mental attitude on the part of the patient during the antenatal period.[14]

While this debate goes on, the program seems to be finding favor with the parents of the country. Women are reading about it in magazines and in accordance with the tempo of the times are anxious to try something new. Those who succeed eagerly try to convert others.[15]

---

[13] Nicholas J. Eastman, "The Middle of the Road in Obstetrics," *Obstetrical and Gynecological Survey* (April, 1951).

[14] Lull and Kimbrough, *op. cit.,* p. 162.

[15] *December 20, 1954;* the television film "The Search," made in co-operation with the Child Study Center at Yale University, showed a woman in labor during a "natural childbirth." Her newborn baby co-starred. Irving Gitlin of CBS, producer of "The Search," maintains that "the natural childbirth scene used . . . is one of the most beautiful and fear-reducing scenes of childbirth ever filmed, for it strips away some of

Time alone will bring the answer. For the present, the marriage counselor would do well to leave to the obstetrician the choice of the method of delivery and the selection of those patients best suited for natural childbirth.

MORAL EVALUATION OF PAINLESS CHILDBIRTH

On January 9, 1956, Pope Pius XII, speaking before a meeting of physicians which had been arranged by the Rome Institute of Genetics, delivered an address dealing with "natural painless childbirth."
Excerpts from this talk make clear his position:

> We have received information concerning a new acquisition in the field of gynecology, and We have been asked to pass judgment thereon from the moral and religious point of view. It is a question here of natural, painless childbirth, in which no artificial means is used, but the mother's natural forces alone are called into action.

> First of all, painless childbirth considered as a general fact is in clear contrast with common human experience today, as well as in the past, even from the earliest times.

---

the age-old bugaboos about childbirth. The mother in this film was enjoying a pleasant experience . . . and her wonderful smile and look will not be soon forgotten. . . ."

December, 1950; Grail magazine. Aileen Hogan, "Natural Childbirth." Miss Hogan, an instructor in obstetric nursing at Western Reserve University, writes, in part: "We are following the pattern of Natural Childbirth. Together the parents have learned each step of the way which leads to the baby's birth. Together they have mastered and practiced and made their own the exercises which train the mother's muscles and discipline her will for the one day's hard work."

January, 1955; Family Life, book review of *The A B C of Natural Childbirth,* by Barbara Gelb, 190 pp., price $2.95 (from W. W. Morton & Co., 101 Fifth Avenue, New York 3, N. Y., 1954). "This is a book by a young mother who describes her experiences in having a baby the 'prepared' way. It is well written with many humorous touches, colorful descriptions and simple explanations of some of the complex matters about which the expectant mother needs to know. By way of telling the course of instruction at the New York Hospital the author covers the information adequately for the average reader. It is really a blow-by-blow account including long quotes from the nurse-midwife who taught the course. While most of the information is valuable, some of it is new even to me (I have had two children by 'natural delivery' and studied the program at Yale University before the first), a good deal of it is misleading. The reason for this appears to be that what happens in one particular hospital is told in such a way that it can be interpreted as general practice. As long as this story is taken strictly as *one* story, the way it might happen at *one* particular hospital it can be very valuable. In the opening all the objections to 'natural delivery' are voiced by the author's husband and friends. The way in which these objections are dealt with is the most important contribution of this book. All exercises taught in the preparatory class are illustrated with the Maternity Center Association drawings and with the exception of those dealing with how to carry and lift a baby or toddler are reliable." — Mary Jane Hungerford.

Most recent research indicates that some mothers give birth without feeling any pain, even though no analgesic or anesthetic has been used. It also shows that the degree of intensity of pain is lesser among primitive peoples than among civilized peoples; that is, in many cases, this intensity is medium, yet it is high for the majority of mothers, and it is not rare that it even prove to be insupportable. Such are observations as currently noted.

The same must be said of past ages, in so far as historical sources permit the fact to be verified. The pains of women in childbirth were proverbial; they were referred to in order to express the most lively and anguished suffering, and literature, both profane and religious, furnishes proof of this fact. Indeed, this way of speaking is general even in the biblical texts of the Old and New Testaments, especially in the writings of the prophets.

We shall cite a few examples of this. Isaias compares his people to the woman who is in pain and cries out when she draws near the time of her delivery (cf. Is. 26, 17); Jeremias, viewing the approaching judgment of God, says: "I have heard the voice as of a woman in travail, anguishes as of a woman in labor of a child" (Jer. 4, 31). The evening before His death, Our Lord compared the situation of His Apostles with that of a mother awaiting the moment of childbirth: "A woman about to give birth has sorrow, because her hour has come. But when she has brought forth the child, she no longer remembers the anguish for her joy that a man is born into the world" (John 16, 21).

All this permits the affirmation, as of a fact accepted among men in the past and now, that mothers give birth in pain. To this the new method opposes itself.

Is this method morally irreproachable?

The answer, which must take into account the object, end and motive of the method, is enunciated briefly: "Considered in itself, it contains nothing that can be criticized from the moral point of view."

There remains to be said a word of theological and religious evaluation, in so far as this is distinguished from the moral value in the strict sense.

The new method is often presented in the context of a materialistic philosophy and culture and in opposition to Holy Scripture and Christianity.

The ideology of a researcher and of a scholar is not in itself a proof of the truth and the value of what he has discovered and expounded.

The theorem of Pythagoras or (to remain in the field of medicine) the observations of Hippocrates which have been recognized as correct, the discoveries of Pasteur, the hereditary laws of Mendel, do not owe the truth of their content to the moral and religious ideas of their authors.

They are not either "pagan," because Pythagoras and Hippocrates were pagans, or Christian because Pasteur and Mendel were Christians.

These scientific acquisitions are true, because and in so far as they correspond with objective reality.

Even a materialistic researcher can make a real and valid scientific discovery, but this contribution does not in any way constitute an argument in favor of his materialistic ideas.

The same reasoning holds good for the culture to which a scholar belongs. His discoveries are not true or false according as he is descended from this or that culture, from which he has received inspiration and which has left its mark deeply impressed upon him.

The laws, the theory and the technique of natural childbirth without pain, are undoubtedly valid, but they have been elaborated by scholars who, to a great extent, profess an ideology belonging to a materialistic culture.

These latter are not true simply because the scientific results mentioned above are.

It is even much less accurate to say that the scientific results are true and demonstrated as such, because their authors and the cultures from which they derive have materialistic orientation. The criteria of truth are elsewhere.

The convinced Christian finds nothing in his philosophical ideas and his culture that prevents him from occupying himself seriously, in theory and in practice, with the psycho-prophylactic method. He knows, as a general rule that reality and truth are not identical with their interpretation, subsumption or systematization, and that, consequently, it is possible at the same time to accept the one entirely and reject the other altogether.

The Method and Holy Scripture

A criticism of the new method from the theological point of view should in particular give an account of Holy Scripture, because materialistic propaganda claims to find a glaring contradiction between the truth of science and that of scripture.

In Genesis (Genesis, 16), we read: *"In dolore paries filios"* ("In pain shall you bring forth children").

In order to understand this saying correctly, it is necessary to consider the condemnation passed by God in the whole of its context.

In inflicting this punishment on our first parents and their descendants, God did not wish to forbid and did not forbid men to seek after and make use of all the riches of creation; to make progress step by step in culture; to make life in this world more bearable and better; to lighten the burden of work and fatigue, pain, sickness and death, in a word, to subdue the earth (Genesis, 1, 28).

Similarly, in punishing Eve, God did not wish to forbid — nor did He forbid — mothers to make use of means which render childbirth easier and less painful.

One must not seek subterfuges for the words of Sacred Scripture. They remain true in the sense intended and expressed by the Creator, namely: motherhood will give the mother much suffering to bear.

In what precise manner did God conceive this chastisement and how will He carry it out? Sacred Scripture does not say.

There are some who allege that originally childbirth was entirely painless, and that it became painful only at a later date (perhaps due to an erroneous interpretation of the judgment of God) as a result of autosuggestion and heterosuggestion, arbitrary associations, conditioned reflexes, and because of faulty behavior of mothers in labor. So far, however, these assertions on the whole have not been proved.

On the other hand, it could be true that an incorrect behavior, psychic or physical, on the part of those in labor is capable of increasing considerably the difficulties of delivery, and has in reality increased them.

Science and technique, can, therefore, use the conclusions of experimental psychology, of physiology and of gynecology (as in the psychoprophylactic method) in order to eliminate the sources of error and painful conditioned reflexes, and to render childbirth as painless as possible. Sacred Scripture does not forbid it.[16]

---

[16] Pope Pius XII, Address to Catholic Doctors arranged by Rome Institute of Genetics, January 9, 1956, translation by Vatican Press Office, N.C.W.C. News Service.

CHAPTER XVIII

Control of Conception (1)

METHODS USED FOR THE CONTROL OF CONCEPTION

GENERAL

For the information of the counselor who may not be familiar with the terms and methods used for the control of conception, it is considered advisable at this point to discuss them at some length. Around this area arise many of the most disturbing and distressing conflicts encountered by married people. For this reason the marriage counselor should be especially well informed on the subject.

For the sake of clarity the term **birth control** will be avoided. It does not represent exactly what is immoral because this term could apply to celibacy or to continence in married life. The term **contraception** will be used to designate conception control through the use of chemicals, mechanical devices, and withdrawal.

Two errors are to be avoided in discussing conception control:

1. The implication that the immediate interest of the Catholic Church is the increase in the population at all costs. If this were the case, the Church would not be upholding religious and clerical celibacy.

2. The idea that the Catholic Church requires married couples to have as many children as they physically or economically can. Both of these errors were specifically answered by Father Treacy in his digest of the encyclical **Casti Connubii:**

> Birth control is wrong not because the Catholic Church says so. If there were no Catholic Church in the world birth control would be wrong and man left merely to the use of his reason or common sense, could see that it is wrong. For he could see that it is frustrating a law of Nature, which means God's law. The Catholic Church, established

by Christ to proclaim and explain God's law, declares it is wrong and explains why it is wrong. The Catholic Church does not make it wrong.

The advocates of birth control often claim that their only opponent is the Catholic Church, because she advocates each family having an unlimited number of children. Both statements are false. Everyone who believes in the Ten Commandments, everyone who with the light of reason to guide him, knows what the Law of Nature means, is against birth control. The most representative members of the medical profession are against birth control for the same reason that the Catholic Church opposes it, because it violates Nature's Law and God's Law.[1]

HISTORY OF CONCEPTION CONTROL

In a work, **De Officio Cherubyn,** which dates from the fourteenth century, the author asserts that "those who desire to prevent birth and conception do a great many and fantastic things." Brother Rudolphus, who wrote the work as a guide for the clergy, goes on to relate that some women, in order to avoid conception, sat or lay on their fingers, believing that this practice would enable them to avoid conceiving a child for the number of years equal to the number of fingers they held under themselves.[2]

He could have referred to a large number of rituals and incantations which were already known and exercised. The Roman historian, Pliny the Elder, in his **Historia Naturalis,** says that it was commonly believed that a couple could avoid the natural consequences of the marital act if they placed the testes and blood of a dunghill cock under the bed during intercourse.[3]

Not all of these magic rites and incantations are confined to the ancients, however. Yao women still place roots under their pillows at night[4] and Maiori women throw some blood into a fire while they pronounce incantations.[5]

Women of the Skaler mountain region of Galicia believe that they have a magic method of knowing whether or not they will have

---

[1] Gerald C. Treacy, S.J., *Love Undying,* simplified edition of the encyclical *Casti Connubii* (New York: Paulist Press, 1944).

[2] *De Officio Cherubyn.* The sole copy of this work extant is now in the Library at the University of Leipzig, Germany.

[3] *Historia Naturalis,* Vol. 30, p. 49. In an old Arabic formula the testicle of a wolf is used to cure venereal disease! Ibn-al-Baitar (ca. 1240) wrote that if a woman took the right testicle of a wolf, rubbed it in oil, and then inserted it as a vaginal suppository, she would be cured of any venereal diseases.

[4] Norman E. Himes, *A Medical History of Contraception* (Baltimore: The Williams and Wilkins Co., 1936), pp. 6–7.

[5] *Ibid.,* pp. 23–24.

children; and, knowing this, decide whether they want to conceive them or to avoid them altogether. This is done by a woman who takes a few drops of her first menstrual blood and allows it to flow into a hole in the first egg of a young hen. The egg is then buried in a hole for nine days and nights. When the egg is dug up again it will contain worms with black heads. The number of worms found in the egg is the number of children which she will have if she so desires. If she throws the egg into water she will have the number of children indicated. But if she throws the egg into fire, she will have none.[6]

There seems to be no end to the amount of ingenuity which the human race has employed in avoiding the responsibilities of conception. A general list of these ingenious attempts would include not only the forementioned rites and incantations but also vaginal and cervical astringents, special foods and potions, muscular agility, surgical operations, pastes, douches, jellies, withdrawal and mechanical devices. Even without considering the moral objections, there is no such thing as the perfect contraceptive.[7] Some of them may effectively prevent conception but are inconvenient to use. Some of them are not inconvenient to use, but are dangerous to health. This is especially true of home-made contraceptives.

There is nothing new about the use of contraceptives. They were known back in ancient Egypt, though they were never so widely known by the general populace as they are today. On a papyrus which is still extant[8] one may find the formula for a vaginal paste in which crocodile dung is a major ingredient. (Elephant dung may be substituted when crocodile dung is unavailable.)

The ancient Greeks used olive oil more than anything else.

---

[6] *Ibid.*, p. 174.

[7] Abraham Stone, "Medical Aspect of Marriage," *Marriage Counsel in Relation to Planned Parenthood, An Outline for Clergymen* (New York: Planned Parenthood Federation of America, Inc., n.d.), pp. 17–47. "The ideal contraceptive still remains to be developed. It should be not only harmless and reliable, but also simple, practical, inexpensive, and esthetically satisfactory. The methods in use today do not meet all these requirements" (p. 34).

R. de Guchteneere, *Judgment on Birth Control* (Baltimore: The Carroll Press, 1950), p. 154. At the International Birth Control Congress in 1922, Doctor Killick Millard reported the result of a questionnaire sent out to the leading gynaecologists in England; only one method of contraception found favor with a third of the persons consulted; no other method was approved by any appreciable number.

[8] F. L. Griffith, *The Petri Papyri — Hieratic Papyri from Kahun and Gurob (Principally of the Middle Kingdom)* (London: Bernard Quaritch, 1898), prescription no. XXI.

Aristotle, in his **Historia Animalium,** indicates that some of his contemporaries avoided conception by anointing "that part of the womb on which the seed falls with oil of cedar, or with ointment of lead or with frankincense, commingled with olive oil."[9]

Soranos of Ephesus (A.D. 98–138) taught that certain fruits (pomegranates and gall nuts, for example) had astringent powers in their acids. These acids, he said, could be used to contract the cervical os, thus closing it off and, he believed, preventing the entrance of male spermatozoa.[10]

The ancient practice of smearing an irritant on the cervix has not been altogether abandoned in the present day. Some natives of Constantinople still prevent conception by inserting a sponge soaked in lemon juice against the cervix before intercourse, then by daubing the same area afterward with tobacco juice.[11]

Some groups attempted contraception by muscular control. Ancient Jewish prostitutes frequently tried to avoid having offspring by practicing a jerking movement of their pelvic region immediately after intercourse. The purpose of this jerking movement was to get rid of the male sperm.[12]

Soranos of Ephesus suggested a similar method. He said that a woman should withdraw her body a little and hold her breath while the male was ejaculating. Then she was to get up directly after intercourse and sit with her knees bent. While in this position, she was to try to induce a violent attack of sneezing.[13]

The belief in passivity as a means of avoiding conception is still found more frequently than one may first imagine. On the Malay Archipelago a great many women believe that they can avoid conception by remaining passive throughout intercourse. And this idea of passivity is not confined to the Orient. There are many women in our own society who still believe that a woman cannot conceive unless she achieves orgasm during intercourse. This is, of course, far from true. **It is not at all necessary for a woman to arrive at orgasm in order to become pregnant.**

There was another form of muscular control which is still found

---

[9] Aristotle, *Works: Historia Animalium,* Vol. 7, no. 3, 583, a. 23, ed. J. A. Smith and D. W. Ross (New York: Oxford University Press, 1910), Vol. 4.

[10] Soranos of Ephesus, *Die Gynäkologie des Soranos von Ephesus,* Uberzetzt von Dr. Phil. H. Luneburg (München: Lehmann, 1894), p. 44.

[11] Himes, *op. cit.,* p. 183.

[12] *Ibid.,* p. 75.

[13] Soranos of Ephesus, *op. cit.,* p. 44.

practiced in some parts of Asia. In these areas there are elderly women who acquire a high degree of skill in manipulating the position of organs in the abdominal cavity; and this enables them to render the uterus of any woman in such a position that it may effectively aid or deter any possible conception. If a woman wishes to avoid conceiving children, she goes to one of these women who throws the uterus out of alignment. If the same woman later wishes to conceive children, she returns to the old woman who kneads and presses the uterus back into alignment.[14]

Physical operations were to be found among the ancients. These were performed on members of both sexes. One of them was removal of the ovaries. Athenaeus of Naucrates said that Adramyttes, a king of the Lydians, was the first man who castrated women and used female eunuchs.[15]

An ancient type of physical operation which is still practiced among some aboriginal groups may be described best as a suburethral incision. In this operation an incision is made into the urethra on the underside of the penis near the scrotum. Since this leaves an opening, the result is that sperm and seminal fluid trickle out of the incision and dribble over the testicles during ejaculation.[16] There is a second kind of operation which was used by the ancients and still in frequent use. This is a cutting of the **vasa deferentia** so that sperm no longer flows into the urethra.

Mechanical devices were as well known to earlier groups as they are today. They are also well known to aboriginal groups of our own time. Natives of Dutch Guiana use a vegetable condom which is made by inserting in the vagina a 5-inch pod cut off at one end.[17] Some natives of Sumatra insert a small ball of opium in the vagina.[18] The Marquesans of Oceania insert a sliver of bamboo in the uterus. The fact that the mortality rate from this operation is much lower than one might imagine is quite probably due to their rather skillful knowledge of human anatomy.[19]

One of the most effective chemical contraceptives used by natives

---

[14] H. H. Ploss, *et al., Woman* (London: Wm. Heineman, Ltd., 1935), Vol. 2, p. 293.

[15] Athenaeus of Naucrates, *The Deipnosophists or Banquet of the Learned of Athenaeus,* trans. C. D. Yonge (London: Bohn, 1854), Vol. 3, p. 826.

[16] Himes, *op. cit.,* p. 40.

[17] *Ibid.,* p. 18.

[18] *Ibid.,* p. 38.

[19] *Ibid.,* p. 23. Their skillful knowledge of anatomy is probably due to their practice of cannibalism.

seems to be the tannic-acid suppositories which are found in use among the natives of Sumatra.[20]

Oral forms of contraceptives have been used extensively and continuously. St. Jerome (ca. 384), in a letter, **De Castitate Virginum,** which he wrote to Eustochium, the daughter of his friend Paulus, deplores the fact that some women drank a potion before coitus in order to remain sterile. Others, he says, when they had felt that they had conceived **de scelere** ("in crime"), thought about "poisons of abortion."[21] Oral contraceptives are found in both liquid and solid forms. Whatever their form, the greatest effectiveness of both seems to be in producing headaches and violent retching.[22] Liquid potions vary from the innocuous and ineffective ancient brew of willow leaves boiled in water to a contemporary North African concoction which has a prime ingredient of gunpowder.[23] In some parts of Estonia the native women take mercury.

The number of solid forms of oral contraceptives seems to be as large as the number of liquid forms. Sun-Ssu-Mu, an ancient Chinese (died A.D. 695) suggested a pill which was a mixture of oil and quicksilver. The recipe is as follows: Take some oil and quicksilver. Fry this continuously for a whole day. At the end of this time, shape it into a pill the size of a jujube seed. This should be swallowed on an empty stomach. This contraceptive, he said, was better than most for two reasons: first, it will **really** prevent a woman from becoming pregnant; and second, it will not cause injury.[24]

The notion of fasting for a whole day is also contained in an old Mohammedan formula which recommended that a woman eat beans on an empty stomach.[25]

Some Malayans chew tree bark and betel nuts. Among the

---

[20] *Ibid.,* p. 39.

[21] *Aliae vero sterilitatem praebibunt et necdum sati hominis homicidium faciunt. Nonullae cum se senserint concepisse de scelere, abortii venena meditantur, et frequenter etiam ipsae commortuae, trium criminum reae, ad inferos perducuntur, homicidae sunt, Christi adulterae, necdum nati filii parricidae. Istae sunt qui solent dicere "Omnia munda mundis"* (Rom. 14:20). *Sancti Eusebii Hieronymi Stridonensis Presbyteri Opera Omnia,* Vol. 1 (*Patrologiae Cursus Completus,* Vol. 22) (Paris: J. P. Migne, 1859), p. 402.

[22] In his *Gynaecology,* Soranos of Ephesus mentions that many of the contraceptives which were then in use caused "indigestion, vomiting and a heavy head." Cf. Luneburg, *op. cit.,* p. 45.

[23] Himes, *op. cit.,* p. 8.

[24] This recipe of Sun-Ssu-Mu is quoted in a Chinese work published in 1237, translated as *Complete Collection of Valuable Prescriptions for Women.*

[25] This is cited in a medical encyclopedia by Ibn al-Jami (ca. A.D. 1180).

Cherokee women of North America the practice was to chew and swallow for four consecutive days the roots of spotted cowbane.[26]

One should mention, in connection with this Cherokee practice, that it was common only to prostitutes. If a Cherokee male found his wife practicing contraception, he would kill her. This seems to have been the practice among the greatest number of social groups. It is certain that among the Egyptians the methods of contraception were quite limited.[27] Contraceptive knowledge was probably not given to prostitutes in Islamic society.[28] And in ancient Rome, the knowledge of contraception was kept for the most part among physicians and scholars.[29]

It was not until the year 1822 that the knowledge of mechanical contraceptive methods was given wide distribution in any social group. The founder of modern birth control and the initiator of its widespread application today was a self-taught workingman, Francis Place, who was the first to give this information to the working classes.[30] In 1822, he wrote a work called **Illustrations and Proofs of**

---

[26] Himes, *op. cit.*, p. 13.

[27] *Ibid.*, p. 68.

[28] This conclusion is based on the fact that Mohammedan philosophers and theologians, while condoning the method of *coitus interruptus,* assert that it should be limited to cases where married women are in danger of death by pregnancy. Cf. al-Razi (ca. A.D. 910), Ali-ibn-Abbas (ca. A.D. 980), and Avicenna (ca. A.D. 1020).

Here is the teaching of Algazel (d. ca. 1111) on *coitus interruptus:*

". . . Doctors of the Law are in disagreement on the permissible or condemnable character of the act. There are four opinions on this matter: a) some declare it entirely permissible on all occasions; b) others declare it to be forbidden in every case; c) certain ones hold that it is permissible when consented to by the wife; it seems that according to this point of view, the wrong done would not be on account of an injustice to the wife; and d) finally, there are those who say that it is allowed in respect to a concubine but not in respect to a free woman.

"In our opinion, the best view is that it is something permissible . . . if it is to be condemned, it is so in the sense of neglecting something which might have been preferable or more suitable." (*GHAZALI: Le Livre des bons usages en matière de marriage,* trad. francaise par L. Bercher et G. H. Bousquet [Paris: A. Maissoneuve, 1953], pp. 88–89.)

[29] Himes, *op. cit.*, p. 96.

[30] Like so many proponents of contraceptive methods, Place failed to consider theological and philosophical objections to the problem. Place merely saw contraception as the solution to a pressing economic problem. The following is taken from a handbill which he published in 1823:

"It is not intended to produce vice and debauchery, but to destroy vice, and put an end to debauchery.

"It is a great truth, often told and never denied, that when there are too many working people in any trade or manufacture, they are worse paid than they ought to be paid, and are compelled to work more hours than they ought to work. . . .

". . . By limiting the number of children, the wages of both children and of grown-up

the **Principles of Population.** Place was not the first Englishman to **recommend** birth control to the population. Twenty-five years before, Jeremy Bentham, the economist, had already recommended the use of the sponge among the poorer classes so as to keep down their number.

Previous to Bentham's work, an Anglican clergyman, Thomas Malthus, had issued a warning against the growth of population. He affirmed that the population of the world was increasing by a geometrical progression, whereas the food supply was increasing only by an arithmetical progression. Malthus suggested that the impending catastrophe of hunger could be avoided only if people began practicing "moral restraint" — which to him meant postponement of marriage until a couple could support their offspring.

METHODS USED IN CONTROL OF CONCEPTION

These contraceptive methods may be divided as follows:
1. Those which interfere before coitus:
   a) Irradiation of ovaries or testicles;
   b) Ligation or partial removal of vas deferens;
   c) Salpingectomy;
   d) Cauterization of uterine cornua.
2. Those which interfere during coitus: Condoms.
3. Those which frustrate the coital act:
   a) Coitus interruptus;
   b) Diaphragms;
   c) Cervical caps;
   d) Tampons;
   e) Chemical substances;
   f) Intrauterine pessaries;
   g) Abnormal forms of coitus, e.g., anal, buccal, and so forth.
4. Those which interfere after coitus: Douches.
5. Those which do not interfere with coitus:
   a) The Rhythm.
   b) Abstinence.
   c) Lactation.
   d) Coitus reservatus.

persons will rise, the hours of working will be no more than they ought to be; you will have some time for recreation, some means of enjoying yourselves rationally, some means as well as some time for your own and your children's moral and religious instruction" (*Place Handbill:* "To the Married of Both Sexes of the Working People," dated 1823. Place Collection, The British Museum).

PROLONGED PROTECTION

More permanent means for the control of conception may be obtained by a variety of procedures which are seldom employed and
some of these may still be regarded as experimental in nature and not
available for clinical use. Among the more certain measures are:
(1) irradiation of the ovaries or testicles with X rays; (2) salpingectomy
(removal of the Fallopian tubes); (3) vasectomy (removal of a portion
of the vasa deferentia); (4) cauterization of the uterine cornua to
produce stricture of the openings of the Fallopian tubes into the uterus.

Experimentally, the following measures have been tried for the
control of conception: (1) application of prolonged heat to the
testicles to stop spermatogenesis; (2) use of hormones to stop ovulation
or spermatogenesis; (3) hypodermic injection of sperm to produce
spermatotoxins. The latter are immune substances or antibodies such
as would be produced by the injection of a vaccine. They react
to destroy the spermatozoa.

Sterility may also be produced by removal of the ovaries or testicles,
but since this would be accompanied by very unpleasant reactions, it
is never recommended as a contraceptive measure.

THE CONDOM

The condom, also referred to frequently as a "rubber" or sheath,
is the most common device used for contraception. It consists of a
thin sheath which is shaped to fit over the erect penis and retain the
semen which is ejaculated. The condom may be made of rubber, latex,
or "fishskin." The latter is in reality made from the peritoneal covering of the caecum of animals. The extreme degree to which condoms interfere with the spontaneity of sexual intercourse may be inferred from the following warnings given by a recent writer on the
subject.[31] He warns: (1) to test the condom before using by blowing
it up with air; (2) before applying condom (which is not done until
all the preliminary acts are over), it must be rolled and the distal
half inch pinched off to permit a free portion to remain; (3) after use
the sheath should be tested by filling with water and distended to see
if there are any leaks; (4) if a defect is observed, the woman should
immediately take a hot douche; (5) if a condom is used, the male
organ should be immediately withdrawn to prevent leakage; (6) dur-

---

[31] Robert Latou Dickinson, *Control of Conception* (Baltimore: The Williams and
Wilkins Co., 1938), pp. 135–136.

ing withdrawal, care must be exercised to see that the sheath does not slip off; (7) to prevent leakage, he suggests placing a rubber band around the upper end of the sheath; (8) in newlyweds he advises a contraceptive jelly or cream in addition to the condom. After observing these precautions, the couple is prepared to **spontaneously enjoy** the marital act! The moral aspects of the use of these various contraceptive measures are discussed in Chapter XX.

COITUS INTERRUPTUS

Withdrawal of the penis just before emission is perhaps the most common and yet probably the oldest method of birth control. It is mentioned in the Book of Genesis (38:8–10) as the sin committed by Onan and because of which he was struck dead. Some non-Catholic theologians have asserted that Onan was not killed for the act of withdrawal but for refusing to obey the ancient Jewish custom of having a family by his brother's widow. The semen is deposited outside of the vagina. Although it would seem that such a method would give almost complete protection against pregnancy, it not infrequently fails.[32] The principal reason for failure is the fact that the secretion at the male meatus during sexual excitement frequently contains spermatozoa even before ejaculation and these are deposited in the vagina. Another common cause of failure is premature ejaculation. The medical literature dealing with the possible harmful effect of coitus interruptus in general agrees that the practice is detrimental, but a great many of these statements are unsupported by evidence. It seems likely that the harm which results from this practice is more psychological than physical. The disturbance in the patient is more or less directly proportional to his attitude toward it. If he believes that the practice is harmful he develops nervous manifestations; if he gives no thought to its possible harmful effects, he has none.

VAGINAL DIAPHRAGMS

The vaginal diaphragm consists of a rubber dome and a base containing some springlike material which allows it to be compressed but to quickly resume its shape when pressure is removed. This diaphragm is inserted into the vagina by the woman before intercourse. It is made to be lengthwise of the vagina, cupped around the cervix in the posterior fornix. These diaphragms are made in various

---

[32] *Ibid.*, pp. 118–120.

sizes and must be fitted to the patient. The combination of a diaphragm with a jelly is usually considered as the most effective contraceptive.

Cervical Caps

The purpose of the cervical cap is to act as a mechanical barrier to the entrance of the spermatozoa into the cervix of the uterus. As their name implies they are shaped to fit over the cervix and are usually applied by the woman before intercourse and removed about twelve hours later. The cap may be made of hard rubber, soft rubber, celluloid, or metal. These caps are now of only historical interest.

Tampons

Tampons are plugs made of various materials such as cotton, gauze, soft rubber sponge, or paper which are placed in the vagina to act as mechanical obstacles to the passage of the sperm. These tampons are frequently medicated.

Chemical Contraceptives

Chemical contraceptives are usually applied in the forms of jellies, pastes, creams, suppositories, or tablets. They are intended to serve a twofold function: (1) to serve as a mechanical barrier to the passage of the sperm; and (2) to destroy or paralyze the spermatozoa. The jellies, pastes, and creams are usually supplied with a long applicator nozzle which is curved to fit the vagina so that the jelly may be applied directly to the cervix. A recent writer points out that the most practical advantage of the jelly is that the device is easy to hide! This same author claims about 80 per cent effectiveness for the jelly as a contraceptive. Since the spermatozoa are easily destroyed by a slight acid reaction most of the chemical contraceptives consist fundamentally of mild acids.

Intrauterine Devices

The devices for use in the cavity of the uterus are usually of two types, one a Y-shaped pessary and the other a flexible spring made of silver wire. These devices are usually inserted into the uterus and left for long periods of time. They are a frequent source of trouble and are seldom used at the present time although they were once very popular. This type of intrauterine pessary must not be confused with the vaginal pessary used to correct malpositions of the uterus. The latter type has no value as a contraceptive.

DOUCHES

Douches are extremely unreliable as a contraceptive measure. No matter how quickly they are taken after intercourse they are likely to be ineffective because any spermatozoa which are deposited into or on the external os of the cervix are quite likely to be beyond the reach of the douche. The intrauterine douche sometimes referred to by moralists is practically a surgical procedure and not available to women in general. The only purpose which the douche serves is for cleansing by washing out the semen. For this reason medicated douches are unnecessary. In spite of this, one not infrequently is called on to treat a woman who has severely burned herself by using a strong solution of lysol or iodine. Although it is impossible to know exactly when the spermatozoa have entered the cervical canal it would probably be safe to say that a douche taken as long as one hour after intercourse would have no contraceptive value. The effectiveness of the douche as a contraceptive measure is variously quoted as from 16 to 70 per cent.

ORAL PREPARATIONS

From time to time some individual attempts to devise a new contraceptive which is proven soon afterward to be as inadequate as any of its predecessors.

The most recent of these contraceptives is a pill developed by a Boston physician. In **Science** magazine for October 10, 1952, Doctor Benjamin F. Sieve[33] announced the development of an antifertility pill which contained phosphorylated hesperidin. In this article Doctor Sieve states:

> Since 1949 the author has been working on an orally administered factor that promises safe and controllable antifertility activity. This work was undertaken after Beiler and Martin's discovery of a new antihemorrhagic factor which in vitro and in vivo in animals, had direct inhibitory action on the enzyme hyaluronidase. They found that the sulfonated and phosphorylated hespiridins inhibited materially the enzyme action of hyaluronidase. Recent reports have specifically established a relationship of hyaluronidase to the coronal cells of the ova

[33] Benjamin F. Sieve, "A New Antifertility Factor," *Science,* Vol. 116, no. 3015 (October 10, 1952), pp. 373–385.

by a dispersion action. This action is identical with the so-called spreading factor of Duran-Reynals, which was corroborated later by McClean.

Hyaluronic acid is a mucopolysaccharide acid found in almost all animal tissues. Myer's classic experiments showed that the gels formed by hyaluronic acid are a part of the viscous barriers that regulate the exchange of various metabolites and water. Earlier experiments proved that at strategic points in the organism hyaluronic acid gels are disaggregated and depolymerized by the action of the enzyme hyaluronidase. This action reduces the viscosity of the "tissue cement." Myer further demonstrated that the enzyme hyaluronidase acts specifically by hydrolyzing hyaluronic acid.

It was this work that formed the basis for the hypothesis that when the hyaluronidase is in proper concentration in the cells of the spermatozoa and ovum and in the surrounding interstitial fluids, a hesperidin derivative at the proper saturation may act as an inhibitor, and this inhibitory action on the hyaluronidase occurs at the moment when the sperm comes in contact with the coronal cell layer of the ovum. It is now known that in the presence of the hesperidin derivative the entire coronal cell layer remains intact, and, in addition, more "tissue cement" is formed, both of which surround the ovum to form an impregnable barrier to the piercing spermatozoa.

In the present study of 300 married couples the antifertility action of the drug was complete except for 2 cases described. The 2 so-called failures are of no scientific significance, because of the lack of cooperation of the couples, as revealed by the method of dispensing medication. The tablets were bottled in lots of 100, each bottle recorded on a tally card for the patient to whom it was given, with the date and dosage for that patient. No one but members of the office staff dispensed the tablets. When a patient applied for more tablets he was required to return any remaining from the previous lot. Before more tablets were dispensed, a tally was made against the previous date and daily dosage. The number of tablets returned plus the number calculated should be equal to the total number dispensed for that period.

The necessity of divided dosage over a 24-hour period (is discussed). This was important to establish a blood saturation level, which remained fairly constant over a 24-hour period. Experience has proved that the drug is best administered with meals; when necessary, a fourth dose can be given at bedtime. The author's general rule was to prescribe 4 doses for the wife, and 3 doses for the husband during the 24-hour period. A constant observation in all couples taking this medication was the lack of rebellion against taking the medication in divided doses. Patients who have been opposed to taking pills all their lives seemed willing to take this factor. It is most important to impress upon the couples this distribution of dosage, as success depends upon the blood saturation.

This drug is an oral medication, physiological in action, which can be taken indefinitely without toxic effects or permanent inhibition of fertility. The medication must be taken for 10 consecutive days by both partners before anti-fertility action can be assured, and thereafter continuously by both partners at the prescribed daily divided dose. Fertility can be restored merely by omitting the drug for a 48-hour period. Should medication be omitted for 48 hours by either member of the couple, the 10 consecutive days of therapy must be repeated by both partners in order to reestablish fertility control. Following pregnancy, these 10 consecutive days of medication should not be started until after the first menstrual period postpartum. Phosphorylated hesperidin has been given clinically along with other substitution factors, such as vitamins, endocrines, amphetamine derivatives, and decholic acid derivatives without apparent interference in its action. As has been shown in both the text and tables, its antifertility action is not inhibited by trauma, infectious diseases, or systemic diseases. Again a word of warning must be expressed — it must be remembered that only one specific radical of this drug, phosphorylated hesperidin has antifertility activity.

It must be realized that this preliminary report is presented for its experimental value only. Much more clinical data must be accumulated before the general use of this antifertility factor is warranted.

Objections

To a cautious person Doctor Sieve's results, even apart from their moral implications, were unacceptable. Aside from the fact that his results were too perfect, the following difficulties might be mentioned:

1. In rats he had 60 per cent failures.

2. There is no proof that hyaluronidase is responsible for the penetration of the ovum.

3. There is no proof that the hesperidin helps a layer of cells around the ovum to clump together and keep the sperm out as Doctor Sieve contended.

4. It is hardly likely that 596 patients (out of 600) would religiously take pills three times every day for months.

5. There is no proof except the statement of the patients that they were not simultaneously using other contraceptives.

Moral Aspects of Oral Contraceptives

The Very Reverend Francis J. Connell, C.SS.R., in response to this publication, states the Catholic attitude toward this development as follows:

The moral principles of the Catholic Church provide a clear and definite solution to the problem of the morality of the antifertility pill. The use of this pill, whether by man or by woman, like the use of any other positive procedure whose direct purpose is to render a person sterile, is a grave violation of the law of God.

It is true, there are some features about this drug (phosphorylated hesperidin) which might seem to make it different from the usual means of contraception.

First, it is taken orally, so that those who make use of it need not pervert their conjugal act in order to obtain the desired result. But this in no wise affects the morality of the procedure.

It is just as truly a frustration of God's plan of conception to interfere with the internal sexual process as it is to use an artificial contraceptive device in the external act of intercourse or to imitate the detestable act of Onan (Genesis, 38:9).

In all these cases there is the same purpose in the method employed — the positive and direct frustration of the primary effect of sexual intercourse, as God established it.

Secondly, some might wonder if the fact that this new drug effects sterilization only temporarily (as long as the pills are used) would affect the morality of its use. The answer is that any direct sterilization, even though only temporary, is a serious violation of God's law.

The act of coition between husband and wife is the occasion on which in God's plan, He cooperates with His creatures toward the sublime work of the creation of a human being, destined to immortal happiness. Hence, to thwart God's plan in so important a matter is mortally sinful, even if it occurs only once.

In branding sterilization and contraception as sinful we referred to them as a direct frustration of the primary purpose of sexual intercourse. This implies that there can be cases in which a person finds it necessary to use a medical or surgical means for the direct purpose of curing some dangerous malady, though the means will have as another effect the sterilization of the sick person. In such a case the sterilization would be an indirect effect.

What are the moral principles applicable to the case of a couple, one of whom renders himself or herself sterile, by the use of these pills while the other refuses to follow this course? Pope Pius XI gave the answer in his encyclical on Christian Marriage. He said, with reference to the spouse who will not practice contraception: "There is no sin, provided that, mindful of the law of charity, he or she does not neglect to seek to dissuade and to deter the partner from sin." Needless to say, this principle is applicable only when there is a sincere and honest effort on the part of the non-cooperating partner to induce the other to desist from sin. A mere "token" resistance would be sheer hypocrisy.[34]

Perverse Forms of Coitus

The methods of contraception described above have presumed a normal form of coitus, i.e., intromission of the male penis into the female vagina. There are other forms of coitus which prevent conception but which are abnormal.

1. **Anal Coitus** — Intromission of the penis into the anus of the partner. As a contraceptive method, this is not frequently employed. It is used more among couples with jaded sexual appetites, or who are of relatively low intelligence. The type of individual who would once have employed this method is now better versed in less disgusting methods. It is more frequently found in use among male homosexuals, although even in these cases the frequency of occurrence is not too high.

2. **Buccal Coitus** (fellatio) is intromission of the penis into the mouth of the partner. The partner may, by drawing on the penis, produce orgasm. Prostitutes may sometimes employ this as a different means of producing sexual pleasure. They may or may not swallow the semen ejected. Rarely ever will buccal coitus be employed as a contraceptive method. It is more often a means of sexual stimulation in married couples.

There are other methods of satisfaction to which sexual partners may resort:

1. **Vulvar Coitus** — Coitus in which ejaculation takes place on the external genitalia of the female. The male ejaculates between the labia without entrance into the vagina. It is a method for avoidance of pregnancy frequently resorted to by engaged couples. The possibility of pregnancy under such circumstances is, however, very great. It is not uncommon to see pregnancy in a woman with an intact hymen.

2. **Interfermoral Coitus** — Ejaculation in this case takes place between the thighs. Although the possibility of pregnancy is not as

---

[34] *The Catholic Standard*, Washington, D. C., October 17, 1952.

great in this case as in that of vulvar coitus, it remains a distinct possibility.

3. **Mutual Masturbation** — This is seldom employed by married couples as a measure in birth prevention, although it is more frequently regarded as a safe method of sexual satisfaction between lovers.

4. **Coitus Saxonicus** (blocked emission) — Pressure at the base of the penis during orgasm will cause the semen to flow backward into the urinary bladder. This was a common practice in ancient India.

CONCLUSIONS

Apart from all moral considerations, the perfect contraceptive, as a contraceptive, has yet to be produced. Scott's dictum is as correct today as it was in 1935 when he wrote: "Every contraceptive method involves a certain amount of trouble and unpleasantness to one partner or the other in the sex act, and in certain instances to both parties."[35]

---

[35] Cf. also John J. Lynch, S.J., "Fertility Control and the Moral Law," *Linacre Quarterly*, Vol. 20 (August, 1953), pp. 83–88; "Another Moral Aspect of Fertility Control" (November, 1953), pp. 119–123.

CHAPTER XIX

Control of Conception (2)

METHODS OF CONCEPTION CONTROL WHICH DO NOT INTERFERE WITH COITUS

Certain practices of spacing children are in themselves quite permissible, whereas certain other methods are always intrinsically wrong. The fundamental difference between licit and illicit practices depends on whether or not the act is properly performed and the natural processes connected with the act are allowed to achieve their natural end. In licit practices of conception control the natural functions proceed to their end without any outside interference. Illicit practices, on the other hand, interfere with the processes either before, during, or after the sexual act. Therefore, it is desirable **to define the nature of the sexual act.**

The complete sex act consists of entrance of the penis into the vagina, orgasm on the part of the male, and ejaculation of his semen at least at the orifice of the vagina.

With this in view, let us discuss the practices by which one may control the conception of children.

ABSTINENCE

First, there is the method of absinence. Abstinence consists in refraining from the sex act. If a man and a woman wish to live as brother and sister, they may do so morally, provided certain conditions are fulfilled.[1] It is unlawful for only one partner to practice abstinence at the expense of the other. Abstinence, however, is rarely, if ever, practiced by two individuals as a method of birth control except for short periods. It is more frequently used as a penance. In the Middle Ages it was a common practice for a husband and wife to practice abstinence during Lent.

[1] Cf. Chapter XXX.

267

Abstinence in the celibate is entirely practical and presents as a rule little, if any, difficulty. Abstinence in the married is impractical except for relatively short periods. During sickness, during the latter part of pregnancy, and the first six weeks after childbirth, abstinence is more or less the rule. For two healthy and loving married persons, however, prolonged abstinence is usually detrimental and frequently leads to the development of neurotic manifestations in one or both parties. Only where both husband and wife are frigid or impotent would prolonged abstinence be free from great difficulty. Unfortunately, we frequently see marriages in which one party is frigid or impotent and the other partner normal. The effect on the normal partner is psychologically harmful, unless he is able to completely sublimate his sexual desires. During pregnancy there is no need for abstinence. It is frequently recommended during the first six to eight weeks because of the fear of miscarriage, and during the last few months when, due to the increased size of the abdomen, the woman may find it uncomfortable, or when it may induce premature labor. During enforced abstinence due to prolonged illness all possible erotic stimuli should be avoided.

LACTATION

Sterility during the period of lactation is as yet an unsettled question. Traditionally this period has been regarded as one of total sterility. It has long been pointed to as the method of aborigines for the spacing of their children. The mothers would continue to nurse the baby until they were ready for another child. However, sexual intercourse during the period of lactation is forbidden in many tribes and this may account for the low incidence of pregnancy during this period. It is known that three out of four women will not menstruate in the first three months of lactation. There is fairly good evidence that the menses occurring during the period of breast feeding are not accompanied by ovulation and are therefore sterile. There is no doubt that conception is unlikely during this time. Where the baby is entirely breast fed pregnancy is least likely.

THE RHYTHM METHOD OF PERIODIC ABSTINENCE

The Rhythm Method of periodic abstinence is based on the fact that conception can take place in the human female only during certain parts of the menstrual month. Fertilization depends on the union of the spermatozoon and the ovum. As explained above, a single ovum is liberated from the ovary each month; consequently, conception can take place only during the life of this cell. All other parts of the month would result in sterile intercourse. The fact of monthly ovulation has been known for some time, but interest was revived by the studies of Ogino and Knaus.[2] Interest in this country has been particularly stimulated by the studies of Latz and Reiner.[3]

The principles upon which this theory is based are:

1. That all women ovulate at approximately the same time each month, and that they ovulate only once each month.

2. That the interval during which the ovum (after ovulation) is capable of fertilization is approximately twenty-four hours.

3. That the spermatozoa after ejaculation are capable of causing fertilization for a period of approximately seventy-two hours.

As pointed out before, there is a marked variability of the menstrual cycle even in the same woman. The most regular woman fluctuates by about four days on either side of the average length of her cycle. In those women who are less regular the variation between the length of the various cycles may be as high as twelve or thirteen days. Many women will not believe this and many are amazed to find out how irregular they are when they keep a written record.

It is generally admitted that a woman will ovulate only once during each menstrual cycle. It is the time at which this event takes place which is the cause of dispute. Much work has been done by a large number of investigators in an effort to determine exactly when ovulation occurs. None of this work has been conclusive. Studies based on the occurrence of pregnancy following a single isolated coitus show that pregnancy has resulted from intercourse on each day of the 28-day cycle. The majority of such instances were, however, in the early part of the cycle with relatively few pregnancies occurring in the last portion. The curve of incidence falls off very rapidly after the seventeenth day of the cycle. From this evidence we must believe that ovulation may occur on any day of the menstrual cycle. Evidence gathered from all sources (ovaries observed at operation, mittel-

---

[2] Kyusaku Ogino, *Conception Period of Women,* English trans. Dr. Yonez Miyagawa (Harrisburg, Pa.: Medical Arts Pub. Co., 1934). Hermann Knaus, *Die Periodische Fruchtbarkeit und Unfruchtbarkeit des Weibes* (Wine: W. Maudrich, 1934). This work has been translated into English at different times by two different authors: D. H. Kitchen, 1934; G. Horowitz, 1951. Father John A. O'Brien wrote a work on periodic fertility with advice from Raoul de Guchtneere, Henry Schmitz, and Knaus himself: *Natural Birth Control Without Contraception* (Champaign, Ill.: The Newman Co., 1938).

[3] Leo J. Latz, *The Rhythm of Sterility and Fertility in Women* (Chicago: Latz Foundation, 1939).

schmerz, endometrial studies, estimation of hormones, vaginal smears, monkey ovulation, bio-electric studies) seems to indicate that the majority of women ovulate before the sixteenth day of the menstrual cycle. The largest number fall between the tenth to the sixteenth day. Ogino maintains that ovulation occurs between the twelfth and sixteenth day before the onset of the next menstruation regardless of the cycle. He allows five days for minor variations in any given number of regular cycles. Knaus believes that ovulation takes place fourteen to sixteen days before the beginning of the next menstrual period.

Tests for Ovulation

It must be admitted that there is no accurate way of estimating the time of ovulation within the 12 to 24-hour period of its occurrence. This fact is important to realize. The following suggestions have been offered for determining the time of ovulation:

1. **Mittelschmerz** — This consists of the occurrence, about mid-menstrual cycle, of symptoms suggestive of the onset of the menses. The woman experiences sensations which are similar to those which she would usually have just before the onset of her menses. These may be associated with slight staining and lower abdominal pain. Those symptoms have been considered to be due to the rupture of the ovarian follicle. Actually the cause of these symptoms is unknown. It may be due to preovulatory distention and stretching of the ovarian capsule over the mature follicle, or it may be due to the irritation of blood upon the pelvic peritoneum.

2. **Endometrial Studies** — Progesterone produces definite and clearly recognized cellular changes in the endometrium. Studies have revealed that this change occurs three to four days after ovulation, so that it is of little use in the conception control.

3. **Vaginal Cytology** — Studies of daily smears made from the vagina reveal cellular changes which are fairly typical of ovulation. Even in the hands of an expert, the changes in the cornified cells are usually not sharp enough or specific enough to establish a diagnosis on the basis of a study of only a few days. A study of a series of smears over a period of at least ten days in the middle of the cycle would be necessary to reveal the beginning of the progesterone effect which would in turn be indicative of ovulation.

4. **Appearance of Pregnandiol in the Urine** — The discovery of pregnandiol in the urine is of little value in determining the time of

ovulation. It is less reliable than either the basal temperature estimation or endometrial studies.[4]

5. **Basal Temperature** — This is probably the most commonly used method of determining the time of ovulation. The woman is instructed to take her temperature each morning upon awakening, except during her menstrual period. The thermometer should be left in place at least five minutes. Oral temperatures are usually satisfactory, although vaginal or rectal temperatures may be taken. For this purpose, a thermometer graduated in tenths of a degree is more accurate and easily read. These are available commercially from several manufacturers. The temperature is then recorded. More specifically, the instructions given to the patient are as follows:

The Basal Temperature Graph
Instructions for the Patient

Basal temperature graphs are helpful in determining whether and when ovulation occurs. Ovulation is the release of an egg (ovum) from the ovary, and ordinarily happens only ONCE in each menstrual cycle. Conception can take place ONLY if intercourse takes place at or near this time, during the interval of transition between low and high temperature levels.

A woman who wishes to become pregnant may increase the chance of conception greatly by having intercourse at the time of ovulation, or she may decrease the chance of conception by avoiding intercourse then. And one may use her knowledge of the fertile interval for avoid-

RECORD OF BASAL BODY TEMPERATURES

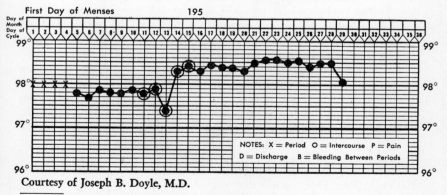

Courtesy of Joseph B. Doyle, M.D.

[4] S. H. Sturgis, "The Clinical Value of So-called Ovulation Tests," *Bull. New England Med. Center.* Vol. 14, no. 1 (February, 1952), pp. 6–12.

ance of conception for some time by natural means, then use it for a planned pregnancy, "natural child spacing."

The basal temperature graph reflects slight body changes taking place during the menstrual cycle (the interval between the beginning of one period and the start of the next period). Theoretically, the maximum normal temperature of a healthy, active, awake individual is 98.6 degrees. Actually, there are always slight variations from this figure. The "basal" *resting* temperature in the first part of the cycle is usually well below 98.6; in the last two weeks or so of the cycle, the basal temperature is closer to 98.6. Most important, the shift from the lower to the higher temperature level occurs about the time of ovulation.

The variations in the temperature before and after ovulation are slight, often only a few tenths of a half degree, so it is important that the temperature be taken carefully and recorded accurately. Special thermometers are available for this purpose; they record temperatures within the usual range of cyclic variation in tenths of a degree and are easier to read than the ordinary "fever thermometers," although the latter may be used.

Directions:

1. Be sure you know how to read your thermometer.

2. Take your temperature every morning except when you are menstruating (at about the same time every morning).

3. Put the thermometer under your tongue for five minutes immediately upon awakening, BEFORE you get up, move around, eat, drink, smoke, talk — if possible, while you are still "half asleep."

4. Start a new graph with every monthly period. The first day of your menstrual period is day "1" of the new cycle. Mark an "X" in the space for that day, and an "X" for each day the flow continues.

5. The morning after the flow has stopped, take your temperature as described in Number 3; record it by a dot in the column for that day on the line for that temperature. Then shake down the thermometer so it is ready for the next morning. Do this every morning until the next period begins, when again it is time to start a new graph.

6. Make additional notations on the graph to help your doctor interpret it. Encircle the temperature dot on the days when intercourse occurs, and write "A.M." or "P.M.," as the case may be, above the circle. Note any pain, any bleeding or spotting, any unusual vaginal discharge. (Some women can recognize ovulation by a twinge of pain or a few drops of blood, or a thin vaginal discharge.) Any recognized cause for temperature change — fever, cold, alcohol, indigestion, emotional disturbance, restless sleep, etc. — should be recorded.

7. Bring your graphs to the doctor at *each* visit.

There will be many variations in individual graphs which can only be interpreted by your physician. He will give further specific directions for use of these records in your particular case after you have kept them for several months.[5]

Physiologically, this rise in temperature is thought to be the result of the following sequence of events: After rupture of the Graafian follicle, luteinization of the corpus hemorrhagicum (the ruptured follicle into which hemorrhage occurred) proceeds rapidly, and well-functioning luteal cells are present in 48 to 72 hours. Within this same period, the production of progesterone probably occurs in sufficient amount to produce effects. One of these is its action on the thermal center in the brain, producing a rise in temperature.

It may readily be seen from this brief description that the temperature rise does not accurately reflect the time of ovulation, because the rise in temperature lags a day or more behind the rupture of the follicle.

From these statements it is apparent that no hard and fast rule can be stated for the exact time of ovulation. In the large majority of women the safest conclusion to be drawn is that ovulation probably occurs on or before the sixteenth day of the cycle, and that intercourse taking place 24 hours thereafter and up to the beginning of the next cycle will probably be sterile. A small percentage of women may determine the day of ovulation by observing in themselves the symptom of mittelschmerz. This refers to the fact that at certain times during the menstrual month symptoms occur which resemble those which are present at the onset of the menses. They are, however, short in duration and soon disappear. There is fairly good evidence that this marks the occurrence of ovulation.

"THE RHYTHM"

The popularization of the Rhythm theory of birth prevention in this country has been done largely by the book called **The Rhythm** prepared by Doctor Leo J. Latz, and published by the Latz Foundation.[6] Although the general principles upon which the rhythm of fertility and sterility is based are well understood, the application of these principles to an individual case is not always simple or accurate.

[5] *Schering Graph*, distributed by the Schering Corporation. There are numerous charts to assist in calculating the Rhythm and in keeping temperature records, e.g.: *Temp-O-Graf* and *Rhythm-Cal*, by Henry A. Fallon, published by R-C Pub. Co.

[6] Cf. footnote 3 above.

About 70 per cent of women menstruate on a regular 28 day cycle. In this group the determination of the fertile period is quite accurate.

Day of Month	
1	Menses
2	*
3	*
4	*
5	*
6	Sterile
7	*
8	*
9	Safety Factor
10	Life of Sperm
11	*
12	*
13	Ovulation
14	*
15	*
16	Life of Ovum
17	Safety Factor
18	Sterile
19	*
20	*
21	*
22	*
23	*
24	*
25	*
26	*
27	*
28	*
29	Menses
30	*
31	*

THE RHYTHM

Slight variations in this cycle such as 27 or 29 days are also quite reliable. In those cases in which there is a variation of three days or more, special care must be used in calculating the fertile period.

Bearing in mind the principles upon which the theory is based (p. 269 ff.) and making reference to the diagram on the left, the rhythm for this group of women may be calculated as follows:

1. Indicate the menstrual period (from the first sign of a flow).

2. Indicate ovulation which is most likely to occur on the 13–14–15 days of the cycle counting from the first day of the menstrual period. In some methods of calculating the rhythm ovulation is determined by counting backwards the 14th, 15th, and 16th days before the next expected period. In the case here under consideration, whether the period of ovulation is counted from the menstrual period which has occurred or the one which is next expected, the result is the same. Therefore ovulation is considered to occur on days 13, 14, and 15 of the cycle.

3. Since the spermatozoa are capable of causing fertilization for a period of 72 hours the three days preceding ovulation must be considered as potentially fertile days. Therefore days 10, 11, and 12 are marked to indicate their life span.

4. The ovum is considered capable of fertilization for a period of 24 hours, so 24 hours after ovulation must be considered as potentially fertile.

5. As a precaution, a 24-hour period is added at each end of the fertile period to allow for possible fluctuations in the cycle. Therefore days 9 and 17 are marked as potentially fertile.

The cycle in this case would therefore be Sterile (1 to 8 and 18 to

28), Fertile (9 to 17). There should be no guess work in connection with determining the length of the cycle. Menstrual records for at least 6 months, preferably for a year, are very important. Where the cycle varies more than 27 to 29 days it would be desirable to attempt to determine the time of ovulation by some other means (p. 270 f.), such as temperature readings, before too much dependence is placed on the sterile periods. The attempt of Dr. Latz in **The Rhythm**[7] to reduce every cycle to a mathematical formula ignores the human variability which must be constantly borne in mind.

Farris offers a formula for fertility based on his Rat Hyperemia Test for the determination of ovulation, which may be used in reverse to avoid pregnancy. He finds that, if the average is taken of three recent, consecutive menstrual cycles to the nearest whole day (a day being added if the fraction of a day is greater than one half) and this average is divided by two to get the mid-cycle day, ovulation is most likely to occur on one of the three days immediately before this mid-cycle day.[8]

According to the sixth edition of **The Rhythm** only 29 complaints had been received after the sale of 150,000 copies of the book. The picture of success painted by this author is too optimistic. Almost every physician that one questions can point to one or more failures in the method. There is no doubt, however, that the period of sterility is not always intelligently worked out.

The most common mistakes are: (1) Trying to recall the date of the last menstruation from memory and consequently attempting to determine the period of fertility on unreliable data — written records are absolutely essential.

(2) Permitting entrance of the penis into the vagina even without ejaculation, because during the period of sexual excitement a few spermatozoa may be liberated. Most of the actual failures occurring with this method are in the period immediately following the menstrual period.

---

[7] *Ibid.*, p. 104.

[8] Edmond J. Farris, Ph.D., *Human Ovulation and Fertility* (Philadelphia: J. B. Lippincott Co., 1956), p. 93.

Other methods of calculating the rhythm consist of calendars made of superimposed discs which are rotated to give the dates of sterility and fertility. Among these methods might be mentioned: Rhythm-Cal, R-C Publishing Company, Kansas City 4, Mo.; Femin-O-Graph, Southern Medical Supply Co., P.O. Box 1168, Atlanta, Georgia; Rhythmeter, Rhythmeter Co., P.O. Box 8646, Wilkinsburg, Pa. Charts to record temperatures may also be obtained from these companies.

In conclusion it may be stated:

1. The "safe period" is not always safe.

2. The "safe period" is safest in those women whose menstrual cycles are regular and between 26 and 28 days.

3. No contact of any kind should be had during the fertile period.

4. Written records are essential.

5. The "safest period" is from the seventeenth day of the menstrual interval to the onset of the next menses.

6. No mathematical formula is as successful in determining the Rhythm as the dates worked out by the physician in an individual case after the most accurate estimate of the date of ovulation which is possible. The date of ovulation is basic in determination of the rhythm. This calculation should be made by a physician. He is the individual most qualified by his professional training to understand the physiological conditions involved.

7. A great deal more study is needed before the enthusiasm of Latz will be shared by the majority of physicians.

THE VERY SAFE METHOD

The method of determining the sterile period just described is the one usually practiced. While pregnancy has occurred on every day of the menstrual cycle, practically all pregnancies occurred during the first half of the cycle. This fact, in addition to the general belief that ovulation occurs on the twelfth to the fourteenth day of the cycle, gives substance to the belief that the safest part of the safe period is that part of the cycle which occurs in the post-ovulatory phase. If, therefore, ovulation occurs on the twelfth to the fourteenth days, one more day should be added for the period during which the ovum can be fertilized, and an extra day for safe measure. This would bring the unsafe period up to the sixteenth day, inclusive. From the seventeenth day should, therefore, be a safe period on both scores, until the beginning of the next menstrual period occurs.

This period, from the seventeenth day on to the next menstrual period, has been a very safe period and is evidenced by a long experience in practice.

EXTENT OF USE OF THE RHYTHM METHOD

Although extensive figures are available concerning the use and effectiveness of contraceptives, there is very little information available concerning the extent to which the Rhythm Method is used and its effectiveness. Schnepp and Mundi, as the result of a survey of St. Louis doctors in 1949, gave the following summary of their findings.[9]

The survey covered a total of ten thousand patients, some of whom were Catholic, some Protestant, and some Jewish. (Schnepp and Mundi do not give figures nor percentages for these.)

Almost 66 per cent of the doctors queried felt that the Rhythm Method was simple enough to teach to most women. About 50 per cent of the doctors felt that there had been an increase in use of the Rhythm.

Of almost ten thousand patients, about 31 per cent were reported to be using the Rhythm Method. Twenty-four per cent were using the Rhythm Method alone; and 7 per cent were using the Rhythm in conjunction with some artificial contraceptive.

The doctors reported a mean average effectiveness for use of artificial contraceptives as 85 per cent; the corresponding mean average effectiveness for the Rhythm Method was 65 per cent. This means that of the total number of patients considered and of the total number of times when Rhythm had been employed, it was effective as a control factor 65 per cent of the time. For the same group of patients the median average was 93 per cent effectiveness for contraceptive methods, and 71 per cent for the Rhythm Method. Since the median average is an average obtained by determining the point where there are as many items below it as above it in the series, it would indicate that of the patients using Rhythm there were as many who had a better than 71 per cent average success in use of the Rhythm as there were those who had less than 71 per cent effectiveness in use of the Rhythm.

It was noted by Schnepp and Mundi that younger physicians tended to have more confidence in Rhythm than older physicians did. The mean age of physicians who gave Rhythm a 70-plus rating was 44 years. The mean age of those who rated it less than 69 per cent was 48 years.[10]

Christopher Tietze and others[11] made another study of 409 individuals who used the method for a month or more. The average (mean) age group was 31 years; the average duration of marriage,

[9] Gerald J. Schnepp and Joseph P. Mundi, "Sociological Implications of Rhythm Method Practice," *Linacre Quarterly*, Vol. 19, no. 2 (May, 1952), pp. 44–48.

[10] *Ibid.*, p. 45.

[11] Christopher Tietze, *et al.*, "Clinical Effectiveness of the Rhythm Method of Contraception," *Current Medical Digest of Recent Advances in Diagnosis and Therapy*, Vol. 18, no. 12 (December, 1951), pp. 25–27.

8 years, and the average number of previous pregnancies, 3.4 per woman, corresponding to 0.4 pregnancies per year of married life.

The 409 users were observed for an aggregate period of 7267 months, or 605.6 woman-years. More than one half of the group (224) participated for less than one year, but these patients contributed only 1134 months, or 15.6 per cent of the aggregate exposure to the risk of pregnancy. The remaining 84.4 per cent were furnished by the 185 patients observed for a full year or longer. In a number of instances the use of the Rhythm was interrupted by one or more pregnancies, voluntary or accidental. The total number of periods of use, separated by pregnancies, was 462. If each of these periods of use is counted as a separate "case," the number of "cases" observed for a full year or longer was 202, contributing 82 per cent of the aggregate exposure.

The number of accidental pregnancies recorded during the period of observation was 57. It can be estimated that 30 pregnancies were concealed in the group of patients who had discontinued participation without further contact with the clinic, thus making the total number of accidental pregnancies 87. At least a portion of these 87 pregnancies is believed to have resulted from the patient's failure to follow exactly the instruction given her by the clinic, either because she had not understood them or because the couple "took a chance."

The 87 accidental pregnancies, observed and estimated during 605.6 woman-years of observation, correspond to a rate of 14.4 plus 1.5 conceptions per 100 years of exposure to the risk of pregnancy, or 1 unwanted conception to almost 8 years of reliance on the Rhythm Method. This rate of 14.4 is much higher than the rates reported for the most successful users of the diaphragm and jelly or of condoms (6 to 7 per 100 years of exposure), but it is in line with the results of several other clinics in urban and rural areas of the United States, prescribing mechanical and/or chemical contraception, and serving a type of patient presumably comparable to those in this type of clinic in understanding and foresight and in their interest in family limitation.

These findings and my own observation lead me to believe that the Rhythm Method is in extensive use. If used intelligently, it is believed that its effectiveness would be higher than the 65 per cent noted in the above study. By intelligent use is meant that ample time should be allowed both before and after the carefully estimated date of ovulation to allow for variations and that there be no genital contact during the fertile period.

EFFECTS OF USING THE RHYTHM

Entirely aside from its value in controlling conception, the Rhythm Method may have other beneficial results which are not usually thought of by those who complain so bitterly about the fact that their sex life is measured by the calendar. Schnepp and Mundi point to three of these:

1. It may bring about a greater development of emotional maturity among some married couples, since Rhythm requires self-control if it is to be practiced successfully.

2. It abolishes the harmful psychological states which result in some women after the use of contraceptives. On the other hand, it increases the delight in the marital relationship which follows after it has been put off for a time. The result should be an increase in the ratio of happily married couples.

3. Knowledge of the fertility periods in the cycle would permit the conception of more children who were desired.[12]

The clear conscience of the couple who use the method licitly is not to be overlooked.

THE MORALITY OF THE RHYTHM METHOD

POPE PIUS XII ON THE RHYTHM

Pope Pius XII in his talk to the Italian midwives on October 29, 1951, gave the most complete and authoritative statement yet made by the Church on the morality of the use of the Rhythm Method. Because of the importance of this talk, those sections of it relating to this matter will be quoted in full:

> Then, there is the serious question today as to whether and how far the obligation of ready disposition to serve motherhood can be reconciled with the ever more widely diffused recourse to the periods of natural sterility (the so-called agenetic periods of the woman) which seems to be a clear expression of the will contrary to that disposition.
>
> It is rightly expected that you be well informed from the medical point of view about this period and of the progress that is likely to be made in it. It is also expected that your advice and aid be not based on popular publications, but founded on scientific objectivity and the authoritative judgment of specialists in medicine and biology. *It is your office, not that of the priest, to instruct married people either when they come for private consultations or through serious publica-*

---

[12] Schnepp and Mundi, *op. cit.*, p. 47.

tions on the biological and technical aspects of the theory, without, however, allowing yourselves to be let in for propaganda that is neither right nor decent. In this field, too, your apostolate demands of you as women and Christians that you know and defend the norms of morality to which the application of this theory is subordinated. Here it is the Church that is the competent judge.

There are two hypotheses to be considered. If the carrying out of this theory means nothing more than that the couple can make use of their matrimonial rights on the days of natural sterility too, there is nothing against it, for by so doing they neither hinder nor injure in any way the consummation of the natural act and its further natural consequences. It is in this respect that the application of the theory of which We have spoken differs from the abuse already mentioned which is a perversion of the act itself. If, however, it is a further question — that is, of permitting the conjugal act on those days exclusively — then the conduct of the married couple must be examined more closely. Here two other hypotheses present themselves to us. If at the time of marriage at least one of the couple intended to restrict the marriage right, not merely its use, to the sterile periods, in such a way that at other times the second party would not even have the right to demand the act, this would imply an essential defect in the consent to marriage, which would carry with it invalidity of the marriage itself, because the right deriving from the contract of marriage is a permanent, uninterrupted and not intermittent right of each of the parties, one to the other.

On the other hand, if the act be limited to the sterile periods in so far as the mere use and not the right is concerned, there is no question about the validity of the marriage. Nevertheless, the moral licitness of such conduct on the part of the couple would have to be approved or denied, according as to whether or not the intention of observing those periods constantly was based on sufficient and secure moral grounds.

The mere fact that the couple do not offend the nature of the act and are prepared to accept and bring up the child which in spite of their precautions came into the world would not be sufficient in itself to guarantee the rectitude of intention and the unobjectionable morality of the motives themselves.

The reason for this is that marriage obliges to a state of life which, while conferring certain rights, also imposes the fulfillment of a positive work in regard to the married state itself. In such a case, one can apply the general principle that a positive fulfillment may be omitted when serious reasons, independent from the good will of those obliged by it, show that this action is not opportune, or prove that a similar demand cannot reasonably be made of human nature.

The marriage contract which confers upon husband and wife the right to satisfy the inclinations of nature, sets them up in a certain state of life, the married state. But upon couples who perform the act peculiar to their state, nature and the Creator impose the function of helping the conservation of the human race. The characteristic activity which gives their state its value is the bonum prolis. The individual and society, the people and the state, the Church itself, depend for their existence in the order established by God on fruitful marriage. Therefore, to embrace the married state, continuously to make use of the faculty proper to it and lawful in it alone, and, on the other hand, to withdraw always and deliberately with no serious reason from its primary obligation, would be a sin against the very meaning of conjugal life.

There are serious motives, such as those often mentioned in the so-called medical, eugenic, economic, and social "indications," that can exempt for a long time, perhaps even the whole duration of the marriage, from the positive and obligatory carrying out of the act. From this it follows that observing the non-fertile periods alone can be lawful only under a moral aspect. Under the conditions mentioned it really is so. But if, according to a rational and just judgment, there are no similar grave reasons of a personal nature or deriving from external circumstances, then the determination to avoid habitually the fecundity of the union while at the same time to continue fully satisfying their sensuality, can be derived only from a false appreciation of life and from reasons having nothing to do with proper ethical laws.[13]

Based on these comments the following conclusions may be drawn:

1. It is the function of the doctor and not that of the priest to instruct married people in regard to the physiological aspects of the Rhythm.

2. **Per se,** there is a positive duty on the part of individual married couples who use their rights to procreate. This is contrary to the opinion of certain theologians who have held in the past that no such positive obligation existed for individual couples but that there was only a general obligation on the human race to preserve itself.

3. Since each couple has a positive duty to procreate, the question arises as to whether such a duty is limited by the excusing causes mentioned by the Holy Father, or does it independently of these causes refer only to a reasonable or average contribution to the preser-

---

[13] Pope Pius XII, *Moral Questions Affecting Married Life,* allocution to Italian midwives, October 29, 1951 (New York: The Paulist Press, n.d.), pp. 13–15. Emphasis added.

vation of the race? Father Gerald Kelly, writing in the **Linacre Quarterly,** said in reference to this question:

> If only the *words* of the Pope are considered, one might argue, I think, that for those who choose to exercise their marriage rights, the only limitation on the duty to procreate is to be found in the serious reasons of a medical, eugenic, social, or economic nature. Consequently, in the absence of these reasons, the couple who can have ten children by leading a normal sexual life are not justified in using Rhythm to limit their family to less than that number.
>
> On the other hand, if the duty to procreate is considered in the light of similar obligations toward society, as well as toward one's neighbor, it is in itself limited. It would bind each couple to make an ordinary, or an average, contribution in terms of the population needs. This would mean that every fertile couple that chooses to use their marriage rights should have a family of perhaps four or five children, if they can, because that seems to be approximately the number required of each couple in order to make proper provision for the population needs.
>
> If the second interpretation of the duty to procreate were taken as a sort of working norm of obligation, it would allow for the following practical rules: *To have more than four or five children is an ideal which should be encouraged.* To use the Rhythm to limit the family to four or five children *is permissible, even without special excusing causes, provided both parties are willing and able to practice it. To use Rhythm to limit the family to less than four children requires one of the justifying reasons mentioned by the Pope.*
>
> I would favor the second interpretation. But I would not propose it as certain. And, even supposing that the general idea of a limited duty to procreate were certain, I would not say that the norm I have suggested here — four or five children — is not open to debate.[14]

Father Kelly's theory on the duty of individual couples to make an ordinary, or average, contribution in terms of population needs, is very vaguely grounded in ethics. There is no other theologian I know of who holds this doctrine. "Duties toward society" are never evaluated quantitatively, except in the case of property, and then only on principles of contract law. There is no analogy in this connection.

The scriptural norm is enough and much less likely to lead to trouble. Father Francis Connell is also in disagreement with Father Kelly.[15]

---

[14] Gerald Kelly, S.J., "Official Statement on Rhythm," *Linacre Quarterly,* Vol. 19, no. 2 (May, 1952), p. 43.

[15] Francis J. Connell, C.SS.R., of the Catholic University of America, takes up the last point which Father Kelly says is open to discussion:

4. A marriage entered into with the understanding beforehand that the right to sexual relations would be restricted to the sterile periods only would be invalid.

5. For sufficiently serious reasons, "medical, eugenic, economic, and social," the Rhythm may be used "for a long time, perhaps even the whole duration of the marriage."

6. The sin involved in the habitual use of the Rhythm, without valid reasons, is a sin against social justice, the neglect of the duty to contribute to the preservation of the race.

7. In those cases where there is a sound medical reason and the use of the Rhythm is not feasible for some reason, the only moral course for those who wish to avoid pregnancy is abstinence from intercourse.

Sufficiently serious causes for the use of Rhythm would be:

1. Chronic illness in the wife which would be aggravated by pregnancy.

2. Wife is suffering from the Rh factor and most probably would not be able to give birth to a living child.

3. Poverty to the extent that the family could not decently support another child.

4. Inability to find housing for a larger family.

5. Husband going to college for a year or so and wife must work.[16]

Griese lists the following as sufficiently serious causes for permanent use of the Rhythm:

1. Because conception will very probably result in death or a permanent state of bad health for the mother.

2. Because it is almost certain that the mother cannot bring forth living children.

3. Because the mother can bring forth only abortive children (i.e., miscarriages).

"I am of the opinion . . . that the divinely imposed obligation to procreate remains substantially unmodified, even when a couple have had seven or eight children, presuming that they wish to make use of their rights and have no serious reason for not having more children. Certainly, a couple who have given life to so many would often have sufficient reasons to avoid an increase in the family because of financial limitations, housing difficulties, etc. But I cannot admit that the mere fact that Divine Providence is prepared to give them more children, when they already have a considerable number, is of itself a sufficient reason to exempt them from further exercise of parenthood" (Francis J. Connell, C.SS.R., "Questions and Answers," *The American Ecclesiastical Review*, Vol. 127, no. 2 [August, 1952], p. 140).

[16] Francis J. Connell, C.SS.R., "Rhythm in Marriage," *Catholic Men* (October, 1953), p. 15, items 2–5.

4. Because it is practically certain that the children will be born with serious and incurable hereditary defects, especially insanity.

5. Because it is morally impossible for the husband to support another child.

6. Because the mother has proven to be utterly incapable of fulfilling the usual maternal duties relative to the care and training of children, either physically or morally.

7. Because one of the spouses is absolutely opposed to having children or another child. If there is no just cause for such an attitude, the other party (not the opposing one) would be **justified** in using the Rhythm Method. If the opposing party cannot be persuaded to change that attitude, the practice may be **permitted** to that party as the **lesser** of two evils.

8. Because it is the only way of stopping or preventing the use of onanistic methods in marital relations. The remarks made in reference to the above motive (7) are applicable in this case as well.

9. Because it is morally certain that one of the parties will otherwise fall into sins of incontinence. (Cf. remarks concerning motive number 7.)[17]

Griese lists also a series of motives which would be considered sufficient for the **temporary** practice of the Rhythm:

1. Because of a temporary physical weakness or period of convalescence on the part of the mother, e.g., gaining strength after childbirth or after an **illness.**

2. Because of the **extraordinary** inconveniences and expenses associated with childbirth in an individual case, e.g., Caesarean deliveries.

3. Because of the exceptional fecundity of the mother; necessary to space births.

4. Because of difficult financial conditions at the present time: unemployment, misfortunes, etc.

5. Because the young wife is not yet physically fit to assume the cares of motherhood.

6. Because of a temporary nervous strain on the part of the wife.

7. Because the birth of another child will actually render the mother incapable of properly rearing the children already born, at least for the time being.

---

[17] Orville N. Griese, *The Morality of Periodic Continence* (Washington, D. C.: Catholic University Press, 1942), pp. 76–77. In reference to point 4 in the list, it should be emphasized that theologians as a group are cautious about advocating the use of Rhythm for eugenic reasons.

8. Because the wife has to work and help support the family; husband's salary is insufficient, or employment irregular, etc.[18]

COITUS RESERVATUS

There is relatively little difficulty in discussing the morality of abstinence, prolonged lactation, and use of the Rhythm Method. But there is a great deal of discussion on the permissibility of a fourth method which is called **coitus reservatus**. **Coitus reservatus**, or as it is also called, **amplexus reservatus**, means intercourse in which penetration takes place and is continued for a time so that neither partner experiences orgasm before, during, or after the act. The discussion of this method is lengthy because of numerous unsettled questions in its regard.

This method was given a great deal of impetus in Europe, especially in France, where it was recommended by some clerics as a solution for the difficulties under which most married couples labored when there was no alternative but forced abstinence. Chanson says that married couples "have not only the right, but the duty" to practice incomplete sexual acts, since these are not only an "indispensable method for appeasing the senses," but also "for advancing conjugal love." The three books of Paul Chanson (**The Art of Love, The Art of Love and Conjugal Continence, The Art of Love and Christian Spiritual Life**) have been ordered withdrawn from circulation and "aucune nouvelle édition ou traduction ne devroit être autorisée."[19] The following excerpts from **The Art of Love and Conjugal Continence** explain his ideas and rather vividly portray his rather lyrical approach to the subject:

> Concretely, conjugal continence relates to three essential modalities; ascetical, amorous and that continence which I take the liberty to call by its true name, *neurasthenique*.
> Ascetical continence is the appanage of a small number of the elect. Let us bow to them and go on.
> Amorous continence is the privilege of those who are masters of the art of love, who, unhappily, are not many in number.
> Thus neurasthenic continence is the lot of almost all husbands, since their lack of temperance on one part and lack of skill on another condemn them in theory to a suitable allowance of nominal intimacy and in practice to unsuitable behavior resigned to the so-called necessity of

---

[18] *Ibid.*, pp. 77–78.

[19] Letter sent to the Archbishop of Paris, August 12, 1950, by the Holy Office, quoted in *La Documentation Catholique*, T. 47, Col. 1292.

involuntary orgasms (or which are presumed to be so), without flaunt-
ing convention, and whose most admissible excuse is that neurasthenic
continence eliminates the minimum of happiness, which, according to
the well-known phrase of Aquinas, is necessary for the exercise of virtue.

And, of course (in a way which is not identical but analogous),
development in the art of love has enabled the orientals, for a long
time now, to determine experimentally the degree of excitation compatible with the retention of seminal emission; in other words, the
protophase of the conjugal act. The popularization of *coitus reservatus*
is, after all, only the rediscovery by the occident of a technique whose
origin is probably thousands of years old, and ignorance of which is
(let us say it without equivocation) only one of the aspects of human
corruption.[20]

MORALITY OF COITUS RESERVATUS

Proponents of the method have held that since no unnatural impediment was placed in the way of the act, it was entirely licit and
could be recommended as a legitimate method of allaying concupiscence and of furthering conjugal love. Some theologians, however,
have been opposed to **coitus reservatus** since, they say, it tends to invert
the relationship between the conjugal act and the pleasure which accompanies it.

It has been the tradition of the Church to oppose any view which
made sexual pleasure an end in itself. Pope Innocent XI (1676–1689),
for example, had condemned this in the proposition *"opus conjungi
ob solam voluptatem exercitum omni penitus caret culpa ac defectu
veniali."*[21]

In his allocution, **Ad Patres Familiae e Gallia,**[22] His Holiness Pope
Pius XII expressed in even stronger terms a condemnation of all those
who would seek to make pleasure of the marital act an end in itself.[23]
After his allocution to Italian midwives[24] it was generally understood
by theologians that this condemnation could be readily applied to the
practice of **coitus reservatus.** After the **Monitum** on **amplexus reservatus**
(**coitus reservatus**) which was issued by the Holy Office on June 30,
1952, there was no doubt that **coitus reservatus** is looked upon as a
practice not without dangers. In the **Monitum** priests were warned

---

[20] Paul Chanson, *L'Art D'Aimer et la Continence Conjugale* (trans. mine, J. R. C.)
(Paris: Editions Familiales de France, 1950), p. 27 ff.
[21] D. B., n. 1159.
[22] Delivered on September 18, 1951.   [23] *Acta Apostolica Sedis,* 43, pp. 730–734.
[24] Delivered October 19, 1951.

that "they should not presume to speak about **amplexus reservatus** as if there were nothing objectionable about it."

The **Monitum** of the Holy Office on **amplexus reservatus** reads as follows:

> The Holy Office has noted with grave concern that in recent times some writers in treating of the conjugal life have been descending to treat it in an unreserved and shamelessly detailed manner: especially some who are describing, praising and recommending a certain act known as *amplexus reservatus*. (The Holy Office) gravely warns the forementioned authors that they must desist from this manner of acting. (The Holy Office) earnestly urges bishops and pastors to exercise strict vigilance in these matters and to apply suitable remedies.

> Priests in the care of souls and in the direction of consciences should never, either of their own accord, nor when asked, presume to speak of *amplexus reservatus* as if there were no objection to it from the standpoint of Christian law.[25]

In commenting on the **Monitum,** Marius Castellano, O.P., enumerates three opinions which were generally held on **coitus reservatus:**

1. It is simply licit, chaste, and commendable to all.

2. It is not evil in itself but only in view of the end or circumstances attending the act which make it or can make it illicit.

3. It is evil in itself either gravely or venially.[26]

Father Castellano, who is himself a consultor to the Holy Office, says that the latter intended to condemn only the first proposition. The second and third propositions are still open to discussion.

The present status of moral opinion regarding **coitus reservatus** is well summarized by Father Gerald Kelly, S.J.:

> It is one thing to say, without qualification, that *coitus reservatus* is licit; another thing to say it is intrinsically evil. Reputable theologians

---

[25] *Gravi cum sollicitudine Apostolica Sedes animadvertit non paucos scriptores his ultimis terporibus, de vita conjugali agentes, passim palam et minute ad singula eam spectantia inverecunde descendere: praeterea nonnullos actum quemdam, amplexum reservatum nuncupatum, describere, laudare et suadere*

. . . omnes praedictos auctores graviter monet, ut ab huiusmodi agendi ratione desistant. Sacros quoque Pastores enixe hortatur ut in his rebus sedulo adviligent et quae opportuna sint remedia sollicite apponant.

Sacerdotes autem, in cura animarum et in conscientiis dirigendis, numquam, sive sponte sive interrogati, ita loqui praesumant quasi ex parte legis christianae contra "amplexum reservatum" nihil esset obiciendum (Acta Apostolica Sedis, 24, p. 346).

The *Monitum* was issued on June 30, 1952.

[26] Marius Castellano, O.P., "Adnotationes ad monitum S.S.C.S. Officii de 'amplexu reservato,'" *Ephemerides iuris canonici,* Vol. 8, no. 4 (1952), pp. 341–345.

readily see in it the possibility of sinful circumstances, e.g., the danger of solitary orgasm, of a "birth-control" mentality, of a perversion of marital values; consequently, they would judge the practice sinless only in concrete cases (which they consider to be very rare) in which such dangers would be sufficiently removed. Hyacinth M. Hering, O.P., does not limit his condemnation to circumstances. He holds that *coitus reservatus,* even without danger of orgasm, is intrinsically evil and gravely so.[27]

Father Hering's view is that **coitus reservatus** is not an **actus per se aptus ad generationem,** and therefore does not serve the purposes of marriage.[28] It is precisely at this point that he is opposed by others:

Theologians who hold no brief for the practice of *coitus reservatus* (because of its dangers and disadvantages) rightly contend that an incomplete venereal act can serve the purposes of marriage by fostering love and preserving mutual sex attraction. It is true that it is not proximately and actually procreative; but by preserving mutual sex attraction, it remotely and habitually serves the procreative purpose.[29]

This view is sustained by Father Hürth in his discussion of the subject in **Periodica:**

It is certainly agreed that: from the standpoint of Christian Law there are several objections to be made against *amplexus reservatus;* and moreover, this method of acting can never in any way be called "simply licit." On the other hand, it is not thus far proven with certainty (either from the nature of the thing itself, nor from the common opinion of moralists, nor from the monitum of the Holy Office) that *amplexus reservatus* is in itself against the right order and therefore can never be licit. This . . . seems to be what one must conclude: (If in a particular case it is certain that because of special demands of the circumstances nothing else is to be advised; if, moreover, it is certain that husbands and wives thus acting are led by serious and just motives) it is not agreed that *amplexus reservatus* can never be performed without sin.[30]

Among concrete circumstances in the article referred to, Father Hürth cites

[27] Gerald Kelly, S.J., "Notes on Moral Theology, 1952," *Theological Studies,* Vol. 14, no. 1 (March, 1953), p. 59.
[28] Hyacinth M. Hering, O.P., "De amplexu reservato," *Angelicum,* Vol. 28 (October-December, 1951), pp. 313–345. Cf. also his article, "Adnotationes ad monitum de litteratura sexuali et de amplexu reservato," *Monitor Ecclesiasticus,* Vol. 77, no. 4 (1952), pp. 568–585.
[29] Kelly, *op. cit.,* p. 59.

. . . spouses who are earnest and full of reverence toward God and who affirm that:

1. In acting thus neither of them often undergoes a proximate danger of orgasm either during the act itself nor afterwards as a result of the act posited.

2. They are not led by sexual lust removed from the control of right reason.

3. They, for grave and completely just reasons (declared by the Supreme Pontiff in the allocution cited above) wish to avoid progeny and therefore restrain themselves in exercising this act.[31]

The most complete summary to date on this whole question is an article by Jules Paquin, S.J., in **Sciences Écclésiastiques** (Montreal) for May, 1953.[32]

---

[30] F. X. Hurth, S.J., "De re morali," *Periodica*, Vol. 41 (December, 1952), pp. 251–269.

Conclusio: Certo constat: contra amplexum reservatum ex parte legis christianae plura esse obiicienda; ideoque hunc modum agendi non posse umquam ullo modo dici "simpliciter licitum." Ex altera parte, hucusque non (neque ex natura rei, neque ex communi Moralistarum sententia, neque ex MONITO S. Officii) certo probatur: amplexum reservatum in se esse contra rectum ordinem, ideoque numquam posse esse licitum. Hinc (saltem interim) concludendum videtur: (si in casu particulari certum est ob pecullares condiciones ex parte circumstantiarum nil monendum esse; si insuper certum est conjuges ita agentes duci seriis et iustis motivis): non constare amplexum reservatum "non posse" umquam peragi sine peccato.

Inter circumstancias concretas, decurrente articulo, Fr. Hurth nominat:
. . . conjuges serii et timoratae conscientiae attestantur:

se ita agentes saepe non subire (in neutro conjuge) periculum proximum orgasmi (neque in ipso actu neque postea vi actus positi) . . .

se non duci sexuali cupidine, dominio rectae rationis subducta . . .

se ob graves et omnino justas rationes (agnitas a Summo Pontifice in supra allegata Allocutione (Oct. 29, 1951) evitare velle prolem ideoque se in hoc actu exercendo sistere).

[31] *Ibid.*

[32] Jules Paquin, S.J., "L'étreinte réservée," *Sciences Écclésiastiques*, Vol. 5 (May, 1953), pp. 81–106.

CHAPTER XX

Control of Conception (3)

MORAL OBJECTIONS TO SPECIFIC CONTRACEPTIVES

Abstinence and the use of the Rhythm Method are not intrinsically evil because they do not frustrate the natural consequences of the sexual act. On the other hand, those practices of birth prevention which are called contraceptive are morally evil because they interfere with the functioning of a natural act. The Catholic prohibition against any form of **contraception** is not based on a Church law which might be changed at a later date (such as abstaining from meat on Fridays). The Catholic Church prohibits contraception because it is prohibited by the natural law itself. And the Catholic Church does not have the authority to change the natural law. The Catholic Church merely points out that the natural law exists and must be observed. Reference has already been made to this issue in the quotation from **Casti Connubii** on page 250 f., but it cannot be overemphasized since the Catholic attitude on this point is so frequently misunderstood.

Permanent or semipermanent procedures (such as irradiation of the ovaries, salpingectomy, vasotomy, vasectomy, cauterization, etc.) are gravely sinful if performed for the purpose of hindering conception. The evil of these procedures lies in the fact that in some of them spermatozoa are prevented from being deposited in the vagina; in other cases the ovum either does not develop at all, or is never allowed to pass through the Fallopian tubes down into the uterus. It is to be noted, however, that while it is gravely sinful for an individual to have these operations performed specifically in order to avoid conception, it is entirely legitimate to have these operations performed for certain other reasons (such as to remove tumors or cancerous tissue from these organs). In such cases, coition between married people, one or both of whom may have had such an operation, is permissible regardless of whether the operation was legitimate or not.

They should, however, seek to rectify the condition if this is possible.

Coitus interruptus (onanism properly so called) is gravely sinful because one of the essential requirements of the act is not fulfilled, i.e., depositing of the semen in the vagina.

Condoms are morally wrong because their use prevents the depositing of semen in the vagina. Since the spermatozoa are collected in the condom, which is then washed out or discarded, the sperm are not allowed to complete their normal activity, i.e., ascending into the uterus or Fallopian tubes in order to unite with a developed ovum. Use of a condom in regular sexual intercourse is strictly forbidden by moral theologians. But could a condom ever be used in order to collect semen for a male sterility test? It is universally maintained by theologians that use of a **sealed** condom for this purpose could never be allowed, since the effect of this would be the same as use of condoms during intercourse — the seed would not be deposited in the vagina.

On the other hand, would it be equally immoral to use a **perforated** condom? In the case of the perforated condom **some** semen would be retained in the condom, whereas **some** would be deposited in the vagina. Would this be considered a frustration of the sexual act?

At present there are two general opinions on the matter. Father Gerald Kelly, S.J., says that use of the perforated condom is "probably licit." An action is called "probably licit" when the moral goodness or evil of the act has not been estabished with complete certainty. Until the moral issues of the problem have been more clearly resolved, physicians may use the method, providing "there is some soundly probable reason for approving it."

While this method of obtaining seminal specimens is only "probably licit," Father Kelly lists four methods which moralists generally consider as licit:

1. The semen is accidentally obtained as a result of an involuntary emission.

2. Removal of semen, about an hour after normal coitus, from the genital tract of the wife.

3. Expression from the male urethra of the semen remaining there after normal coitus is completed.

4. The use of a vaginal cup — that is, of a rubber cup which is inserted in the vagina after coitus, and which will catch semen that would otherwise be lost.[1] (Some theologians add that the woman

---

[1] Gerald Kelly, S.J., "Moral Aspects of Sterlizing Tests and Artificial Insemination," *Linacre Quarterly,* 16:1 (January–April, 1949), p. 31.

would not be allowed to perform any action for the direct purpose of allowing the semen to flow into the cup until one hour has passed after intercourse. See p. 334 f. for further discussion.)

At the present time two of the most noted opponents of the perforated condom are Father Arthur Vermeersch, S.J., of the Gregorian University, Rome, now deceased, and Father Francis J. Connell, C.SS.R., of the Catholic University of America. Two noted theologians who consider the perforated condom as "probably licit" are Father J. McCarthy of Maynooth College, Ireland, and the late Father John J. Clifford, S.J., of St. Mary of the Lake Seminary, Mundelein, Illinois.

All other chemical and mechanical devices used by the woman (diaphragms, caps, tampons, pessaries, chemicals, jellies, etc.) which are used to hinder the action of the semen or to destroy it outright are gravely immoral.

Use of the douche for purposes of cleanliness after normal coitus is usually considered morally correct when one hour has elapsed after the act of intercourse. Use of the douche after that period will not be a hindrance to the action of the sperm. Probably even sooner the spermatozoa are beyond the effectiveness of a douche. However, if a woman at any time after intercourse were under the impression that the douche could be used as a contraceptive method and actually used one for that purpose, she would have subjective guilt.

ATTITUDE OF OTHER RELIGIONS ON CONTRACEPTION

Catholicism is joined by Orthodox Judaism in denouncing every method of contraception. Conservative and Reformed Judaism, on the other hand, both allow the use of contraception in some instances. The majority of Protestant sects either recommend its use or at least tolerate it in some circumstances. Mohammedanism is not opposed to contraception, but strongly forbids any type of abortion.

The Orthodox Jewish attitude is based on the command of God to the first parents, "Be fruitful and multiply." **The Book of Codes**[2] states that it is forbidden to bring out sperm and this sin is more grievous than all the transgressions of the Torah. In the same section is found a prohibition against any activities whatever that may arouse an unlawful sexual passion.

It is generally agreed by teachers of Orthodox Judaism that not only was Onan slain for a wasteful discharge of seed, but also that

---

[2] Aruch, Schulchan, Eben Haezer I, Chap. 23, *Laws of Marriage and Morals,* subject: "Bringing Out Sperm for No Good."

the generation of Noah was destroyed principally for the same reason.

The Orthodox Jewish position on the role of parenthood in the married state is that, except for unusual conditions, parents should have at least two children before they are entitled to practice even natural methods of birth control, such as the Rhythm or complete abstention.

The Conservative and Reform Jewish attitude toward contraception: according to these groups, **absolute prevention** of offspring would be reprehensible. On the other hand, they believe that **limitation** of offspring is, in some cases, desirable or at least permissible, even if couples resort to contraceptive methods. According to Talmudic teachers, certain situations warranted use of contraception:

1. When pregnancy endangered the life of the mother;
2. When pregnancy endangered the life of the child;
3. Where a child was likely to be stillborn;
4. Where children already born of the marriage are defectives, either mentally or physically.[3]

Since these views are based on economic, eugenic, and medical reasons, they will be discussed in a more detailed section on page 297.

The general Protestant attitude is one of toleration. There is no Protestant sect which is strictly opposed to contraception. Many groups leave the question to each married couple as a matter of their own conscience. The general argument is that married couples ought to have children if they are able; but if they feel that for some serious economic, eugenic, or medical reason, they cannot have more children, they may adopt contraceptive techniques.

Some Protestant sects have gone further than mere toleration. The Planned Parenthood Federation of America, Inc.,[4] lists five groups which have formally recognized contraception as **acceptable** to their religious views. These are:

1. The American Unitarian Association;
2. Lambeth Conference of Anglican Bishops;
3. The Methodist Church;
4. The Protestant Episcopal Church;
5. The Universalist General Convention.[5]

---

[3] This teaching was most notably expressed by MaHaRSHaL (Solomon Luria) (1510–1573).

[4] Prior to 1941 the Planned Parenthood Federation of America, Inc., was known as the Birth Control League.

[5] *Marriage Counsel in Relation to Planned Parenthood, An Outline for Clergymen* (New York: Planned Parenthood Federation of America, Inc., n.d.), p. 45.

In February, 1946, the Federal Council of Churches declared itself in favor of "planned parenthood" (which in the context implies contraception as well as other birth-control techniques). It was noted at the time that no biblical or patristic authority was cited in support of the decision and that no theological considerations had been involved. The secretary of the committee which drafted the recommendation, Doctor L. Foster Wood, is quoted as replying: "We don't have to bring in a theological basis for every social question. We think social questions have a theological significance in their own right."[6]

In June, 1954, the Augustana Body (membership 500,000) of the Lutheran Church **officially recommended** "planned parenthood" during its ninety-fifth annual synod:

> An unrestrained production of children without realistic regard to God-given responsibilities involved in rearing children . . . may be as sinful . . . and selfish as is the complete avoidance of parenthood. . . . The power to reproduce is His blessing, not a penalty, upon the sexual relationship in marriage.

The statement calls upon husbands and wives

> so to plan and govern their sexual relations that any child born to their union will be desired both for itself and in relation to the time of its birth. . . . Any planning for the number and spacing of the births of their children must be practiced prayerfully in accord with the fruits of the Spirit rather than in indulgence of the lusts of the flesh, and in the full freedom of the redeemed believer who feels his stewardship responsibility to his Lord.[7]

Erik W. Modean remarks on this in **The Christian Century,** "Three decades ago (the document) would have created a sensation. . . ."[8]

The Mohammedan Religion allows contraception, but forbids abortion. It forbids the destruction of life once the sperm and the ovum have been united, but it allows contraceptive techniques which would prevent union of sperm and ovum. (However, if the authority of the state declared that contraception was harmful to the welfare of the state, then it would become an immoral act of disobedience.)

---

[6] "Protestant Babies," *Time,* XLVII:5 (February 4, 1946), p. 46. The Federal Council is composed of 22 Protestant and 3 Orthodox sects whose total membership is approximately 29,000,000.

[7] Erik W. Modean, "Augustana Left to 'Go It Alone,'" *The Christian Century,* LXXI:27 (July 7, 1954), pp. 828–830. Reprinted by permission.

[8] *Ibid.*

The prohibition against abortion is considered by Mohammedan theologians as a logical deduction from those texts in the Koran which forbid the killing of children.[9] Since the fetus is a child **in utero,** it may not be killed any more than a child **ex utero.** Mohammedanism allows contraceptive techniques (notably **coitus interruptus)** which would prevent sperm from uniting with an ovum because, though there be **life** present in the separate sperm and ovum, they believe that it is not a **human** life.

The Mohammedans, in other words, look at the problem from consideration of what constitutes a human life. The Catholic and Orthodox Jewish attitude is based on a more fundamental consideration — the natural law — in this case upon the capacity of human reason to determine the precise nature and purpose of the function of sex. Since the culmination of the sexual act is obviously the deposition of semen in the vagina, the latter groups believe that the act must be allowed to achieve its natural end.

Nobody will deny that the truly human sexual act is far more than depositing semen in the vagina. Concomitant with it is a whole complexity of activities which engage man's emotional and even intellectual nature. The sexual act, properly performed, will cause an increase in mutual affection, in mutual aid, and will promote the ultimate good of both partners. But the **primary** physical end of the sexual act must not be overlooked. It would be safe to say that there are few activities which engage so many faculties of the human being all at once as does the sexual act. But the **whole act** has to be considered — not just one part of it. Pleasure which accompanies the sexual act is pleasure which accompanies every natural function: pleasure in rest, pleasure in activity, in eating, etc. The amount of pleasure associated with the act is in proportion to the importance of the vital function with which it is connected. Any one of these vital activities could be carried out merely for the pleasure it affords. The ancient Romans, for example, had a practice of tickling their throats after eating a heavy meal so that they might vomit up what they had eaten and begin eating again on an empty stomach. Most people today would consider this practice as disgusting. Yet the practice of contraception is like this: the final purpose of the action is subordinated to its pleasure.

With these considerations in view, one may see part of the fallacy

[9] Koran, Surah VI, 152. Also in Surah XVII, 31, where it is stated: "Slay not your children, fearing a fall to poverty. We shall provide for them and you. . . ."

in the following argument in a booklet of the Planned Parenthood Federation of America, Inc.:

> *The Groom:* I read somewhere that birth control is contrary to the natural law.
>
> *The Minister:* We should recognize that natural law rightly interpreted directs human beings to make use of forces in the natural world for the maximum benefit of the family and of society.
>
> Happy and reasonably frequent sexual union of husbands and wives is natural and beneficial. Since nature itself does not provide for the most desirable spacing of children, married people must themselves assume this responsibility.[10]

Before answering the question further, it should be pointed out that the author of the article is confused in his understanding of the natural law. The author is really speaking about the law of nature, whereas he should be speaking of the natural law itself, which is defined as:

> Practical universal judgments which man himself elicits. These (universal judgments) express necessary and obligatory rules of human conduct which have been established by the Author of human nature as essential to the divine purposes of the universe and have been promulgated by God solely through human reason.[11]

However, the confusion of the minister in regard to a definition of the natural law is the least serious error in his answer. Implicit in the answer is an almost complete denial of the spirituality of man — especially that phase of man's nature called free will. It is rather astounding that the answer comes from a minister serving the spiritual needs of his parish. The most serious mistake in the answer lies in the author's failure to consider the **complete** nature of man and the relation of man and his acts which is found in the natural law: Man can and has employed his intelligence to discover that he himself is free in **some** of his acts. That is to say, in some of his actions man has the capacity to act or not to act, depending upon the permissibility or nonpermissibility of the circumstances. By his same intelligence, man can also understand the nature and end of natural acts, including the sexual act. He recognizes that the climax of the sexual act is the

---

[10] Rev. L. Foster Wood, "Ethical Aspects of Marriage," *Marriage Counsel in Relation to Planned Parenthood, An Outline for Clergymen, op. cit.,* pp. 13–14.

[11] Thomas J. Higgins, S.J., *Man as Man* (Milwaukee: The Bruce Publishing Co., 1951), p. 88.

deposition of semen in the vagina. Therefore, when he performs the sexual act according to nature, he should expect the act to culminate in its natural climax (deposition of semen in the vagina). The fact that the sexual act does not **always** bring about the generation of a new human life is not the point at issue. Whether or not a life will follow is the prerogative of nature. Man's prerogative is to perform or not to perform the act. But if he performs the act, the natural effects must be allowed to follow.

There is all the difference in the world between abstaining from performing an act and performing the act but frustrating its end. This is why the Rhythm Method, **in itself,** is not a sinful practice. But, as mentioned before, use of the Rhythm Method can be morally wrong for those couples who, without grave excuse, regularly practice it over a long time, since they are avoiding one of the duties in their state of life — the procreation of children.

PRINCIPAL ARGUMENTS ADVANCED IN FAVOR OF CONTRACEPTION

The argument from the natural law which has been outlined before is a solid one and will hold against any objections which may be brought against it, if the argument is correctly understood. Proponents of contraception avoid coming to grips with this moral argument because there is no way of refuting it. They prefer, rather, to advance reasons from the fields of eugenics, economics, medicine, or sociology.

Economically, they see a danger of overpopulation if man continues to bring children into the world at the present ratio of increase. The reason most frequently advanced from the field of **sociology** is the difficulty of supporting larger families at the present time, and the close relation which is said to be found between crime and poverty. The **eugenic** argument is concerned with a desire to reduce the number of potential idiots and other undesirables who, it is alleged, are likely to be born from parents who have some kind of hereditary defect. **Medical** reasons advanced for contraception are based primarily on the desirability of eliminating therapeutic abortions at the very outset, i.e., by preventing a pregnancy from ever beginning. Contraception is also seen as a way of eliminating the large number of criminal abortions which are performed annually.

These arguments have been given wide distribution, so much so that today there are only 2 (Massachusetts and Connecticut) of the

48 states which oppose all media of disseminating contraceptive information.[12] In view of the fact that these arguments have been accepted uncritically by many in the populace who should know better, it may be profitable to show that **even on their own grounds** the arguments are far from accurate. When these questions are examined in any detail, one usually discovers either that they are based on rather doubtful premises, or they are at best mere expedients which advocates of the position admit in many cases fail to reach the heart of the problem.

Economic argument. The most common economic argument is that of population. The problem of overpopulation as something to be solved by birth control was first raised by an Anglican minister, Thomas Malthus, who in 1798 published his **Essay on the Principles of Population**[13] — a work which was intended to refute the opinions of Condorcet and Godwin,[14] both of whom had asserted that human institutions were the cause of poverty and vice, and that these latter could be eliminated if somehow or other it would be possible to bring about an equal distribution of property. Malthus opposed this view of Condorcet and Godwin, and said that poverty and vice were

---

[12] In 19 states there are no laws of any kind which control the dissemination of contraceptive information. These are Alabama, Florida, Georgia, Illinois, Kentucky, Maryland, New Hampshire, New Mexico, North Dakota, Oklahoma, Rhode Island, South Carolina, South Dakota, Tennessee, Texas, Utah, Vermont, Virginia, West Virginia. In 14 states there are laws which prevent *indiscriminate* dissemination of contraceptive information but exempt the medical profession either by implication or construction. These are: Arizona, Arkansas, California, Kansas, Louisiana, Maine, Michigan, Missouri, Mississippi, Nebraska, New Jersey, North Carolina, Pennsylvania, Washington. The laws of 13 states restrict dissemination of information but specifically declare that the prohibition does not apply to the medical profession. These states are: Colorado, Delaware, Idaho, Indiana, Iowa, Minnesota, Montana, Nevada, New York, Ohio, Oregon, Wisconsin, and Wyoming. Two states forbid any dissemination whatever of contraceptive information. These two states are Massachusetts and Connecticut.

The Federal Government, in an act of 1873, sometimes called *The Comstock Act,* forbade the use of the United States mails for the dissemination of contraceptive information (*U. S. Code Annotated,* tit. 18, par. 1461, "Mailing Obscene and Crime-inciting Matter"). In 1933, in the case of Davis *vs.* the United States, the Supreme Court ruled that to convict a person under this act it must be proven that the purpose of using the information is obscenity. Again in United States *vs.* Nichols, 1938, the Supreme Court ruled that dissemination of contraceptive information was not forbidden *absolutely* but only when such publications are unlawfully employed.

[13] Thomas Robert Malthus, *An Essay on the Principles of Population or a View of Its Past and Present Effects on Human Happiness, with an Inquiry into Our Prospects Respecting the Future Removal or Mitigation of the Evils which it occasions* (London: J. Murray, 1826).

[14] William Godwin, *Thoughts on Man, His Nature, Productions and Discoveries Interspersed with some Particulars Respecting the Author* (London: E. Wilson, 1831). For a study of Condorcet's views cf. J. Salwyn Schapiro, *Condorcet* (New York: Harcourt, Brace and Co., 1934).

the result of overpopulation. He affirmed that the food supply of the
world was increasing in an arithmetical progression (1, 2, 3, 4, 5, etc.)
whereas the human race was increasing in a geometrical progression
(1, 2, 4, 8, 16, etc.) and that a time would soon come when the food
supply would be insufficient for the number of human beings on
the earth.

Malthus taught that the situation could be avoided only by limiting
the number of human beings. He suggested that this could be done
by practicing the method of "moral restraint" — by which he meant
that couples should marry late in life, or not at all, or should limit
the number of children by self-control. Malthus never did advise the
use of contraception for controlling the population.

The followers of Malthus, however, took only **part** of his program
— i.e., his theory of maximum population. They ignored his teaching
on self-restraint and suggested something quite opposite — early marriage and the use of contraceptives.

The question to discuss with the Neo-Malthusians, then, is whether
or not their view of the causes of overpopulation is true.[15] In other
words, is it true that the population of the world is increasing at
such a rate that the world will soon be overcrowded and there will
not be enough food to go around? At the outset, it can be said that
in spite of starvation in some countries of the world, this fear of starvation for the world as a whole is still far away as long as governments
like our own continue to pay sums to farmers in order to keep them
from producing their maximum number of crops.

Proponents of the myth of overpopulation claim that the danger of
overpopulation has been brought about sooner than was once expected
because of the new medical cures which reduce the number of deaths
at an early age. They point to ancient Rome and Greece as countries
whose populations were kept down by war and disease. But Polybius,
one of the most authoritative of ancient historians, says that the
depopulation of Greece was caused not so much by war and disease
as it was by selfishness.[16] Moreover, while it is true that modern civili-

---

[15] In a sense, it could be said that there is a question which would be even more
primary than the one to be discussed. Is it *actually* true that the increase in population
is a universal fact? The answer is no. In 1850, for example, the population of both
France and Germany numbered approximately 35,000,000 each. In 1913, the population of France was 39,600,000 and that of Germany was 67,000,000. According to
Malthusian principles, they should have been the same.

[16] "In our own time Greece has been subject to a low birth rate and a general decrease of the population, owing to which cities have become deserted and the land has
ceased to yield, although there have neither been continuous wars nor epidemics. If then

zation has eliminated some diseases, there are others which are peculiar to the conditions of our own time. Spotted fever, for example, is contagious only under conditions of modern living. Even the bubonic plague which devastated so much of Europe during the Middle Ages, could only have spread under the conditions of crowded city life.

There is another point which could be raised as an objection on the economic level. That is that the whole Malthusian argument fails to accept the tremendous advancement which has been made in the fields of chemistry and agriculture. There is no convincing reason to believe that the sciences of chemistry and agriculture have exhausted themselves and that there is no hope for more development in the future. And, of course, the argument fails completely in any recognition of God's providence.

The economic argument is untenable in two respects. It is based on a supposition which is anything but certain and it simply asserts that some economic advantage is to be gained by limiting the population by contraception. At no time does it face the moral issue.

Sociological argument. The primary arguments from sociology are those concerning a child who is brought into a family where the income is so low that the child will have little chance of receiving a decent upbringing. It is argued that no married couple has the right to bring into the world more children than they can adequately support. The argument is entirely correct, and has been recognized as such.[17] But the difference of opinion lies in how this restriction of family is to be made. The contraceptionist says that limitation of

anyone had advised us to send and ask the gods about this, and find out what we ought to say or do, to increase in number and make our cities more populous, would it not seem absurd, the cause of the evil being in our own hands? For as men had fallen into such a state of pretentiousness, avarice and indolence that they did not wish to marry, or if they married to rear the children born to them, or at most as a rule but one or two of them, so as to leave these in affluence and bring them up to waste their substance, the evil rapidly and insensibly grew. For in cases where of one or two children the one was carried off by war and the other by sickness, it is evident that the houses must have been left unoccupied, and as in the case of swarms of bees, so by small degrees cities became resourceless and feeble" (Polybius, *Histories,* trans. W. R. Paton [New York: G. P. Putnam's Sons, 1927], pp. 383–385).

[17] Cf. Victor White, O.P.: ". . . the Church has constantly asserted the necessity of conjugal chastity, which is precisely the virtue of regulating intercourse and reproduction according to the requirements of right reason.

". . . The ideal fecundity is a *rational* fecundity. The Catholic will not advocate the instinctive fecundity of beasts and savages, but he will hold it to be generally desirable for a man to have as many children as he can *reasonably* and healthily bring up, having in mind all the circumstances" ("The Ethics of Contraception," *The Clergy Review,* VII [May, 1934], pp. 368–369).

offspring is to be effected by artificial methods which interfere with the natural processes. But, since these methods frustrate the end of the natural act and are, therefore, contrary to the natural law, they are not morally allowable. To permit contraception would violate the fundamental principles of ethics that the good end of an act never justifies an immoral means. The only acceptable solutions would be either those which limit marital acts to the sterile periods, or the practice of abstinence.

Another question to be raised in objection to the sociological argument is: What is to be considered a decent family wage? It is well recognized that a large number of those who are practicing contraception are members of the middle-income and higher-income brackets of society. Moreover, things which were looked upon as mere luxuries thirty years ago are considered as necessities today.

Eugenic argument. Eugenic arguments for contraception are based on the thesis that persons who are likely to produce offspring with some physical, moral, or mental defect should be prohibited from ever bringing them into the world, inasmuch as these offspring would more than likely constitute a drain upon society. One may say, first of all, that this view exaggerates the importance of intelligence and virtually equates intelligence with goodness. But a more serious objection lies in the question as to whether the laws of heredity are so perfectly established that their application will indicate infallibly the type of child that any family will produce. One should always assume a circumspect attitude toward the problem.

Contraceptionists are wont to point out the Jukes family in the United States as a notorious example of bad blood.[18] This particular case has been overemphasized. The Jukes study, like the other Kallikaks and Smoky Mountain Pilgrims, has been thoroughly discredited. The methods used in these studies were scarcely scientific. Lange's case in Denmark is less well known. Lange's conclusions are entirely opposite to those of the eugenicists.[19] Doctor F. Lange worked at the Middefart Asylum in Denmark, where he made a study of inmates of that institution and discovered that 70 of them came from 44 families. Some families had as many as 4 members in this institution. Lange checked their family records and discovered that

---

[18] R. L. Dugdale, *The Jukes, a Study in Crime, Pauperism, Disease and Heredity, Also Further Studies of Criminals* (New York: G. P. Putnam's Sons, 1877).

[19] F. Lange, *Degeneration in Families,* trans. by C. C. Sonne (London: Kimpton, 1907; also Glasgow: Stenhouse, 1907).

there had been 358 members who had had some kind of mental or nervous trouble. The argument looked good for the eugenicists; but Lange decided to check on the remaining members of these families. He was able to do so with 28 families and came up with surprising facts. Besides persons of average intelligence and ability, he found that these 28 families had produced:

  2 cabinet ministers
  1 ambassador
  3 bishops
  8 clergymen
  3 admirals
  3 generals
  3 supreme court judges
  4 headmasters
  8 consulting physicians
  9 university professors
 23 doctors of science or of arts
 20 poets
  9 musicians or composers
  8 actors and actresses
  2 inventors
 10 authors
 15 individuals who were either painters, sculptors,
     architects, or engravers

In addition to these there were a large number who had been members of Parliament, town councilors, physicians, teachers, businessmen, government officials, and two of the highest-ranking persons in Denmark at the time.

Discussion of the problem above has been made on the ground of the eugenicists themselves. There are, of course, arguments from other fields which should be considered. From the point of view of ethics, eugenic sterilization is prohibited. One can never injure the innocent; there is no ground for mutilation of an individual who has inflicted no harm. Sterilization might be permitted as punishment for a criminal in order to deter others from committing the same crime. But it is a well-established fact that sterilization has never accomplished this end. Moreover, if sterilization were used originally upon mental and social defectives, the time would soon come when the list of defectives would expand to include almost anybody who was undesirable for one reason or another. This has been the history of divorce, for example. Divorce began originally as acceptable on grounds of adultery. At the present time there is hardly any reason which is not acceptable to one group or other.

From a sociomedical view sterilization would be unsound, inasmuch as the individual sterilized could thereafter evade the procreative consequences of the sexual act. This would lead to a far greater spread of venereal disease.

Medical arguments. Advocates of contraception have suggested it as a means of saving the life of a mother who is unable to bear children without the almost certain possibility of death to herself and to the child. Thus, argue the contraceptionists, the mother of a family where there exist already one or two small children has an obligation to stay alive. No moralist will deny that a mother has an obligation to her family, and that she should have only the number of children which she can properly bear and bring up. But the point at issue is again, how is the problem to be solved? The contraceptionist recommends sexual intercourse as usual except that contraceptive practices are to be adopted. The moralist cannot allow the solution again on the ground that the use of contraceptives is against the natural law itself. If there is an acceptable solution to the problem, it must be one in accordance with the natural law. The two solutions which are now known for this problem are use of the Rhythm or the practice of abstinence. Given sufficiently strong motives, a married couple should be able to sublimate the most part of their sexual drive.

A second medical argument proposed by contraceptionists is that contraceptives would reduce the number of abortions which take place annually. Doctor Frank Taussig made a study in which he indicates that there must be close to 700,000 abortions annually in the United States.[20] This would mean that there is a ratio of 1 abortion to every 3 confinements. Of these 700,000, between 25 and 30 per cent are therapeutic abortions, i.e., induced because of the possibility of death resulting if the fetus is allowed to develop to full term. The remainder (70 per cent to 75 per cent) of abortions are criminal.

Probably one half of these criminal abortions are performed by irregular practitioners, the dregs of an otherwise honorable profession. Another half of these criminal abortions are performed by laymen. Taussig's study indicates that the annual death rate from criminal

[20] Frank J. Taussig, *Abortion, Spontaneous and Induced. Medical and Social Aspects* (St. Louis: C. V. Mosby Co., 1936), p. 26. Taussig's final figure is 681,000 abortions. He arrives at his figure on the basis of statistics compiled separately by Macomber in Boston, Kopp in New York State, and Plass in Iowa.

abortion must be close to 8000.[21] He also asserts that 90 per cent of abortions occur among married women, the majority of whom are between 25 and 35 years of age. There is no substantial evidence that the use of contraceptives has cut down the number of abortions. In fact, if anything, it tends to increase them, since a fetus which develops in spite of contraceptive precautions will still be destroyed if the mother gets anxious enough about it.

Needless to say, all direct abortion is contrary to the natural law (cf. **Moral Aspects of Marriage, p. 523 f.**). Proponents of therapeutic abortion say that destruction of the fetus is necessary to save the mother's life, although many of them will admit that destruction of a fetus in itself is morally wrong. Again the problem is to be solved by the ethical principle that a good end never justifies employing evil means to get to the end. Since destruction of a fetus is the destruction of a human life, and since the fetus is itself innocent, no man nor the state has any right directly to deprive it of life.

It may be said in answer to all the foregoing arguments that none of them is solidly established in its own field. None of them even considers the morality of the act. All of them admit frequently that the method is far from being a completely satisfactory solution.[22] This is to be noticed especially in the Lambeth Resolution drawn up by the Anglican bishops of England. Again it is to be found in the resolution adopted by the Central Conference of American Rabbis in 1929:

> . . . We earnestly desire to guard against playing into the hands of those who would undermine the sanctity of the time-honored institutions through reckless notions and practices. We are especially mindful of the noble tradition obtaining among the Jewish people with respect to the holiness of domestic relations. But, at the same time, we are keenly aware of the many serious evils caused by a lack of birth regulation among those who, by reason of lack of health or of a reasonable measure of economic resources, or of intelligence or all these, are prevented from giving to their children that worthy heritage to which all children are entitled. We, therefore, urge the recognition of the im-

---

[21] *Ibid.*, p. 28. *Re* abortion, Taussig says, "No other group is in a position to appreciate as we do the damage it inflicts upon the integrity of the family." It should be noted that methods of treatment devised since Taussig's estimate of morality have greatly reduced this figure.

[22] To accept contraception as a practical solution without regard to its intrinsic immorality is an unwise procedure. If a patient complained of a headache to his physician, the physician might cut off the patient's head. It would certainly eliminate the headache. But would it be the wisest solution?

portance of intelligent birth regulation as one of the methods of coping with said problems.[23]

Beside the somewhat plausible arguments which have been already advanced for birth control, there are others which border on the lunatic fringe. Take for example the following argument which is found in a booklet issued by the Planned Parenthood Association of America, Inc.:

> *Planned parenthood is a democratic concept* [italics theirs]. It expresses the idea that parents shall have the first choice as to the progeny they will bring into the world. It stands in contrast to the Fascist dogma that parenthood shall be regulated by an authoritarian state.[24]

Is the reader to draw the analogy, then, that since the universe is dominated by physical laws, we are to be considered slaves? Again, is it true that planned parenthood, by which the author intends mostly contraception, is possible only by contraceptive techniques? By no means. It has been shown already that Rhythm and abstinence are **possible,** and practicable.

In another booklet[25] the same organization discusses the question of Rhythm and says that it is merely "a concession by the hierarchy" to those members of the church who desire some kind of birth control. Previous discussion on the subject has shown that there is a total difference in the nature of acts of contraception and of Rhythm. But it may be repeated for another time that Rhythm, **in itself,** does not frustrate the natural end of the sexual act (depositing of semen in the vagina). Rhythm would be morally wrong, however, if practiced for no grave reason, since the husband and wife would be negligent of fulfilling one of the duties of the marital state.

GENERAL ARGUMENTS AGAINST CONTRACEPTION

Few if any advocates of contraception ever take the providence of God into account. But it is a matter of Revelation that God never tempts a man beyond his own strength.[26] In view of this fact, a

[23] A. J. Rongy, "Birth Control," *The Universal Jewish Encyclopedia,* 1940, Vol. 2, pp. 380–381.

[24] *Planned Parenthood* (New York: Planned Parenthood Federation of America, Inc., n.d.), p. 5.

[25] *Marriage Counsel in Relation to Planned Parenthood, An Outline for Clergymen, op. cit.,* p. 46.

[26] Cf. 2 Cor. 12:9. Cf. also the discussion of this point by Pope Pius XI in his encyclical *Casti Connubii,* "On Christian Marriage," with discussion-club outline by Rev. Gerald C. Treacy, S.J. (New York: The Paulist Press, n.d.).

married couple who must face the recognized difficulty of either periodic or sustained abstinence may expect the grace of God to maintain them, provided they co-operate with that grace.

In the section on Rhythm it was emphasized that even under normal circumstances the practice of periodic abstinence heightens sexual pleasure in the same way as a man who has gone without food for a day enjoys a meal more than the man who has just finished a ten-course dinner.

There is also the danger that contraception may foster incompatibility. The truly human sexual act is more than a mere physical sensation of pleasure. Tied in with it is a complexity of emotions, the true aesthetic experience which engages mind, heart, and will of both parties: the desire to rest in the beloved, the desire for the beloved, the joy of mutual understanding, the alliance of purpose. More than they often realize, individuals are reaching for a perfection which they will only find in God. Frequently a couple who are performing the sexual act are really not intent so much upon the act as they are upon everything else that is concomitant with the act. Such a couple could sublimate the act by disengaging the emotional from the physical part of the act and by releasing these same emotions through a more licit procedure than contraception.

There are, of course, far more practical reasons against contraception. For one reason, those who now are engaged in contraceptive practices would not be here to practice it if an ancestor of theirs had adopted the technique. Another reason is that frequent resort to contraception tends to exaggerate the emotional and vegetal nature of man to the detriment of his intellectual faculties. This danger is present at any time when the emotional factor is overemphasized, but it is especially so in the case of contraceptive techniques.

SOME ARGUMENTS FOR THE DESIRABILITY OF HAVING CHILDREN

It may be said that a woman reaches her highest function in the role of motherhood. Parenthood is the participation of two created human agents in one of the most sublime functions which God has ever given to mankind, i.e., setting the conditions for creation of another human soul. One of the great gifts which God gave to Abraham was to promise him an increase of his descendants. Men and women, in carrying out the sexual act, are fulfilling one more of the potentialities with which they are endowed as social beings.

CHAPTER XXI

Infertility

JOHN J. KUHN

Sterility may be defined as the inability to conceive (impotentia generandi). Any couple who have not produced a child within three years of marriage should be presumed to be sterile.

The problem of infertility offers a challenge to the physician. Its successful treatment not only affords the married pair a new outlook on life but is also a source of great satisfaction to the doctor.

Through the history of mankind sterility has always been a problem. Hippocrates, the father of medicine and one of the first scientific workers in the field, developed a unique test to determine the possibility of conception. In a barren woman he recommended that a piece of garlic be placed near the uterus. At a later interval, if the smell of garlic could be detected on her breath, he felt that she could become pregnant. This crude test was one of the first to determine tubal patency.

References to sterility are made in both the Old and New Testaments. When Sarah found that she was not having children, she sent Abraham in to her maid Hegar, who subsequently bore Abraham a child.[1] Later Sarah herself conceived. The development of pregnancy in a woman previously sterile after the adoption of a child is a well-recognized phenomenon. In the New Testament the conception of John the Baptist in the old age of Elizabeth and Zachary is afforded prominent mention.[2]

ANATOMY AND PHYSIOLOGY

STERILITY

In order to understand the problem of the barren couple, certain fundamental facts of male and female genital anatomy and physiology

---

[1] Gen. 16:1–14. [2] Lk. 1:18–25.

must be understood. In the female, the essential organs for reproduction are the ovary, the Fallopian tube, and the uterus. Each of these organs has special adaptive features for the role which it plays in conception and pregnancy. These features are discussed in detail in Chapters II and XVII and will not be repeated here.

Sterility may be primary or secondary. The **primary cases** are those in which no pregnancy has ever occurred. The **secondary cases** are those in which sterility supervenes after a period of fertility. Most of the secondary cases are the result of an infection usually either puerperal or gonorrheal which produces a block in one of the passageways through which the ovum or spermatozoon must travel.

In **primary cases** many factors may play a part. Either the male or female partner may be at fault and both should be investigated. It was formerly believed that the female partner was usually at fault. This is not true. Studies of sterile couples show the male to be at fault in about 40 per cent of the cases.[3]

The **more common causes of primary sterility** are:

1. Constitutional diseases, such as tuberculosis and diabetes;
2. Faulty nutrition;
3. Faulty development of the spermatozoa;
4. Obstruction or occlusion in the male genital tract;
5. Stenosis of cervix or vagina or some other obstruction in the female genital tract such as tubal occlusion;
6. Defective endometrium;
7. Defective ovulation or defective ova;
8. Hostility of secretions in either male or female genital tracts;
9. Endocrine disturbances;
10. Defective coital technique;
11. Psychogenic.[4]

EXAMINATION FOR STERILITY

When a couple who have been married for some time and are infertile consult a doctor as to their problem, no cursory examination is likely to solve the case. A detailed history, comprehensive physical examination, and laboratory tests are necessary of both the husband and wife.

[3] *Texas State J. of Med.* (May, 1941), p. 21. Raoul Palmer, M.D., *New Problems in Medical Ethics,* ed. Dom Peter Folld, O.S.B., Vol. 2, p. 6.

[4] John R. Cavanagh, "Notes on Subjects Important in the Study of Pastoral Medicine" (1946), p. 115.

The Examination of the Male

The program for the husband is carried out first as these studies are less painful and time-consuming than those of the wife. A program for the male would be as follows:

1. History and physical examination;
2. Laboratory examinations:
   a) General — blood count, urinalysis, chest X ray, basal metabolism, and any other indicated studies;
   b) A study of the prostatic secretions and the semen.

In the **history,** special attention is paid to data that have a bearing on reproductive life. Questions are directed toward the family history of childbearing, adverse habits that have a bearing on fertility such as excessive use of tobacco, overwork, and lack of proper rest.[5] Also the man is questioned regarding any past history of marital relations. It is occasionally a matter of surprise for an infertile couple to learn that cohabitation takes place so frequently at times when conception is unlikely.

In the **physical examination,** special attention is paid to those factors which have a known bearing on male sterility. Among these factors are endocrine disturbances such as hypothyroidism, systemic disturbances such as tuberculous and local diseases of the genitalia (e.g., chronic gonorrhea) and congenital diseases of the same organs (e.g., hypospadias, a condition in which the opening of the male urethra is on the underside of the penis, thus preventing the ejaculate of semen from being deposited near the cervix).

Of the laboratory examinations the most important is the **examination of the semen** (see Chapter VI). One sperm count is not diagnostic; several should be done. Pregnancy can take place with quite low counts but as the number decreases the chance of success is decreased.[6]

The Collection of the Semen

The problem confronting the Catholic physician and patient is

[5] Alton Ochsner, *Smoking and Cancer* (New York: Julian Messner, Inc., 1954).

[6] S. A. Kaufman, "What Is Normal Semen," *Human Fertility,* Vol. 2, no. 1 (March, 1946); Gerald Kelly, S.J., *Medico-Moral Notes,* Part 2 (St. Louis: The Catholic Hospital Ass'n. of the U. S. and Canada, 1951), p. 15 ff.; Roy E. Krigbaum, "An Aid in the Study of Sterility," *Am. J. Obst. and Gynec.,* Vol. 34 (December, 1937), pp. 1046–1047; Joseph B. Doyle, "The Cervical Spoon: A New Method of Semen Sampling and Assaying Spermigration; A Preliminary Report," *J. Urology,* Vol. 60, no. 6 (December, 1948), pp. 986–987, 989; Max Huhner, *The Diagnosis and Treatment of Sexual Disorders in the Male and Female* (Philadelphia: F. A. Davis Co., 1937).

the method of collecting the specimen of semen. For the non-Catholic physician this usually presents no problem; he collects masturbatory specimens in a sterile glass container and sends them to the laboratory. This method is not available to those physicians guided by Catholic moral code. See Chapter XXII for a complete description of the various methods proposed on the collection of semen and a discussion of their morality.

EXAMINATION OF THE WOMAN

If the status of the husband is found to be satisfactory, the next step is to proceed to the study of the wife. As this study is a more painful and time-consuming procedure, it is usually left until the husband has been evaluated. If the husband is sterile there is no need to proceed with the examination of the wife. A definite program is once again prescribed, as follows:

1. Complete history and physical examination;
2. Laboratory examination which usually includes chest X ray, blood count, urinalysis, basal metabolism or other tests of thyroid function, and any other tests which may be indicated;
3. Specific studies of the reproductive apparatus to determine the status of fertility — this would include:
    a) Careful internal examination of the female genitalia to exclude the presence of organic disease, e.g., inflammation, tumors, congenital abnormality, etc.;
    b) Determination of ovulation by:
        1) Endometrial biopsy,
        2) Vaginal smears,
        3) Temperature curves;
    c) Determination of Fallopian tubal patency by:
        1) Injection of carbon-dioxide gas (Rubin test),
        2) X-ray study of the tubes after injection of a suitable radiopaque dye to outline them;
    d) Huhner test.

In the history of the wife, questions are asked that may have a special bearing on the problem at hand in addition to obtaining a general medical history. One is interested in obtaining information on the family history of childbearing, any past pregnancies by a previous marriage or otherwise. Details are sought on diet, hygiene, menstrual disturbances, and marital habits. The general physical examination is done to exclude medical disease that may have some

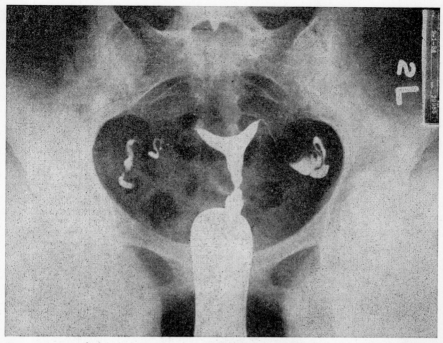

X-ray picture showing lipiodal injection of normal Fallopian tubes. The rounded white shadow at bottom of picture is the speculum used to dilate the vagina. The large central three-pointed shadow is the cavity of the uterus filled with lipiodal. The scattered white areas on the sides of the pelvis represent lipiodal in the Fallopian tubes. (Courtesy of Dr. Alfred Den.)

bearing on the infertility problem and, if normal, to give the patient further reassurance. The general laboratory procedures are done for the same purpose. The examination of the reproductive organs will show any organic bar to pregnancy.

The two most important procedures in the study of the female are:
1. The determination of tubal patency;
2. The establishment of the presence or absence of ovulation.

It is essential that at least one Fallopian tube be open and that ovulation be present for a woman to conceive. The first study on the Fallopian tube usually made is the **Rubin Test**. This test was first devised by Isadore Rubin of New York and was a real milestone in the study and treatment of sterile women. Air was used at first in the test but as it presented a danger from an occasional air embolism, carbon dioxide (a more absorbable gas) has replaced it. The test consists in the insufflation of the Fallopian tubes by an apparatus especially designed for that purpose. This device allows carbon dioxide to be released in measured amounts under the control of the operator. A fall in pressure noted as the gas escapes from the uterus through the Fallopian tubes denotes tubal patency. This can be recorded by a kymograph.

If patency of the tubes cannot be demonstrated by this method, the next procedure would be to visualize the tubes by X ray. This is done by injecting a contrast medium of a radiopaque material. X rays are then taken which will frequently show the location of any obstruction.

Whether or not ovulation has taken place is shown by the **endometrial biopsy.** The endometrium or lining of the uterus is a mirror of ovarian activity. After the ovum, or egg, has left the ovary, a

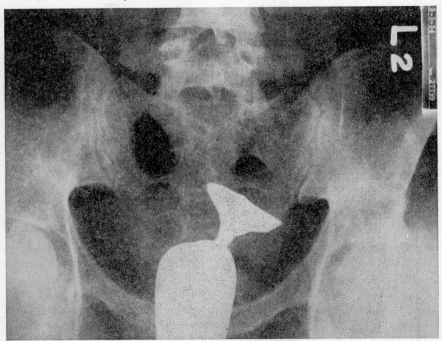

Lipiodal injection of occluded Fallopian tubes. The rounded white shadow at the bottom of the picture is the speculum used to dilate the vagina. The triangular white shadow represents lipiodal in the cavity of the uterus. None of the lipiodal has gotten into the Fallopian tubes. (See normal injection, p. 311.) (Courtesy of Dr. Alfred Den.)

hormone, progesterone, is elaborated from the bed in which the egg was enclosed while in the ovary. This hormone makes the lining of the uterus rich in glands, blood vessels, and nutrient so that it will be a fit receptacle for the ovum if it is fertilized. If this lining is partially scraped from the uterus and suitably prepared for microscopic examination, the character of the cells and glands proves whether or not ovulation has taken place. This particular test is as a rule done on the first day of menstruation. This test is the most reliable method of determining ovulation (see p. 270). For other tests of ovulation see p. 270 f.

PSYCHOGENIC STERILITY

No real studies have been made on the subject of psychogenic sterility, although there has been an increasing awareness of the subject.[7]

The recognition of a psychic factor in the sterility which ceases when a child is adopted is relatively easy. Other types of psychogenic sterility are more difficult to recognize and understand. Fear is probably a potent factor in such cases. Fear of pregnancy can cause sterility by producing spasm of the uterotubal musculature. It is well known that muscular tension resulting from anxiety may affect involuntary muscles elsewhere in the body. The effect of the emotions on the musculature of the bronchial and gastrointestinal organs is well known. The same type of spasm affecting the muscles of the uterotubal junction could easily produce a tubal occlusion. This, of course, represents only one possibility. There are, unfortunately, no

---

[7] Cf. following as examples: Helene Deutsch, "Introduction to the Discussion of the Psychological Problems of Pregnancy," *Problems of Early Infant Care* (New York: Josiah Macy, Jr., Foundation, 1948), p. 12; F. M. Hanson and J. Rock, "The Effect of Adoption on Fertility and Other Reproductive Functions," *Am. J. Obst. and Gynec.,* Vol. 59 (1950), pp. 311–319; G. R. Kamman, "The Psychosomatic Aspects of Sterility," *J.A.M.A.,* Vol. 130 (1946), pp. 1215–1218; K. Kelley, "Sterility in the Female with Special Reference to Psychic Factors," Review of Literature, *Psychosomatic Med.,* Vol. 4 (1942), pp. 211–222; W. S. Kroger and S. C. Freed, "Psychosomatic Aspects of Sterility," *Am. J. Obst. and Gynec.,* Vol. 59 (1950), pp. 867–874; D. W. Orr, "Pregnancy Following Decision to Adopt," *Psychosomatic Med.,* Vol. 3 (1941), pp. 441–446; J. P. Pratt, quoted by H. C. Walser, "Fear an Important Etiological Factor in Obstetric Problems," *Am. J. Obst. and Gynec.,* Vol. 55 (1948), p. 801; L. L. Robbins, "Psychological Study of Sterility in Women," *Bull. Menn. Clinic,* Vol. 7 (1943), pp. 41–44; J. J. Rommer, "Psychoneurogenic Causes of Sterility and Their Treatment," *West. J. Surg. Obst. and Gynec.,* Vol. 55 (1947), pp. 278–287; B. B. Rubinstein, "Emotional Factors in Female Sterility," *Am. Soc. Study of Sterility* (June 7, 1949); J. Stallworthy, "Facts and Fantasy in Study of Female Infertility," *J. Obst. and Gynaec. Brit. Emp.,* Vol. 55 (1948), pp. 171–180.

controlled studies on this subject. The very nature of the disorder makes such studies very difficult. The effects of the emotions on the menses however show how responsive the pelvic organs are to these influences.

Tubal spasm has been noted in a number of studies including tubal fluoroscopy. Such spasm is not always relieved by sedatives. However, it has been reported that women so heavily sedated that they were almost asleep during intercourse became pregnant, although previously sterile.[8]

The condition should be suspected when the physical and endocrinologic studies are negative. In some cases the studies themselves are therapeutic. The tubal insufflation may relieve spasm and in some individuals the discomfort and pain associated with the studies may satisfy a need for punishment. This satisfaction may then result in relief of tension. The treatment of psychogenic sterility should be primarily psychotherapeutic. In occasional cases simple reassurance may be sufficient to bring relief.[9] More thorough psychotherapy is usually needed. This may be given by a psychosomatically oriented gynecologist but psychotherapy of any depth is best done by a psychiatrist.

ARTIFICIAL INSEMINATION

In cases where the husband and wife are unable to have children by ordinary means, and where the couple do not wish to adopt a child, the marriage counselor may be asked about artificial insemination. In the broad sense, this term refers to any process whereby a woman becomes impregnated with semen with the aid of any artificial means.[10]

Reports by Seymour and Koerner and by Murphy and Farris show that artificial insemination may be easily performed by any doctor. Murphy and Farris report that out of 57 inseminations they were able to produce 10 pregnancies. The time of insemination was coincident with the period of ovulation of the woman. This was determined by the rat ovulation test which Farris had developed previously.[11]

[8] W. S. Kroger and S. C. Freed, *Psychosomatic Gynecology* (Philadelphia: W. B. Saunders Co., 1951), p. 291.

[9] *Ibid.*

[10] Rev. William K. Glover, *Artificial Insemination Among Human Beings* (Washington, D. C.: Catholic University of America Press, 1948), p. VII of Introduction.

[11] D. P. Murphy and E. J. Farris, "Treatment of Sterility: Insemination Timed by Rat Ovulation Test," *J.A.M.A.*, Vol. 138, no. 1 (September 4, 1948), pp. 13–14.

In each of these cases the semen used was obtained from the husband. Seymour and Koerner made a survey in which a total of 9489 cases of women impregnated by the method of artificial insemination was reported. Out of this group 5480 were impregnated with semen from their husbands while 3649 were impregnated with semen obtained from some male other than the husband.[12]

There are two possible methods of artificial insemination:

1. **Donor insemination** by some male other than the husband. This violates the natural law in that the marital right to sexual relations must be exercised personally. It cannot be delegated. This method was specifically condemned by the Holy Father.[13]

2. **Insemination by the husband. Insemination by the use of the semen of the husband is permissible only when the semen is obtained by natural intercourse with his wife.** This semen may not then be removed from the vagina but may be assisted by a syringe or other method to gain entry into the cervix of the uterus.

In Chapter XXII, various methods of obtaining semen for examination are discussed. It is now necessary to discuss how such a specimen, once obtained, may be inserted into the genital tract. A better understanding of the difficulties involved is had when the three classes of artificial insemination are distinguished. Artificial insemination **in the strict sense** is any attempt to produce fertilization by other than natural means. Artificial insemination **in the less strict sense** is any act whereby the semen ejaculated into the woman's vagina in normal sexual intercourse is collected by a syringe and expressed into the external os, cervical canal, or uterus to offer a better chance at pregnancy. **In a very wide sense,** it is when an instrument is used to facilitate normal intercourse and to increase thereby the possibility of conception.[14]

The following methods have been suggested as a means of obtaining spermatozoa for insemination: masturbation, natural onanism (withdrawal), artificial onanism (condom), rectal massage of the prostate and the seminal vesicles and pressure put on the ampullae of the vas deferens, and, last, puncture of the testicles or epididymides. All of these are now considered illicit but for a time some theologians felt

---

[12] F. I. Seymour and A. Koerner, "Artificial Insemination: Present Status in the United States as Shown by Recent Survey," *J.A.M.A.*, Vol. 116, no. 25 (June 21, 1941), pp. 2747–2749.

[13] Pope Pius XII, Discourse of His Holiness Pope Pius XII to the Fourth International Congress of Catholic Doctors, Rome (September 29, 1949).

[14] Glover, *op. cit.*, p. 65.

that puncture of the testicles to obtain sperm was permissible. In justice to these theologians it must be emphasized that they expressed their opinions prior to the addresses of the Holy Father on this subject. It is now clear that this method is no longer tenable. As for the other methods enumerated, they are intrinsically wrong and can never be licitly performed even though the husband of the woman be used to obtain the sperm to fertilize her. Father Kelly in 1939 used an argument to show that the husband and wife could use artificial means to produce offspring that went like this:

> . . . so it seems that married people, when unable to generate by the normal means of sexual intercourse, may use abnormal means, provided that these means be not sinful.[15]

It seemed like a sound argument. If a man is unable to eat in the normal way, he can have food intravenously. Why not in the case of the generative act? The answer is found in the address of the Holy Father to the Italian Catholic Union of Midwives:

> In its natural structure, the conjugal act is a personal action, a simultaneous and immediate cooperation on the part of the husband and the wife which by the very nature of the agents and the propriety of the act is the expression of the mutual gift which according to Holy Scripture brings about "union in one flesh only." This is something much more than the union of the two seeds which may be brought about even artificially, without the natural action of husband and wife. The conjugal act, ordained and willed by nature, is a personal act of cooperation, the right to which husband and wife give each other when they marry.[16]

On March 24, 1897, the Holy Office issued a decree approved by Pope Leo XIII that condemned artificial fecundation as illicit. But all theologians did not agree as to the exact content of the condemnation. Some said it condemned all artificial insemination without qualification, while others said it referred only to that type in which the material was obtained through masturbation. Palmieri, who at first held that if the husband and wife could not have natural intercourse they could use the semen if the husband obtained the specimen by masturbation since this ejaculation was directed to the fecundation of a lawful spouse, withdrew his opinion when this condemnation was expressed. Berardi consulted with four learned theologians on the

15 Quoted by Glover, *ibid.*, p. 117.
16 Pope Pius XII, *op. cit.*

subject of this condemnation, and they were all in agreement that it did not include all the possible means available at the time, but only those that involved masturbation and pollution. These were the only "strict means" in use at the time of the decree.[17] Those who held this decree included withdrawal of semen from the epidermis were Cappello, De Smet, Eschbach, Jone, Iorio, Noldin-Schmitt, Sabetti-Barrett, and some others less well known. Father Mahoney was of the opinion that the Holy Office forbade any means used to fecundate the woman artificially and this seems to be substantiated by the statements of Pius XII in his addresses of 1949 and 1951.[18]

The question may then be asked: What methods are available for artificial insemination? There would seem to be only two: (a) the injection of semen obtained from natural intercourse, and (b) the use of the cervical spoon. In the first of these, after natural intercourse between a husband and his wife, a syringe collects the semen deposited in her vagina. Then it is forced further up into the genital tract to aid the natural process. Cappello is quite sure of the liceity of this action:

> Fecundation improperly so-called is licit, not only probably or more probably as some hold, but certainly in our opinion (provided it is done for a just cause) because natural copulation is had.[19]

It is held by some theologians that the syringe is not to be removed from the precincts of the vagina.[20] This method also seems to be licit in the light of the address of the Holy Father to the physicians in 1949. This method might be more correctly termed **artificial assistance to insemination,** since the natural act takes place. Father Connell holds that a physician may licitly use a syringe to aid nature after the married couple have had relations.[21] This opinion is also held by Genicot-Salsmans, Jone, Iorio, Vermeersch, Palmieri, and Sabetti-Barrett. In the second available method the cervical spoon (Doyle) is inserted into the vagina before intercourse to facilitate passage of the spermatozoa into the womb. There is no moral problem in the use of the spoon and a syringe may be used to facilitate the passage of the sperm retained in the spoon to higher levels in the genital tract.

The morality of artificial insemination should be discussed in reference to a **whole** view of man and his acts. The Catholic philosopher

---

[17] Berardi, *Theologia Moralis,* II, 427, n. 891.
[18] Mahoney, *Clergy Review,* Vol. 25 (June, 1945), pp. 268–270.
[19] Cappello, *De Matrimonio,* 450, n. 382, ad 4.
[20] McFadden, Merkelbach, Ubach, and Payen.
[21] Francis J. Connell, C.SS.R., *Ecclesiastical Review* (December, 1944), p. 445.

and theologian look upon man as a creature who has been created "in the image and likeness of God." The image of God which is stamped upon man is the rational soul with its activities of intellect and of will. By these two activities, man is raised higher than the strictly material world in which the lower grades of living beings and the nonliving world find themselves immersed. The specific difference between man and the animals about him is the supremacy of his spirit. Whatever he does, then, must be directed toward the supremacy of that spirit. As Father Tesson remarks:

> Since his end is to establish in himself the reign of the spirit and of charity, (man) can do so only by submitting himself to the plan itself which is written in his nature and which expresses his likeness to God. Seen in this perspective, the human body takes on, the instrument of the soul, a value which lifts it above the level of a mere animal body. . . .[22]

In the light of these principles we can readily understand the position of Pope Pius XII on artificial insemination as he expressed it in his allocution to the Fourth International Congress of Italian Doctors on September 29, 1949.

> The doctor would not respond fully to the ideal of his vocation, if, while making profitable use of the most recent discoveries in medical science and art, he brought into play, in his role of a practitioner, only his intelligence and his skill, and failed to bring in also . . . we would even say, above all . . . his human heart and that charitable delicacy which belongs to him as a Christian. He does not work "in anima vili"; he acts directly on bodies, it is true, but on bodies animated by an immortal, spiritual soul, and — in virtue of the mysterious but indissoluble connection between the physical and moral — his action is efficacious on the body only if he acts at the same time on the soul.
>
> Whether he is dealing with the body or with the human composite in its unity, the Christian doctor will be always on his guard against the fascination of technique, against the temptation to apply his knowledge and his art to other ends than the treatment of the patients entrusted to him. Thank God, he will never have to be on his guard against another, a criminal, temptation to use, in the service of base interests, unavowable passions and in human crimes, the gifts hidden by God in the heart of nature.

---

[22] R. P. Tesson, S.J., "Artificial Insemination and the Moral Law," *New Problems in Medical Ethics,* Vol. 2, ed. Dom Peter Flood (Westminster: The Newman Press, 1954), p. 38.

. . . natural and Christian morality have everywhere their imprescriptible rights. It is from them, and not from any consideration of feelings, or of materialist, naturalist philanthropy, that the essential principles of medical deontology are derived; the dignity of the human body, the fraternity of all men, the sovereign dominion of God over life and destiny. . . .

. . . We cannot allow the present opportunity to pass without indicating, briefly and in broad outline, the judgment of morality on this latter (artificial insemination):

1. The practice of this artificial insemination, when it concerns a human being, cannot be considered, either exclusively or even principally, from the biological and medical view, while ignoring that of morality and of right.

2. Artificial insemination, outside marriage, is to be condemned purely and simply as immoral.

   The Natural Law and the Divine Positive Law lay down that the procreation of new life may be the fruit of marriage only. . . .

3. Artificial insemination in marriage, but produced by the active element of a third person, is equally immoral, and, as such, to be condemned outright.

   The husband and the wife have alone a reciprocal right over their bodies in order to engender new life. . . .

4. As to the lawfulness of artificial insemination in marriage, let it suffice for the moment that We recall to your minds these principles of the Natural Law: the mere fact that the result envisaged is attained by this means, does not justify the use of the means itself; nor is the desire of the husband and wife to have a child — in itself a very legitimate desire — sufficient to prove the legitimacy of having recourse to artificial insemination, which would fulfill this desire. It would be wrong to hold that the possibility of having recourse to this means would render valid the marriage between persons incapable of contracting it because of *impedimentum impotentiae.*

On the other hand, there is no need to point out that the active element can never lawfully be procured by acts contrary to nature.

Although one cannot exclude new methods "a priori" simply because they are new, nevertheless, as regards artificial insemination, not only is extreme caution called for, but the matter must be absolutely dismissed. In speaking thus, we do not imply that the use of certain artificial means solely destined either to facilitate the natural act or to cause the natural act normally accomplished to attain its end, are necessarily forbidden.

Let it not be forgotten that the procreation of new life according to the will and plan of the Creator, *alone* brings with it, and that to an astonishing degree of perfection, the realization of the ends pursued.[23]

In this talk the Pope also states that it is never permissible for an unmarried woman to be artificially inseminated, nor for a married woman to be impregnated with semen from any male other than her husband. If one were to consider the problem from a strictly physiological viewpoint, there would seem to be no problem whatever. But if the problem is viewed in relation to the whole marriage state, then a number of other problems arise.

Insemination of an unmarried woman brings with it the same trail of social, psychological, and physical difficulties as the pregnancy of any unmarried woman brings no matter how the child was conceived.

Insemination of a married woman by a male other than her husband is a plain case of adultery. According to the marriage contract, a man and woman promise each other, among other things, that they will give exclusive sexual rights to each other. The husband will have sexual relations with no other woman but this one, so long as she lives. The wife, in turn, promises that all her sexual activity will be confined to this man and to no other, as long as he lives. In granting this exclusive right to her husband, the woman is promising that he alone will be the father of any children she may bear, so long as he lives. Therefore, if she has children by any man other than her husband, she is guilty of adultery; and so is the third party who furnishes the semen.

Neither can a husband delegate his marriage right to a donor because the natural law does not allow the intrusion of a third party into the natural intimacy of marriage. Marriage is such a strictly personal relationship that each party, husband and wife, commits his and her **whole person** to the contract. (It is quite evident that a donor is expected to give only his semen.) The husband, in delegating to another his marital right as the father of his wife's children, would have to surrender his whole personality.

In speaking to 2000 delegates attending the Second World Congress on Fertility and Sterility on May 21, 1956, Pope Pius XII spoke even more plainly on this subject. On this occasion the Holy Father said that the problem of sterility involves spiritual and ethical values, because "if it is deeply human that a married couple should see in

---

[23] Pope Pius XII, Address to the Fourth International Congress of Catholic Doctors, September 29, 1949.

their child the true and full expression of their reciprocated love, it is natural that they should feel it a painful sacrifice to be forced involuntarily to renounce fatherhood and motherhood."

The fundamental tenet that the "principal object of matrimony, the procreation and education of children, has precedence over every other aim and that all must be subordinated to it" has been a constant teaching of the Church, the Pontiff stated. The Church, he said, has always condemned any theory that might induce a married couple to seek physical self-satisfaction in their own exclusive interest.

The Church is equally opposed, the Holy Father continued, to those who advocate artificial insemination.

"The child is the fruit of conjugal union," the Pope said, "involving not only organic functions and tender feelings, but also the spiritual and disinterested love that animates them. . .

"The relationship that unites father and mother to the child takes its roots from the organic fact and . . . the wish of mutual giving finds its true fulfillment in the human being that they bring into the world.

"Only this consecration of oneself, generous in its beginning . . . since it entails the conscious acceptance of the responsibility involved, can guarantee that the task of educating the children will be carried out with all the care, courage and patience that it requires. It can therefore be said that human fecundity, apart from the physical aspects, assumes essential moral aspects that must be borne in mind even when considered in the light of medical opinion."

In speaking about artificial insemination among humans, the Pope rejected as absolutely immoral attempts at artificial insemination "in vitro" (test tube insemination).

This does not mean, he added, that one must necessarily condemn the use of certain artificial means, with the view of either facilitating the conjugal act or attaining the objective of the normal act.

Artificial insemination is not within the rights acquired by a couple by virtue of the marriage contract, the Pope continued, nor is the right to its use derived from the right to offspring as a primary objective of matrimony.

"The marriage contract does not confer this right," the Holy Father said, "because its aim is not 'progeny' but 'natural acts' capable of generating a new life. Therefore artificial insemination violates the natural law and is contrary to what is right and moral."

The voluntary direct taking of human seed outside the circumstances of legitimate union, the Pope continued, is to be condemned, even in the light of simple, rational ethics. There is no motive whatever to justify it, he added, even that of scientific research.

The right and power to exercise procreative faculties, the Holy Father declared, are not acquired by the mere fact of their existence. Since it is a question of men and not brute animals, the right and power are limited to valid marriage.

LEGAL AND PSYCHOLOGICAL PROBLEMS

But apart from moral problems of donor insemination, **further** questions would be encountered — especially psychological and legal ones. Ficarra says that before anyone attempted donor insemination the following procedures would have to be undertaken:

1. A written request and consent for the procedure signed by both the husband and wife and witnessed in the presence of the physician is obtained.

2. Clinical and laboratory proof of incurable sterility of the husband, i.e., transcripts of statements of specialists who diagnosed or treated the husband, are made available.

3. Physical, mechanical, endocrine, and functional normal fertility of the wife are established by clinical and laboratory tests.

4. A release is obtained by the physician from responsibility for abnormal physical or mental condition of the offspring.

5. No guarantee of success is given.

6. It is clearly understood that a time limit for success cannot be predicted, nor can the number of inseminations which may be required for success be specified.

7. Legal implications and responsibilities must be understood by all parties involved, such as how the birth certificate is to be signed relative to paternity, and the advisability of legal adoption by the husband relative to estate and inheritance rights of the offspring.

8. The physician should be reasonably sure that the couple's marriage is a stable one and their emotional state such that it enables them to adjust to this form of parenthood.[24]

It is considered important that the identity of the donor be kept from the husband and wife and the identity of the husband and wife be kept from the donor because experience has indicated that the donor frequently becomes too interested with the wife over the future

---

[24] Bernard J. Ficarra, *Newer Ethical Problems in Medicine and Surgery* (Westminster, Md.: The Newman Press, 1951), pp. 103–104.

of their mutual child. On the other hand, the husband often develops an unconscious, if not an overt, jealousy or sense of inferiority in relation to the man who can do something which he, by rights, should be doing but cannot do.

In cases of artificial insemination by a donor who remains anonymous there is a further psychological difficulty. The wife often develops an anxiety over the unknown "shadow" in her life. Deutsch says she has treated such cases.[25] She further states that she was able to effect a recovery in some of them. However, while a psychiatrist might eliminate the emotional tension arising from such anxiety, he could not eliminate the knowledge of a mistake from the mind of a patient who really understood the intimate nature of marriage.

One of the eugenic difficulties relating to donor insemination is the fact that it would be a distinct possibility for one donor to procreate as many as 20,000 children in one year. If the same donor were used regularly in the same geographical area, there would be no end to the possibilities of inbreeding. The eugenicists have attempted to solve this problem by suggesting that donors be limited to 100 pregnancies resulting in birth.

The medical and eugenic problems are mild compared to the legal difficulties. According to both French and English law, a wife who becomes artificially inseminated by a donor (either by consent of her husband or without his consent) is guilty of adultery.[26] In the United States the question of donor insemination has not yet been directly the subject of decisions by the courts.[27] It is probable that in

---

[25] Helene Deutsch, *The Psychology of Women*, Vol. 1 (New York: Grune and Stratton, 1944), pp. 206–208.

[26] R. Savatier, "Artificial Insemination and the Law of France," *New Problems in Medical Ethics*, Vol. 2, pp. 15–19; Charles Larère, "Artificial Insemination in England," *New Problems in Medical Ethics*, Vol. 2, pp. 26–30; A. Gemelli, *Artificial Insemination* (Milan, Italy: Catholic University of the Sacred Heart, n.d.); H. U. Willink, "Legal Aspects of Artificial Insemination," *The Practitioner* (London), Vol. 158 (1947), p. 349. The editorial staff of the *British Medical Journal* held that it is generally agreed that a child conceived by artificial insemination from a donor would be illegitimate. Editorial: "Artificial Insemination," *Justice of Peace and Local Government Review*, Vol. 109 (1945), p. 194; *ibid.*, p. 448 ff.

[27] In the Strnad case in New York City, 1947, the former wife of Strnad attempted to prevent him from visiting her child who, she declared, was conceived by donor insemination. The judge in this case refused to make any decision on the question of donor insemination since it was not the immediate issue in the case. Cf. also: J. P. Greenhill, "Artificial Insemination: Its Medico-legal Implications," chapter in *Symposium on Medico-legal Problems*, ed. Samuel A. Levinson (Philadelphia: J. B. Lippincott Co., 1948), pp. 43–87. Judge Gibson E. Gorman (Doornbos v. Doornbos, N. 54 S. 14981; Superior Court, Cook County, December 13, 1954) said:

the United States it would also legally constitute adultery. Seymour, Koerner, and Guttmacher suggest procedures to obviate the difficulties of adultery and illegitimacy. Guttmacher suggests that delivery of the woman be performed by some doctor other than the one who performed the insemination.[28] The reason is so that the doctor who delivers the child could honestly say that, so far as he knows, the husband of the woman is the father of her child. Guttmacher recognizes that lying is involved here but he insists that it is a permissible lie. We wonder, then, arguing from the permissibility to falsify birth records in these circumstances, if Guttmacher would say that it is also permissible for the poor to print their own counterfeit money whenever they feel the pinch of circumstances.

INSEMINATION BY THE HUSBAND

Insemination by the husband is permitted under certain circumstances. Circumstances which have been cited as calling for artificial insemination are the following:

1. When natural vaginal insemination is impossible;
2. When natural ascension of spermatozoa into the uterus is impossible.

When it is a question of the husband's semen, there is no problem of adultery (as there as in donor insemination), but there is a moral problem on how the husband's semen is to be obtained. Pope Pius XII, in his allocution previously cited, states that **all** procreation must be effected by a **physical union** carried out according to the natural process of the act. The obligation of physical union may appear to some at first as an unnecessary complication. But the requirement for physical union is rooted in the nature of the **whole** sex act.

The whole fulfillment of the specifically human sexual act is that it is a union of the **whole persons** of both husband and wife. It is far

---

"Homologous Artificial Insemination (when the specimen of semen used is obtained from the husband of the woman) is not contrary to public policy and good morals, and does not present any difficulty from the legal point of view.

"Heterologous Artificial Insemination (when the specimen of semen used is obtained from a third party or donor) with or without the consent of the husband is contrary to public policy and good morals, and constitutes adultery on the part of the mother. A child so conceived is not a child born in wedlock and therefore is illegitimate. As such it is the child of the mother, and the father has no right or interest in said child." The Ontario (Canada) Supreme Court in 1921 (58 D.R.L. 251) also declared that heterologous artificial insemination constituted adultery.

[28] A. F. Guttmacher, "The Role of Artificial Insemination in the Treatment of Human Sterility," *Bull. of the New York Academy of Med.*, Vol. 19 (1943), p. 590.

more than a merely physical act. It is a mutual compenetration of two human beings who are united body and soul with each other. The sexual act is an incomplete act unless this physical compenetration of persons is effected with its psychical counterpart.

Thus it is not permissible for the partners in a marital act to separate the psychical component of the act from the physical nor the physical from the psychical. Consequently, a husband cannot obtain semen for impregnation of his wife by a simple act of **masturbation** or by **coitus interruptus.** The error in **masturbation** is that the physical and psychic union is never begun; whereas the error in **coitus interruptus** is that the physical and psychic union is begun but the husband turns away before the act is completed. The union between the husband and wife is abruptly destroyed.

The only method of procuring semen then is for the married couple to carry out the act of union according to normal procedure. Once the act has been performed it is permissible for a physician then to move the semen further into the uterus.

Methods of Collecting Spermatozoa and Their Morality

The great benefit of obtaining spermatozoa for examination is evident from the discussion in Chapter XXI. The difficulty of discovering a way which is both practical and licit is great. No really satisfactory method has yet been discovered. Because of its importance, this chapter will be devoted to a study of those methods in current use and a discussion of their practicability and morality.

The following methods have been suggested for the collection of specimens of spermatozoa:

1. Masturbation
2. Use of a condom
3. Use of a perforated condom
4. Coitus interruptus
5. Removal of semen from vagina **immediately** or **very soon** after intercourse
6. Removal of semen from vagina **one hour** after intercourse
7. Aspiration of semen from the testicles or epididymides
8. Expression of seminal fluid by massage from the seminal vesicles
9. Use of a vaginal cup
10. Use of a cervical spoon (Doyle)
11. Testicular biopsy
12. Collection of fluid from involuntary (nocturnal) emission
13. Expression of residual spermatozoa remaining in urethra after normal intercourse.

Masturbation is undoubtedly the method preferred by the majority of medical men. Father Glover describes this preference thus:

> Unfortunately, there can be no doubt whatever that the majority of non-Catholic doctors who desire a specimen of their patient's semen consider and advise masturbation as the best means to obtain it. It

would be tedious and to little purpose to give quotations from all who advocate this method. The following drawn from a section of such men, should suffice to prove the point, if proof be required. Weisman states clearly and briefly the reasons why medical men favor the use of this method: "The ideal method is to have the patient masturbate, in the office of the physician, into a clean carefully dried, widemouthed glass container. The spermatozoa secured in this manner are fresh and free from contaminants, and most closely approximate those of normal ejaculation."[1]

Father Glover also gives the following quotations from Meaker and Hotchkiss:

Masturbation yields semen ideally fresh and free from contamination.[2]

A three-day period of abstinence is advised and the specimen is then ejaculated into the flask. There is little change in the character of the semen whether it be collected by coitus interruptus or by masturbation.[3]

Father McFadden comments:

Masturbation is the technique commonly employed to procure specimens of semen.[4]

In spite of a very considerable weight of medical opinion in favor of masturbation as the method of choice for obtaining spermatozoa for examination there are two authoritative voices to the contrary. An authority of no less prominence than Doctor Huhner dissents from this majority view. He is of the opinion that:

All that is necessary is for the woman to come after coitus. She is placed in the regular gynecological position, the cervix is seen, and with an ordinary platinum loop on a glass rod, a particle of mucous from within the cervical os is placed on a glass slide and examined under the microscope. In normal cases, we will see at once many live spermatozoa. That is all there is to it, yet what a wealth of information is obtained from this few minutes of examination.[5]

---

[1] Rev. William K. Glover, *Artificial Insemination Among Human Beings* (Washington, D. C.: Catholic University of America Press, 1948), pp. 24–25. The quotation by Father Glover from Weisman was obtained from: A. I. Weisman, *Spermatozoa and Sterility — A Clinical Manual* (New York: Paul B. Hoeber, Inc., 1941), p. 44.

[2] S. R. Meaker, *Human Sterility: Causation, Diagnosis and Treatment, A Practical Manual of Clinical Procedure* (Baltimore: Williams & Wilkins Co., 1934), p. 107.

[3] R. S. Hotchkiss, *Fertility in Men* (Philadelphia: J. B. Lippincott Co., 1944), p. 103.

[4] Charles J. McFadden, O.S.A., *Medical Ethics* (Philadelphia: F. A. Davis Co., 1953), p. 97.

[5] Max Huhner, M.D., *Sexual Disorders in the Male and Female Including Sterility and Impotence* (Philadelphia: F. A. Davis Co., 1937), p. 7.

The passage of years and the advance in medical knowledge and skill did not warrant a change in Doctor Huhner's opinion, for years later he still maintained:

> And so we may go through many of the theoretical questions in the etiology of sterility and see how frequently they may be dismissed as a result of this few minutes examination. Perhaps I may be pardoned for my enthusiasm concerning this test but I really know of no other from which so much valuable information can be gained in so short a time.[6]

In the total approach to the study of sterility, Doctor Joseph B. Doyle of St. Elizabeth's Sterility Clinic in Boston seems medically satisfied with his basic program of examination (and thus by inference denies the necessity of masturbation):

> Rectal examination, including palpation and massage of prostate and seminal vesicles, is always carried out to detect associated pathology, usually of an inflammatory nature, in these vital structures.
>
> Routine laboratory studies include a urinalysis and inspection of the expressed prostate secretion, a complete blood count and blood serology, and semen analysis. Material for the latter may be obtained by the use of Doyle's cervical spoon, or by the perforated condom technique.
>
> If complete azoospermia is confirmed by repeated examinations, testicular biopsy, a simple, relatively painless out-patient procedure is indicated, and if the pathologic examination discloses absent spermatogenesis with permanent tubular damage, the case is hopeless.[7]

Condomistic intercourse is a method of collecting sperm in which the penis is sheathed by a condom, which collects the ejaculate and retains it so that it may be examined. It is generally agreed that such a method is unsatisfactory on medical grounds because the semen retained in the condom is contaminated by contact with substances which may be inimical to spermatozoa.

Father Glover gives the opinions of some gynecologists on this:

> It is now quite generally accepted that the prophylatic sheath is the poorest method of collecting seminal fluid for careful analysis. The chemicals and the dusting powders used to preserve the rubber, the

---

[6] Max Huhner, M.D., quoted by Father Clifford, S.J., "Sterility Tests and Their Morality," *American Ecclesiastical Review* (November, 1942), p. 363.

[7] Joseph B. Doyle, "The Role of the Gynecologist," *Linacre Quarterly,* Vol. 21, no. 2 (May, 1954), p. 48.

deterioration of the rubber itself and the chemicals used in the manufacture of liquid latex are all drastic spermicides. (Weisman.)[8]

There is no question that the condom contains elements hostile to the sperm or affords contact with non-physiological substances leading to frequent errors in diagnosis. . . . Consequently the mechanical sheath is to be avoided. (Hotchkiss.)[9]

The use of a perforated condom is closely allied to the method just described; in fact, it is but a variation of this method in which the condom is punctured a few times to allow some of the semen to penetrate the vagina, while some is retained for examination. On medical grounds, it is ruled out by the presence of the same harmful elements as in the case of an unperforated condom.

Coitus interruptus, as its name indicates, involves an act of sexual intercourse which is interrupted before ejaculation. The ejaculation takes place outside the vagina, and is collected in a clean glass receptacle. This means of obtaining semen for examination is on a par with masturbation as a clinically satisfactory method. As Father Glover says:

From the medical point of view, either masturbation or "withdrawal," undoubtedly, have decided advantages over the other methods. For by them the complete ejaculate is obtained. . . . The semen has not been contaminated in any way, as could happen when a condom is used; moreover, it has not been in contact with any hostile secretions, as in the case when the semen is deposited in the vagina.[10]

Post-coital examination is a method whereby some of the sperm are aspirated from the vagina after normal intercourse. As a procedure for obtaining semen for examination it is not considered satisfactory, since the secretions of the vagina may contain elements harmful to the spermatozoa, and hence render it unsatisfactory for examination purposes. Weisman sums up the matter in these words:

Since the vagina is acid (PH 3.5 to 4.5), spermatozoa fare poorly in the vaginal canal. Normally they are dead within three or four hours after entry (Huhner, 1913). Attempts to analyze, with a definite routine, the semen obtained from the vagina by siphonage, aspiration, sponging, or other special mechanisms, were made in the early years of

---

[8] A. I. Weisman, "Recent Advances in the Clinical Evaluation of Spermatozoa," Proceedings of the Second American Congress on Obstetrics and Gynecology (St. Louis, 1943), p. 230.

[9] Hotchkiss, *op. cit.,* p. 102

[10] Glover, *op. cit.,* p. 25.

this century, but they have been abandoned, since the admixture of semen with vaginal contents is now known to render it unfit for study.[11]

In the course of an infertility study, a **Huhner Test** is frequently
employed.[12] This test involves aspirating the contents of the cervical
canal through a pipette about 30 to 60 minutes following coitus. The
presence of viable spermatozoa in the cervical canal demonstrates
that the cervical secretions are not hostile to the sperm. At the time
this is done, a microscopic study of the sample of the seminal pool
in the posterior part of the vagina may reveal the number of normal
spermatozoa. Some physicians feel that this type of examination is
enough to establish the fertility of the male. However, it is not as
satisfactory as one would like and in the presence of too few sperm,
another method would be desirable to get a proper evaluation.

Aspiration of semen from the testicles and/or the epididymis is a
method whereby the testicles and the epididymis are aspirated by
means of a large bore needle and syringe. This usually results in a
very small number of sperm. For this reason, this method is not
widely used or advocated. Another drawback of this method is the
fact that the collected specimen is devoid of the prostatic and vesicular
secretions which form the vehicle of normal ejaculation, and hence
the seminal examination is restricted to spermatozoa out of their
functional elements.

Rectal massage is the term used to describe the expression of
"semen" from the seminal vesicles by digital pressure brought to
bear by the introduction of a finger into the rectum. The fluid thus
expressed is composed of secretions from the seminal vesicles and
prostate gland. The resultant fluid is ordinarily of little utility in sterility testing. Father Glover says that Weisman is of the same opinion:

> Microscopic examination may occasionally reveal some mobile sperm,
> but in the majority of cases none are found, and a little or no informa-
> tion will be provided by this antiquated procedure.[13]

The vaginal cup or cervical spoon methods — both methods involve
variations on the post-coital method. The use of a rubber cup and
cervical spoon is designed to prevent the loss of semen from the
vagina and to the extent that they serve this purpose, they are

---

[11] A. I. Weisman, *Spermatozoa and Sterility,* p. 46.

[12] Max Huhner, M.D., *The Diagnosis and Treatment of Sexual Disorders in the Male
and Female* (Philadelphia: F. A. Davis Co., 1937), p. 7.

[13] Weisman, *op. cit.,* p. 123.

probably the best means of collecting a specimen. The first suggestion of using a rubber cup for this purpose was made by Krigbaum in 1937.[14] A suitable cup is one which was originally designed to retain the menstrual flow (Hy-Cup, Tassette). They are no longer used for this purpose but provide an excellent means of collecting semen. One difficulty which arises is that the material of which the cup is formed may have a spermaticidal effect. To use the cup the patient is instructed to sterilize it and keep it handy. After intercourse she inserts it into the vagina, open end upward, before arising from her back. She should report to her physician soon after this. He will remove the cup with her in a standing position so as to collect a maximum amount of the specimen. (All theologians would not agree with this method.)

The **cervical spoon** was designed by Doctor Joseph B. Doyle. The author describes his method as follows:

An alternate method of semen collection which approximates these criteria and permits normal intercourse and also aids sperm survival and spermigration is herein presented. A concave plastic spoon has been devised to provide an innocuous inner lining of the posterior fornix and vaginal wall. It is inserted beneath the cervix by gently depressing its shaft by flexion of the index finger against the relaxed perineum and posterior vaginal wall, as the patient gently bears down. The cervix can be felt digitally to dip into the spoon. The procedure is demonstrated in the office to both husband and wife. At probable ovulation time as determined by calendar calculation, thermal shift, and/or vaginal smear or cervical mucus study, the vagina is wiped dry and free from accumulated debris in the office. A clean tampon is left in place in the vagina to absorb the secretion until the patient is ready for coitus at home. The spoon has been washed in hot tap water and allowed to dry. Before coitus the husband then places the spoon beneath the cervix. Intromission from above is readily attained. Deep, gentle penetration with minimal coital movement will result in the deposition of the ejaculate into the spoon where it mingles freely with the cervical mucus. . . . The wife remains supine for 30-60 minutes. Complete liquefaction so necessary to maximum motility of the sperm requires 30 minutes on the average. The vaginal temperature further stimulates motility. The exclusion to [sic, probably means "exclusion of"] the acid vaginal secretion permitted the pH of the seminal pool in the spoon to remain 6.5–7.5 in 8 cases of 1 hour contact. The spoon is then withdrawn by the husband as the wife gently bears down to relax the perineal floor. The

14 Roy E. Krigbaum, "An Aid in the Study of Sterility," *Am. J. Obst. & Gynec.*, Vol. 34 (December, 1937), pp. 1046–1047.

spoon is inverted to deposite the ejaculate plus traces of cervical mucus in a small glass jar which is promptly capped to prevent escape of CO_2. . . .

This is a preliminary report of a new method of obtaining a physiologic post coital semen sample, especially for motility and viability assay.

The cervical spoon aids sperm deposition and sperm survival for maximum utilization of the migration potentiality of the sperm population.

The method is simple and acceptable psychologically and morally.

Simultaneous assay of sperm survival and degree of motility in the cervical mucus and in the pool offers a new method of estimating sperm migration.[15]

If it can be shown that this method does actually provide a suitable sampling, free from hostile secretions and agents, one might find here another method which can favorably compare with masturbation and "withdrawal" as sound and satisfactory medical means of procuring semen for examination purposes. Such is the contention of the inventor, Doctor Doyle, who describes his method as a protective measure against vaginal acidity and as an aid to spermigration — thus:

Since 1948 there has been available to husbands a method of semen sampling which reputable Catholic theologians agree is entirely consonant with moral law and the teaching of the Church.[16]

Testicular biopsy as a method of examining the spermatozoa is comparatively new. There is not much written as to its value, so one may conclude that its effectiveness and utility are not completely determined at the present time. After describing testicular and epididymal punctures, Doctor Hamblen describes this method in the following words:

The testicular biopsy is a more valuable test than those just described. It is done in general as follows: Following antiseptic preparation and anesthetization of the overlying scrotum, a small incision about one-half inch in length is made in the scrotal skin to expose the testis. The coating of the testis is barely pricked with a knife. Slight pressure on the testis then forces out a small amount of frothy looking seminal tissue.

---

[15] Joseph B. Doyle, "The Cervical Spoon: A New Method of Semen Sampling and Assaying Spermigration; A Preliminary Report," *J. Urol.*, Vol. 60, no. 6 (December, 1948), pp. 986–987, 989.

[16] Joseph B. Doyle, "The Role of the Gynecologist," *op. cit.*, p. 44 ff.

A small shaving, no longer than a fifth of a thin dime, is taken from this extruded tissue for microscopic study.[17]

Nocturnal emission. Before bringing to a close this discussion of the various methods of obtaining sperm, two other possibilities of obtaining seminal fluid for testing should be noted. These are mentioned by Father Gerald Kelly, who, in speaking of licit ways of procuring semen, states: "The semen is accidentally obtained as a result of an involuntary emission . . . (2) expression from the male urethra of the semen remaining there after normal intercourse is completed. . . ."[18]

MORAL EVALUATION OF THE VARIOUS PROPOSED METHODS OF OBTAINING SEMEN

Masturbation. As far as masturbation, or self-pollution, is concerned, it is an act which is intrinsically evil, being contrary to the Divine and Natural Laws. It is never lawful, even for a laudable purpose, to use the generative faculty in an unnatural way. The bases for this common and certain teaching of the Church are:

1. Condemnation by Innocent XI (on March 4, 1679) of the proposition: **"Pollution is not forbidden by the law of nature. Consequently, if God had not forbidden it, it would often be good and sometimes of grave obligation."**

2. The condemnation by the Holy Office in 1929 of the proposition that it would be licit to directly procure masturbation for seminal examination concerning a diseased condition.

3. The argument from **reason,** which is that the generative organs are by nature directed to the propagation of the species, and hence solitary use is a deordination.

Condomistic intercourse. This method is but a form of masturbation. Its morality is judged on the same principles. There is universal agreement of all theologians that condomistic intercourse is intrinsically evil.

Perforated condom. This method of obtaining semen is the subject of dispute among theologians. Father Glover, following the opinion of Fathers Connell and Vermeersch, concludes: "The use of a pierced condom to obtain a specimen of semen is a deliberate impeding of whatever semen is retained from its ordination toward

[17] E. C. Hamblen, M.D., *Facts for Childless Couples* (Springfield, Ill.: Charles C. Thomas, 1950), p. 47.

[18] Gerald Kelly, S.J., *Medico-Moral Problems,* Part II (St. Louis, Mo.: The Catholic Hospital Association of the United States and Canada, 1950), p. 17.

generation and is, therefore, unlawful."[19] This subject is discussed more fully on page 291.

Coitus interruptus. Also known as withdrawal. This method of obtaining a seminal sample for examination is universally condemned by Catholic moralists. It is the sin of Onan, whom God slew because of his sin.[20] Glover[21] summarizes the Catholic position by stating that onanism, or any other manner of performing copulation which is deprived of its natural ordination toward generation, is intrinsically against nature and is thereby essentially and gravely evil; he presents this opinion as the **certain** teaching of the Church, based on **Casti Connubii** of Pius XI, Sacred Scripture, the teaching of the moralists, and the arguments of reason.

Post-coital examinations. In his book, **Morals in Politics and Professions,** Father Francis J. Connell suggests:

> . . . the only certainly lawful methods of obtaining a specimen would be to wait until that period of time has passed after which a woman may lawfully use a douche for the direct removal of semen from the vagina (that is, at least an hour after intercourse) and then to take a specimen from what remains in the vagina, or to utilize what may have been accidentally (that is, not of direct purpose) deposited outside the vagina, at the time of relations.[22]

There is no argument among moral theologians that after about an hour some semen might be removed for examination. Some of the older moralists would have demanded a longer time, up to six or eight hours, but at present it may be stated that, after intercourse between a husband and his wife, it is certainly licit to remove some semen from the vagina after one hour. Father Vermeersch maintained that after one-half hour the semen could be removed, since by that time the sperm would no longer be of use for fertilization. Father Kelly also writes that some theologians argue for a shorter length of time on the basis of a permissible mutilation, and concludes: ". . . if physicians find it necessary to remove some semen immediately or soon after intercourse, they may do so."[23] To remove

---

[19] Glover, *op. cit.*, p. 76.

[20] Gen. 38:9–16.

[21] Glover, *op. cit.*, p. 84 ff.

[22] Francis J. Connell, C.SS.R., S.T.D., *Morals in Politics and Professions* (Westminster, Md.: The Newman Press, 1951), pp. 125–126.

[23] Kelly, *op. cit.*, p. 17. Father Vermeersch and the theologians referred to by Father Kelly are not talking about the same thing. Father Vermeersch is talking about removing semen from the vagina after it has had ample opportunity to pass through the cervix.

spermatozoa before an hour has passed is debatable and constitutes only a probable opinion. It would seem that the better basis for the probability is that the sperm's function has been achieved, rather than the idea of justifiable mutilation. Doctor Hamblen points out that the trend in medicine is to assign a very short time to the process whereby the sperm achieves its purpose:

> Most physicians believe that the spermatozoa which are deposited in the vagina properly play no role in fertilization, and that direct insemination of the cervix at the time of the husband's orgasm is the normal mechanism.[24]

In my opinion, this belief has a sound formation; it may be properly termed a medical fact, and therefore the moral judgment concerning the time element should undergo drastic revision. On this basis, it would be licit to remove some semen from the vagina immediately after intercourse. However, there is little or no literature on the subject, and the majority of moralists cling to a minimum time of one hour before removal, with the result that, at present, this radical opinion bears but slight probability. Even so, it would appear that to remove the sperm within 15–30 minutes after coitus constitutes a probable opinion. Father Lynch comments as follows:

> Note that in the second and third categories of the preceding outline (2b and 3b) a distinction is made between a seminal sample extracted from the vagina about an hour after normal intercourse, and one which would be obtained within a substantially shorter period. The first method is declared to be *certainly* licit when legitimate reason prompts it; and the vast majority, if not all, of the theologians have long agreed with that conclusion. The latter method, however, has not been so clearly evident as lawful, and many moralists would be inclined to argue against the morality of the practice. This insistence on a time interval is not an instance of theological hair-splitting, but only a conscientious attempt to abide by the prime principle that deliberate interference with natural post-coital processes is morally reprehensible. It is only on condition that nature be left substantially unimpeded in the normal process of spermigration that moral theology can countenance any method of semen sampling after coitus.[25]

He estimates this time as *"post semi-horam vel unam horam."* The theologians referred to by Father Kelly are talking about the removal of semen before that time; hence they liken it to a sort of mutilation of the conjugal act, considered in its entirety.

[24] Hamblen, *op. cit.*, p. 57.

[25] John J. Lynch, S.J., "Some Moral Phases of Infertility Problems," *The Linacre Quarterly*, Vol. 21, no. 2 (May, 1954), pp. 55–56.

In discussing the morality of the cervical spoon we have the same problem as to the minimal time requirement before the spoon can be removed. As will be noted in the discussion of this method, Father Lynch[26] explains the medical reasons behind the moral opinion that the semen may be removed prior to the elapse of one hour; in substance, it is the medical belief that only those comparatively few spermatozoa which come into contact with the cervical mucus at the time of coitus have any chance of achieving union (fecundation) with the ovum.

Aspiration of the epididymis. This method was, and still is, the subject of debate among theologians. Father Vermeersch argued that since it did not excite venereal pleasure, it was not an abuse of the sex faculty, and, hence, lawful. In opposition, Father Merkelback retorted that man's sole right to use his semen is confined to the conjugal act. Following Vermeersch, Fathers Clifford, Kelly, and Lynch all hold for its probable liceity.[27]

The Holy Father, in his address to the Catholic doctors, rules out such a method to obtain semen for artificial insemination, but he does not definitely settle the problem of its use to obtain a sampling for sterility testing.

Father Lynch considers this method still probably licit for purposes of examination, at the same time acknowledging that the Pope forbids it as a means to artificial insemination:

> But then His Holiness took up a phase of the question which previously had been open to debate, and by implication apparently resolved a doubt which had been discussed by moralists for some thirty years. His statement regarding "new methods" of insemination has since induced moralists to conclude that only through the medium of natural coitus can human procreation be licitly effected — an opinion which the majority had maintained even prior to the pronouncement. Hence the minority, who had previously held as probably licit the artificial impregnation of a wife with semen legitimately obtained from her husband independently of intercourse, now find reason to believe that their opinion was contradicted in the papal allocution. No theologian to my knowledge has since questioned that interpretation of the words of Pius, while many have explicitly avowed it.[28]

Vaginal receptacles. Father Kelly sums up the common teaching of the theologians as to the liceity of these methods in these words:

---

[26] *Ibid.,* p. 57.   [27] Glover, *op. cit.,* p. 76.   [28] Lynch, *op. cit.,* p. 60.

"Sterility tests are **certainly licit** when the male specimen is obtained in one of the following ways . . . the use of a vaginal cup — that is, of a rubber cup, which is inserted into the vagina after coitus and which will catch semen that would otherwise be lost."[29] As to the removal of the cup, we again run into the dispute concerning the time element — after one hour, being **certainly licit;** within a shorter time, being **probably licit.** The basic reason why there is no objection to this procedure is that in it there is involved no interference with the normal processes of sex, but merely a "saving" of sperm which would go to waste in the normal course of events.

With regard to Doctor Doyle's cervical-spoon method, there seems to be no moral prohibition, for it is an aid to spermigration, and only accidentally provides a sampling for testing purposes. It would thus fall under the words of the Pontiff: "With such a pronouncement one does not necessarily proscribe the use of certain artificial methods intended simply either to facilitate the natural act or to enable the natural act, effected in a normal manner, to attain its end. . . ."[30] Father McFadden gives the moral evaluation in these words:

> This method of aiding nature in the effecting of conception and of securing the material for semen analysis appears to be both practicable and moral. Emphasis must be placed on the point that the spoon must not be withdrawn too soon. If the spoon is left in place at least a half hour, preferably an hour, after coitus, the procedure appears to be morally permissible.[31]

It is the latter point — the time element — which again proves to be the bone of contention. On the basis of recent medical data, Father Lynch feels that there is no need for insistence on a minimal time of one hour before the spoon may be removed. As he states:

> For it seems to have been established that sperm deposited in the acid vagina will normally die there rather quickly unless contact is made with the alkaline cervical mucus. In fact, it has been estimated that in normal intercourse 80% of the sperm do for that reason perish intravaginally, and that it is the vanguard 20% upon which nature de-

[29] Kelly, *op. cit.,* p. 17. Father Connell agrees with Father Kelly that the cup may be used at any time to collect semen that would otherwise be lost. His objection is that a woman *immediately after intercourse* may not rise with the express purpose of pouring into the cup semen that might be effective toward conception.

[30] Pope Pius XII, Address to Fourth International Congress of Catholic Doctors, September 29, 1949.

[31] McFadden, *op. cit.,* fourth edition, 1956, p. 99.

pends for conception. If, however, the seminal pool can be protected
from vaginal acidity and at the same time brought in closer contact
with the cervical mucus, spermigration is allegedly so improved that
within 15–30 minutes more sperm will have penetrated the cervix
than would ordinarily ever survive the vaginal acid bath in normal
circumstances. That appears to be the basic principle underlying the
cervical spoon; and if the theory is medically sound, there seems to be
no theological reason for insisting upon an hour's interval before allowing the spoon to be withdrawn and its residual contents subjected to
fertility tests.[32]

Nocturnal emission. There is little question as to the liceity of
using sperm collected through nocturnal emission, and sperm remaining in the urethra after normal intercourse, but neither method is
practical and neither has any clinical use.

CONCLUSION

It may be concluded that the best method of collecting sperm
for examination both **morally** and **medically** would be either testicular
biopsy or the use of the cervical spoon. The best method of collecting
sperm for artificial assistance to insemination by the husband after
natural intercourse both **morally** and **medically** is by use of the
cervical spoon.

---

[32] Lynch, *op. cit.*, p. 56.

CHAPTER XXIII

Abortion

An abortion is the termination of pregnancy before the child is viable. It may be **spontaneous** or **induced**. A spontaneous abortion is one that is brought about by natural physical causes. An induced abortion is one caused by human agent. Legally, **induced abortion** may be **criminal** or **therapeutic**.

INCIDENCE OF SPONTANEOUS ABORTION

About every sixth pregnancy results in a spontaneous abortion. Guttmacher[1] stated that in 1000 consecutive pregnancies there were 98 spontaneous abortions or 9.8 per cent. The frequency of these abortions was not affected by the number of previous pregnancies. Seventy-two per cent of the abortions occurred during the first three months. The cause of such premature ejections of the fetus is often unknown, but it seems most frequently to be due to defective germ plasm. It has been estimated that 70 per cent of all spontaneous abortions are due to this cause. Defective germ plasm may be the result of (a) a defective spermatozoon or ovum; (b) a defect in the process of fertilization; or (c) a defect in the implantation of the fertilized ovum.

In the other 30 per cent of abortions, the cause is unknown. It is sometimes related to severe maternal illness, to excessive amniotic fluid, and to abnormalities of the reproductive organs such as fibromyomata or ovarian cysts. Syphilis, if untreated, may be the cause of stillbirth, but is seldom a factor in the induction of abortion. Traditionally, overexertion or accidents have been considered important causative factors, but according to Guttmacher,[2] neither of

---

[1] Alan F. Guttmacher, *Abortions and Miscarriages in Successful Marriage,* ed. Morris Fishbein and Ernest W. Burgess (Garden City, N. Y.: Garden City Books, 1951), p. 207.
[2] *Ibid.,* p. 210.

these is considered an etiologic factor. Also, according to Guttmacher,[3] shock, grief, and fear rarely cause abortion. Kroger and Freed,[4] on the other hand, are strongly inclined to believe that emotional factors are causative of abortion in many cases. These authors have adopted the **Malpas formula**[5] as a method of ruling out the factor of chance in evaluating the results of psychotherapy in cases of frequent spontaneous abortions. Malpas, in a study of 6000 abortions, found that if a woman had had one abortion, she had a 78 per cent chance of not having another. If there were two previous abortions, she had a 62 per cent chance of not having another; with three previous abortions, her chance of not having another is 27 per cent; and with four previous abortions, there is only a 6 per cent chance of not having a recurrence. Thus, it was claimed by Malpas that not until the patient has had three consecutive abortions can the factor of chance be reduced to give significant results.

Kroger and Freed strongly recommend psychotherapy in habitual abortion (about 4 per cent of all spontaneous abortions).

Spontaneous abortions, in sharp contrast to the induced type, are seldom a source of serious difficulty to the patient. The availability of blood and penicillin has greatly reduced the morbidity which was previously present.

BAPTISM OF FETUS

The expulsion of the fetus, especially in the early months, is practically always preceded by its death. The baptism of well-preserved fetuses is indicated, especially those ejected after a short labor. It is probably useless in most instances, however, because in practically every case, the death of the baby occurred before the labor started. It is certainly unnecessary to baptize where degenerative changes have already begun.

INDUCED ABORTION

Induced abortion may be **therapeutic abortions,** i.e., those induced by a physician after due consultation for a medical reason, or **criminal abortions,** those induced by a large variety of physicians, irregular practitioners, or laymen at the request of the patient, without any

---

[3] *Ibid.,* p. 211.

[4] William S. Kroger and S. Charles Freed, *Psychosomatic Gynecology* (Philadelphia: W. B. Saunders Co., 1951), p. 142 ff.

[5] P. Malpas, "A Study of Abortion Sequences," *J. Obst. and Gynec. of Brit. Emp.,* Vol. 45 (1938), pp. 932–949.

medical reason to be offered in justification. By far the largest number of abortions performed are criminal abortions. Attempts by the patient or others to induce abortion by the use of abortifacient drugs are useless. As far as we know, no drug administered by mouth or by injection will cause an abortion.

INCIDENCE OF THERAPEUTIC ABORTION

There can be no doubt that along with the many operations performed in our modern hospitals, the operation known as therapeutic abortion is very common, and looked upon by many as medically and morally justified. While not having at hand any official statistics with regard to the number of therapeutic abortions performed in this country in recent years, there is good reason to believe that the number, if known, would be appalling. Ten years ago, various attempts were made to indicate the number of abortions, including criminal abortions, which were performed annually in the United States. Many authorities, according to a Grand Jury report, regarded the figure of 100,000 abortions annually in the city of New York alone as approximately accurate. That would be more than 273 a day. Doctor A. J. Rongy, in his book, **Abortion: Legal and Illegal,** went so far as to estimate that 250,000 abortions were performed each year in New York City. In setting his figures for the United States, Frederick J. Taussig stated that he believed that there were 681,000 abortions performed each year (1867 a day), and this would be a minimum judgment. Doctor William Bickers put the national total at 550,000.[6] These figures do not apply to therapeutic abortions alone, but also include criminal abortions. We may be sure, however, that a good percentage of this number falls under the category of therapeutic abortions.

In the year 1939, it was estimated that the number of abortions in England ranged between 110,000 and 150,000 annually, and of these only 40 per cent were criminal; the rest were either spontaneous or therapeutic.[7]

No doubt in this age of easy marriage and comfort and materialism, the trend of increasing abortions has kept a steady pace with the general decay of morality which seems to exist in the world, especially

---

[6] J. Gerard Mears, "In Fear and In Secret They Do Damnable Deeds," *America,* Vol. 67 (1942), pp. 96–97.

[7] Richard O'Sullivan, "The Committee's Report on Abortion," *Clergy Review,* Vol. 17 (1939), p. 395.

as regards the marriage bond. The increase of divorce, birth control, and other evils is matched by the increase of the lax spirit in regard to the practice of therapeutic abortion. The dignity, sanctity, and beauty of marriage have lost their meaning, and along with them the very purpose of marriage itself. In his encyclical **Chaste Marriage,** Pope Pius XI points out that

> amongst the blessings of marriage the child holds the first place, and indeed the Creator of the human race Himself, who in His goodness wished to use men as His helpers in the propagations of life, taught this when, instituting marriage in Paradise, He said to our first parents, and through them to all future spouses, "Increase and multiply, and fill the earth. . . ."[8]

In the same encyclical, the Holy Father writes:

> If a true Christian mother weighs well these things, the dignity and beauty of her office, she will indeed understand with a sense of deep consolation that of her the words of our Savior were spoken: "A woman . . . when she hath brought forth the child remembereth no more the anguish, for joy that a man is born into the world." And proving herself superior to *all the pains* and cares and solicitudes of her maternal office . . . she will rejoice in the Lord, crowned as it were with the glory of her offspring.[9]

This is the Christian outlook on the propagation of children. Through marriage a couple is given the right to co-operate with God in the production of new life, and that very co-operation is the greatest glory that a man or woman can have both in this life and in the next. It is the very foundation of the bond of matrimony. How then can the lawfulness of therapeutic abortion be upheld? How can the destruction of life in therapeutic abortion be reconciled with the office of man and woman in sacred matrimony? Nothing can be so opposed to their primary office of co-operating with God in the production of new life and a soul for heaven as the destruction of life which is brought about in therapeutic abortion.

MEDICAL ASPECTS

The **medical indications** for the induction of abortion have been greatly decreased in number in recent years. As knowledge has in-

---

[8] Pope Pius XI, "Encyclical Letter on Christian Marriage," *The Ecclesiastical Review,* Vol. 84 (1931), p. 228.

[9] *Ibid.,* p. 229.

creased and obstetrical skill improved, most physicians consider that the abortion is more harmful to the patient in most cases than allowing her to go to term. Before a therapeutic abortion is performed it is customary for two physicians to consult and declare in writing that the operation is necessary. Williams[10] lists the following indications for abortion: (1) pernicious vomiting of pregnancy; (2) occasional cases of pre-eclamptic toxemia or pronounced renal insufficiency; (3) infection following attempts at criminal abortion; (4) diseases of the ovum, such as hydatidiform mole; (5) occasional cases of uterine hemorrhage; (6) constitutional diseases, e.g., tuberculosis, heart disease, diabetes, and so forth. Williams stresses very strongly that interference with the pregnancy should always take place in the case of tuberculosis. DeLee[11] gives practically the same indications as the above but feels that the operation is rarely indicated. Dickinson,[12] on the other hand, feels that facilities for the induction of abortion should be increased and its indications liberalized. He urges that the same publicity be given to it as to birth-control procedures. In his opinion economic and "humanitarian" indications should be added to the medical. By "humanitarian" he apparently means that where birth-control procedures have failed, the woman should be free to have an abortion performed.

As the various conditions, which were once considered by the medical profession as urgent indications for the interruption of pregnancy, have become better understood, fewer physicians advise abortion. There is no doubt that pregnancy may have an adverse effect in some diseases.

The most common diseases in which pregnancy is considered a serious complication are tuberculosis, heart disease, diabetes mellitus, and nephritis. Abortion itself, however, is not without risk as is evidenced by the fact that over 24 per cent of women who die as a result of pregnancy die following such a procedure. The occurrence of pregnancy in a woman having one of these diseases calls for the best possible care. These are not cases for the general practitioner; they require the care of a specialist. Such special care can always be provided even when the patient cannot afford to pay. She should have

[10] J. Whitridge Williams, *Obstetrics* (New York: D. Appleton and Co., 1927), pp. 419–421.

[11] Joseph B. DeLee, *The Principles and Practice of Obstetrics,* 2 ed. (Philadelphia: W. B. Saunders Co., 1915), pp. 1045–1046.

[12] Robert L. Dickinson, *Control of Conception,* 2 ed. (Baltimore: The Williams and Wilkins Co., 1938), p. 271.

not only an obstetrical specialist, but also a specialist in the disease from which she suffers. Under these circumstances the patient will probably do well. The risk becomes greater with each succeeding pregnancy.

From the medical viewpoint there can be no doubt that the attitude of medical science has been changing over a period of decades. With the great progress in medical science, especially in this century, any doctor, worthy of the name, should consider it an admission of incompetence in his profession to be forced to have recourse to therapeutic abortion to save the life of an expectant mother. As G. Clement writes in his book **Thou Shalt Not Kill:**[13]

> If all the forms of complications in childbirth are examined, the old imposing list of medical indications for abortion is being gradually narrowed, till it has almost disappeared under the united endeavors for progress in therapeutics. This abandonment of the old interventionist practices is especially striking in the pathological states which a few years ago constituted for practicing physicians the classic indications for the interruption of pregnancy, and the sacrifice of the child; contracted pelvis, albuminuria, eclampsia, uncontrollable vomitting. This reversal of opinion *has not been dictated by doctrinal concern,* and by the speculative demands of the moral law. It has been caused by the objective comparison of the results of different methods, by a closer analysis of facts, and a more judicious use of the varied resources of therapeutics.[14]

In this same book, written in 1930, the author points out how the attitude of medical men has changed with regard to the individual "indications" for abortion. Thus he shows how modern research and medicine have ruled out the necessity of abortion when treating such complications of pregnancy as serious hemorrhage, the various toxemias, vomiting, renal tuberculosis and serious nephritis, diabetes, heart disease, and so forth.[15] And, as stated above, this change of attitude has not been motivated by moral principles, but rather by the great steps that have been made in medical research and methods. Thus the author points out that from a purely medical view, therapeutic abortion can hardly ever be justified.

Since 1930, when G. Clement wrote his book, the general attitude

---

[13] G. Clement, *Thou Shalt Not Kill* (Philadelphia: Reilly, 1930), p. 134.

[14] At the time the book was written, Clement was chief surgeon at the Cantonal Hospital, Fribourg, member of the Gynecological Society, French Switzerland.

[15] *Ibid.,* pp. 100–133.

of many medical men has swung more and more to the idea that
therapeutic abortion has no place in the modern medical practice. As
late as February of 1953 the **Linacre Quarterly** presented a lengthy
article in which it was clearly shown that therapeutic abortion "is
never justified from a strictly scientific standpoint."[16]

> Among the modern doctors, eminent in their profession as obstetri-
> cians, who in recent years have condemned the practice of therapeutic
> abortion on scientific grounds alone, there are such men as Samuel A.
> Cosgrove of Columbia University, Albert Schweitzer, Barnes, Skillen,
> DeLee, Jacobs. The latter stated, after analyzing the medical literature
> for the past forty years, that, "If abortion is to have any scientific
> justification, evidence must be sought showing that in general the
> harmful effects are avoided if the pregnancy is being interrupted. A
> study of the literature will soon convince any impartial person that
> no such evidence exists."[17]

Others who might be included in this list are Bowles, Damzalski,
Stewart, Simmons, Jameson, Matthews, Barone, Cohen, Reid, Hoff-
man, Jeffers, Gorenberg, Correll, Rosenbaum, and many others.[18]
It might be noted that many of these, if not most, are non-Catholic,
and therefore cannot be accused of a Catholic bias.

In an impressive survey conducted on the indications of therapeutic
abortion, Doctor Roy J. Heffernan, M.D., and Doctor William A.
Lynch, M.D., assembled conclusive data to the effect that this practice
is never justified from a strictly scientific standpoint. Tuberculosis,
for example, which ranks highest in mortality from puerperal causes,
is not an indication for abortion. As far back as April, 1930, Barnes
and others, in reviewing the records of 410 pregnant tuberculous
women, concluded that their investigations "lend little support to
the view that emptying the gravid uterus in either the minimal or
the far advanced cases has value as a remedy for pulmonary

---

[16] Roy J. Heffernan and William A. Lynch, "Is Therapeutic Abortion Scientifically
Justified?" *The Linacre Quarterly*, Vol. 19 (1952), pp. 11–27.

[17] *Ibid.*, p. 13.

[18] *Ibid.*, pp. 12–16; cf. also: Lull and Kimbrough, who give no specific indications for
therapeutic abortion but state: "Every means must be utilized to establish with
certainty the absolute necessity of the procedure," Clifford B. Lull and Robert A.
Kimbrough, *Clinical Obstetrics* (Philadelphia: J. B. Lippincott Co.), pp. 260–261.
Incidence of therapeutic abortion at Los Angeles County Hospital fell from 1 in
every 106 deliveries in 1931 to 1 in every 2864 in 1946–1950, to 1 in every 8383 in
1950. Russell states that despite the greatly lowered incidence of therapeutic abortion,
maternal mortality progressively declined (Keith P. Russell, "Changing Indications for
Therapeutic Abortion," *J.A.M.A.*, Vol. 151 (January 10, 1953), pp. 108–111.

tuberculosis."[19] In 1938, James Skillen and others concluded, from a study of 10,000 patients admitted to the Olive View Sanatorium in California, that "by and large it seems that the tuberculous woman who becomes pregnant has a case not greatly different so far as her tuberculosis is concerned from her tuberculous sister who does not become pregnant. While so far as her pregnancy is concerned she does not differ greatly from other pregnant women."[20] In 1943, DeLee said, "If the patient with active tuberculosis become pregnant, abortion is not indicated; proper care will enable the patient to go through her pregnancy unharmed."[21] "A survey by Barone in 1947 showed that the mortality for patients who had delivered spontaneously was 19.2 per cent. The mortality for the patient who had delivered by Caesarian section was 36.3 per cent. The mortality for the patient in whom the pregnancy was interrupted was 38.5 per cent. The best results in this survey were obtained in those patients who were delivered spontaneously regardless of the extent of the tuberculosis."[22] Thus, medical research shows that interruption of pregnancy in tuberculous patients may even increase the hazards of this disease.

In the same survey made by Heffernan and Lynch, it was found that heart disease is not an indication for therapeutic abortion. Thus, for example, Gorenberg concludes, from a view of at least 500 cases of pregnancy complicated by heart disease: "It is probable that practically every pregnancy encountered in a patient with heart disease can be brought to a successful spontaneous termination if adequate prenatal care is instituted and if absolute bed rest is enforced when indicated."[23]

Besides tuberculosis and heart disease, the following other diseases were carefully studied as possible "indications" for therapeutic abortion: multiple sclerosis, chronic nephritis, hypertension, benign pelvic tumors, cancer of the pelvic organs, tumors of the brain, sickle cell anemia, disorders involving the Rh factor, virus diseases, otosclerosis, ulcerative colitis, and a number of neurological and mental disorders.[24] The impressive evidence, among all these forms, against therapeutic abortion is such that, at a recent Congress of the American College

[19] Harry L. and Lena R. Barnes, "Pregnancy and Tuberculosis," *Am. J. Obst. and Gynec.,* Vol. 44 (August, 1942), p. 183, quoted by Heffernan, *op. cit.,* p. 13.

[20] *Ibid.,* p. 13.

[21] *Ibid.*

[22] *Ibid.,* p. 15.

[23] *Ibid.* p. 16.

[24] *Ibid.,* pp. 18–24.

of Surgeons, Doctor Roy J. Heffernan stated, "Anyone who performs a therapeutic abortion is either ignorant of modern medical methods of treating the complications of pregnancy or is unwilling to take the time to use them."[25]

In another impressive survey published by Samuel A. Cosgrove, M.D., and Patricia A. Carter, M.D., the significant figure is presented of only 4 "necessary" abortions among 67,000 deliveries at the Margaret Hague Maternity Hospital.[26] Doctor Cosgrove did not hesitate to label therapeutic abortion as murder and to justify it only in extreme cases.[27] It should be noted that Doctor Cosgrove is not a Catholic.

The evidence accumulated against the feasibility of this practice is borne out by medical investigations both in the United States and abroad. Thus, for example, the most outstanding physicians in Spain have come to the conclusion that therapeutic abortion is never a necessary means of saving the mother.[28] After taking account of a good cross section of medical opinion on the subject, Father Kelly remarks, "In therapeutic abortion, as in other matters, present day medical findings show that good morality is good medicine."[29]

MORAL ASPECTS

From the moral standpoint the case against therapeutic abortion can be briefly stated as being one of plain and simple murder. By murder we mean the direct killing of an innocent person. Now, the fetus, however undeveloped it may be in its biological structure, is in every sense a human person endowed with both a body and a soul. It possesses, therefore, the right to live. That the fetus is an innocent person would hardly need to be stated, were it not for the contention of a few moralists of past years who held that, in the case where pregnancy constitutes a threat to the mother's life, the infant might be considered, at least materially, as an unjust aggressor. However, this view is no longer tenable, for it has been explicitly condemned by the Catholic Church. By its very nature the operation involved in therapeutic abortion can have no other immediate and direct effect than the extinction of life. The action of the operating

---

[25] *Ibid.*, p. 24.

[26] Gerald Kelly, S.J., *Medico-Moral Problems*, Part 3 (St. Louis: The Catholic Hospital Association of the United States and Canada, 1951), p. 16.

[27] *Ibid.*, p. 16.

[28] *Ibid.*, p. 19.

[29] *Ibid.*, p. 16.

surgeon is as objectively one of murder as the action of the assassin who brings down his victim with knife or gun.

It is commonly pleaded that therapeutic abortion is motivated by a lofty purpose, that of saving the life of a belabored mother. The plea is a specious one. An action that is evil by its very nature cannot be divested of its evil by any amount of good intentions. To say, "I do not mean to kill the child, I merely want to save the mother," does not in the least acquit therapeutic abortion of its specific character of being a direct killing. The end does not justify the means.

That therapeutic abortion is an intrinsic evil is further shown by comparison with indirect abortion. In a typical case of indirect abortion a woman is stricken, e.g., with cancer of the uterus, the treatment of which will inevitably result in the death of the fetus. It is perfectly licit for her to take medicine or submit to treatment necessary for her safety and directly conducive to it, even if at the same time the infant is ejected or dies in the womb. This unfortunate effect, though evil, is neither intended, nor does it follow from the very nature of the treatment. It is rather a secondary effect, or by-product of the procedure, and is not its sole immediate effect. In this case we do not have the employment of an evil means to obtain a good end, but rather the application of the principle of double effect. The surgical operation itself is good — it is applied to the infected organ, not to the fetus. The good effect itself is not procured by means of the evil effect (the death of the fetus), but rather the evil effect is either produced simultaneously with it in the order of causality or follows from it. Finally, there is sufficient reason for permitting the evil effect to happen,[30] the saving of the mother's life.

The medicomoral code for Catholic hospitals in the United States and Canada has enunciated the above-mentioned principles of the natural law as follows:

12. The direct killing of any innocent person, even at his own request, is always morally wrong. Any procedure whose sole immediate effect is the death of a human being is a direct killing.

13. Risk to life and even the indirect taking of life are morally justifiable for proportionate reasons. Life is taken indirectly when death

---

[30] Cf. Henry Davis, *Moral and Pastoral Theology*, Vol. 1 (New York: Sheed and Ward, 1945), p. 13; Edwin F. Healy, S.J., *Moral Guidance* (Chicago: Loyola University Press, 1943), p. 174.

is the unavoidable accompaniment or result of a procedure which is immediately directed to the attainment of some other purpose, e.g., the removal of a diseased organ.[31]

Applying these principles to abortion, the code goes on to state:

15. Direct abortion is never permitted, even when the ultimate purpose is to save the life of the mother. No condition of pregnancy constitutes an exception to this prohibition. Every procedure whose sole immediate effect is the termination of pregnancy before viability is a direct abortion.

Before the decisions of the Holy Office were issued on this subject, a few Catholic moralists were still not convinced of this absolute position of the vast majority of theologians. The difficulties raised by them tended either to justify direct abortion or to reduce certain cases to a mere indirect killing of the fetus. Some attempted to justify direct abortion by pleading that, in extreme cases where the only way to save the mother's life is to terminate pregnancy, such a course would be permissible on the grounds that the fetus is a materially unjust aggressor. The unsoundness of this analogy was pointed out very aptly by Father Aertnys: "But the child is making no attempt upon its mother's life; it is only trying to be born, and it is only by a natural concourse of circumstances that this effort becomes a cause of death to the mother. The child, therefore, is not an aggressor, and much less an unjust aggressor."[32] Father Lehmkuhl, S.J., formerly defended, or at least suggested, the analogy with the situation of a storm at sea where a man voluntarily sacrifices his life by yielding to a friend a plank which is not large enough to save both of them. He later pointed out the weakness of this argument by showing that in such a situation death follows as an indirect result of the man's action, while in therapeutic abortion death is a direct effect of the action, however much one may presume the willingness of the infant to relinquish its own life for the sake of its mother's.[33] Other theologians invoked the principle of the conflict of rights. The mother, they claimed, had the prior and stronger right to life; therefore, when both could not be saved, the fetus could be sacrificed. But, as the opposition was quick to observe, here there

---

[31] *Ethical and Religious Directives for Catholic Hospitals,* second edition (St. Louis: The Catholic Hospital Association of the United States and Canada, 1955), p. 4.

[32] Quoted by Kelly, *op. cit.,* p. 12.

[33] *Ibid.,* p. 13.

is no question of a conflict of rights. It is rather the question of two innocent people, each having an equal and clear title to life.[34]

No less vulnerable is the argument, among others, advanced by those who are squarely opposed to the Catholic position; faced with two evils, the doctor must choose the lesser; but it is a lesser evil to sacrifice the child than to have both mother and child die. This plea amounts to the erroneous statement that it is a less evil to **murder** one person than to **permit** the death of two persons. Certainly, the moral evil of murdering the fetus is far greater than the mere physical evil involved in the unavoidable death of both mother and child.[35] Thus, all the arguments set up in defense of therapeutic abortion fall before the principle that it is never lawful to procure a good end by an evil means.

The Catholic position on therapeutic abortion has been given official sanction by recent declarations of the Holy See. The Church has made it quite clear, through several pronouncements of the Holy Office, that every operation that directly kills the fetus is unlawful.[36] It will be noticed that in its decree of August 19, 1889, the Holy Office explicitly aims its condemnation at all operations which directly kill **either mother or child**. "These last words should be carefully noted. They are a clear refutation of the calumny that the Church always prefers the life of the infant to that of the mother. From the very beginning the official Catholic position has been that each life is inviolable and that neither may be directly killed to save the other."[37]

Pope Pius XI strongly reaffirmed the unlawfulness of therapeutic abortion in his encyclical on Christian Marriage, December 31, 1930:

> As to the medical and therapeutic indications to which, using their own words, "We have made reference, Venerable Brethren, however much we may pity the mother whose health and even life is gravely imperiled in the performance of the duty allotted to her by nature, nevertheless what could ever be a sufficient reason for excusing in any way the direct murder of the innocent?" This is precisely what we are dealing with here. Whether inflicted upon the mother or upon the child it is against the precept of God and the law of nature, "Thou shalt not kill." The life of each is equally sacred, and no one has the power, nor even the public authority, to destroy it.

---

[34] *Ibid.*

[35] *Ibid.*, p. 14.

[36] May 28, 1884; August 19, 1889; July 24, 1895; May 4, 1898; March 5, 1902.

[37] Kelly, *op. cit.*, p. 10.

This position was more recently declared by Pope Pius XII in a discourse to delegates attending the Congress of the Italian Catholic Union of Midwives.[38]

THE Rh FACTOR

The strongest arguments proposed by non-Catholics in support of therapeutic abortions are based on the desire of counteracting the Rh factor (see p. 84 ff.). The Catholic position on this states that Rh sensitization never constitutes moral justification for the termination of pregnancy by abortion to prevent the live birth of an erythroblastic child, because it is a direct abortion and, hence, an act of murder. On the medical side there is absolutely no way of determining prior to the birth of the precise hematological condition of the fetus. Even the most careful study of the mother's blood during pregnancy does not give us very precise information. If clear evidence of sensitization of an Rh-negative expectant mother is at hand there is admittedly a sound probability that the child will be erythroblastic. Clear evidence of sensitization of the mother's blood, however, does not make it possible to determine the precise nature of the pathology present in the infant. On the moral side therapeutic abortion is never permissible.

Under due conditions Rh sensitization may provide a moral justification for radical obstetrics in the form of Caesarean section or premature delivery. It must be stated, however, that the best scientific thought on this subject has undergone a notable change during the past two years. Until a year ago, it was very commonly believed that babies could and should be protected from the action of Rh antibodies by premature induction or Caesarean section. This view is no longer held by the best authorities in this field.

The moral justification of Caesarean section and premature induction depends upon the verification of a medical fact. Does sound scientific evidence indicate that this obstetrical procedure provides, without undue risk to the mother, the most likely method of obtaining a healthy baby? In the present state of our knowledge of the matter, it would appear morally permissible for a doctor to have recourse to Caesarean section whenever expert medical judgment regards it as the best means of protecting the child from erythroblastosis without undue risk to the mother. On the other hand, the doctor must keep

---

[38] Discourse delivered on October 29, 1951: English version published by the N.C.W.C. News Service, November 3, 1951.

in contact with the progress of medical science and if research shows that Caesarean section does not confer a benefit on the child which is proportionate to the risk which it inflicts on the mother and child, then this radical obstetrical procedure would not be morally permissible.

Finally, our present knowledge of the Rh factor is so unsettled that it should be used with extreme care as a determining factor in the selection of a spouse. From all that has been said, it should be evident that both from the medical and moral viewpoints Rh incompatibility should be set up as a partial determinant in the selection of a spouse and as a basis for judging the problems which are to be anticipated in the married life.[39]

---

[39] Francis J. Connell, C.SS.R., *Ecclesiastical Review,* Vol. 115, No. 1 (July, 1946), pp. 63–65. In this article Father Connell suggests that it might be commendable to take into consideration the Rh factor in selecting a mate.

SECTION IV

SOCIAL
ASPECTS
OF
MARRIAGE

And He said: "Therefore, now they are not two, but one flesh. What therefore God hath joined together, let no man put asunder." Mt. 19:6.

CHAPTER XXIV

Divorce[1] in Its Social Aspects

The family group is a society, and is the cornerstone of civil society. Society is defined as "a stable union of two or more for a common purpose attainable by co-operative activity. Society . . . is natural when its nature, purpose and bond are fixed by the moral law or the Author of Nature."[2]

Societies are called natural when they "respond perfectly, either adequately or inadequately, to the inborn aptitudes, inclinations and needs of the human race."[3]

In spite of these facts, it is unfortunately true that little respect exists today in the minds of many for the integrity and indissolubility of marriage. Some marriages are contracted and abandoned with even less thought than the purchase of an automobile or the planning of a vacation.

The result of this disrespect is a staggering increase in divorce in the United States.

The appalling state of divorce today can be illustrated from statistics gathered by the United States Census Bureau.[4] In 1867 the crude divorce rate was 0.3 per 1000 population. It remained at this point until 1880 when it rose one tenth of a point up to 0.4 per 1000 population. By 1911 it had reached an average of 1 divorce per 1000 population. The rate climbed until 1946 when it reached a rate

---

[1] It is to be understood that whenever the term "divorce" is used hereafter it connotes the correlative of contracting a second marriage during the life of the partner to the first marriage. If the term is used in a more limited sense, the context will so indicate.

[2] Timothy J. Brosnahan, *Prolegomena to Ethics* (New York: Fordham University Press, 1941), p. 302.

[3] *Ibid.*, p. 303.

[4] U. S. Department of Health, Education and Welfare, National Office of Vital Statistics, *Vital Statistics of the United States: 1950* (Washington, 1954), 1:73, fig. 5C.

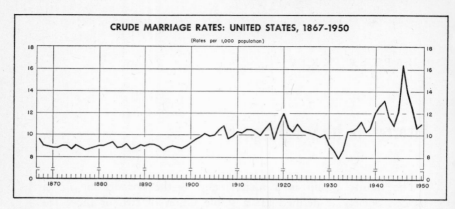

U. S. Department of Health, Education and Welfare, National Office of Vital Statistics, Vital Statistics of the United States: 1950 (Washington, 1954), 1:73.

of 4.3 divorces per 1000 population. In other words, between 1879 and 1946 — a period of 67 years, the crude divorce rate multiplied fifteen times. In 1879 there were granted 17,083 divorces. In 1946 there were granted 610,000 divorces.

Between 1946 and 1950 the number dropped a little more than one third. In 1950 the crude divorce number was 385,144. This still leaves us with a divorce rate which is almost nine times greater than the rate for 1879.

Taking the United States as a total, the crude divorce rate for 1950 was 2.6. The crude rate varied considerably from one state to another. In Nevada the rate was 55.7 per 1000 population. In New York the rate was 0.8 per 1000. If one is to judge by statistics, it would seem that the state of Nevada wins its doubtful distinction without much competition. The second highest divorce rate in 1950 was 6.5 per 1000 in the state of Florida. The third highest was Oklahoma, with a rate of 6.2. The 385,144 divorces for the year 1950 were distributed geographically as follows:

New England States	14,027
Mid-Atlantic States	29,274
East North Central States	77,249
West North Central States	30,702
South Atlantic States	53,722
East South Central States	30,736
West South Central States	65,500
Mountain States	27,931
Pacific States	55,973

Further divorce statistics for the year 1950 indicate that for the United States as a whole, 27.8 per cent of divorces were granted to the husband, and 72.1 to the wife. (These figures were estimated on the basis of reports from twenty states, and should be accepted only within the limits which this basis allows.)[5]

Among the individual states the differences in percentage varied from 61.3 per cent for wives in Mississippi to 79.9 per cent for wives in Massachusetts.

In sixteen reporting states 44 per cent of the divorces were granted to couples with children while 56 per cent were granted to couples who had no children.

In sixteen reporting states, taken as a whole, the median average duration of the marriage before divorce was 5.8 years. This median average varied from 9.5 years in Connecticut to 4.2 years in Wyoming and Idaho. In two states the largest number of divorces were granted to persons married less than one year; in five states, to persons in the second year of marriage; in four states in the third year; in three states in the fourth year; and in two states in the fifth year. (The report does not specify which individual states these were.)[6]

There are a number of reasons for the increase in divorce: a materialist attitude prevailing among a large number of people, a decline in the sense of individual responsibility, intervention of the state in an area which is not within its province. We do not deny that the state has an interest in marriage; on the contrary, we affirm that very fundamental interests of civil society are tied into the

---

[5] *Ibid.*, p. 75, Table 5.12.
[6] *Ibid.*, p. 69.

decision of two citizens to contract a marriage. But the state, while being a necessary third party to any marriage, does not have the right to dissolve a marriage to the extent that it can allow either of the two parties to contract a second marriage while the partner of the original marriage still lives.

> . . . the end or meaning of marriage and the family is independent of the will of the state as well as of the will of the parties to the marriage contract. Marriage and the family produce rights and duties that are grounded in the very nature of these institutions.[7]

In other words, individuals are free to enter the state of marriage. But once they have entered upon it they acquire both the rights and obligations of marriage. Some of these obligations are rooted in the very essence of marriage. One of these characteristics which flows from the very essence of marriage is its indissolubility while both parties to the contract are alive. The marriage can be dissolved only by the death of one of the parties.

> The essential limitations (of marriage) forbid plural marriage, race suicide, sexual excess, unnecessary separation, and absolute divorce.[8]

We can add, then, that the increase in divorce is attributable not only to the causes listed before but to an even more deeply rooted cause — i.e., a failure to understand the essence of marriage.

The conditions today which result from easy divorce laws were recognized by Pope Leo XIII as a danger in his encyclical **Arcanum Divinae**. This encyclical was written in 1888 (when the divorce rate was 0.5, or less than one fifth of what it is today).

The words of His Holiness were prophetic. In 1888 he stated in part:

> *Divorce once being tolerated, there will be no restraint powerful enough to keep it within the limits fixed or foreseen.* Great is the force of example, and the violence of passion even greater. With such incitements it must needs follow that the eagerness for divorce, daily spreading by devious ways, will seize upon the minds of many like a virulent contagious disease, or like a flood of water bursting through every barrier. These are truths that are clear in themselves, but they will become clearer yet if we call to mind the teachings of experience. So soon as the road to divorce began to be made smooth by law, at once quarrels, jealousies and judicial separations largely increased; and

---

[7] Heinrich Rommen, *The Natural Law*, trans. Thomas R. Hanley (St. Louis: B. Herder Book Co., 1949), p. 239.

[8] Charles Macksey, "Society," *Readings in Ethics*, ed. J. F. Leibell (Chicago: Loyola University Press, 1926), p. 748.

such shamelessness of life followed that men who had been in favor of these divorces repented of what they had done, and feared that, if they did not carefully seek a remedy by repealing the law, the commonwealth itself might suffer disaster.[9]

MARRIAGE IS PERMANENT AND INDISSOLUBLE

For Catholics there can be no doubt that marriage is permanent and indissoluble. This doctrine is found not only in the words of Christ, but in the proclamations of many Councils of the Church. The Council of Trent (1545-1563), for example, stated:

> If anyone should say that on account of heresy or the hardships of cohabitation, or a deliberate abuse of one party by the other, the marriage may be loosened, let him be anathema.[10]

And again:

> If anyone should say that the Church errs in having taught, or in teaching that according to the teaching of the Gospel and the Apostles, the bond of marriage cannot be loosed because of the sin of adultery of either party, or that neither party, even though one be innocent, having given no cause for the sin of adultery, can contract another marriage during the lifetime of the other and that he commits adultery who marries another after putting away his adulterous wife, and likewise that she commits adultery who puts away her husband and married another: Let him be anathema.[11]

The Third Council of Baltimore (1884) decreed:

> The pain of excommunication, reserved to the Bishop, to be incurred *ipso facto* by those attempting marriage after obtaining a civil divorce.

ST. MATTHEW ON DIVORCE

Unfortunately, the services of the marriage counselor are frequently sought by those who wish to attempt to justify a divorce with remarriage. Many of these will be people well read in religion, who may attempt to find in the words of the Gospel justification for their action. Many Christians who attempt to justify divorce do so by means of certain words of Christ quoted from the Gospel of St. Matthew. For this reason, the marriage counselor should be aware of this passage and its interpretation. He should be prepared to explain

[9] Pope Leo XIII, *Arcanum Divinae Sapientiae*, trans. Gerald C. Treacy, S.J. (New York: The Paulist Press, 1942), p. 18.

[10] H. J. Schroder, O.P., *Canons and Decrees of the Council of Trent*, original text with English translation (St. Louis: B. Herder Co., 1941).

[11] *Ibid.*

the Catholic attitude on the indissolubility of marriage, and to explain the difference between marriage as a sacrament and marriage as a civil contract. (These matters are discussed at greater length in the chapters "Marriage as a Sacrament" and "Canon Law of Marriage.")

Because of the importance placed upon the words of Christ in the Gospel of St. Matthew by various individuals, it is quoted here in full:

> (3) And there came to Him some Pharisees, testing Him, and saying: "Is it lawful for a man to put away his wife for every cause?" (4) But He answered and said to them: "Have you not read that He Who made man from the beginning made them male and female?" And He said: (5) "For this cause shall a man leave father and mother, and cleave to his wife, and they two shall be in one flesh. (6) Therefore, now they are not two, but one flesh. What therefore God hath joined together, let no man put asunder." (7) They said to Him: "Why then did Moses command to give a bill of divorce, and to put away?" (8) Jesus saith to them: "Because Moses by reason of the hardness of your heart permitted you to put away your wives, but from the beginning it was not so." (9) "And I say to you that whosoever shall put away his wife *except it be for fornication* and marries another, commits adultery; and he who marries a woman who has been put away commits adultery" (Mt. 19:3–9).

If the clause "except it be for fornication" is taken out of context and considered only by itself and without regard to other pronouncements made by Christ, it would seem to allow the remarriage of the husband. However, as any lawyer would state, any declaration made must be considered as part of the whole, and that other statements made by the same person may be used to interpret the total meaning of all of his statements. If all of the statements are taken into account, the most that the statement could mean was that such immorality would be justification of a limited separation **(a mensa et thoro).** In considering this passage from St. Matthew some theologians offer the explanation that Christ was speaking of divorce as allowed by God in the Old Law. There were two schools among the Jews as to the reason required for such a divorce. Our Lord was asked whether a man might put away his wife (in the Old Law) for **every** reason. His answer was — No — but only because of fornication (i.e., adultery). The New Law was stated by His Apostles. Consider, for example, this statement from St. Mark:

> When the tempting Pharisees had left, His disciples went back to the question again and this time the Master was very explicit. And

he said to them: "Whoever shall put away his wife and marry another committeth adultery against her. And if the wife shall put away her husband and be married to another, she committeth adultery" (Mk. 10:11–12).

Next to Christ Himself, His Apostles and disciples in their inspired words and writing were well qualified to give the doctrine as He had taught it. They were delegated by Divine Authority to speak in God's name:

For Christ, therefore, we are Ambassadors (2 Cor. 20).

What did these ambassadors say in regard to the marriage bond? St. Paul stated:

A woman is bound by the law as long as her husband liveth: but if her husband die, she is at liberty (1 Cor. 7:39).
Whilst her husband liveth, she shall be called an adulteress if she be with another man (Rom. 7:3).

And in order to make it evident that what he states is divine truth, he says:

To them that are married, not I, but the Lord commandeth, that the wife depart not from her husband. And if she depart, that she remain unmarried (1 Cor. 7:10, 11).

St. Luke repeats the same doctrine:

Everyone who puts away his wife and marries another commits adultery; and he who marries a woman who has been put away from her husband commits adultery (Lk. 16:18).

For anyone who is willing to be convinced, this would be sufficient. Those who are unwilling would not accept more. For further discussion of this subject see the chapter "Marriage as a Sacrament."[12]

The indissolubility of marriage is the keystone upon which the whole structure of marriage is built. If this is attacked the security of the marriage relationship is weakened, and this in turn renders the family itself insecure. Anyone who advocates more lenient divorce laws must remember the far-reaching effects which easy divorce will have on society as a whole.

As Chesterton remarked:

Because someone bumps into a thing, he calls it the nearest obstacle;

---

[12] See pp. 499 ff.

though the obstacle may happen to be the pillar that holds up the whole roof over his head. He industriously removes the obstacle; and in return the obstacle removes him. . . .[13]

Even those, who, for one reason or another, countenance divorce as a solution, still are aware of its impact upon society at large. In its decision on the case of Williams **vs.** North Carolina, the Supreme Court of the United States observed that:

Divorce, like marriage, is of concern not merely to the immediate parties. It affects personal rights of the deepest significance. It also touches basic interests of society. . . .[14]

HIDDEN CAUSES OF DIVORCE

A divorce may be obtained on a number of legal grounds; but it is well recognized that these are rarely the true cause. The parties to a divorce select a charge which is close enough to the real problem so that the case goes through without much opposition.

Groves, who recognizes this disparity between the legal and the real grounds, goes on to say that:

Often the reasons that appear to justify a divorce, as soon as they are closely and calmly examined, become more complex than they appeared at first sight. There is more root to them than we expected. Rarely are they entirely related to the other person. Even when they are clearly the consequence of the action of the other spouse, their significance is, in part at least, due to the personal history and disposition of the individual seeking the divorce.[15]

The number of situations which can break up a marriage is almost limitless. Some are so obvious they scarcely deserve attention; whereas

---

[13] G. K. Chesterton, *The Superstition of Divorce* (London: Chatto and Windus, 1920), p. 5.

[14] Williams *vs.* North Carolina, 325 U. S. 226, 89 L. ed. 1577, 65 Sup. Ct. 1092.

[15] Ernest R. Groves, *Conserving Marriage and the Family* (New York: The Macmillan Co., 1945), p. 5.

The National Office of Vital Statistics prefaces its data on divorce with the following remarks: "Although it is widely recognized that legal grounds (or causes) for divorces and annulments may be quite different from the underlying 'true' reasons for family breakup . . ." (*Divorce and Annulment Statistics, Specified States: 1948* [Washington, 1950], 35:12).

"Legal grounds are seldom the true causes. You have no choice but to select the one that seems most feasible from whatever number the law of your state permits" (Groves, *op cit.*, p. 4).

"Many of the apparently foolish and trivial grounds for divorce as reported in

others are so carefully hidden that the person mainly at fault may often fail to see his full responsibility.

Assuming good will on the part of both parties in their attempt to make the marriage work, the following table gives the most common hidden causes of divorce, as any marriage counselor of experience can verify. It is not, however, exhaustive.

1. Financial Problems
2. In-Law Troubles
   a) Momism
3. Sexual Maladjustment
   a) Ignorance
   b) Fear of pregnancy
   c) Infidelity
   d) Frigidity
   e) Impotence
   f) Lack of love-making
   g) Flirting
   h) Failure to keep attractive
4. Emotional Immaturity
5. Mental Illness
6. Neurotic Traits
   a) Alcoholism
   b) Disillusionment
   c) Pleasure philosophy
   d) Nagging
   e) Lack of confidence
   f) Lack of consideration
   g) Vulgarity
7. Social Factors
   a) Employment of wife
   b) Ease of divorce
   c) Lessened respect for integrity of marriage
   d) Prolonged separation
   e) Disagreement over how to raise children

These hidden causes of divorce should not be considered as isolated entities. A marriage does not usually break up for only one reason.

---

the daily papers or by friends, represent substitutions for the actual causes of something less intimate but more readily accepted by society at large" (Fred Brown and Rudolph T. Kempton, *Sex Questions and Answers* [New York: Whittlesey House, 1950], p. 210).

The breakup may begin because of one difficulty but hostility arising in this area soon spreads to others.

Many of these topics are discussed in other chapters so that not much need be said about them here.

FINANCIAL PROBLEMS

There is little doubt that poor management and misunderstanding about finances causes much marital discord. How could there fail to be difficulty when a girl who has been accustomed to supporting herself and spending her money as she sees fit marries a man who keeps such a tight hold on the purse strings that he is unwilling to give her even an allowance for her necessities. What is sometimes even more surprising is that such a girl will permit a state of affairs to develop wherein she has absolutely no spending money, even for cigarettes, Coca-Colas, or a sandwich with a friend whom she meets downtown. This type of control of the family finances by the husband can lead only to unhappiness and frequently to disaster. On the other hand, we frequently see a thoughtless wife who seems to feel that her husband's resources are unlimited, and who spends money either frivolously or for unnecessary things. Budgetary restrictions are undoubtedly necessary for most families. This should be worked out between the two parties acting as sensible adults who recognize their financial limitations, and who make the most of the funds which are available to them. It may be observed that failure to have an allowance would be a frivolous cause for serious marriage maladjustment. This is certainly true if one thinks only of direct cause and effect, but in regard to the hidden causes of divorce the mechanism is usually not cause followed immediately by effect. The process is much more intricate than this, and the real cause may even elude the couple who seriously attempt to discover the cause of their marital difficulties. What happens usually is that the minor factor acts as an irritant which by a process of radiation begins to include secondary situations so that, for example, hostility generated by no allowance may begin to effect other areas of life so that multiple annoyances begin to occur. These lead to further misunderstandings, and ultimately to a major break in the marital relation.

IN-LAWS

Problems of in-laws have already been discussed in the chapter on courtship and marriage. As has been pointed out, the difficulties here are more likely to arise in regard to the mother of the husband, than the mother of the girl. The male parent is not to be completely exonerated, but is certainly less frequently a major source of discord. Persistence of "The Silver Cord" seems to occur most frequently between the mother and son.[16]

SEXUAL MALADJUSTMENTS

Many of the subjects included under this title are discussed in greater detail in other chapters. They are mentioned here only for the sake of completeness.

Sexual ignorance and the need for education in sex are discussed in Chapter X.

Frigidity and impotence are covered in Chapter XIII.

The need for love-making is discussed in Chapter XII.

Fear of pregnancy is a very real but often unconscious cause of marital difficulties. Numerous cases could be given where fear of pregnancy has caused lifelong anxiety with a consequent sexual maladjustment. Some of this is due to misunderstanding of the attitude of the Church on the subject. The belief that intercourse may be performed only for the purpose of inducing pregnancy is a not uncommon belief. There are numerous individuals who misunderstand the teaching of the Church in the use of the Rhythm (see p. 279 ff.). There are others, who although understanding both of these properly have such a fear of pregnancy that they limit the relationship to only one or two days a month or who can only tolerate the relationship while strongly influenced by alcohol. Others will permit the relationship only during the menstrual period because of their mistaken belief that pregnancy cannot occur at this time. Lest one believe that such fear exists only in the female partner, I must add that although it is less frequent the male also suffers seriously from similar fears of having another child and will either abstain from sexual relations or act immorally to overcome it.

"Sex by the calendar" is a frequent comment made by those men whose wives insist on the use of the Rhythm Method of conception control. Even those husbands who fear future pregnancies ridicule the natural method. They seem to take it as a personal affront that they must practice abstinence as a method of controlling the size of the family. They should give thought, however, to these facts: First,

---

[16] Edward Strecker, *Their Mother's Sons* (Philadelphia: J. B. Lippincott Co., 1946).

that any sexual satisfaction too frequently indulged will produce a sense of satiety and no longer be as enjoyable; for this reason sexual relations bring greater satisfaction when they follow a period of abstinence. Second, that since the anticipation is always greater than the pleasure that abstinence heightens the pleasure. Third, that there is greater happiness in the marriages of those who lead a moral life which permits them more complete enjoyment which comes when there is no associated feeling of guilt. Fourth, that although it is true that the woman's greatest sexual desire occurs at the time of ovulation, there is a period of equally great desire just before and after the menstrual periods. Fifth, that any man or woman who is unable to control his or her sexual impulses for a few days each month is hardly a normal person and is in need of training to develop greater moral stamina. They are weak, immature individuals. Sixth, that for those individuals employing the Rhythm, the first day of each sterile period becomes an event and should be so regarded by both partners. There is no greater feeling of rejection than that of the husband, who has waited for two weeks, than to have his wife appear on this special evening with her hair in curlers and the statement, "I am dead tired and I am going to bed with the children."

Infidelity. Except for the emotionally and sexually immature individual who has never developed any proper moral sense or control, the "other woman" is a sign of serious marital difficulty. It is important for the counselor to remember that the appearance of the "other woman" is seldom the beginning of the difficulties between the husband and wife. She is more often an end product of already existing difficulties. In discussing the question of infidelity, great care should be exercised because this idea is a frequent first manifestation of a mental disorder. For this reason it is especially important to discuss the question with both partners and perhaps with the other members of the family. Be sure first to obtain permission from the individual who first sought your help. Do not make accusations against one party on the basis of allegations made by the other. Aside from the fact that the marriage counselor should be nonjudgmental, it is unwise to act or speak before one is sure of the facts.

Flirting. Some women, and also some men, have the mistaken notion that flirting stimulates the interest of their husband or wife in them. Nothing is further from the truth. They should be completely disabused of the idea that flirting is helpful in any way. It is destructive, annoying, creates tensions, and leads only to jealousy and com-

unhappiness. If one finds that, under the influence of alcohol, he makes amorous advances toward members of the opposite sex, he should limit his indulgence in alcohol. Not only does he stir up marital discord; he creates a great deal of criticism and scandal — not only for himself but for the people toward whom he directs his advances.

EMOTIONAL IMMATURITY

If there is one basic cause of marital difficulties, emotional immaturity undoubtedly deserves first rank.

We have already dealt with the subject in the chapter on courtship and marriage; but a few more remarks are applicable here.

The emotionally immature person is the emotionally unstable person — the individual who lacks control over the strong instinctual drives which, if employed for their specific purposes, further his or her welfare. All instinctual drives are co-ordinated by the power of reason in a person who is emotionally stable so that they work for the good of the whole person. But in the emotionally unstable these drives are un-co-ordinated and, instead of fulfilling their natural purpose, take over the individual and push him from one direction to another. Such an individual is incapable of pursuing for long any direct course in his or her emotional life. Incapable as they are of any sustained purpose, they are commensurately incapable of genuine love.

Adult human love possesses a number of distinct attributes among which is the capacity to give without getting something immediately in return. The immature, impetuous, or narcissistic individual never has attained this capacity. He or she thinks only in terms of immediate wish-fulfillments, immediate satisfaction. Like the man who killed the goose that laid golden eggs, the emotionally immature person demands immediate fulfillments which in the long run may have a harmful effect on his person.

When immediate satisfactions are not forthcoming, he projects his inadequacy in the form of hostility.

It is not hard to see how two people who are living together and do not have the capacity to love maturely are almost inevitably doomed to constant bickering, misunderstanding, fighting, and eventual hatred for each other. Appeals to their sense of duty, to their sense of moral obligation in making a solemn promise in the marriage contract, are of no avail. The immature want pleasure here and now. They say that they are entitled to it, that all they want is happiness, and they are searching for it. The fact is that they never can find happiness or achieve it on a lasting plane because the fault lies within themselves. It lies in their inability to give without getting.

With the loss of the first physical glow, with increased responsibilities, with the recognition that the partner has faults which during courtship he chose to ignore, the emotionally immature partner feels that he (or she) has been denied the right of free expression and happiness and that he is free to seek whatever he wants.

Such people are constantly blaming their difficulties on their environment. They jump from one partner to another, becoming more confused each time, and finally end their search in utter frustration.

MENTAL ILLNESS

This is a subject so broad in scope that it cannot be discussed properly in the narrow limits of this chapter. The term "mental illness" includes all varieties of psychiatric disorders. These may be classified as:

1. Personality disorders;
2. Psychoneuroses;
3. Psychoses;
4. Somatopsychic disorders;
5. Defect states including mental deficiency.

For the information of the counselor we will define these terms.

Those who are psychotic and mentally deficient are unable to properly contract a marriage because they do not have the mental capacity to do so. **Psychoses are either temporary or prolonged grave deviations from normalcy in judging, reasoning, and willing which are the result of the individual's failure to adequately solve his conflicts and which may result in disturbed or inappropriate emotions, delusions, seriously irregular conduct, and deep-seated personality disorganization, and other symptoms.**[17]

Mental deficiency is defined in the classification adopted by the American Psychiatric Association as follows:

Here will be classified those cases presenting primarily a defect of intelligence existing since birth, without demonstrated organic brain disease or known prenatal cause. This group will include only those cases formerly known as familial or "idiopathic" mental deficiencies.

[17] John R. Cavanagh and James B. McGoldrick, S.J., *Fundamental Psychiatry* (Milwaukee: The Bruce Publishing Co., 1953), p. 288.

The degree of intelligence defect will be specified as mild, moderate, or severe, and the current I.Q. rating, with the name of the test used, will be added to the diagnosis. In general, mild refers to functional (vocational) impairment; as would be expected with I.Q. of approximately 70 to 85; moderate is used for functional impairment requiring special training and guidance, such as would be expected with I.Q.'s of about 50–70; severe refers to the functional impairment requiring custodial or complete protective care, as would be expected with I.Q.'s below 50. The degree of defect is estimated from other factors than merely psychological test scores, namely, consideration of cultural, physical and emotional determinants, as well as school, vocational and social effectiveness. The diagnosis may be modified by the appropriate qualifying phrase, when, in addition to the intellectual defects, there are significant psychotic, neurotic or behavioral reactions.[18]

A **psychoneurosis** may be described as follows:

1. Neuroses are defensive mechanisms which are utilized to preserve the individual from the result of deflating experiences that threaten his ego.
2. They are a group of personality reaction patterns produced by warped habits which had their origin in insecurity, fear, and worry.
3. Neuroses are disorders of psychogenic origin characterized by more or less habitual personality deficiencies and erroneous attitudes toward life caused by unsolved conflicts, early frustration, and an urge to escape depressing emotions.
4. They are disorders in which psychic forces beget various mental and physical symptoms which serve as a means of escape and protection from irritating emotions.
5. Neurotic symptoms symbolize unsatisfactory patterns of adjustment to conflicts that threaten the personality.
6. Neuroses are syndromes which represent a balance or type of equilibrium reached by the individual between his own psychic forces and the disintegrating influences of his environment.
7. The neuroses are psychic disorders in which disabling symptoms arise consequent to the deep and profound realization that life's conflicts have not been adequately solved.[19]

A neurotic individual has most of his libido invested in himself and becomes an increasingly poor marriage risk in proportion to the severity of his neurosis.

---

[18] American Psychiatric Association, Mental Hospital Service, *Diagnostic and Statistical Manual of Mental Disorders* (1952), pp. 23–24.
[19] Cavanagh and McGoldrick, *op. cit.*, p. 220.

A **personality disorder** is described by the standard nomenclature as follows:

These disorders are characterized by developmental defects or pathological trends in the personality structure, with minimal subjective anxiety, and little or no sense of distress. In most instances, the disorder is manifested by a lifelong pattern of action or behavior, rather than by mental or emotional symptoms. These may manifest themselves in the following types:

1. Inadequate personality

    Such individuals are characterized by inadequate response to intellectual, emotional, social and physical demands. They are neither physically nor mentally grossly deficient on examination, but they do show inadaptability, ineptness, poor judgment, lack of physical and emotional stamina and social incompatibility.

2. Schizoid personality

    Inherent traits in such personalities are (1) avoidance of close relations with others, (2) inability to express directly hostility or even ordinary aggressive feelings, and (3) autistic thinking. These qualities result early in coldness, aloofness, emotional detachment, fearfulness, avoidance of competition and day dreams revolving around the need for omnipotence. As children, they are usually quiet, shy, obedient, sensitive and retiring. At puberty, they frequently become more withdrawn, then manifesting the aggregate of personality traits known as introversion, namely, quietness, seclusiveness, "shut-in-ness," and unsociability, often with eccentricity.

3. Cyclothymic personality

    Such individuals are characterized by extratensive and outgoing adjustment to life situations, an apparent personal warmth, friendliness and superficial generosity, and emotional reaching out to the environment, and a ready enthusiasm for competition. Characteristics are frequently alternating moods of elation and sadness, stimulated apparently by internal factors rather than by external events. The individual may occasionally be either persistently euphoric or depressed, without falsification or distortion of reality. The diagnosis in such cases should specify, if possible, whether hypomanic, depressed or alternating.

4. Paranoid personality

    Such individuals are characterized by many traits of the Schizoid personality, coupled with an exquisite sensitivity in interpersonal relations, and with a conspicuous tendency to utilize a projection mechanism, expressed by suspiciousness, envy, extreme jealousy and stubbornness.[20]

No general statement can be made in regard to these personality types as marriage risks. Each must be investigated and evaluated individually. The inadequate and paranoid personality types are those most poorly adapted to marriage.

Somatopsychic disorders may be defined as:

> Those whose onset and development require as a necessary prerequisite the presence of cerebral or spinal degeneration, organic disease, trauma, or some other type of physical disturbance in which the development of mental manifestations is the result of the patient's psychic response to the presence of the disease.[21]

SUMMARY STATEMENT REGARDING MENTAL ILLNESS

No further comment will be made here in regard to these psychiatric disorders. If the reader has had special training in psychiatry, anything which would be said would be repetitious. If the reader has had no training, anything which could be said would be inadequate. Beware of being an amateur psychiatrist. If there appears to be a real psychiatric problem get professional help.

NEUROTIC TRAITS

Alcoholism. This has been discussed in a separate chapter (see Chapter XVI).

Disillusionment. Much of the disillusionment concerning marriage comes from an initial failure on the part of the couple to recognize reality as it is. A great deal of their failure comes about because they hold on to a **pleasure philosophy of life.** The couple have usually been acquainted for only a short time before their marriage. The obvious solution for this is a longer period of courtship so that the couple may get to know each other in all types of situations.

Vulgarity. This is sometimes unknown or unsuspected before marriage. When it appears, it produces more than mere disillusionment — it may actually produce revulsion — which may result in the development of severe neurotic traits in the offended person. An instance of this was the case of a wife who became seriously ill and required

---

[20] American Psychiatric Association, *op. cit.,* pp. 35–36.
[21] Cavanagh and McGoldrick, *op. cit.,* p. 415.

hospitalization on several occasions; her husband, whom she described as oversexed, was in the habit of walking around the house with little on but his shorts, and often with his genitals showing — and all this in the presence of their adolescent daughters!

Failure to keep attractive. This fault is closely akin to vulgarity. Too often the husband or wife fail to keep themselves physically attractive and acquire slovenly habits of dress. When it comes to remaining attractive, a wife ought to remember the advice given by Mrs. Eisenhower: "A wife does not have to be 'dolled-up' in expensive clothes all the time, but I think it is dreadful for a pretty bride to go around in cold cream or curlers, or a sloppy dress. Who ever heard of a secretary wearing a spotted dress to work because 'It is just the office and no one will see but just the boss.' Your husband is the boss, and don't forget it."[22]

If keeping neat and attractive needs further emphasis, these words of Thomas Jefferson may be quoted: "Some ladies think they may under the privileges of the deshabille be loose and negligent of their dress in the morning, but be you from the moment you rise until you go to bed as cleanly and properly dressed as of the hours of dinner or tea."

SOCIAL FACTORS

Employment of wife. During the period immediately after marriage it is quite feasible for a woman to work outside her home. It may even be desirable for a woman who has vitality and whose household is not yet large enough to occupy her for the whole day. However, if a wife continues work for a short time after marriage, her attitude toward the work ought to be that it is something temporary, something subordinate to the interests of her married life. She ought never to consider her outside work so important that she gives up a chance of having children to advance her career. Having taken on the married state, she has adopted the vocation of a wife and mother. If she is continuing her outside work against the objections of her husband, she is doing him an injustice. A man has a right to demand of his wife more than a casual acquaintance.

The husband can err similarly when, in carrying out his role as the breadwinner of the family, he becomes totally preoccupied with his work and fails to become a companion to his wife and a father to his children.

---

[22] Llewellyn Miller, *Today's Woman*, June, 1948.

Contrariwise, we find husbands and wives erring in the opposite direction. The wife, after marriage, severs all contact with outside influences and becomes overly preoccupied with the home. She becomes a crashing bore, and discourages all rapport between herself and her husband. The result is that he loses interest, and this can be dangerous. A wife should always realize that, though she is physically absent, she is unconsciously subjected by her husband to comparison with other women whom he meets during working hours. However kindly his disposition may be, a husband may find it difficult to find common ground between himself and the "homebody" whose most interesting bit of conversation is that the milkman forgot to leave two quarts of milk or who discusses in detail a new recipe for white sauce.[23]

Prolonged separation. Enforced separation, particularly long separations such as occurred in World War II when men were overseas for a year or more, may contribute directly to divorce. Separation for some may lead to infidelity, for others to a feeling of independence, but for most it leads to an overidealization of the loved one. This overidealization causes the individual in phantasy to forget most of the irritating qualities of his spouse and to exaggerate her perfections. This occurs particularly in the male, who as a result of overidealization forgets that he has married a nice but ordinary girl who has imperfections as well as perfections; who is probably not the most beautiful girl in the world but also not the worst-looking; instead, in phantasy he places her upon a pedestal and endows her with many qualities which she does not have. As a consequence, when he returns to the everyday world of civilian life she fails to measure up to his idealized concept of her. She falls from her pedestal with a crash, and as a consequence the marriage gets into serious difficulties. Absence undoubtedly makes the heart grow fonder, but this fondness must stay within realistic limits.

In the period of separation husband and wife are subjected to different influences which may change their character if the separation is sufficiently prolonged. Many couples were unsuccessful in their attempts at readjustment and simply dissolved the marriage.

SUMMARY

It would be ideal if all people were outgoing, emotionally mature, and had a proper love of God and their fellow men. A marriage

---

[23] See footnote 8, Chapter XXVI, p. 407.

between two people in this category is almost bound to succeed because their capacity to adjust to each other and to future difficulties of any nature is sufficient to carry them through. In a like manner, it is highly probable that if one partner is mature and the other is an immature, dependent, possessive type, the marriage will succeed so long as the demands made on it are not too severe. However, with two emotionally unstable, immature, neurotic, and egocentric individuals who contract a marriage, it is almost impossible to see how it can succeed. Some do because of external factors like money, religion, or habit; but with each internal or external stress the partners retreat into their own egotistical sphere and project their inadequacies on the other.

The rule of divorce will decrease only when people are able to accept their responsibilities, acknowledge their obligations, and deflate their egos and to accept the unchanging laws of God as made known by reason and revelation. Modern man too long has been driven and motivated by a pure pleasure principle, seeking now this and now that, only to find that these vaporous goods have no appeal once they are attained.

Divorce is wrong not only because it undermines human society, but also because it is a breach of an obligation which was entered into with the utmost solemnity at marriage. And it need hardly be mentioned that in those cases where only one partner desires the divorce, he or she is purchasing happiness at the expense of the other.

CONCLUSION

There are practically no instances where an absolute divorce is necessary or desirable. As pointed out by Pope Pius XI in the encyclical letter **Casti Connubii,** separation from bed and board eliminates the need for legal divorce. His Holiness stated:

> This separation, which the Church herself permits and expressly mentions in her Canon Law in those canons which deal with the separation of the parties as to marital relationship and co-habitation, removes all the alleged inconveniences and dangers. It will be for the sacred law and to some extent also the civil law, insofar as civil matters are affected, to lay down the grounds, the conditions, the method and precautions to be taken in a case of this kind in order to safeguard the education of the children and the well-being of the family, and to remove all those evils which threaten the married persons, the children and the State.[24]

[24] Pope Pius XI, *Casti Connubii* (New York: The Paulist Press, n.d.), pp. 28–29.

TABLE 5.07. MEDIAN AGE OF BRIDE AND OF GROOM AT MARRIAGE, BY RACE: 20 REPORTING STATES, 1950

(By place of occurrence)

AREA	BRIDE			GROOM		
	Total	White	Non-white	Total	White	Non-white
TOTAL . . .	22.5	22.5	22.8	24.9	24.8	26.4
Alabama	21.0	20.8	21.5	24.3	24.1	24.8
California . . .	23.3	23.2	24.6	25.7	25.5	28.3
Connecticut . . .	24.0	24.0	24.4	26.8	26.7	27.2
Delaware	23.3	23.2	23.7	25.8	25.5	27.3
Florida	23.8	24.0	22.7	26.9	27.1	26.0
Idaho	21.5	21.5	(¹)	24.6	24.6	(¹)
Iowa	21.7	21.7	23.9	24.2	24.1	27.1
Kansas	21.6	21.5	23.5	24.2	24.2	26.6
Louisiana² . . .	21.9	21.7	22.4	24.7	24.4	25.7
Maine	21.9	21.9	(¹)	24.4	24.4	(¹)
Michigan	22.4	22.4	23.3	24.5	24.4	26.7
Mississippi . . .	21.2	20.7	22.3	24.6	24.3	26.2
Missouri	23.0	22.8	24.7	25.5	25.2	28.5
New Hampshire .	23.5	23.4	(¹)	26.1	26.0	(¹)
New York³ . . .	22.9	22.9	23.7	25.0	24.9	26.7
South Dakota . .	21.7	21.7	23.0	24.5	24.5	28.1
Tennessee . . .	22.0	21.9	23.4	24.4	24.3	27.2
Vermont	22.1	22.1	(¹)	24.6	24.5	(¹)
Virginia	22.7	22.7	22.5	24.7	24.6	25.2
Wyoming . . .	22.8	22.8	(¹)	25.2	25.1	(¹)

[1] Median not computed for frequencies of less than 100.

[2] Excludes the following 9 parishes: Beauregard, Bienville, De Soto, Jefferson, Orleans, Pointe Coupee, St. Martin, Vermilion, and Webster. Estimated State total, 26,900.

[3] Excludes 82,535 marriages for which licenses had been issued in New York City.

NOTE — Medians computed from distributions of marriages by 5-year age groups.

This chart is taken from Vital Statistics of the United States, 1950, Vol. I, p. 71, U. S. Department of Health Education and Welfare (U. S. Government Printing Office, 1954).

CHAPTER XXV

Canon Law of Marriage

ROMAEUS O'BRIEN

Christ entrusted the government of man's salvation to the Church which He established. To this Church, the Catholic Church, He gave the power of infallibly declaring and interpreting the natural law binding upon all human beings. Moreover, He left His Church as the indisputable custodian of all His means of sanctification. Since the sacrament of marriage is one of these means instituted by Christ, its custody is in the hands of the Church. Accordingly, the Church has the right and the obligation to preserve so sacred an institution as the sacrament of marriage from any possible profanation or abuse. To cope with this responsibility the Church has developed a body of laws governing the sacrament of marriage.[1] It is this body of laws which is to be examined in the present chapter. Before explaining these laws, however, it is necessary to delineate briefly the authority of the Church and State over marriage.

THE AUTHORITY OF THE CHURCH OVER MARRIAGE

In the first place, it must be noted that marriage is a divine institution governed by certain laws beyond all human authority.[2] These are the **laws of unity, perpetuity, indissolubility, and of the individual man's right to marriage.** A knowledge of these laws is native to man

---

[1] These laws are to be found in the official law book for the Latin Church, namely: *Codex Juris Canonici Pii X Pontificis Maximi iussu digestus, Benedicti Papae XV auctoritate promulgatus* (Romae: Typis Polyglottis Vaticanis, 1917). The pertinent canons on marriage are found in the section from Canon 1012 to Canon 1143. Hereafter reference to this work will be made by citing the canon, e.g., Canon 1012.

[2] Encyclical letter of Pope Pius XI, *On Christian Marriage (Casti Connubii)* (Rome, 1930), paragraph 5. Translation from the Latin printed and published by the Paulist Press, New York. Hereafter reference to this encyclical will be made by the title and paragraph number.

independently of all revelation. By **the law of unity** marriage is an exclusive contract between one man and one woman to the absolute exclusion of all others. **Perpetuity** insures a permanent transfer of mutual love by the conferring of reciprocal rights to each other. The **indissolubility** of marriage insures a lasting contract which even the partners cannot dissolve. Finally, the encyclical of Pius XI clearly establishes the **primeval right of man to marriage** as a right beyond the authority of human power. Because these laws are of divine legislation no human power has authority to dispense in these matters.[3] Recognizing the divine establishment of such marriage laws, one can understand the egregious error of the State in permitting remarriage while a previous bond exists. Nor is it possible to defend the State's occasional claim to an absolute right of impeding marriage for punitive or eugenic reasons:

> As regards State laws requiring medical certificate of freedom from disease as a prerequisite either for licitness or validity of marriage . . . in the case of baptized persons, they exceed the limits of the State's authority.[4]

The State, however, may forbid for eugenic reasons the marriage of the unbaptized for a time.[5] Actually, the right of the State over marriage is quite circumscribed, for as Pope Pius XI teaches: "The family is more sacred than the State. . . ."[6]

When **two baptized persons** contract a valid marriage they receive and give a sacrament and enter upon a sacred union which is intended by Christ to be an unfailing channel of grace. The Church alone, as the custodian of Christ's sacraments, has the native and exclusive right to legislate for the validity of that sacrament.[7] Thus she alone may create impediments to the sacrament and establish conditions necessary for its reception.[8] In this sacramental sphere marriage is beyond the scope of the State's jurisdiction. This doctrine is true in

---

[3] *Ibid.,* paragraph 8.

[4] T. Lincoln Bouscaren and Adam Ellis, *Canon Law,* 2 rev. ed. (Milwaukee: The Bruce Publishing Co., 1951), p. 462, n. 23. Hereafter, reference to this work will be made as follows: Bouscaren-Ellis, *Canon Law,* p. . . . .

[5] Louis Nau, *Manual on the Marriage Laws of the Code of Canon Law,* 2 rev. ed. (New York: Pustet Co., 1934), p. 20. Hereafter reference to this work will be made as follows: Nau, *Marriage Legislation,* p. . . . .

[6] Pope Pius XI, *On Christian Marriage,* paragraph 69.

[7] H. J. Schroeder, O.P., *Canons and Decrees of the Council of Trent,* original text with English translation (St. Louis: B. Herder Book Co., 1941), Canons 1 and 12, pp. 180–181.

[8] Canon 1038, § 2.

all marriages of two validly baptized persons, whether they be Catholic or Protestant, for their valid baptism elevates their marital contract to the dignity of a sacrament and subjects it to the law of Christ's Church. The authority of the State is limited strictly to the area of merely civil effects, for example, right to the husband's name on the part of the wife, the right of succession, etc.[9]

With sincere concern, however, for the validity of the marriages of baptized non-Catholics, Church law grants **two noteworthy exemptions** in their behalf. In the first place, the marriage of a baptized non-Catholic to an unbaptized person is exempted from the impediment of **disparity of cult** so that the contract is valid even though no dispensation has been obtained for the marriage.[10] Second, a baptized non-Catholic contracting marriage with another baptized non-Catholic **is not obliged to have his marriage witnessed by a priest,** unless he or the other party is one who has lapsed from the Catholic faith.[11] It is worthy of note that the Church is sometimes accused of denying the validity of all marriages contracted before a judge or a minister. Such an accusation is far from the true Catholic teaching. Only a Catholic or a lapsed Catholic is obliged to have his marriage witnessed by a priest and two witnesses under penalty of invalidity. The marriages of other people not subject to ecclesiastical law are certainly valid, presupposing that there are no impediments to the marriages and that there are fulfilled all the requisites of the natural law.

Although it is certain that the marriage of a baptized person to an unbaptized person is not a sacrament, it is nevertheless true that such a marriage is governed exclusively by Church law. Both parties to the marriage enter into a divinely established union which is sacred in the law of nature itself. For the baptized person it is even more: it is an action with a particular bearing on his sanctification and, therefore, an action in which the Church is vitally interested. Regarding the competence of either Church or State over such a union, authors disagree.[12] Some would maintain that the State laws must be observed, because the unbaptized person is subject to them. Nevertheless, since the contract (regardless of the subjection of the partners to different

---

[9] Canon 1016.

[10] Canon 1070, § 1. The Greek Orthodox are bound by this impediment by the law of the Eastern Church. Cf. Canon 60, *Motu Proprio, "Crebrae allatae,"* February 22, 1949; *Acta Apostolicae Sedis,* XXXXI (1949), p. 102.

[11] Canon 1099, § 1, 1°.

[12] Bouscaren-Ellis, *Canon Law,* p. 463; Nau, *Marriage Legislation,* pp. 16–17.

jurisdictions) is a unified entity, the superiority of the Church's jurisdiction is more commonly held to prevail.

Finally, there are the **marriages of the unbaptized** to be considered. Since these people are not subjects of the Church because they have never been baptized, they do not fall within the scope of her legislation. Her only right over their marriages is the power to give authoritative interpretations and declarations regarding their rights and duties under the natural law.[13] On the other hand, the State enjoys a peculiar authority in matters pertaining to them. The authority of the State is extended into the realm of a religious power over them, not as a purely secular authority to which spiritual power is subordinated, but as the power of a God-given social superior. Thus, the State can legislate in regard to the unbaptized even to the extent of creating invalidating impediments provided these are reasonable and do not derogate from the laws established over marriage by God Himself.[14]

SUMMARY

To summarize, the Church alone can legislate for any marriage involving a baptized person, while the State has a limited competence over the marriages of the unbaptized. For all marriages, however, the State has the right to establish legislation regarding merely civil aspects.

With her God-given authority in the declaration and interpretation of natural law and over the sacrament of marriage, the Church has developed a concise body of laws for the protection of her subjects and the preservation of the sanctity of marriage.

CHURCH LAW ON MARRIAGE

For the sake of order, the following plan has been adopted for the examination of the Church's laws on marriage. In this chapter the first section, which follows immediately, will deal with the prenuptial investigation of the parties and the impediments to marriage. The next section of the chapter will concern itself with the actual marriage ceremony (when it can take place, where, and under what conditions). The third and final section will consider the marriage after the ceremony and will treat mainly of the defects which can make the marriage invalid.

---

[13] Canon 1038, § 1.

[14] Arthur Vermeersch, S.J., and T. Lincoln Bouscaren, S.J., *What is Marriage?* (New York: The America Press, 1931), p. 12.

I. BEFORE THE MARRIAGE CEREMONY

PRENUPTIAL INVESTIGATION

Previous to every marriage an investigation must be held to ascertain whether the parties are entering the marriage willingly and with complete freedom. Moreover, it must be clear that neither party is laboring under any impediment to the marriage.[15] Ordinarily this **prenuptial investigation** takes place in the parish of one of the parties, and this, of course, raises a question regarding the proper parish for the marriage. The parish of the bride is normally the parish in which the marriage should take place, but it may be celebrated in the presence of an authorized priest even outside the parish of either party with due permission of the proper pastor.[16] The bride's pastor is competent to give permission for the marriage to be celebrated elsewhere. Even the groom's pastor may give the permission if a good reason exists for asking him in preference to the bride's pastor. Likewise, either pastor may accede to the request of the parties and authorize some other priest to come into the parish and witness the marriage.[17] The reason for the ruling that the marriage be performed in the parish of one of the parties is based on the presumption that less chance for deception exists where the parties to the marriage are interrogated by one who knows them. Moreover, the pastor is the specific shepherd of the spiritual lives of his parishioners and it is only proper that he witness, or at least be consulted about, the marriage of a subject.

When the couple present themselves to the parish in which they are to marry, they should bring **a recent baptismal certificate** if they have been baptized elsewhere. Baptism is a necessary prerequisite for the reception of the other sacraments, and so the priest must be certain that the parties have actually been baptized. It is well to note that the certificate must be a recent one (i.e., one issued within the past six months).[18] The certificate may offer information concerning the person: what sacraments have been received, whether he has taken religious vows or whether he has been previously married. It may greatly aid the pastor in determining the status of the person; how-

---

[15] Canon 1019, § 1.
[16] Canon 1096.
[17] *Ibid.*
[18] Canon 1021; *Instruction of the Sacred Congregation of the Sacraments,* June 29, 1941; *Acta Apostolicae Sedis,* XXXIV (1941), p. 300.

ever, if it is very old, there is no certainty that the certificate gives a complete picture of the party's true status.

After the preliminary details have been arranged with the priest, the parties are interrogated individually according to a well-planned questionnaire which is to be filed afterward in the parish. The list of questions may differ from diocese to diocese but they agree universally in essentials. The questions aim to establish the fact that the parties are entering the marriage of their own accord and that they are laboring under no canonical impediments (see p. 432 f.).

IMPEDIMENTS

An **impediment is an obstacle that stands in the way of marriage** and it may be one of two types. One type is called **prohibitive,** the other is called **diriment.** If two people marry while still under a prohibitive impediment, their action is unlawful but the marriage is valid; if two people marry while under a diriment impediment, no true marriage takes place, for the diriment impediment makes it impossible to contract a true marriage bond until the impediment ceases or a dispensation is obtained. Hence, for one to hide a prohibitive impediment and contract marriage would be a grave sin, but the marriage would be valid. But with a diriment impediment, in addition to grave sin there would be no real marriage, nor could there be one until the cessation of, or dispensation from, the impediment.

Knowledge of the impediment is not required for actual subjection to it. Thus, even non-Catholics who may have no knowledge of impediments fall under them. For this reason some allowance is made in favor of Protestants in order to safeguard the validity of their marriage; as mentioned earlier, they are not held to the impediment of **disparity of worship** and so they may marry an unbaptized person without any dispensation. The Church can waive her right in such fashion with regard to ecclesiastical law, but not with regard to the divine law.[19] Hence, she cannot permit anyone to contract marriage in cases where a previous bond exists, or in a case of premarital and perpetual sexual impotency.

A. The Prohibitive Impediments

1. Vow. A vow is a free promise made to God.[20] According to

---

[19] Francis J. Connell, C.SS.R., *Outlines of Moral Theology* (Milwaukee: The Bruce Publishing Company, 1953), p. 30.

[20] Canon 1307, § 1.

Church law, anyone who makes a vow which is opposed to the rights or obligations of marriage is forbidden to marry until a dispensation from the vow has been obtained. Such a vow would be the simple vow of chastity professed in religious congregations and societies. Likewise, a private vow freely and deliberately made not to marry, or to remain a virgin always, or to observe perfect chastity, or to receive Holy Orders, or to enter the religious life would prohibit marriage.[21] For a serious reason the Church may relax her prohibition to marry by granting a dispensation but a priest would have to be consulted in each case.

2. **Legal adoption. This impediment has no binding force in the United States,** but is included here for the sake of completeness. It obliges in those places where civil law makes illegal a marriage between an adopted person and the adopting person. The law of the Church states that legal adoption is an impediment only in those places where the civil law considers it so.[22] Since the civil law in the United States permits marriage between these parties, no dispensation is necessary for there is no impediment.

3. **Mixed religion.** The final prohibitive impediment concerns itself with marriage between baptized persons, only one of whom is a Catholic.[23] This impediment and the diriment impediment of **disparity of cult** constitute the two "mixed-marriage" situations. Although the effect of violation of each of these differs (the former merely prohibits the marriage; the latter not only prohibits but actually invalidates), what is to be said concerning the dispensation of one holds equally true for the other.

The Church is strongly opposed to mixed marriages. Pope Pius XI in his encyclical on marriage insists upon the Church's prohibition of these marriages:

> They, therefore, who rashly and heedlessly contract mixed marriages, from which the maternal love and providence of the Church dissuades her children for very sound reasons, fail conspicuously in this respect

21 Canon 1058, § 1. The vow of virginity excludes the first complete act of venereal pleasure, while the vow of perfect chastity excludes every act of carnal pleasure. Virginity is irreparably lost by an external, complete act; the vow is thereby rendered impossible of fulfillment and no longer binds. But chastity can be observed even though virginity has been lost.

22 Canon 1059. We were unable to confirm the statement of Father Healy that legal relationship is a bar to civil marriage in Connecticut, Massachusetts, and Rhode Island. (Edwin F. Healy, S.J., *Marriage Guidance* [Chicago: Loyola University Press, 1948], p. 185.)

23 Canon 1060. See Chapter XXVIII.

(against the Sacredness of Marriage), sometimes with danger to their eternal salvation. The attitude of the Church to mixed marriages appears in many of her documents, all of which are summed up in the Code of Canon Law: "Everywhere and with the greatest strictness the Church forbids marriages between baptized persons, one of whom is Catholic and the other a member of a schismatical or heretical sect."[24]

The **attitude of the Church toward mixed marriages** is based upon the disadvantages created in such marriages for the parties and children. Differing upon such a fundamental issue as religion, the partners have less chance for unity of thought and sentiment than if their beliefs were the same. Moreover, marriage is intended by Almighty God to be a means of mutual sanctification for the partners. The fulfillment of this end is more difficult in a mixed marriage. Finally, there is serious danger that, despite promises to the contrary, the religious observance of the Catholic party will deteriorate. With regard to the children, there is a danger of inculcating religious indifference when they see the different observances of their parents.

Mixed marriages are prohibited by the divine law if there is danger of perversion of the Faith for the Catholic party or children to be born of the marriage.[25] **If,** however, **such danger is not present,** a dispensation from the ecclesiastical impediment may be granted **for a serious reason.** Before dispensing, the Church demands assurance that this danger of perversion will not be present. This assurance is obtained by requiring the non-Catholic to agree explicitly to a policy of noninterference with the practice of the Faith by the Catholic party and by requiring that both parties promise that all children who will be born will be baptized and brought up as Catholics.[26]

In addition to the above promise by the non-Catholic, the various dioceses of the country frequently add amendments to the general law. Depending upon the practice of the particular diocese, one or all of the following promises may also be demanded: (1) no other ceremony will take place after the Catholic ceremony; (2) the Church's law on marriage and birth control will be observed; and (3) on the death of the Catholic party, the non-Catholic will provide for the Catholic education of the children. Through such additional promises, the priest is able to give greater credence to the promises demanded by the general law and thus acquire moral certitude that the marriage is lawful before the divine law.

---

[24] *On Christian Marriage,* paragraph 82.
[25] Canon 1060.   [26] Canon 1061, § 1, 2°; see Chapter XXVIII.

Of course, it would almost be meaningless to give a sheet of promises like the above to a non-Catholic without any instructions regarding them and their fulfillment. The signing of the promises should, therefore, follow a series of instructions which explain the Catholic doctrine on marriage. These instructions will likewise explain the different obligations that are required of the non-Catholic party. If the instructions and promises are properly executed, there will ordinarily be sufficient assurance that the divine law will be observed and, reasons warranting it, an ecclesiastical dispensation may be sought for the marriage.

B. The Diriment Impediments

1. **Age.** The only age required by the natural law for marriage is that age at which the parties have the use of reason and the mental capacity for matrimonial consent. The legal age established by civil law varies greatly but all civil jurisdictions go beyond that required by the natural law.

Canon Law states that the man must have completed his sixteenth year; the woman, her fourteenth year.[27] But even these age limits are a minimum requirement, for the Church does not wish to encourage such early marriages. In fact, she counsels her priests to follow the civil law and the custom of the place.[28] For instance, although a valid marriage can be contracted in the Church by a boy of sixteen years and a girl of fourteen, ecclesiastical authorities will be prone to follow the civil law if such a marriage is therein prohibited. Such a policy of the ecclesiastical authority is not founded upon a sense of subordination to civil authority, but rather upon a recognition of legitimate variant customs.

The unbaptized are not bound by the canonical age unless they contract marriage with a baptized person. They are governed by the natural law and the civil law of the place where the marriage is contracted.

2. **Impotence.** The impediment of impotence arises when previous to the marriage ceremony one of the partners is permanently and perpetually incapable of the marital act.[29] The subject of impotence

---

[27] Canon 1067, § 1.

[28] *Ibid.*, § 2.

[29] Canon 1068, § 1; Card. Petrus Gasparri, *Tractatus de Matrimonio*, Vol. 1, ed. nova (Romae: Typis Polyglottis Vaticanis, 1932), pp. 299–338. Hereafter reference to this work will be as follows: Gasparri, *De Matrimonio*, Vol. . . ., p. . . . .

has been treated earlier.[30] It must be repeated, however, that **impotence differs from sterility;** for while impotence prevents the marital act itself, sterility hinders only conception. **Sterility does not invalidate or impede marriage in any way; impotence does.**

Impotence prevents those marriage acts which of themselves are suitable for the generation of children. The bestowal and acceptance of the right to such acts constitute the essence of the marriage contract. Consequently, the impediment of impotence affects all persons, baptized or unbaptized.

3. **Previous bond.** Anyone who is still bound by a previous marriage tie cannot validly contract another marriage, except in the instance of the Privilege of the Faith.[31] It must be remembered that **civil divorce has absolutely no effect upon a valid bond;** the fact that a divorce has been obtained after a valid marriage in no way entitles one to remarry. This impediment, like impotence, is binding upon the unbaptized as well as the baptized.

The death of a former spouse must be a proven fact before remarriage is permitted. The practice of presuming death after the passage of a period of years has no validity before the ecclesiastical law. Unless some positive evidence sufficient for moral certainty or proof of the death of a former spouse is forthcoming, no permission to remarry will be given. The Church never dispenses when there is even probable danger of violating the divine law.

It should also be noted that anyone who goes through a marriage ceremony, even an invalid one, must establish proof of freedom to marry at a later date. That is why a Catholic who has attempted a civil marriage must obtain an official declaration of nullity of this marriage before he is allowed to contract marriage in the Church.[32]

4. **Disparity of worship.** This impediment invalidates any marriage contracted by a Catholic and an unbaptized person.[33] All that has been said above regarding the Church's attitude to marriage with a baptized non-Catholic applies **a fortiori** to a marriage where the impediment of disparity of worship exists.

The requisites necessary to obtain a dispensation from the impediment of disparity of worship are the same as those mentioned above in the treatment of the prohibitive impediment of mixed religion. The difference between the two situations has already been indicated,

30 Cf. pp. 178 f.
31 Canon 1069, § 1.
32 *Ibid.,* § 2.
33 Canon 1070, § 1.

namely: if no dispensation has been obtained, the impediment of mixed religion makes the marriage merely unlawful, whereas the impediment of disparity of worship makes it invalid. Like the impediment of mixed religion, this impediment arises from the law of the Church and binds those baptized in the Catholic Church. The divine law, however, prohibits the marriage when there is danger of perversion of the Faith of the Catholic party or of the children to be born of the union.

5. Holy Orders. According to the established law of the Church, no one who has embraced major orders (i.e., has been ordained a subdeacon, deacon, or priest) can validly marry.[34] This impediment originates with ecclesiastical law, dating back in its present form to the Second Council of the Lateran (A.D. 1139).

Besides making sacred orders a diriment impediment the Church has established a penalty of excommunication for any cleric in major orders and his accomplice who attempt to contract marriage. Only with difficulty will the Church dispense a subdeacon or deacon from his obligations of the sacred order. With regard to the obligations of the priesthood, there have been times in history when special favors have been granted. Thus Pope Julius III (1550–1555) gave a general dispensation in England after the Protestant Revolt, and Pope Pius VII (1800–1823) acted similarly in 1801 for France after the French Revolution. The persons dispensed were reduced to the lay state and not permitted to function as priests. In modern days, however, no such dispensations have been given. In fact, Pope Benedict XV stated on the matter of clerical celibacy: "We solemnly testify that the Holy See will never in any way mitigate, much less abolish, this most sacred and most salutary law."[35] In certain recent cases involving the conversion of married Protestant ministers to the Faith, Pope Pius XII has permitted them to be ordained to the Catholic priesthood.

6. Solemn vows. Vows may be private or public, simple or solemn. Private vows are those made by an individual to Almighty God in his personal efforts to strive after perfection. Public vows, however,

---

[34] Canon 1072, § 1. A similar law (Canon 62) is now binding upon members of the Oriental Rites. Cf. Pope Pius XII, *Motu Proprio "Crebrae Allatae,"* February 22, 1949, Canon 62 — *Acta Apostolicae Sedis,* XXXXI (1949), p. 102.

[35] Pope Benedict XV, *Allocutio,* December 16, 1920 — *Acta Apostolicae Sedis,* XII (1920), 585.

are those vows professed by a member of a religious community and received officially in the name of the Church by some representative of the Church.[36]

In the section on the prohibitive impediments it was stated that a vow of chastity does not invalidate marriage. A solemn vow of chastity, however, is an exception to this rule. A **solemn vow of chastity** is a vow taken only by members of certain religious orders (for example, the Carmelites, Augustinians, Dominicans). Those who have taken such vows cannot validly contract marriage without a dispensation from the vow from the Holy See.[37] A vow taken by a private person never constitutes a solemn vow in this sense. By **special exception,** the simple vow of chastity in the Society of Jesus is also included under this impediment. Hence, a Jesuit in simple vows would be bound in the same manner as a solemnly professed religious.

7. **Abduction.** Because marriage is a voluntary and free contract with another party, the Church has established the impediment of abduction. Simply stated, abduction means that an impediment arises whenever a man either takes a woman away against her will with a view to marriage, or detains her unwillingly for that same purpose.[38] This impediment exists whether the man intending marriage commits the abduction personally or through agents. For the duration of the time the woman is in his power, this couple is incapable of marriage. Once the woman is free, the impediment ceases, and if she then desires to marry the man, she may do so.

The impediment is one derived from ecclesiastical law and binds the baptized alone.

8. **Crime.** **Crime is a technical term** and represents an impediment designed by ecclesiastical law to discourage marital infidelity and to protect the dignity of the contract of marriage by impeding unworthy persons from entering it.[39] **There are three degrees to this impediment.** Crime in the first degree, however, is the chief interest in this brief treatment of the impediment. As an impediment, crime binds only the baptized.

Crime in the first degree is an impediment whereby one guilty of adultery is rendered incapable of marriage with his or her accomplice

---

[36] Canon 1308, § 1.
[37] Canon 1073.
[38] Canon 1074.
[39] Gasparri, *De Matrimonio,* I, p. 401.

if there is joined to the sin of adultery a promise or attempt at marriage.[40] It is multiplied as an impediment if both accomplices are validly married at the time of their delinquency. Adultery which gives rise to this impediment must be complete and recognized as adultery by both parties.

Crime in the second and third degrees are still more unpleasant topics. For crime in the second degree, there must be adultery with a manifestation of an intention to marry, and then conjugicide by one of the accomplices.[41] Crime in the third degree, the most heinous of all the degrees, is committed by two accomplices who by mutual co-operation, physical or moral, with intent to marry, kill the lawful spouse of one or the other.[42] So serious a matter is crime in the second or third degree that the Church reserves the dispensation in either case to the Holy See itself.

9. **Consanguinity. Consanguinity is an impediment prohibiting marriage between certain individuals because of blood relationship.**[43] Before examining this impediment, it will be wise to explain the different terms which must be understood to compute the degree of relationship.

First of all, **two lines of relationship** are spoken of. Relationship is in the **direct line** when each of a series of persons descends directly from another, as, for example, father, son, and grandson. The relationship is said to be in the **collateral line** when one person does not have his origin directly from another, but from a parallel line of ancestors. Thus, two first cousins descend from a brother and sister. This diagram will help to illustrate:

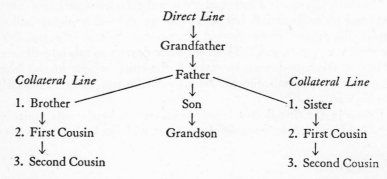

40 Canon 1075, § 1; Vermeersch-Creusen, *Epitome Juris Canonici,* Tomus II, ed. VII (Romae: H. Dessain, 1954), p. 251. Reference to this volume will hereafter be made as follows: *Epitome,* p. .....
41 Canon 1075, § 2.   42 *Ibid.,* § 3.   43 Canon 1076.

The degree of the impediment indicates the generations existing between the person in question and the common ancestor. Thus, according to the illustration, the **grandson** is related to the **grandfather** in the third degree of consanguinity in the direct line. The **second cousin** is related to the **father** on the chart in the third degree of consanguinity in the collateral line. Degrees are determined in both lines by counting the number of generations inclusive of the person involved but exclusive of the common ancestor.

The **impediment of blood relationship occurs whether it is derived from lawful wedlock or not.** Thus, the consanguinity is legitimate when based on lawful wedlock; illegitimate, if it is not.[44]

Finally, **consanguinity may be complete or incomplete.** It is complete if it arises from a union of two common ancestors; incomplete, if there is only one common ancestor.[45]

Bearing these terms in mind, **the impediment of consanguinity may be defined as blood relationship prohibiting marriage in all degrees of the direct line, and in all relationships in the collateral line up to the third degree, inclusively.** In the degrees of the direct line the impediment arises from the divine law, as also, according to the more common opinion, does the first degree of the collateral line.[46] In all other degrees, the impediment arises from ecclesiastical law and affects the baptized alone.

For serious reasons, the Church can dispense from the impediment of consanguinity in the second and third degrees of the collateral line. The Church could dispense from the impediment in the second degree of consanguinity of the collateral line when it touches upon the first degree, i.e., an uncle and a niece.[47] Never, however, will she dispense beyond these degrees since any further dispensation would impinge upon a matter probably prohibited by the divine law.

Consanguinity may be multiplied in several ways. A multiple impediment arises in the following cases: if a man marries a woman who is related to him; if a man or woman marry a sister-in-law or brother-in-law and children are born of the first and second marriages; if two brothers marry two sisters.

---

[44] Cf. Abbo-Hannan, *The Sacred Canons* (St. Louis: B. Herder Book Co., 1952), Vol. II, pp. 281–285.

[45] *Ibid.*

[46] *Epitome,* p. 253.

[47] Beste, *Introductio in Codicem,* editio altera (Collegeville, Minn.: St. John's Abbey Press, 1946), p. 548.

In each instance of contemplated marriage where a blood relationship exists, an illustrative diagram should be carefully drawn and presented to the priest so that an examination of relationship may be made to determine the necessity for a dispensation.

10. **Affinity.** The impediment of affinity also deals with relationships, but this time the relationship is strictly ecclesiastical in origin and is binding upon the baptized alone. **The impediment arises from a valid marriage of the baptized and creates a bond between the wife and the blood relatives of her husband and between the husband and the blood relatives of his wife.**[48] It is computed in lines and degrees in the same way as the impediment of consanguinity. Historically, the concept of affinity stems from the notion that a certain closeness of family ties arises between persons through marriage. Although a relationship arises between one spouse and the blood relatives of the other, no relationship arises between the blood relatives of the one spouse and those of the other.

The impediment of affinity forbids a person to enter marriage with the spouse's blood relative in any degree of the direct line or to enter marriage with relatives up to, and including, the second degree (first cousins through marriage) in the collateral line. For example, a widower could not validly marry his deceased wife's mother, sister, or first cousin.

11. **Spiritual relationship.** Spiritual relationship is an impediment of the ecclesiastical law arising both between the minister of baptism and the person baptized, and between the person baptized and his (her) sponsors.[49]

In connection with the impediment of spiritual relationship it might be well to mention a specific case to be guarded against. Sometimes one of the prospective marriage partners is converted before marriage and desires to have his or her fiancé(e) as sponsor. If the fiancé(e) acts as sponsor, a diriment impediment may arise, thereby necessitating a dispensation from the invalidating impediment.

The impediment must exist with certainty; a doubtful impediment has no effect. Accordingly, the sponsor at conditional baptism does not contract the impediment unless he or she were also sponsor at the first baptism whose validity is questioned.

12. **Public honesty.** This impediment of ecclesiastical origin states

---

[48] Canon 1077.
[49] Canon 1079.

that one who has been invalidly married or who lives in public and open concubinage cannot validly marry his consort's relatives in the direct line.[50] Like the impediment of crime, this impediment strives to preserve the dignity of the sacrament by preventing such closely associated persons from entering a particular union. Moreover, it affords a measure of protection to the divine law. Thus, a man may not marry the daughter of a woman with whom he has lived in an invalid marriage; not only is the union undesirable, but the daughter might also be a direct descendant of the man.[51]

The nature of public honesty may better be understood by taking note of its parallel, the impediment of affinity. Affinity is an impediment based on closeness of relationship through lawful marriage; public honesty is an impediment based on closeness of relationship through unlawful union.

Canonical Reasons for Dispensation From the Impediments

Throughout this section on the impediments to marriage it has frequently been stated that the Church will grant a dispensation for serious reasons alone. There is no necessity for an enumeration of these reasons here. It is sufficient to state that the persons usually indicate some need for a relaxation of the law in order to ward off serious spiritual harm for the individuals or for society. Each particular case must be examined by the bishop or his delegate in order to verify whether a dispensation is warranted.

The Banns of Marriage

After the pastor has completed the prenuptial investigation, the banns of marriage are to be announced, if the contracting parties are both Catholics. The marriage banns are an announcement on three successive Sundays (or Sundays and holydays) that a marriage between two specified persons is going to take place.[52] The purpose of the banns is to safeguard the validity of the marriage and to protect the parties from possible fraud and deceit. In the event that someone has information militating against the marriage, he has the serious obligation of disclosing it to the pastor.

The banns must be announced in the parish church of each party.

---

[50] Canon 1078.
[51] Cf. Gasparri, *De Matrimonio*, I, p. 446.
[52] Canons 1022–1023.

The bishop may dispense from this announcement if special circumstances warrant it and he is certain that no impediment stands in the way of the marriage. Normally they are never announced for a mixed marriage.

ADMONITION

One final word remains to be said regarding the prenuptial investigation demanded by Church law. The adequate performance of the investigation may create inconvenience for all concerned; for the priest, for the parties, and for those who may have to offer testimony in behalf of the parties. **If the inconvenience is notable, all participants should remember that such prenuptial requirements are prompted by a desire not only to protect the holiness of marriage but also to procure lasting peace and happiness for the marriage partners.**

II. THE MARRIAGE CEREMONY

When the prenuptial investigation has been satisfactorily completed and all other canonical and civil requirements satisfied, the parties are eligible to participate in the marriage ceremony. In this section the following points pertaining to the marriage ceremony will be considered: (1) the time for the marriage; (2) the place for the marriage; and, finally, (3) the witnesses to the marriage.

1. THE TIME FOR THE MARRIAGE

Marriage may be permitted at any time during the year.[53] This includes even the "forbidden seasons" of Advent and Lent. In these seasons, however, the solemn nuptial blessing may be allowed only with the special permission of the bishop; even then, the parties are to refrain from elaborate pomp and splendor in their wedding.[54]

The **nuptial blessing** is a special blessing given during the Canon of the Mass. It may be received but once in a lifetime. In this blessing the Church pleads that the woman be chaste, pious, fruitful, and an instrument of her husband's sanctification. With the permission of the bishop this blessing may also be given outside Mass, and even subsequent to the marriage ceremony itself. If the blessing for some reason has not been received at the time of the marriage, e.g., if the marriage were a mixed marriage, the blessing may be given later if the non-Catholic is converted to the Catholic Faith.

[53] Canon 1108, § 1.
[54] *Ibid.*, §§ 2–3.

Particular conditions in a diocese may prompt the bishop to establish certain restrictions on the time for marriage. Consideration of public order or the common good, for example, may dictate the necessity for a law that all weddings be celebrated before a certain time of the day.

2. The Place for the Marriage

The **ordinary place for the marriage of Catholics is the parish church** if both parties are from the same parish; if they are from different parishes, the ordinary place for the wedding is the parish church of the bride.[55] If the parties desire to have their wedding in some other parish, they must obtain the permission of their pastor or bishop. The pastor of the bride or of the groom is competent to give this permission, although preference should be shown to the bride's pastor.

Church law specifies that **marriages are not to be performed in convent or seminary chapels.**[56] Only in an extraordinary case is marriage permitted in a private home. In such an instance, there must be a justifying reason and permission must be obtained from the bishop. For example, the bishop may permit the wedding in a home or in a hospital if the bride or groom is confined there. The reasonableness of the requirement that marriage be celebrated in a church is evident to one who realizes the sacredness and public nature of the marriage contract. Garden weddings and ceremonies at home generally deprive marriage of the sacred dignity which is its due.

The law states that **mixed marriages are to be celebrated outside the church.**[57] If the bishop judges that this cannot be observed without giving occasion to greater evils, with prudent discretion he may dispense from this requirement. In recent years many of the bishops of this country have permitted mixed marriages in churches, hoping to counteract the all-too-common materialistic concept of marriage by means of this added recognition of its enduring spiritual import. All sacred rites, however, are forbidden unless the bishop foresees greater evils resulting from this prohibition; the celebration of Mass is always prohibited.[58]

Regarding the details of time and place for marriage, the Church law prudently confers discretionary authority on the local bishop. Recognizing the difficulty of legislating for all peoples upon matters

---

[55] Canon 1109.
[56] *Ibid.*

[57] *Ibid.*, § 3.
[58] Canon 1102, § 2.

of details, the Church concedes to the local bishop certain rights to adjust the general law to the local circumstances.

3. THE WITNESSES OF THE MARRIAGE

Church law requires the observance of certain formalities when Catholics wish to contract a valid marriage. **A Catholic is ordinarily obliged to celebrate his marriage before a priest and two witnesses.** This is known as the **form of marriage.** It will be discussed in the following section where its relationship to the validity of marriage will be examined.

Witnesses must have the use of reason (although they need not be adults) and **must be physically present** for the exchange of consent.[59] They may be of either sex and should be Catholic. The bishop, however, may grant permission for a non-Catholic to act as a witness if there is a justifying reason. For instance, a convert to Catholicism may desire a brother or sister to act as a witness; the bishop could allow this if a refusal of permission would bring hardship to the convert.

The priest is the official representative of the Church at the marriage of a Catholic. It is the priest's duty officially to witness the ceremony and to record the wedding as a public fact in the church registers.[60]

III. AFTER THE CEREMONY

Once the marriage ceremony has taken place **the Church is slow to admit that it was not a real marriage.** Accordingly, when the validity of a marriage is contested by either of the partners, the Church is meticulous in its investigation of the case for a twofold reason. On the one hand, the common good of society dictates that a marriage ceremony and a presumed bond be strongly upheld; on the other hand, the natural law demands that a person shall not be deprived of his natural right to a lawful marriage. Only after certain establishment of an essential defect in the contract will a declaration of nullity or an annulment be granted. The effect of this declaration of nullity is that the partners regain their freedom to marry.

There is another class of marriage cases whose solution does not depend upon some essential defect but rather upon the power resting in the pope as the Vicar of Christ. These are cases where a special privilege may be given either because the marriage is non-

---

[59] Cf. Canon 1094.
[60] Canon 1103.

sacramental or because the partners have not lived as husband and wife.

In order to examine the instances where the Church may restore the freedom to marry, a brief treatment of both types of cases will be presented in the following order:

A. Cases involving invalidity and nullity of the marriage;

B. Cases involving a dissolution of the bond.

A. CASES INVOLVING INVALIDITY AND NULLITY OF THE MARRIAGE[61]

1. When a Catholic enters marriage, whether it be with another Catholic or not, the marriage must be performed before an authorized priest and two witnesses in order that it be a valid contract.[62] This requirement is known as the canonical **form of marriage** and was introduced by the Church to eliminate the evil of clandestine marriages. The Catholic is obliged to observe this **form** at all times except in two instances: **(a)** if he is in danger of death and no priest is available; and **(b)** in the unusual circumstances when no priest is available or will not be available for a month.[63] In these two exceptional circumstances a marriage before two witnesses alone will be valid. This is known as the **extraordinary form of marriage.**

In connection with the **form of marriage, another exemption** should be mentioned. From May 19, 1918, the day the Code of Canon Law went into effect, until January 1, 1949, an exemption from this rule was granted in favor of children born from mixed marriages if they were baptized in the Catholic Church but reared from infancy in heresy, schism, infidelity, or no religion at all.[64] Since January 1, 1949, however, every person who has been baptized a Catholic must have his marriage celebrated before a priest and two witnesses unless the **extraordinary form** is allowed.[65] For a Catholic to do otherwise is

---

[61] The adjectives *null* and *invalid* are used interchangeably today to describe a union of two parties which is not recognized as a valid marriage. Strictly speaking, however, a distinction between the two phrases can be made, although it will not be adhered to in this section. *Null* in the strictest sense applies to a marriage in which there is a lack of marital consent. *Invalid* is applied to a marriage when the naturally sufficient consent of the parties is rendered juridically ineffective by a diriment impediment or by lack of the proper canonical form (cf. Harrigan, *The Radical Sanation of Invalid Marriages,* The Catholic University of America Canon Law Studies, No. 116 [Washington, D. C.: The Catholic University of America, 1938], p. 99).

[62] Canon 1094.

[63] Canon 1098, §§ 1–2.

[64] Canon 1099, § 2.

[65] Pope Pius XII, *Motu Proprio,* August 1, 1948 — *Acta Apostolicae Sedis,* XXXX (1948), p. 305.

to enter a union that is invalid before God and the Church. Moreover, the Catholic has a serious obligation in conscience to terminate such a union or have it rectified before the Church. Should he decide to rectify the union before the Church, he must go through the procedure outlined in the first part of this chapter, a procedure which he sinfully bypassed when he attempted marriage outside the Church.

If the Catholic decides to terminate his sinful union, he should separate and get a civil divorce. It is well for the Catholic to seek permission for this divorce from the priest in his parish. In this way he has prepared the way for an introduction of his case into the proper hands, namely those of his parish priest who thus has the opportunity of instructing him on any pertinent diocesan regulations. He has also cleared his name in advance in the event that any publicity be given to the legal proceedings. When this step has been accomplished, the Catholic will have to supply as a minimum: (1) proof that he is a Catholic; (2) proof of his marriage and divorce; and (3) finally, proof that his marriage has not been rectified in the Church. When this information has been gathered, together with any additional evidence requested by the bishop or his delegate, it will be possible to state officially that the attempted marriage of the Catholic was absolutely invalid. Such a statement is known as a **declaration of nullity.**[66]

2. The second instance where a declaration of nullity can be granted involves a summary judicial process in the bishop's court. Through an oversight, deceit, or some other reason, it may happen that a particular marriage is contracted before a priest despite the existence of a certain invalidating impediment, e.g., previous marriage, disparity of cult (for which no dispensation was obtained). If one or both of the parties themselves are unaware of the impediment, the marriage, unlike the attempted marriage outside the Church, has a certain appearance of validity because it was celebrated before a priest and two witnesses. It is, therefore, known as a **putative marriage,** and children born from the union are legitimate.[67] Nevertheless, the fact remains that the marriage is invalid.

The bishop or his delegate need only establish proof: (1) that the impediment existed at the time of the marriage; and (2) that there was no cessation of the impediment and rectification of the marriage until the present time. Once this is established and the parties are

---

[66] Cf. Canon 1069, § 2.
[67] Canon 1114.

summoned to appear in court, he may declare the marriage null and void from its inception.[68] Both parties are then free to contract a valid marriage.

The process in this instance has been called a summary judicial process. The reason for this classification is that the process follows judicial norms, but nevertheless, is not as detailed and formal as the process in which an annulment is sought on the basis of an essential defect in the contract.[69]

3. An annulment of a marriage may be granted whenever there is some essential defect in the matrimonial contract. To simplify the treatment of this question a study of **the nature of the matrimonial contract** will be undertaken.

Earlier in this chapter it was mentioned that marriage between Christians (baptized persons) is a sacrament, whereas marriage between a baptized person and an unbaptized person, or between two unbaptized persons, is not a sacrament. Regardless of the sacramentality, however, if a true marriage exists it is **always a contract**, albeit a unique one.

A contract is an agreement between two parties in which rights and obligations are mutually granted and accepted. Thus, when a person agrees to give another person a certain sum of money in exchange for a particular quantity of goods, a contract arises. One party assumes the obligation of paying the other for the goods and acquires the right to the goods. The other person assumes the obligation of delivering his goods; in turn he receives a right to the money offered. In this example the ideas of agreement, right, and obligation are embraced in the notion of the contract.

Marriage may be compared to such a contract. The one difference between the case stated above and the marriage contract is that once the agreement or consent is given, marriage binds the parties exclusively and perpetually. In this the marriage contract is unique, for in every other contract the parties can withdraw from the agreement or make concessions to a third party, if they so agree.

The contract entered into by the partners of marriage is the granting and accepting of the perpetual, exclusive right over one another for conjugal purposes; the obligation entailed by such agreement is the moral duty of acquiescing to the partner's right in accordance with the moral laws of marriage.[70] In the marriage agreement, then, if either

---

[68] Canon 1990.   [69] Cf. Canons 1960–1989.   [70] Canon 1081, § 2.

the right is not given perpetually and exclusively, or no real intention of fulfilling the marital obligation is had, there is a defective contract. An essential defect of this kind renders the marriage invalid.

Let us examine this concept of "contract" further. **First** of all, the parties who enter the contract must know what they are doing. It is obvious, therefore, that those who lack the use of reason are unable to marry. Also, those who lack the knowledge of the rights and obligations of marriage are incapable of marriage. Regarding the minimum requirement of knowledge for marriage, authors agree that the partners must know that marriage is a somewhat permanent union in which some kind of bodily contact is made for the begetting of children. Once a person reaches the age of puberty, Canon Law presumes that ignorance of the notion of marriage is not present.[71]

But if ignorance of the essentials of the contract can be proven in the ecclesiastical court, the marriage contract may be declared invalid.

Second, if the interior assent of the will is destroyed because of external force or impaired by fear, the marriage contract will be affected. It is obvious that violence will invalidate the contract when one is forced to embrace marriage against his will. The exclusion of internal consent makes the marriage null and void by the natural law. Fear, however, is more difficult to analyze. That fear may vitiate the marriage contract, it must be a serious fear, externally and unjustly induced, and such that one is forced to embrace marriage in order to escape from it.[72] The fear must be a serious fear, namely, some notable danger or evil must be imminent. It must also be occasioned by some external agent who acts unjustly in urging the marriage. Thus, fear of embarrassment to a girl over a broken engagement might be a source of fear for her but not one brought about by some other person. If, however, a girl were severely threatened with a beating by an imperious parent unless she married a particular person, the presence of serious and unjust fear might be established. A serious and unjust fear, so inflicted as to force entrance into marriage, destroys the freedom of matrimonial consent required by Church law. It is disputed among authors whether the invalidity arises merely because of Church law or also because of the natural law.[73]

---

[71] Canon 1082, § 2.
[72] Canon 1087, § 1.
[73] Cf. Gasparri, *De Matrimonio,* II, p. 52; Cappello, *De Matrimonio,* Vol. II (Romae: Officina Libraria Marietti, 1939), p. 62, n. 809.

Third, substantial error regarding the identity of the other party would make the contract invalid.[74] Thus if fraud were perpetrated upon a blind person so that he exchanged consent with a person he thought was someone else, there would be substantial error. The marriage would be invalid since his will-act was made with regard to some entirely different person.

Ignorance or error which is not substantial may be morally reprehensible in so far as the one who perpetrates it is concerned, but it will not invalidate a marriage.[75]

Fourth, if conditions are attached to the marriage consent, they can nullify it. Thus, if the conditions are contrary to the very contract itself, they nullify the marriage.[76] Hence, a restriction upon the nature of marriage or the marriage rights and obligations (e.g., an agreement to terminate the marriage whenever desirable to the parties) would certainly nullify the contract. Or again a condition might be placed as an essential requisite upon one's consent, e.g., an intention to marry a girl provided she is a virgin. Such a condition would make the matrimonial consent valid or invalid, depending upon the virginity of the girl. It should be noted that the placing of a condition upon one's consent is unlawful unless the express permission of the bishop has been obtained.[77]

Finally, there must be some external manifestation of consent. The Church does not recognize tacit matrimonial consent.[78] With the exception of mutes, Canon Law demands that this consent be spoken.[79] Those who are not bound by Church law (the unbaptized) need not manifest consent by words. In this case signs or even a letter are sufficient.[80]

It must be borne in mind that these defects in the matrimonial contract are all anterior to the marriage ceremony and actually exist at the time of the ceremony. The preservation of the marriage contract from such defects is the precise reason for the prenuptial investigation treated in the first part of this chapter.

B. Cases Involving a Dissolution of the Bond

Although marriage is a divine institution the stability of which is upheld by the law of nature, certain marriages are nevertheless dis-

---

[74] Canon 1083, § 1.
[75] Ibid., § 2.
[76] Canons 1086, § 2; 1092.
[77] Cf. Bouscaren-Ellis, *Canon Law*, p. 511.

[78] Canon 1088, § 2.
[79] Ibid.
[80] Gasparri, *De Matrimonio*, II, p. 66.

soluble in virtue of the power resting in the Church by the will of Christ. Thus, for a spiritual good the Holy Father can dissolve the natural bond of certain nonsacramental contracts or that of a sacramental contract if the parties have not consummated the marriage. Speaking of this power in the Church over the stability of the bond of marriage in these instances, Pope Pius XI said:

> And if this stability seems to be open to exception, however rare the exception may be, as in the case of certain natural marriages between unbelievers, or amongst Christians in the case of those marriages which though valid have not been consummated, that exception does not depend on the will of men nor on that of any merely human power, but on divine law, of which the only guardian and interpreter is the Church of Christ. However, not even this power can ever affect for any cause whatsoever a Christian marriage as it is plain that here the marriage contract has its full completion, so by the will of God, there is also the greatest firmness and indissolubility which may not be destroyed by any human authority.[81]

An analysis of the Pope's statement discloses three points: (1) the marriage bond admits certain exceptional dissolutions; (2) when the dissolution of a marriage bond occurs it is derived from the power of Christ which rests in the Holy Father or in the Church; and (3) only death can dissolve the bond of a consummated marriage of two Christians. The practical application of these points is evidenced in a consideration of the following exceptional dissolutions of the marriage bond.

1. **Pauline Privilege.** Although a marriage between two unbaptized persons is valid and has been consummated, it can nevertheless be dissolved by the Pauline Privilege in favor of the Faith.[82] This exception to the indissolubility of marriage is based on the following text of St. Paul in the First Letter to the Corinthians:

> For to the rest I say, not the Lord: If any brother has an unbelieving wife and she consents to live with him, let him not put her away. And if any woman has an unbelieving husband and he consents to live with her, let her not put away her husband. For the unbelieving husband is sanctified by the believing wife, and the unbelieving wife is sanctified by the believing husband; otherwise your children would be unclean, but, as it is, they are holy. But if the unbeliever departs,

---

[81] *On Christian Marriage,* paragraph 35.
[82] Canon 1120, § 1.

let him depart. For a brother or sister is not under bondage in such cases, but God has called us to peace.[83]

In this passage of St. Paul, three facts are evident: (a) St. Paul is talking about two unbaptized persons who have validly married and consummated their marriage before baptism; (b) one of the parties is converted; and (c) the other party refuses to be converted or to live at peace with the baptized party. Tradition has interpreted this passage in the sense that under such circumstances the infidel partner is at fault. Accordingly, to safeguard the newly baptized person's Faith, the privilege of remarriage is granted the convert to the Faith. Regarding this exception to the law of stability of marriage, authors are divided as to whether St. Paul promulgated this law as a matter of revelation explicitly made by Christ or as a matter implicitly contained in the apostolic power granted by our Lord.[84]

The **Pauline Privilege** is an instance where the power of Christ to dissolve a natural bond rests in the Church. Thus, when the Church permits the qualified convert to embrace a new marriage with a Christian, the bond of the previous marriage contracted in infidelity ceases at the exact moment that the new bond arises.[85]

2. **Privilege of the Faith.** The **Privilege of the Faith** signifies the dissolution of a marriage bond in favor of a convert to the faith. When the term is used in this broad sense, it may include even the Pauline Privilege. The name, however, is used here in a restricted sense and applies to the specific instance where the Holy Father, as the Vicar of Christ, dissolves the bond of marriage existing originally between an unbaptized person and a baptized person in favor of the Faith, when either of the parties is converted to the Faith.[86] This specific case is sometimes referred to as the **Petrine Privilege** in view of the fact that it rests upon the special power of the Pope. At other times this case is called a **Helena Case** because such a case was submitted from Helena, Montana, and granted shortly after

---

[83] 1 Cor. 7:12–15.

[84] Nau, *Marriage Legislation*, p. 176.

[85] Canon 1126.

[86] Nau, *Marriage Legislation*, pp. 168–189; Bouscaren-Ellis, *Canon Law*, p. 560; Bouscaren, *Canon Law Digest*, II, pp. 342–343. When the unbaptized party is baptized before the dissolution of the marriage contracted in infidelity, the marriage is considered to have become sacramental in nature. It must then be established that cohabitation of the partners has not taken place since the infidel's baptism, before the Holy Father can dissolve the marriage bond on the basis that the marriage has not been consummated.

the promulgation of the Code of Canon Law.[87] The Privilege of the Faith differs from the Pauline Privilege in the following ways: (a) the Privilege of the Faith applies to a marriage in which one partner is already baptized, whereas the Pauline Privilege applies to a marriage contracted by two unbaptized; (b) the bond of marriage is dissolved by the Holy Father in a case of the Privilege of the Faith, whereas the bond of marriage involved in the Pauline Privilege is dissolved by the new marriage of the Christian. Both cases agree, however, in this, that the natural bond is dissolved in favor of a convert to the Faith.

It is but natural that such a privilege is granted only for special reasons. Each case must be examined carefully by the bishop who will decide whether or not the circumstances warrant petitioning the Holy Father for the special favor.

3. **Nonconsummated sacramental marriage.** It has been seen that the marriage of two baptized persons is a sacramental union. Although it is a sacramental union it is not absolutely indissoluble until the parties have lived together as man and wife. If they have not done so, the Holy Father may, in special circumstances, use his power as the Vicar of Christ and grant a dissolution of the bond. The bond of such a marriage is likewise dissolved if one of the partners pronounces solemn vows in a religious community.[88] Even in this case, however, the matter must be brought to the attention of the Holy See since the party could not validly be admitted into religious life without permission from the Holy See.[89]

4. **Separation and divorce.** Although a sacramental marriage which has been consummated cannot be dissolved except by death, a right for a canonical separation may arise for one of the partners. Such a right may come into being for the innocent party if the other partner is guilty of adultery. Likewise, separation may be permitted in the event that the partners prove to be absolutely incompatible.[90]

Since separation of marriage partners may always be a source of scandal or wonderment, it should not be undertaken on private initiative. The case should always be submitted to the bishop of the diocese for his authorization.

Divorce may sometimes prove to be the only adequate way to

---

[87] November 5, 1924 — Bouscaren, *The Canon Law Digest*, Vol. 1 (Milwaukee: The Bruce Publishing Co., 1934), p. 553.

[88] Canon 1119.

[89] Canon 542.

[90] Canons 1129, § 1; 1131.

protect the rights of the innocent party in an unfortunate marriage. In such an instance, the bishop may grant permission for legal action. The **individual, however, should never proceed legally against his or her partner without the proper permission of the ecclesiastical authority.** Since the couple have entered into a union which has been sanctioned by the public authority of the Church, they have the obligation to approach that same public authority again if they wish to terminate the union. Moreover, in seeking the Church's permission to institute divorce proceedings, an opportunity is given ecclesiastical authority to take preventive measures against any further attempt at marriage.

REVALIDATION OF AN INVALID MARRIAGE

It has been seen that a Catholic is obliged to observe the **form of marriage,** namely, to go before a priest and two witnesses in order to contract marriage validly, unless circumstances justify the **extraordinary form of marriage.** If a Catholic fails to observe the required form, an attempted marriage is absolutely invalid before God and the Church. Although the marriage is invalid, it may nevertheless be rectified before the Church. **This rectification of a marriage is known as its validation, revalidation, or "blessing."** That such a marriage, invalid because lacking the prescribed form, be rectified before the Church, it must be contracted anew in the proper form.[91] This is the ordinary procedure, although the marriage may also be validated without renewal of consent (as will be seen in the next section).

The parties should approach a priest, preferably the parish priest, and indicate their desire to have the marriage validated. They must then satisfy all the requirements of the prenuptial investigation. When the priest is satisfied that they are free to enter marriage, a dispensation from the banns is obtained. Consent is renewed before the priest and two witnesses in the same manner as if the parties were contracting the marriage for the first time. Actually, in the eyes of the Church, it is only now that they do contract the marriage. Since at the time of this ceremony they mutually administer and receive the sacrament of marriage, they should prepare themselves devoutly through a contrite confession of their sins.

The acquisition of a new civil license for marriage is not necessary

---

[91] Canon 1137.

for this validation of the marriage. In the eyes of the State, they are already legally married; therefore, a new license is not necessary.

It may likewise happen that the marriage is invalid because of some impediment or essential defect (e.g., lack of consent) although the proper form was observed. For example, through deceit or oversight a marriage may have been entered despite the existence of some diriment impediment for which a dispensation has not been obtained. If the impediment was occult, a private renewal of consent is sufficient, after the impediment has ceased, or has been dispensed from.[92] Likewise, a private renewal of consent is sufficient, if the withholding of the consent was occult. If, however, the impediment or essential defect is something public, able to be proven in the external form, the procedure described above for convalidating a marriage, the giving of consent before a priest and two witnesses, must be followed, after the cessation or dispensation of the impediment, or the removal of the essential defect.[93] This is the ordinary procedure for convalidating a marriage that is null and void because of some diriment impediment. The extraordinary procedure for convalidating such a marriage — **sanatio in radice** — will be described below.

THE "SANATIO IN RADICE"

The term **sanatio in radice** is generally used in the Latin form since it is a technical term. Literally, the phrase means "the healing in the root." **In two cases, the Church allows a sanatio in radice. First,** a marriage may be invalid because of lack of canonical form or because of a diriment impediment or essential defect in the agreement. One party may desire the validation of the marriage in order to be reconciled to the sacraments (which have been forbidden because of the invalid union), while the other party refuses to go before a priest and renew consent according to the prescribed form. **Second,** a marriage may be invalid though neither party is aware of the fact. Relative to either case the law states: "The healing of a marriage **in radice** is its validation, involving, besides the dispensation or cessation of the impediment, a dispensation from the law requiring renewal of consent, and retroactivity, by fiction of law, with regard to canonical effects." The law continues in the second paragraph: "The validation takes place at the moment when the favor is granted; but the retroactivity is understood as going back to the beginning of

---

[92] Canon 1135, 2, 3.
[93] Canon 1136, 2, 3.

the marriage unless express provision is made to the contrary." Finally, in the third paragraph, the law states: "The dispensation from the law requiring renewal of consent can be granted even without the knowledge of one or both of the parties."[94]

Although a discussion of this unusual form of validation really goes beyond the scope of a survey, it should be noted that there are two broad concessions in the **sanatio,** besides a dispensation from any impediment from which the Church can dispense. These concessions are: (1) dispensation from the ordinary law of Canon 1137 which requires the renewal of consent; and (2) retroactivity by fiction of law so that in regard to canonical effects the marriage is considered as valid in the past. Through this retroactivity, certain benefits are derived for the parties concerned. Thus, for example, children born from the marriage during the period of its invalidity are legitimated before Church law. The **sanatio in radice** shows the Church's true solicitude for her children. She recognizes cogent reasons for dispensing with the ordinary validation of an invalid marriage. Consequently, she permits unusual measures to provide sacramental benefits for partners in marriage.

The foregoing represents a very brief survey of the Church's law on marriage. **Even from such a cursory study, it is patently evident that the Church's law, though at times difficult of comprehension and complicated in its application, has been enacted solely for the protection and guarantee of the sacred institution of marriage.** To the Church, in a special way, has been entrusted the fearful responsibility of custody, declaration, and interpretation of God's law in the matters pertaining to matrimony. Thus, over the centuries, in fulfillment of her august duties, she has formulated and crystallized in her Code of Canon Law the legislation best fitted to serve God and man alike.

---

[94] Canon 1138.

CHAPTER XXVI

Civil Law Concerning Marriage

MATTHEW F. MC GUIRE

It was James Bryce[1] who said:

> Of all legal institutions, Marriage is that which most profoundly affects the structure and character of society. The State, it is often said, depends upon the Family; and the Family is constituted by Marriage.[2]

This observation is no truism. If, then, as Toynbee categorically states, "Western Christendom was essentially the creation of the Catholic Church,"[3] certainly marriage, as a legal institution affecting as Bryce has said "most profoundly" the "structure and character of society" both in its nature and its incidents, has been shaped and fashioned by the Christian concept and teaching with respect to it.[4]

HISTORY AND BACKGROUND OF CIVIL LAW

By the civil law concerning marriage as it relates to this chapter is meant the secular law generally in what is called civil society, and more specifically the law relating to marriage as it was and is presently affected by the substantive law of England and America.

Marriage consists of the union of one man and one woman for life, and it has been called variously a civil contract,[5] an institution,[6] a

---

[1] James Bryce, D.C.L., author of *The Holy Roman Empire, The American Commonwealth, etc.,* formerly Regius Professor of Civil Law in the University of Oxford, Honorary Fellow of Oriel and Trinity Colleges, Corresponding Member of the Institute of France, and former British Ambassador to the United States.

[2] James Bryce, *Marriage and Divorce* (Preface) (New York: Oxford University Press, American Branch, 1905).

[3] Arnold Toynbee, *A Study of History,* abridgment of Vols. 1–6 by D. C. Somervell (New York: Oxford University Press, 1947), p. 153.

[4] Westermarck, *The History of Human Marriage,* 5 ed. (London: Macmillan and Co., Ltd., 1921), Vol. 3, p. 331.

[5] Jewell's Lessee *vs.* Jewell, 42 U. S. 219, 1 How 219, 11 L. Ed. 108.

[6] Sweigart *vs.* State, 213 Ind. 157, 12 N.E. 2d 134, 114 A.L.R. 1117; Maynard *vs.* Hill, 125 U. S. 205, 8 S. Ct. 723.

domestic relation,[7] and a status,[8] with a religious ceremony not being considered a prerequisite.

It has been judicially held to be contractual in character and essence. It differs, however, from the ordinary contract in that it cannot be rescinded or its terms changed by agreement of the parties, and under American law it is not such a contract as is within the purview of the Fourteenth Amendment to the Constitution of the United States.[9] Agreements directed toward its restraint are usually held to be invalid. It is a relationship which results in a status. A **status** is that condition of a person by which the nature of his **legal personality** and his **legal capacities** are determined. In simpler terms, status is the relationship which a person bears in a legal way to the state, the community, in short to civil society.[10] It is a condition which arises out of such circumstances as infancy, guardianship, sex, mental capacity, crime, alienage, public station, or marriage.

At common law, that is, law in the absence of statutory enactment, marriage effected a merger of the legal identity of the wife with that of the husband. This was the great characteristic of early common-law marriage. The effect of such merger basically was that the act of the wife became the act of the husband. From this legal fiction have sprung many technical rules of law, particularly of property. These rules today, since the idea of merger is no longer widely held, are for the most part outmoded.[11]

Nearly half of the states of the American Union have statutes, that

---

[7] Cook vs. Cook, 14 N.W. 33, 56 Wis. 195, 43 Am. Rep. 706.

[8] Graham vs. Graham, D.C. Mich. 33 F. Supp. 936; Williams vs. North Carolina, 325 U.S. 226, 89 L. Ed. 1577.

[9] Vernier, *American Family Laws* (Stanford, Calif.: Standford University Press, 1951), Vol. 1, p. 51.

[10] Restatement, Conflict of Laws, Sec. 119, p. 181.

[11] The status of husband and wife today has widely departed from that under the common law. This is true as to marital property, custody and control of children, power of husband over wife, and in the general economic self-sufficiency of the wife (John W. Morland, *Keezer on Marriage and Divorce,* 3 ed. [Indianapolis, 1946], p. 33).

Wills: At common law a man's will was not revoked by marriage (marriage *plus* birth of issue did act as revocation, though). A woman's marriage, however, revoked a will made by her prior to marriage, whether she subsequently survived her husband or not. Today many states have statutes which provide that marriage revokes a man's will, unless the will contains provision contrary thereto, or makes a provision in contemplation of marriage. Most states have statutes leaving a woman her antenuptial will in full force, but a substantial number still adhere to the common-law rule.

is, legislative enactments relating to the nature of marriage.[12] Kansas goes so far as to state that it "may be regarded either as a civil ceremony or a religious sacrament."[13] We know, too, in ancient times among such civilizations as those of the Chinese, Egyptian, Greek, and Roman, some religious significance or symbolism was often attached to marriage. This is particularly true with reference to the Hebrews, possessed as they were of Revelation.

Monogamy was the usual form of marriage. Westermarck, a recognized authority in the field, in his classic **History of Human Marriage** states categorically "that monogamy prevailed as the only legitimate form of marriage in Greece and Rome. . . ."[14] Despite deviations, it also prevailed among most Indo-Europeans. Even in those places where polygyny was at times tolerated there was always one legal, principal wife,[15] bearing out the law of nature that marriage consists of the union of one man with one woman for life.[16] Monogamy prevailed generally, also, among all peoples of which we have any record, with deviations at times, however, of either a polygynous or polyandrous character.[17]

THE LAW OF ENGLAND

So much for general history and background. As far as the law of England was concerned, from which our law with respect to marriage for the most part stems, marriage and all problems arising in or out of it, such as those of annulment, separations, guardianship of children, etc., were in the spiritual forum, that is, before the ecclesiastical courts and not in those of the common law,[18] thus reflecting the profound effect of the teaching of the Church with respect to this fundamental relationship.

This was so not only during the period that England was formally

---

[12] Seventeen states and Alaska refer to marriage as a "civil contract" while six other states characterize it as a "personal relation growing out of a civil contract."

[13] Vernier, *op. cit.,* p. 51.

[14] Westermarck, *op. cit.,* p. 50.

[15] *Ibid.,* p. 35.

[16] "Monogamy as pattern and prototype of human marriage . . . is universal." "Monogamy is, has been and will remain the only true form of marriage. . . ." (Bronislaw Malinowski, "Marriage," *Encyclopaedia Britannica,* Vol. 14, 1956 ed., p. 950).

[17] Polygyny was the union of one man with many women; polyandry, the union of one woman with many men.

[18] Pollock and Maitland, *History of English Law,* 2 ed. (Cambridge at the University Press, 1923), Vol. 2, p. 367.

Catholic and united with Rome, but continued to exist for a long time after the separation of England from the Church.

As recently as 1843 it was the judgment of the House of Lords that a ceremony of marriage at which no clergyman was present was no marriage.[19] The secular law of the realm had no doctrine of marriage for it never, as we have seen, was within its purview to say categorically in words whether a valid marriage had been contracted. Adultery, bigamy, and incest were not crimes within the ambit of the criminal law. True, however, the civil courts had often to decide such matters as dower and inheritance, so that the question as to whether there was a valid marriage or not might come before them incidentally. When it did, however, it was immediately referred to the ecclesiastical court and upon that court's finding the lay court predicated its judgment.[20]

THE AMERICAN LAW

With the establishment of the American colonies, since there were no ecclesiastical tribunals, the questions we have alluded to were disposed of by the civil courts. A religious rite was neither required nor recognized, an appearance before a magistrate being sufficient, in fact necessary, for a valid marriage. In still other jurisdictions, so-called common-law marriages resulted from the mere fact of the parties agreeing to live with each other as husband and wife and holding themselves out as such for an appreciable time in the community in which they lived.[21] It is interesting to note that banns or the public promulgation of intention to marry were customary in some Christian countries before being made mandatory by the Lateran Council in 1215.[22] The purpose of banns was to prevent clandestinity and to bring to light any impediments to the marriage prior to its solemnization. In some states today we have legislation dealing with this form of advance notice. Others have prescribed a statutory form which must be complied with. These statutes fall into two categories. One requires that application for license to marry be made or notice of intention to marry be filed one to five days before the ceremony; the other issues a license to marry at once but specifies that it not be used until a specified number of days elapses. Other jurisdictions permit this so-called waiting period to be cut down or waived under

---

[19] *Ibid.*, p. 372.
[20] *Ibid.*, p. 374.

[21] E.g., the District of Columbia.
[22] Pollock and Maitland, *op. cit.*, p. 370.

certain conditions.[23] In the District of Columbia this period may not be cut down or waived under any condition.

MARRIAGE LICENSE LAWS

All of the states and territories have what are called marriage license laws. Their basic purpose is to insure that persons who intend to marry must give formal notice of the same and receive formal permission to do so from the state in the form of a license. This is understandable as the state and community and society as a whole have a special interest not only in the creation of the family status but in what is often overlooked, its maintenance, since the family is the very foundation upon which the entire structure of civil society rests.

It is to be noted that although all American jurisdictions have marriage license laws, the inference should not be drawn by virtue of this fact that in all cases a license is essential to the validity of marriage in the eyes of the state.

AGE AT MARRIAGE

At common law, males of the age of 14 and females of the age of 12 could make a binding contract of marriage.[24] In all but three states, however, these minimum-age requirements have been raised by specific enactment. It can be said that the most generally adopted age standard in the United States is 18 for males and 16 for females. This is the standard presently in 24 states. If the parties are under age the marriage is usually regarded by the courts as not a void marriage but a voidable one. At common law parental consent was not required. Today, however, in most states, the law requires that minors above the age of consent but below a certain definite "age of parental consent" must formally secure the consent of parent or guardian. The contractual aspect of marriage in its very nature demands that the element of **mutual** consent[25] be present and so for this reason we have statutes and regulations governing not only consent but the capacities of the parties to give consent.

---

[23] Vernier, *op. cit.*, p. 54.

[24] England's Age of Marriage Act, 1929, fixed the minimum age for both sexes at 16.

[25] Canon 1081, Code of Canon Law, Book III, Part I, Title VII, Chapter 5, "Matrimonial Consent," Typis Polyglottis Vaticanis.

IMPEDIMENTS TO MARRIAGE

Again, for reasons which need no elaboration, society dictates certain basic prerequisites for entering the status, and as a consequence certain marriages are prohibited. For example, some of these are where the parties are closely related by consanguinity and affinity, bigamous marriages, and, in certain states, marriages between persons of different races. In some states, these latter marriages may be void. These regulations or standards spring for the most part from religious and moral considerations, or from the social standards or conventions of the particular community, and out of a manifest desire on the part of society to safeguard its physiological well-being. Consanguinity is blood relationship or descent from a common ancestor. Other prohibited marriages are those involving (1) impotency on the part of either party; (2) insanity; (3) affliction with a contagious or loathesome disease; (4) where either party is an habitual criminal, drunkard, or drug addict; (5) where one of the parties is or was related by marriage to a blood relative of the other (affinity).

DIVORCE

No treatment of the subject matter can be regarded as full without at least a reference to divorce. Here, however, it is necessary to distinguish carefully with respect to terminology. The term "divorce" is often loosely used to designate a suit for the annulment of a marriage, but this is a misnomer because the purpose of that proceeding, i.e., annulment, is the attainment of a decree to the effect that by virtue of certain inherent and essential difficulties no valid marriage in law ever existed. The term "divorce" means "a dissolution of the bonds of matrimony based upon the theory of a valid marriage, for some cause arising after the marriage, while an annulment proceeding is based upon the theory that, for some cause existing at the time of marriage (sic), no valid marriage ever existed."[26] Some of the grounds usually advanced for annulment are: want of mental capacity, intoxication, duress, disease, impotence; ceremony in jest; fraud and misrepresentation, etc., in short, similar generally to impediments with respect to marriage listed above.

A separation is actually what has been called in the books a **divorce a mensa et thoro.** In other words, the status still exists and the bond

---

[26] Millar *vs.* Millar, 175 Cal. 797; 167 Pac. 394; L.R.A. 1918B, 415, Ann. Cas. 1918E, 184.

attaches but the parties for reasons approved by the court are living apart; that is, the marriage tie is not dissolved and neither party is free to marry again. As it has been rather naïvely put, a separation just frees the "innocent party from the presence and control of the guilty one until they agree to renew cohabitation."[27] Such separation agreements have been held valid as early in 1758 in England.[28]

With reference to actual divorce, namely the severing of the bond by civil authorities, statistics are usually faulty and afford no accurate predicate as bases for sound conclusions, despite the awe which they somehow seem to inspire (see Chapter XXIV). There is no doubt, however, that the high incidence of divorce in Western countries, particularly in the United States, constitutes a great evil and a threat to the stability of society. Today in most American jurisdictions it is comparatively easy of attainment[29] and is granted for many trivial reasons and upon perjured and collusive evidence extremely difficult to detect. The modern trend seems to be to regard marriage as a status only in the subordinate sense, the relationship being primarily that of contract, which can be abrogated or dissolved and with considerably more ease than one could extricate one's self from the liabilities arising out of one of a business relationship.

An interesting sidelight is that while the status is purportedly destroyed by court action resulting in divorce, certain incidents arising from it remain, such as the right of custody of children and of maintenance or support. These rights or incidents may still be enforced, **although** the status out of which they sprang and to which they attach is no longer in existence.[30] Again, in the United States by virtue of diversity of jurisdiction, it is possible for a man or woman to be unmarried in one state and married in another, the latter state holding the divorce decree of the former invalid. The result is they are either fowl or fish, depending upon the place in which they find themselves. Litigation in such circumstances, instead of resolving their problem, merely confuses and compounds it. There has been as a consequence, over the years, considerable but sporadic agitation for a uniform divorce law, but the difficulties in the way, constitutional and otherwise, are great.

---

[27] Morland, *op. cit.*, Sec. 244, p. 305.

[28] Rex *vs.* Mead, 1 Burr. 541, 97 Eng. Rep. 440.

[29] Thirty-nine distinct causes for absolute divorce were recognized by United States courts as far back as 1931. Living separate and apart is a ground for divorce in more than twenty jurisdictions.

[30] Estin *vs.* Estin, 334 U.S. 541, 545.

The present divorce rate in the United States is extraordinarily high, indeed if not the highest among all Occidental countries (see Chapter XXIV).

Evil though divorce is, and a great evil that saps at the very foundation of society, it would appear that very little up to now has been done to salvage those marriages which can be salvaged. Once a case gets into the courts the result in nine cases out of ten is certain, and another inroad into the integrity of family life has been accomplished. Many states have gone too far in the matter of easy divorce, adopting the view that if two parties can no longer live together in the relationship of husband and wife there ought to be an end to it — a decree of divorce in the circumstances being merely a public validation of the existing fact of separation.[31]

This is the easy way out and an affirmation of the fact that the personal wishes of the individuals concerned take precedence over the general welfare of the community. The result has been easy divorce, presumed satisfaction for the litigants involved, but havoc for the children concerned.[32]

Up to 1936 divorce was easy in the Soviet Union. This was understandable, committed as it is to the Marxian doctrine that since there can be no private property, then obviously marriage, out of which has sprung the family status and the root source of private property, was to be no longer regarded as the basic political entity of the State, but rather the individual was to be recognized as this entity. Experience, however, has caused this viewpoint to change, despite what appears to be political heresy, and divorce has become increasingly more difficult to obtain in Russia.

At the present time in this country there is a strong movement afoot to stem this continually rising tide of divorce[33] by the institution of therapeutic measures of a preventive character. One in particular is the creation of an agency known, for want of a better name, as the Family Court. This court would have all the powers now vested in courts in which jurisdiction of this type of litigation is lodged,

---

[31] Park *vs.* Park, 116 F. 2d 556. 73 App. D.C. 93.

[32] Cf. Howard Witman, "Divorce Granted," *Reader's Digest* (Vol. 65, October, 1954, p. 11), condensed from Des Moines *Register and Tribune,* p. 11 ff.

[33] "Monthly Vital Statistics Report," U. S. Department of Health, Education and Welfare, National Office of Vital Statistics, Vol. 2, No. 10 (December 18, 1953), Table 8: "Divorces Reported by Specified States September 1952 and 1953, and cumulative figures: 87,447 for 1953; 85,732 for 1952; percentage increase 2.0, only 21 areas reporting."

with this difference: its primary purpose would be that of salvage by the expenditure of every possible effort to maintain the integrity of the bond. This would mean the engagement of the services of all of the social forces in a given community interested in the achievement of this end.

It qualifiedly is a step in the right direction. It will not eradicate the evil as such but, if rightly implemented, it would go quite a long distance on the road toward the amelioration of some of its more disastrous effects.

In conclusion, let it be said:

> The problems raised by the divorce legislation of our own time are among the gravest which society has now to face; and they deserve more consideration than they have yet received. Different as were the conditions of life, and especially of religious life, in the Roman Empire, the experience of Rome may not be without some warning for our own time.[34]

APPENDIX TO CHAPTER XXVI

THE MARRIAGE COUNSELOR AND THE LAW

Divorce is a legal process. The marriage counselor may frequently have to discuss this matter with his clients. Consequently, the marriage counselor should be very careful because he runs the risk of getting into legal difficulties. Professor John S. Bradway points out some of these difficulties:

1. The risk of being accused of practicing law without a license.

2. The law permits an engaged person or spouse to sue other persons (including marriage counselors) for alienating the affections of the other engaged person or spouse.

3. The law provides that information given to representatives of certain professions and only to those persons may be held inviolate and confidential.

4. The court might decide that it was illegal for a counselor to tell a client he could get a divorce or to tell the client the grounds for divorce.

5. The law favors marriage and attempts to deter people from

---

[34] Bryce, *Marriage and Divorce* (Preface).

interfering with the formation of the marriage contract and from breaking up the family once it is organized.

6. The marriage counselor may be called as a witness, and if he refuses to testify he may be punished for contempt of court.

A marriage counselor is strongly advised, as Professor Bradway points out, that "the counselor should carefully study his position in relation to the law, and at least be aware of the risks that he is taking."[35]

GROUNDS FOR CIVIL DIVORCE

Much interest has been shown in the specific grounds required for civil divorce in various states. For this reason the following summary is added:

Desertion (45 states and the District of Columbia)
Cruelty (43 states)
Conviction of a felony (40 states and the District of Columbia)
Alcoholism (36 states)
Impotence (31 states)
Insanity (27 states)
Neglect to provide (23 states)
Separation (15 states and the District of Columbia)
Bigamy (14 states)
Pregnancy at the time of marriage (13 states)
Drug addiction (11 states)
Fraudulent contract (11 states)
Indignities to the person (8 states)
Violence (6 states)
Attempt to take the life of spouse (3 states)
Prohibitive decree of consanguinity (3 states)
Communication of venereal disease (1 state)
Corruption of children (1 state)

In other instances some of the less frequent causes for the granting of a divorce have been:

Immoral conduct before marriage
Incompatibility
Membership in religious groups which are opposed to marriage

---

[35] John S. Bradway, "Some Domestic Relations Laws that Counselors in Marital Difficulties Need to Know," *Social Forces,* Vol. 17 (October, 1938), pp. 83–89.

Contracting leprosy
Sexual perversion
Vagrancy
Ungovernable temper

Needless to say, a detailed treatment of all these is beyond the scope of this book. But a brief treatment of the more important ones may be useful for those who are not familiar with the terms.

Adultery is defined as the voluntary sexual intercourse of a married person with a person other than the offender's husband or wife. In general it is necessary that only one of the offenders be married for the act to be considered adultery.

Desertion (also referred to as willful desertion; abandonment; willful, obstinate, and continued desertion; willful and malicious; utter and continued; intentional). Desertion may be a voluntary separation of one of the married partners from the other for purposes of obtaining a civil divorce. The period of separation varies from six months to five years, depending upon the state. The usual length of time is one year. Desertion may also occur when one of the parties may refuse to renew a suspended cohabitation without some justifiable reason.[36]

Cruelty (other expressions are extreme cruelty, cruel and inhuman treatment, intolerable cruelty, extreme and repeated cruelty).[37]

Bouvier's Law Dictionary defines acts of cruelty as,

> Those acts which affect the life, the health, or even the comfort of the party aggrieved, and give a reasonable apprehension of bodily hurt. . . . What merely wounds the feelings is seldom admitted to be cruelty, unless the act be accompanied with bodily injury, either actual or menaced. Mere austerity of temper, petulance of manners, rudeness of language, a want of civil attention and accommodation, even occasional outbreaks of passion, will not amount to legal cruelty.[38]

Conviction of a crime (usually a felony) which is followed by a sentence of imprisonment is considered grounds for divorce in all

[36] Some states hold that obstinate refusal to have sexual intercourse is probably desertion. So too is the refusal of a wife to follow her husband to a new place of domicile or an unjustified refusal to begin cohabitation.

[37] John W. Morland, *op. cit.,* Sec. 355, p. 407.

[38] *Bouvier's Law Dictionary,* ed. William Edward Baldwin (Cleveland: Banks-Baldwin Law Publishing Co.), p. 258. The following are some charges where divorces were granted on grounds of cruelty: attempt to kill, attempt to poison, choking, kicking, whipping, spitting in the face, communicating venereal disease, inexcusable neglect during sickness, false charge of adultery (whether uttered privately or in public), commission of rape, keeping a mistress, forcing a wife to submit to an abortion.

states except seven. In some states the required period of imprisonment is two years or more. Other states require a life sentence before an absolute divorce is granted. When a person has been divorced because of sentence for crime, he does not regain conjugal rights upon release from prison.

Alcoholism or habitual drunkenness — the usual criteria for this are three: **(a)** an irresistible habit of getting drunk; **(b)** a fixed habit of drinking to excess; **(c)** such frequent indulgence to excess as to show a formed habit and inability to control the appetite. The habit must be a confirmed one, but it does not have to be a daily occurrence. The complaining partner must show that he or she had no knowledge of the habit prior to their marriage.

Impotency — the inability of the male partner to produce an erection so as to perform satisfactorily the act of copulation (see Chapter XIII).

Insanity is "a deprivation of reason such that the subject is no longer capable of understanding and acting with discretion in the ordinary affairs of life."[39] This is a legal definition of insanity. Medically, this condition is known as a psychosis and is very difficult to define (see p. 368 f.). As I have stated before, "In attempting to arrive at a satisfactory definition of a psychosis, one is inclined to agree with Lord Blackburn, who wrote more than fifty years ago, 'I have read every definition (of insanity) which I would meet with and never was satisfied with one of them, and I have endeavored in vain to make one satisfactory to myself. I verily believe it is not in human power to do it.' "[40]

Since it is impossible for a person to make a valid contract except when in control of his faculties, most states affirm that a marriage contracted at a time when one of the partners has been proven to be insane is dissolved.[41]

In cases of psychoses which develop after marriage, there has been much agitation in recent years to allow a divorce under this circumstance. At the present time civil divorce on grounds of insanity is permitted in the following states:

Alabama (7 years)   Connecticut (5 years)
California (3 years)   Delaware (5 years)
Colorado (5 years)   Idaho (not specified)

---

[39] *Ibid.*, p. 555.

[40] John R. Cavanagh and James B. McGoldrick, S.J., *Fundamental Psychiatry* (Milwaukee: The Bruce Publishing Co., 1953), pp. 287–288.

[41] In some states this definition of insanity includes drunkenness.

Indiana (5 years)
Kansas (5 years)
Kentucky (5 years)
Maryland (3 years)
Michigan (not specified)
Minnesota (5 years)
Mississippi (3 years)
Montana (not specified)
Nebraska (5 years)
Nevada (2 years)
New Mexico (not specified)

North Carolina (10 years)
North Dakota (5 years)
Oklahoma (5 years)
Oregon (5 years)
South Dakota (1 year)
Texas (5 years)
Utah (not specified)
Vermont (5 years)
Washington (2 years)
Wyoming (2 years)

Refusal to support — this is a grounds for divorce when the husband abandons his wife or willfully neglects to provide adequate support. In many cases this does not constitute grounds in a civil court for an absolute divorce, but only for a partial divorce.

Exceptional cases which come under consideration are included in some states under the more common grounds listed above. Gross neglect of duty, for example, is a distinct ground for divorce in three states. In some states the same circumstances would constitute desertion or refusal to support.

Living separated and apart — when two parties have been living separate and apart for a given period of time, they may have their marriage dissolved in nineteen states. The period of separation varies from two years to ten years.

Indignities against the person — vulgarity, unmerited reproach, habitual contumely, studied neglect, intentional incivility, manifest disdain, abusive language, and malignant ridicule may be cited as examples of indignities against the person for which divorces have been granted. Further examples are refusal on the part of a spouse to perform marital duties except for pay or with danger of the communication of a loathsome disease. On this charge, every divorce is judged according to its particular circumstances.

Unsafe and improper cohabitation may be included under cruelty in some states. This charge includes any acts which would make cohabitation unsafe, any acts which are likely to cause injury to the person or health of the spouse; for example, intoxication accompanied by acts of cruelty, repeated acts of violence. Under this ground it is not enough to merely hurt the feelings of the wife; there must be real danger of bodily injury.

Incompatibility as such is grounds for divorce in only two states: Idaho and New Mexico. In 1933, the legislature of the state of New Mexico passed a law allowing judges in district courts the power to grant a divorce when they believed that evidence directly presented before them proved that a couple were incapable of maintaining harmonious relations. Incompatibility does not mean that the parties merely disagree or exchange unkind words. They must be mutually repellent to each other and, in the opinion of the court, absolutely incapable of harmonious association.

When the definition of incompatibility is applied to particular cases, it is often found to be an elusive one, and is subject to quite a different interpretation in various jurisdictions.

Of all the causes listed above, cruelty and desertion far exceed the rest in number. Annual reports from the National Bureau of Vital Statistics suggest that cruelty is the basic charge in from 50 to 75 per cent of divorce cases in the United States.[42] In some states cruelty alone constitutes more than 75 per cent of the grounds. In both Michigan and Oregon, for example, the number is well above 80 per cent. The national rate for charges of desertion is considerably lower than that for cruelty, but in certain states it exceeds the latter. Desertion is the principal cause in 75 per cent of all divorce cases in the state of Virginia.

---

[42] It is impossible to arrive at an *exact* figure for the United States as a whole because information is not available from every state. This is further complicated by a lack of uniformity in procedures for reporting data. However, the figures reported are believed to accurately reflect *trends,* especially when they are viewed over a long period of time.

CHAPTER XXVII

Economic Problems in Marriage Counseling

ALPHONSE H. CLEMENS

Every counselor seasoned by experience is aware of the frequency of economic maladjustment in marriage today. Not only the illiterate but also the most highly educated are victims of this type of problem. It is not too uncommon to find in need of economic counseling Doctors of philosophy who could furnish an intelligent answer for reducing the national debt, but who are unable to balance their own family budget. The silence of our homes and schools on matters of family economics together with the miseducation accruing from much of our current advertising and salesmanship have resulted in a generation illiterate in a true sense of economic values. It would be amazing if this all-pervading distortion of true values did not infect the area of family economics also.

ECONOMIC PROBLEMS A SOURCE OF FRICTION

Economic problems are some of the most frequent sources of friction in marriage today. A recent review of the cases of the Marriage Counseling Center of the Catholic University of America disclosed that in 79 per cent of the cases there was some type of economic maladjustment. The exact relative importance of economic factors in marital difficulties is not really known. There are, on the basis of so-called scientific studies, presently three theories concerning the importance of economic factors in marital maladjustment. **First,** we are told that there is no such thing as an economic tension problem; rather do some psychologists prefer to believe that economic friction is due to personality deviations.[1] This school of thought would, doubtless, displace expert economists at international conferences with expert psychiatrists to resolve world economic tensions. **Second,**

[1] L. M. Termon, *et al., Psychological Factors in Marital Happiness* (New York: McGraw-Hill Book Co., Inc., 1938).

there are those who believe economic matters the most frequent cause of dispute between husbands and wives.[2] **Third,** we find those who believe, on the basis of studies, that economics can be a causative factor in breakdown but it is usually not the dominating reason for family failure.[3]

MORAL ASPECTS OF ECONOMICS

To the Catholic marriage counselor and the Catholic couple, however, the question of economics as a factor in marital failure is accompanied by a deep sense of the moral implications of family economics. No less an authority than St. Thomas Aquinas insists that family virtuous living is closely associated with and conditioned by family economics.[4] To a thinking person, furthermore, the family income and its use is not merely a question of good economic science; it is also a question of morality, of the virtues of prudence, detachment, thrift, and others. Family income is not to be used at one's own discretion and for one's own whims; on the contrary, it is to be expended in accord with the **moral** purposes of married life. Since, according to St. Paul, marriage is for generation, **the first claim to family finances is that of the children — their generation and education.** Personal luxuries and conveniences need to give way to this basic and primary moral imperative. As a result, the spending of family income on "gadgets" and superfluous items at the expense of adequate economic security in the event of death, the proper Catholic education of the children and provision for the future security of the children as adults, is a violation of several economic virtues and, as such, immoral. Some theologians hold that parents are bound to afford even a college education to children who are willing and able to profit by it.[5] The Catholic counselor and couple will see beyond the moral to the ascetical implications of family economics. He will recognize the hardships and difficulties of wise money management and of industry, as invaluable vehicles on the road to sanctity and holiness. If the practice of poverty is deemed one of the three great "expediters" to perfection for religious orders, it is no less for families.

[2] Gallup Poll, August 31, 1946.

[3] J. Thomas, *The American Catholic Family* (New York: Prentice-Hall, 1956).

[4] The following citations from St. Thomas confirm this position: *De Reg. Prin.*, L. I, c. 14; *S. T.*, Ia–IIae, q. 4, art. 7c; *S. T.*, IIa–IIae, q. 134, art. 3ad–4um.

[5] F. J. Connell, C.SS.R., *Some Moral Problems in Marriage Education and Counseling* (Washington, D. C.: Catholic University of America Workshop Papers, 1952).

ECONOMIC SENSE OF VALUES

The basic difficulty found in counseling cases with economic problems is that one or both members of a couple have lost their sense of values. The loss of the vision of Christian principles and virtues in matters economic; the predatory pressures of harmful advertising and salesmanship; the neopagan, materialistic example of all about them who strive to "keep up with the Joneses" — have given most couples a set of entirely false attitudes. Amid the confused environment of today, they have become perplexed and muddled about the most obvious, common-sense facts.

Few of them are any longer able to distinguish between necessities and superfluities. In current culture, an automobile, a television set, an automatic washer are necessities — but life insurance is not! These couples need re-education in primary, basic, common-sense facts of economic life. They need to recapture **the threefold distinction,** laid down by St. Thomas centuries ago, **of the types of wealth.**[6] First, are **the absolute necessities** — food, clothing, shelter, health needs, education, recreation, and religion, etc. **Second, are the "social" necessities** — those things truly necessary to maintain a family's rightful (not exaggerated) professional and social position. **Third, are those limitless items and services which** (not being necessary in either an absolute or social sense) **are genuinely superfluous.** Another basic value progressively on the decline in our current culture is the import of "home production." A profit-mad economy is more interested in **selling** us a finished product than encouraging us to produce things ourselves. Yet the bold fact remains, attested by scientific studies, that the average housewife can be worth $2,000 to $5,000 a year as a producer in the home!

With such facts and principles at hand, the marriage counselor and couple can come to a resolution of most economic troubles in marriage. Even before marriage, counsel needs to be given indicating the need for savings by young couples. A proper sense of values clearly indicates that **starting a life-insurance program before marriage** and storing up a tidy sum for the heavy burdens of family life **should take precedence** over the purchase of a red convertible and other luxuries. While industry and thrift before marriage will help lay the economic foundations solidly, learning well the home arts and crafts will likewise, in time, be a significant factor in bolstering the family

---

[6] *S. T.,* Ia, q. 5, art. 6c; Ia–IIae, q. 84, art. 4c.

economy. There is little wonder that Pius XI had a "special word of praise for schools of domestic economy." The young man who brings to his family a skill in making and repairing many of the varied items of a modern household will, in time, substantially add to his family's security and standard of living. The young woman who similarly comes to her family responsibilities well trained in the skills of child rearing, child training, cooking, sewing, and interior decorating approaches the description of the "valiant woman" inspired by the Holy Spirit in the Old Testament. "Far and from the uttermost coasts is the price of her. . . . Her children rose up, and called her blessed: her husband, and he praised her."[7] **During the courtship all money matters should be prearranged,** a pattern of economic life together agreed upon, and a system of budgeting devised. Not only will this serve the purpose of closing out in advance many potential points of friction; it will also afford an opportunity of determining how well mated they are in matters other than romantic love.

HOME IS FOR CHILDREN

Couples entering marriage with merely a modest saving and income would be well advised to resist the pressures of our age for expensive furniture. Again that uncommon common sense assures us that a home is to be chiefly **for children,** not adults. In practice, this means selecting furnishings which will readily withstand the not-too-careful use by children; it will mean selecting a house with ample space for sleeping and recreating. In brief, it will mean setting up a household **not to impress the Joneses** but to serve as a center of work, play, love, recreation, education, and religion for a family with children. It means a homelike place, not a show place.

WORKING WIVES

A question frequently asked the counselor in marriage is whether the wife should work in the early part of marriage and before the advent of the first child.[8] Some would hasten to advise that she do

---

[7] Prov. 31:10–28.

[8] The problems arising because of working mothers are so numerous and serious that it seems worth while to quote at length an allocution on the subject by the Holy Father. His Holiness Pope Pius XII addressed these eloquent words *to working mothers* in a talk delivered on October 21, 1945. He said in part:

"We see a woman who, in order to augment her husband's earnings, betakes herself also to a factory, leaving her house abandoned during her absence. The

so provided her earnings are saved and not spent, and provided the first child be not deferred for the sake of working. This advice seems unrealistic, impractical, and un-Christian in spirit. It is unrealistic because most couples simply will not save the wife's earnings while many will delay the having of the first child. These are matters of common observation; only the valiant few will resist these temptations. It is impractical because a wife is worth more economically to the family as a producer in the home than as a wage earner. The statistical

---

house, untidy and small perhaps before, becomes even more miserable for lack of care. Members of the family work separately in four quarters of the city and with different working hours. Scarcely ever do they find themselves together for dinner or rest after work — still less for prayer in common. What is left of family life? And what attractions can it offer to children? To such painful consequences of the absence of the mother from the home there is added another, still more deplorable. It concerns the education, especially of the young girl, and her preparation for real life. Accustomed as she is to see her mother always out of the house and the house itself so gloomy in its abandonment, she will be unable to find any attraction for it, she will not feel the slightest inclination for austere housekeeping jobs. She cannot be expected to appreciate their nobility and beauty or to wish one day to give herself to them as a wife and mother.

"This is true in all grades and stations of social life. The daughter of the worldly woman, who sees all housekeeping left in the hands of paid help and her mother fussing around with frivolous occupations and futile amusements, will follow her example, will want to be emancipated as soon as possible and in the words of a very tragic phrase 'to live her own life.' How could she conceive a desire to become one day a true lady, that is, the mother of a happy, prosperous, worthy family?

"As to the working classes, forced to earn daily bread, a woman might, if she reflected, realize that not rarely the supplementary wage which she earns by working outside the house is easily swallowed up by other expenses or even by waste which is ruinous to the family budget. The daughter who also goes out to work in a factory or office, deafened by the excited, restless world in which she lives, dazzled by the tinsel of specious luxury, developing a thirst for shallow pleasures that distract but do not give satiety or repose in those revue or dance halls which are sprouting up everywhere, often for party propaganda purposes and which corrupt youth, becomes a fashionable lady, despises the old nineteenth century ways of life. How could she not feel her modest home surroundings unattractive and more squalid than they are in reality? To find her pleasure in them, to desire one day to settle in them herself, she should be able to offset her natural impressions by a serious intellectual and spiritual life, by the vigor that comes from religious education and from supernatural ideals. But what kind of religious formation has she received in such surroundings?

"And that is not all. When, as the years pass, her mother, prematurely aged, worn out, and broken by work beyond her capacity, by sorrow and anxiety, will see her return home at night at a very late hour, she will not find her a support or a help, but rather the mother herself will have to wait on a daughter incapable and unaccustomed to household work, and to perform for her all the offices of a servant. And the lot of the father will not be any better when old age, sickness, infirmity and unemployment force him to depend for his meager sustenance on the good or bad will of his children. Here you have the august holy authority of the father and mother dethroned."

average increment to the family income by wage-earning wives is about $1,000 a year; that of a busy home producer is more than twice that amount as a minimum, according to expert investigations. It would indicate greater vision and insight were the first year spent in learning and perfecting home-producing arts. These arts and skills would continue to provide a family increment throughout the life of the family, long after wage-earned income has ceased. Employment for the wife is not in accord with Christian tradition which impelled Pope Leo XIII to write in his encyclical: "Women are best fitted by nature for the duties of home-making." This same tradition envisions wage-earning wives to consider the loss of femininity, refinement, and modesty which accompanied women's emergence in the work-world of the male. However, the rampant pragmatism and secularism of our age effected, in this question of working wives, what Cardinal Manning called "a lack of a decisive Christian conscience."

In spite of these very good arguments, we must recognize that there are certain situations where it is desirable and necessary for the wife to work. A wife's contribution may not always be made in the home. Each couple should carefully investigate all aspects of the problem before the wife decides to seek employment.

THE QUESTION OF ALLOWANCES

Another problem facing couples early in their life together is that of "allowances" for husbands and wives. Such allowances are fixed sums of money and as such present a restriction on spending. It would seem that allowances (as other budgetary restrictions) are indicated when and if either or both parties have uneconomic habits of spending. A truly thrifty, economical person does not need an allowance system other than perhaps a temporary one for a periodic check on his or her expenditures for various classes of goods. Grandmother saved more without budgets and allowances than her granddaughters saves with them! But grandma was frugal and thrifty by training and education, if not by force of circumstances.

BUDGETING

The same holds true of the question of whether a couple should budget or not. Again truly wise spenders and frugal couples will find little use for budgeting. They will have the best possible budget in their proper sense of economic values, in their economic prudence, and in their habits of self-control and self-denial. Realism, however, forces us to acknowledge that, again, only the valiant few enjoy the above traits; most do stand in need of a budgetary system. At this point a counselor is faced with the very practical problem of what type of budget to advise. If he is setting up a budget for a couple in his city, he will need to know the local price levels of various items quite accurately. He will further need to know the peculiar economic responsibilities of a given married couple. He will need to have a true sense of values between naturally necessary items, social-professional necessities, and luxuries. Fortified with these data, facts, and principles, he can then set about devising a scientific budget. But even then he will need to caution the couple that change of relative prices or family responsibilities or social-professional advancement, etc., will make imperative a revision of this budget.

It is because of such changes that the usual type of budget (until recently widely urged by economic dilettantism) based upon fixed percentages (20 per cent for housing, etc.) is most often misleading and not infrequently harmful. No fixed percentage can be practical for all couples in the face of varying costs and prices, varying needs of couples, varying preferences, and so forth. The scientism of our age and the shortsighted practicability of the pragmatist have foisted this impractical type of budget upon couples to their distinct disadvantage. Budgets, like clothing, must be tailored to the time, place, and family; they cannot be devised by a magic rule-of-thumb, even though under the guise of being "scientific."

WORKING CHILDREN

The practices of children working for wages and of children's allowances also are frequent points of inquiry and advice. **The ideal environment for children to work is,** of course, **under the supervision of the parents.** A home which still produces a significant amount of its own goods and services will afford such opportunities. Working outside the home has undoubted advantages also. But parents need to be cautioned against the dangers that often lurk in the adult environment of the filling station and other places of employment for children. Repeated studies have pointed out the danger to morals which exists in such places.

Children's allowances have distinct educational advantages if properly handled. Giving such allowances with no supervision over their use usually means the children's developing habits of unwise spending or luxury. Only if children are taught how to handle money wisely will allowances serve their intended purpose.

THE NECESSITY OF GOOD BUYING HABITS

There are families, however, who, despite attempted budgeting and allowances, seem unable to make any economic progress. Usually the reason lies in their inexpert buying habits. Just as it has been estimated scientifically that a family by home production can reduce its expenditures 15–20 per cent, so research also indicates a similar saving possible through wise buying. The rules of good purchasing habits are simple, though their application demands considerable effort. Wise buying means little more than knowing when to buy, where to buy, and how to buy a given commodity or service, and what to buy. **When** implies the proper time or season of the year; **where** implies coming to know the outlets for goods which have a given article at the best price; **how** means the knowledge of qualities and the ability to judge items on their true merits rather than superficial appearances. **What** implies buying necessities before conveniences; conveniences before luxuries. The mastery of these four rules spells success in purchasing and a considerable enhancement of the family income. A competent counselor will, as a matter of personal experience and study, be prepared to advise couples as to the best times and places in his locality for the purchase of various articles and services. He will be acquainted with sources of information which counselees may and should consult.

INVESTMENTS

Perhaps one of the greatest tragedies observable at times in families who have been industrious, frugal, and wise in expenditures, is witnessing their hard-won savings disappear through **unwise investment.** Here, as elsewhere, a proper sense of values is important. The **first savings** should be placed in a liquid position for emergency purposes — someplace (as a checking or savings account) where it can be gotten quickly and easily. The **second claim upon savings** should be adequate insurance. The Very Rev. F. J. Connell, Dean of the School of Theology of the Catholic University of America, points out that adequate insurance protection would seem to be a moral obligation on the head of a family which would be impoverished if he were suddenly summoned by death. **Third,** under normal circumstances and under normal conditions, savings should be used to buy a home. If there are still further savings at this point, only the most secure type of investment should be purchased until the family has all the economic security it needs for both the present and the future. After such security needs are provided, superfluous savings might be placed in more risky and speculative ventures — but not before they are provided. Ordinary observation will indicate a rather widespread failure to follow the above sequence.

THE HIGH COST OF CHILDREN

One more problem often confronting counselors in marriage is the fear of staggering costs of having more children. In part, this is due to the exaggerated standard of living to which many believe they are entitled. In part, it is due to exaggerated costs publicized by scientific agencies. In some studies the cost of bringing a child to its eighteenth year is estimated at $20,000! Parents on a small income and with five children might well wonder where they would ever obtain the $100,000 to raise their children. The fact should be recognized that **these studies are usually unscientific, unrealistic, and grossly exaggerated.** Actually, the true cost can be closer to half that amount. Home production, frugality, thrift, wise buying, children's chores, and so forth, are omitted in these studies while luxury costs are included.

In our age when family economics takes on the complexities of our general culture and civilization, and when grievances over economic matters are so prolific, the counselor in marriage and the successful parent must have a considerable competency and fund of knowledge in things economic. In addition, they should have a grasp of the Christian philosophy of economics and integrate it into their economic planning. Such counsel cannot remain sterile with theoretical generalities. It must not be fraught with pseudo-scientific errors or based upon shortsighted practicability. In things economic "a little knowledge is a dangerous thing; drink deep or taste not the Pierian spring."

CHAPTER XXVIII

Mixed Marriages

Catholics form one fifth of the total population of the United States.[1] This proportion between Catholics and non-Catholics is not evenly distributed in all areas, however. In the Ecclesiastical Province of New York — which includes all of New York state — for example, the **Official Catholic Directory** lists 4,562,296 Catholics, whereas the total population for that same area — according to the 1950 Census — is 14,830,192 persons. On the other hand, the Catholic population of the Province of Portland, Oregon — which includes the states of Oregon, Idaho, and Montana — is 292,369. The total census for the same area is 2,701,002 persons. In other words, Catholics number approximately one out of three in the New York area, whereas they number one out of ten in the Oregon area. Roughly speaking, this will mean that on a national average Catholics may expect to have dealings with four times as many non-Catholics as they may have with members of their own faith. It should not be a matter of surprise, therefore, to find that a large number of Catholics marry persons who do not subscribe **in toto** to the teachings of the Catholic Church. For the year ending May, 1955, there were 70,520 marriages between Catholics and non-Catholics, while there were 218,169 marriages where both parties were Catholic. In two dioceses the number of marriages to non-Catholics is almost double the number of Catholic marriages. In a third diocese the number of marriages to non-Catholics is almost triple.

A marriage between two persons of different religions is called a **mixed marriage.**

---

[1] *Yearbook for American Churches,* ed. for 1956 (New York: National Council for the Churches of Christ, 1955).

429

POPE PIUS XI ON MIXED MARRIAGES

The evils of mixed marriages are described in the following words of Pope Pius XI in his encyclical letter **Casti Connubii:**

They, therefore, who rashly and heedlessly contract mixed marriages, from which the maternal love and providence of the Church dissuades her children for very sound reasons, fail conspicuously in this respect, sometimes with danger to their eternal salvation. This attitude of the Church to mixed marriages appears in many of her documents, all of which are summed up in the Code of Canon Law: "Everywhere and with the greatest strictness the Church forbids marriages between baptized persons, one of whom is a Catholic and the other a member of a schismatical or heretical sect; and if there is, added to this, the danger of the falling away of the Catholic party and the perversion of the children, such a marriage is forbidden also by the divine law." If the Church occassionally on account of circumstances does not refuse to grant a dispensation from these strict laws (provided that the divine law remains intact and the dangers above mentioned are provided against by suitable safeguards), it is unlikely that the Catholic party will not suffer some detriment from such a marriage.

Whence it comes about not unfrequently, as experience shows, that deplorable defections from religion occur among the offspring, or at least a headlong descent into that religious indifference which is closely allied to impiety. There is this also to be considered that in these mixed marriages it becomes much more difficult to imitate by a lively conformity of spirit the mystery of which We have spoken, namely that close union between Christ and His Church.

Assuredly, also, will there be wanting that close union of spirit which as it is the sign and mark of the Church of Christ, so also should be the sign of Christian wedlock, its glory and adornment. For, where there exists diversity of mind, truth and feeling, the bond of union of mind and heart is wont to be broken, or at least weakened. From this comes the danger lest the love of man and wife grow cold and the peace and happiness of family life, resting as it does on the union of hearts, be destroyed. Many centuries ago indeed, the old Roman law had proclaimed: "Marriages are the union of male and female, a sharing of life and the communication of divine and human rights." But especially, as We have pointed out, Venerable Brethren, the daily increasing facility of divorce is an obstacle to the restoration of marriage to that state of perfection which the divine Redeemer willed it should possess.[2]

---

[2] Pope Pius XI, *Casti Connubii.*

A mixed marriage is obviously anything but an ideal one. The different religious groups tolerate it only in order to prevent greater evils — such as sinful and invalid marriages. The dangers of mixed marriages are legion; and they involve more than religious difficulties. From a purely religious viewpoint they result often in (a) religious indifference, (b) a loss of faith, and (c) neglect of the religious education of the children. The Catholic Church has long recognized them to be the greatest single source of apostasy.[3] It can be readily seen how these difficulties arise: religious indifference arises because of the reluctance on the part of the husband or wife to raise a subject of disagreement. In order to stay out of that field they refuse to consider anything even remotely connected with it. So too with the loss of faith which arises from indifference or from more serious problems (see below). The fear of discord grows when it is a question of the religious education of the children. Rather than insist upon the Catholic education of the children, the Catholic parent first tends to make minor concessions — hoping that each one will be the last.

There is an even greater objection to mixed marriages from the Catholic standpoint. Marriage is a sacrament. Unlike all other sacraments, marriage is conferred by the parties to the marriage on each other. This will mean, then, that the Catholic member is having the sacrament of matrimony conferred upon him by a non-Catholic.

Apart from the religious question there are other reasons which militate against mixed marriages. A mixed marriage creates "a house divided against itself," and it can never possess one of the prime requisites for successful marriage, i.e., the mutual sharing of experience in all phases of life. Because where there is a difference in religious outlook there is a fundamental point of disagreement which although a couple may choose to ignore during their engagement period, they will, nevertheless, have to face as a practical difficulty once they are married. For example, if the Catholic partner sincerely intends to remain a Catholic, he will be bound by the law of God on birth control as taught by the Catholic Church. Indirectly these same obligations will be forced upon the non-Catholic member who might have chosen to act otherwise. In other words, the non-Catholic is put in the position of subscribing to a moral code in which he has no belief. Needless to say, the non-Catholic partner will probably refuse to abide by the decision of the Church if the going gets rough.

---

[3] The official German civil census for 1929 shows that 40,000 apostasized from the Church in one year alone because of mixed marriages.

Another problem may come from the in-laws. Even when the couple themselves have agreed upon a solution for their religious difficulties there is no guarantee that the in-laws will be reconciled to it, especially when children are concerned. Nagging reminders are bound to be heard in the presence of any marital discord.

PROMISES BEFORE MARRIAGE

Before a non-Catholic marries a Catholic, **the Church requires certain promises from both parties.** In addition to these promises, some dioceses add a fourth promise that at no time will either partner resort to contraceptive devices. One very helpful requirement in some dioceses is that the non-Catholic partner must take a brief course in Catholic doctrine before the marriage takes place.

FORM OF PROMISES FOR CATHOLIC

I, the undersigned Catholic, wishing to contract marriage with the non-Catholic mentioned below, sincerely promise in the presence of the undersigned witness, a Catholic Priest:

1. That all children of either sex born of this marriage will be baptized and educated in the Catholic Religion alone.
2. That in the performance of this marriage there will be *only* the Catholic ceremony.
3. That I shall do all that I can by prayer, example and frequentation of the Sacraments to lead the non-Catholic to the Catholic Faith.

. . . .

Signature of Catholic

. . . .

Address

FORM OF PROMISES FOR NON-CATHOLIC

I, the undersigned non-Catholic, desiring to contract marriage with the Catholic named above, propose to do so with the understanding that the marriage bond thus contracted is indissoluble except by death, and I hereby promise in the presence of the undersigned witness, a Catholic Priest:

1. That all the children of either sex born of this marriage shall be baptized and educated in the Catholic Religion alone.
2. That I shall not in any manner hinder the Catholic party in practicing freely and faithfully the Catholic Religion.

3. That in the performance of my marriage, there will be *only* the Catholic ceremony.

. . . .

Signature of non-Catholic

. . . .

Address

I, the undersigned Catholic Priest, hereby declare that the above promises were signed in my presence by the contracting parties named in this petition, and I am morally certain that in making these promises both parties are sincere.

. . . .

Signature of Priest

. . . .

Church

. . . .

Date   *City or Town*

The prescribed course in doctrine and the promises exacted may seem to some to be an unnecessary procedure; but viewed in the proper light, they are benefits to the non-Catholic as well. By studying the Catholic doctrine the non-Catholic realizes what obligations he incurs in marrying a Catholic, and it gives him time to consider these problems before marriage when he may back out if he so desires. Although the Church may seem to some autocratic in exacting these promises, it can take no other course. One must realize that the Church possesses and teaches the Truth as revealed by God Himself. If the Church, therefore, allowed one of its members to subscribe to the teachings of another sect, it would be guilty of treason.[4] It is only with the greatest reluctance that the Catholic Church will grant a dispensation to one of its members to marry a non-Catholic; and a Catholic may not contract a marriage with a non-Catholic partner until he or she has received a proper dispensation.

INVALID AND ILLICIT MARRIAGES

If a mixed marriage has been contracted by a Catholic before he has received a proper dispensation, the resulting marriage is **illicit**.

[4] Some non-Catholic leaders have suggested that the non-Catholic make no concessions to the Catholic partner until the Catholic has studied the non-Catholic position. This would be unacceptable to the Catholic partner. James E. Pike, Dean of the Cathedral of St. John the Divine, in his work, *If You Marry Outside Your Faith*, makes this suggestion.

It may or may not be a **valid** one, depending on other circumstances. By "valid marriage" is meant a **true** marriage. That is to say, the Church recognizes the agreement between the couple as a true marriage contract; and if problems arise later in connection with this agreement, the individuals involved will be considered as bound to each other just as they would have been if the marriage had been wholly licit. On the other hand, an **invalid marriage** is no marriage at all. In this case, the Church would hold that **no real** agreement was ever entered into by the couple because they failed in one respect or another to meet all the requirements for a true marriage to take place. A situation which prevents a couple from meeting the qualifications for a licit marriage is called an **impediment** (see p. 381 f.).

HISTORY

The Mosaic Law prohibited marriage between the Israelites and heretical sects.[5] St. Paul exhorted Christians to avoid mixed marriages.[6] At the time of St. Paul, however, marriages between Christians and infidels were considered valid. They were recognized as such because the number of Christians was so few as to make it difficult for the Christian partner to find another Christian. Schroeder says that these marriages (especially where the wife was Christian and the husband was a heathen) were not uncommon:

> First, because Christian women outnumbered Christian men, and secondly, because the heathen husband was usually too indifferent to interfere either with the religion of his Christian wife or with the rearing of the children as Christians.[7]

Another reason why Christians were allowed to marry heathens was because they had a natural right to marry.

By the twelfth century, however, the **Decretum of Gratian** (ca. 1150) made nonbaptism a diriment impediment. After that time all marriages between Catholics and unbaptized persons were judged invalid except when a proper dispensation had been obtained.

The history of the Church's attitude toward marriage between Catholics and baptized members of heretical sects was similar. Between the third and seventh centuries opposition was expressed

---

[5] Gen. 24:3; 28:1; 3 Kings 9:2; Deut. 7:3.

[6] 2 Cor. 6:14.

[7] H. J. Schroeder, *Disciplinary Decrees of The General Councils* (St. Louis: B. Herder Book Co., 1937), p. 107.

toward such unions by the Councils of Elvira,[8] Arles,[9] Laodicea,[10] and Trullo.[11] But although the Church was opposed to marriages of this kind, it did not always deny them validity. Even after the **Decretum of Gratian** marriages between a Catholic and a baptized adherent of an heretical sect were still considered valid. It was not until the time of the Protestant Revolt that such a marriage was declared invalid, if not contracted in the presence of a priest and two witnesses and after the obtaining of a dispensation (mixed religion). After the Council of Trent, valid marriages could only be contracted **in facie ecclesiae** — that is to say, with a priest of the Church as a witness. The Council enacted this legislation to counteract the unhappiness which was the almost certain outcome of marriages between Catholics and Protestants of that time. In order to prevent such marriages, the Church considered them "clandestine," i.e., contracted without formal recognition by the Church. This action by the Council of Trent must not be considered as something radically new, because we find Tertullian **(De Pudic.)** holding in the second century that such marriages were null and void.

MISCEGENATION

Miscegenation refers properly to a mixture of racial groups, but it may refer sometimes to a mixture of national groups within the same race. There is no argument against miscegenation from purely religious, physiological, or biological viewpoints. There may be even an argument for it, since it often helps to produce a better strain. The Eurasians of the Malay Peninsula, who are considered among the most beautiful people of the world, are a mixture of European and Asian blood. But psychologically speaking, interracial marriages may be a cause of unhappiness when they occur in only isolated cases. Somebody is bound to be harmed in the process. Suppose, for example, an Occidental male who is working in the Orient begins to court an Oriental woman. While she is at home among her own people the differences between her way of life and that of the Occidental will be minimized. But if the Occidental male returns to the Occident with his new wife, she will be placed in a milieu so completely different from her past that she may be unequipped to adjust.

Miscegenation is even more difficult in areas of racial prejudice.

[8] Canons 15 and 16.
[9] Canon 11.
[10] Canons 10 and 31.
[11] Canon 72.

When a couple break through the racial barrier in these areas, they find themselves in a no man's land. They are accepted by neither race. If they have children, things only grow worse. The children are not accepted by the social group — and this can be heartbreaking.

What has been said above applies to interracial marriages when they are isolated instances rather than common practice. These problems are far less difficult in areas where intermixed marriages are frequent. In fact, there may be no problem at all under these circumstances.

Marriage partners who come from different national groups (but who are both of the same religion) are sometimes confronted with milder forms of these problems. But they are not so likely nowadays in the United States since nationalist groups are more communicative to each other than they were up to forty years ago. In the old days there were the great obstacles of language and economic conditions. In a study made on marriage records in New Haven, Connecticut, from the years 1870 to 1950, Ruby Jo Reeves Kennedy concluded that nationalist groups are being assimilated with each other along religious lines. Protestant British-Americans are marrying Protestant Germans and Scandinavians; Catholic Irish are marrying Catholic Italians and Poles; Jews are remaining among themselves.[12] It should be emphasized that the Catholic Church does not forbid miscegenation.

THE ATTITUDE OF NON-CATHOLIC RELIGIONS ON MIXED MARRIAGES

On the whole, one may say that all religious groups are opposed to mixed marriages. The degree of opposition varies.

In the case of Orthodox Judaism, a member automatically cuts himself off from association with his group because the non-Jewish partner is not qualified to participate in the general activities of the group. Orthodox Judaism extends to more than what are ordinarily called "religious observances." The whole social life of the Orthodox Jew is tied into his religion.

Jews of other sects of Judaism have a more "liberal" attitude, and among these mixed marriages may not meet with much opposition. All Protestant sects are opposed to mixed marriages. They are more strongly opposed to mixed marriages with Catholics than they are to mixed marriages with Protestant denominations. The Protestant

---

[12] Ruby Jo Reeves Kennedy, "Single or Triple Melting-Pot?" *American Journal of Sociology,* LVIII (1), July, 1952, pp. 56–59.

attitude on mixed marriages is rooted in the basic position that a man's conscience is a matter directly between himself and God; and that each man should choose for himself whatever religious body best fits his own sincere convictions. Therefore, the only real difficulty between the marriage of two Protestant parties would be when they had opposed views on religious problems. Dean James A. Pike of the Cathedral of St. John the Divine in New York suggests that the easiest solution for Protestants is to have both parties study the religion of each other and see if they cannot find a religious view which they find compatible. Dean Pike also suggests this for Catholics and Protestants. But the Catholic Church could not allow such a procedure in view of its firm conviction that it has the Truth as divinely revealed, and under no circumstances can this deposit of Truth be altered.

Protestant groups are opposed to marriage of their members with adherents of the Catholic Church because they believe that the Catholic Church treats all other religions like "poor relations." Self-respect and justice are lost, they maintain, when the Protestant party makes concessions to a mixed marriage, such as signing the promises.[13]

---

[13] For a detailed treatment of the Protestant views on mixed marriage see: James A. Pike, *If You Marry Outside Your Faith* (New York: Harper and Brothers, 1954).

CHAPTER XXIX

Alcoholism and Marriage

> Whiskey — I like it: I always did, and that is the reason I never
> use it (Robert E. Lee).[1]

It may be asked, "Why a chapter on alcoholism in a book for
marriage counselors?" Actually, no apology is needed for such an
inclusion because next to the in-law problem the abuse of alcohol
is the greatest cause of marital difficulties. In its wake follow poverty,
physical abuse, and sexual difficulties.

Although there is an extensive literature on the subject of alcoholism,
it is somewhat difficult to find in one place a general review of the
topic. For this reason it seems important to include a discussion of
the subject here so that the counselor may be informed. In this way
he may better advise the victim of this unfortunate disease. There
have been many misconceptions about alcohol and alcoholism. Probably the most prevalent of these misconceptions is the belief that
alcohol is the cause of alcoholism. Others might include:

1. That drunkenness and alcoholism are the same thing;
2. That alcoholism is inherited;
3. That alcoholism is due to a lack of will power;
4. That alcohol is a stimulant;
5. That alcohol damages the nervous tissue;
6. That alcohol causes a large percentage of crime.[2]

Alcohol in itself is good. Used moderately and temperately it can
be a useful adjuvant to living.

In this theme St. John Chrysostom wrote:

> I hear many cry when there are deplorable excesses, "Would there
> be no wine! Oh! Folly, Oh! Madness!" Is it the wine that causes this

---

[1] Source unknown.
[2] Selden D. Bacon, Ph.D., "Alcoholism: Nature of the Problem," *Congressional
Record* (Wednesday, September 28, 1949), pp. 3–13.

abuse? No, it is the intemperance of those who take an evil delight in it. Cry rather, "Would to God there would be no drunkenness, no luxury." If you say, "would there be no wine" because of the drunkards then you must say, going on by degrees, "Would there be no steel because of murderers, Would there be no night because of thieves, Would there be no light because of the informers, and would there be no women because of adultery."[3]

Alcohol is used in many religious ceremonies. This is pointed out by Father Magner in these words:

> Despite the religious scruples of some people, it cannot be demonstrated that there is anything evil in alcoholic beverages as such — the ancient observance of the Jewish Passover involved the use of wine, and it was this that Christ took and shared with His Apostles at the Last Supper, together with bread, when He pronounced the immortal words, "This is My Body. . . . Take ye and eat. This is My Blood. . . . Do this in Commemoration of Me." His first public miracle at the Marriage Feast of Cana was to convert water into wine. Saint Paul who was a rigorist prescribed a little wine for the stomach's sake. And so, if a drink helps to calm one's nerves or to induce a brighter view on life it may be regarded as one of God's good gfts, not as a poisonous draft of the devil. What is one man's meat, however, may be another man's poison; and drink is no exception.[4]

Horace spoke of alcohol in these terms:

> What wonders does not wine! It discloses secrets; ratifies and confirms our hopes; thrusts the coward forth to battle, eases the anxious mind of its burden; instructs in arts. Whom has not a cheerful glass made eloquent! Whom not quite free and easy from pinching poverty![5]

But, unfortunately, man will not always be moderate and tends to excess, so that alcohol is not always used as it should be:

> Wine was created from the beginning to make men cheerful, not to make them drunk.[6]

The Bible also warns of the danger of the insidious onset of alcoholism:

---

[3] St. John Chrysostom, *Homilies 1.*

[4] Rev. James A. Magner, *Mental Health in a Mad World* (Milwaukee: The Bruce Publishing Co., 1953), pp. 152–153.

[5] Louis Goodman and Alfred Gilman, *The Pharmacological Basis of Therapeutics* (New York: The Macmillan Co., 1941), p. 109.

[6] Ecclus. 31:35.

Take heed to yourselves, lest your hearts be overburdened with self-indulgence and drunkenness and the cares of this life and that day may come upon you suddenly.[7]

INCIDENCE OF ALCOHOLISM

The use of alcohol as a beverage is very extensive. All such use is not harmful. The damage, however, may be very great. In this regard Doctor Munch states:

Alcoholic "thirst" . . . is known to have disabled more than 6,000,000 persons in this country last year [1952]. It also caused 12,000 deaths, an estimated loss of four hundred thirty-two million dollars in wages alone, and an estimated seven hundred fifty million dollars in terms of disease, crime, poverty — despite the fact that a majority of such losses did not appear in published statistics.[8]

O'Brien offers more embracing and revealing figures:

In the United States, which has a population of 138,000,000 people, there are more than sixty-five million who drink, mostly in moderation. About 3,750,000 of these are repeatedly in trouble because of their excessive use of alcohol and more than half of these 3,750,000 are ill men and women. This illness is defined in terms of disorganization. These 2,000,000 persons are suffering from physical, psychological, or spiritual disorder(s) or a combination of disorder(s) at all three levels. . . . There are at least 750,000 in the final stages of the disease, 12,000 individuals die each year from chronic alcoholism. The social, moral and financial losses are staggering.[9]

The following figures will give an idea of the extent of the use of alcohol in the United States. These figures are for the year 1954:

Number of distilleries — 224
Number of wholesale houses — 1500
Number of retailers — 192,000
Number of employees — 800,000
Federal tax — $2,000,000,000
Money spent on alcoholic beverages — $9,000,000,000
Distilled spirits processed — 184,876,858 gallons

---

[7] Lk. 21:34.

[8] Dr. J. C. Munch, "New Hope for the Alcoholic," *The American Weekly* (November 29, 1953).

[9] Patricia O'Brien, "Facts on Alcoholism," National Committee for Education on Alcoholism, as quoted in "Casework Treatment with Alcoholics" (Washington, D. C.: Catholic University Press, 1950).

Distilled spirits inventory — 864,343,131 gallons
Bottled output of whisky — 141,255,835 gallons
Per capita consumption of distilled spirits — 1.23 wine gallons[10]
Tax on the retail price of whisky — 56 per cent
U. S. production of wine — 125,700,000 gallons
Users of alcohol — 60 to 80 million
Alcoholics in the United States — 4 million
Alcoholics below the age of fifteen — None
Alcoholics below the age of twenty — Almost none
Alcoholics between the ages of twenty and sixty-five — 95 per cent, of whom 85 per cent are males

Although the number of alcoholics in the United States seems tremendous, according to the World Health Organization, percentage-wise the United States has only the fourth-highest rate of alcoholism in the world, the country having the highest rate being Switzerland, the next Chile, and the next France.

Therapeutic Facilities

1. Out-patient clinics — 92
2. Alcoholics Anonymous — 5421 groups
   Total members, approximately 128,296 in the United States and 58 other countries.

ALCOHOLIC BEVERAGES

Most married people drink and, on the basis of percentages, many of them are problem drinkers. The marriage counselor should, therefore, be well informed on the topic.

Some individuals, probably including many marriage counselors, group all alcoholic beverages into one class. They fail to distinguish one group of beverages from another. Consequently, they fail to reach their client who has contempt for them because of their ignorance. It is very important, therefore, for the marriage counselor to have some basic information concerning alcohol and alcoholic beverages. In order to avoid such ignorance, the next few pages will be devoted to this subject. An intelligent grasp of the subject will give greater confidence to the counselor in dealing with the alcoholic.

---

[10] Definition of wine gallon: A wine gallon is the same as an ordinary United States gallon of four quarts. It was originally intended in England to be equivalent to a cylinder of 7 inches in diameter and 6 inches in height.

For the information of the counselor, it may be pointed out that alcoholic beverages are produced in one of two ways (a) by distillation; (b) by fermentation.

Distilled beverages are whisky, rum, brandy, gin, cordials, and liqueurs. **Fermented beverages** are wine and beer.

WHISKY

The word "whisky" is derived from the Gaelic **uisque-beatha,** afterward contracted to **usquebaugh,** meaning "water of life." It is defined as "an alcoholic liquor obtained by distilling the fermented mash of any of several cereal grains, and aging the distillate in wooden kegs."[11]

The following **descriptive terms** are used in describing whisky:

1. Rye	5. Malt
2. Bourbon	6. Bonded
3. Scotch	7. Blended
4. Corn	

Whisky usually contains about 40 or 50 per cent of alcohol by volume, which is usually indicated on the label as the proof. A **proof** represents one half of 1 per cent, so that 90-proof whisky would be 45 per cent alcohol by volume.

a) Rye whisky is made from a mash which contains more than 50 per cent rye grain.

b) Bourbon whisky is made from a mash which contains 50 to 80 per cent corn.

c) Scotch whisky is made from barley mash. The grain used to prepare this mash is "cured" or dried over open peat fires which gives it its characteristic smoky flavor.

d) Corn whisky is produced from a mash of more than 80 per cent corn.

e) Bonded whisky is held in government warehouses to age for at least four years. Before being bottled for sale, the alcohol content is adjusted to 50 per cent (100 proof).

f) Blended whisky is a mixture of several whiskies. It may consist of a mixture of good, aged whiskies or of a mixture of 95 per cent neutral spirits and 5 per cent whisky (so-called spirit whisky).

Gin consists of alcohol and water to which the juniper flavor has been added.

[11] *The New Funk and Wagnalls Encyclopedia,* Vol. 35, pp. 13, 137 (New York: Unicorn Publishers, Inc., 1950–1951).

WINES

A wine is a beverage produced by the natural fermentation of the juice of ripe grapes. It usually contains from 10 to 16 per cent of alcohol.

Wine is probably the oldest and best known of alcoholic beverages. It was produced in Egypt about 2400 B.C. and in China before 2000 B.C. Many persons have written of its charms and delights. Even the usually prosaic **Encyclopaedia Britannica** becomes lyrical in describing it:

> Wine is, indeed, a living thing, brash in its youth, full-blossoming in its maturity, but subject, if not used in time, to senility, decay and death. It is gregarious, appearing at its best in the company of food, and as a constituent of food; and in the society of moderate men and women, priming their wit, assisting at their worship, and serving as a medicine for some of their ills.[12]

Wines are usually described as:
a) Dry
b) Sweet

A **dry wine** is one in which the sugar has been fermented away. The term means the opposite of sweet without meaning sour. Dry wines usually have a lower alcoholic content than sweet wines.

A **sweet wine** has not had all the sugar fermented away, has a higher alcoholic content, and a sweeter taste.

A **sparkling wine** is one which has been bottled before fermentation is complete and will, therefore, bubble when poured from the bottle. Champagne is the best known sparkling wine.

A **fortified wine** is one to which alcohol has been added.

Wines **depend for their quality** on a number of factors, the most important of which are: (1) climate; (2) drainage; (3) exposure to sun and wind; (4) the vineyard from which the grapes are taken. It is obvious, therefore, that some years will produce better wines than others because of varying climatic conditions. This is meant when one speaks of a certain year having been a **good year** for a particular brand of wine.

Each country has its own special brand of wine in which it specializes. France probably is better known for its wines than any other country. In France, as well as in other countries, a wine is known either by the name of the section of the country from

---

[12] *Encyclopaedia Britannica* (Chicago: The University of Chicago, 1950), Vol. 23, p. 652.

which it comes or by the name of the vineyard which produces it. Since it is our purpose here to give only enough information to enable the counselor to speak intelligently on the subject, only a very brief outline will be given.

FRENCH WINES

Most famous of the French wines are those which come from Bordeaux and Burgundy. The Bordeaux wines are usually described according to the area of Bordeaux from which they come. The best known of these areas are:

1. Médoc
2. Graves
3. Sauternes
4. Saint-Émilion
5. Pomerol

Médoc, Saint-Émilion, and Pomerol are best known for claret (a term loosely applied to all red Bordeaux wines). Graves and Sauternes are better known for their white wines; Sauterne being one of the better known of the sweet, white dessert wines. The most famous Sauterne is from Chateau d'Yquem.

The best known **Burgundy wines** are:

a) Côte d'Or   c) Beaujolais
b) Maconnais   d) Chablis

Côte d'Or is usually regarded as the true Burgundy. Maconnais and Beaujolais are light red or white wines. Chablis is a dry, pale golden wine with a somewhat flinty flavor. Other famous red wines are: Romanée-Conti, Romanée St. Vivant, Chambertin, Clos de Vougeot, Le Corton, Beaune-Greves, and Pommard-Rugiens.

Champagne is a sparkling wine which is usually white or pale amber in color. The quality of the champagne depends upon the type of grape used. The reputation of the firm making the champagne is more important than its age because the addition of sweetening can disguise an inferior brand.

Alsatian or **French Rhine wines** come from Alsace. The best known of these wines are:

a) Riesling
b) Gewuerz Traminer   c) Sylvaner

Riesling is dry and fresh flavored. Gewuerz Traminer is less dry and the bouquet is more flowery. Sylvaner is medium dry and soft. It is better when it is young.

German Wines

1. **Moselle wines** (light, fresh, dry; sparkling tang and flowery bouquet):

   a) Piesporter   c) Bernkasteler
   b) Zeltinger

2. **Rhine wines** (more body, softer; may be quite sweet):

   a) Rudesheim   d) Appenheim
   b) Johannisberg   e) Forst
   c) Nierstein   f) Deidesheim

Italian Wines

1. **Piedmont:**
   a) Barolo   b) Barbera

2. **Tuscany:**
   Chianti

3. **Umbria:**
   Orvieto

4. **Sicily:**
   a) Albanello   b) Malvasia   c) Marsala

Barolo and Barbera are red wines, while Orvieto is dry or slightly sweet. Albanello is a heavy sweet white wine and may be dry. Malvasia is a sweet, deep golden wine, and Marsala is sweet and heavy.

Asti Spumante and **Lacrima Christi** are the best known of the Italian sparkling wines.

Vermouth is an **apéritif** and is used as an ingredient of cocktails. It is a white wine, blended, fortified, and aromatized.

Spanish Wines

a) Sherry   d) Malaga
b) Rioja   e) Muscatel
c) Valdepeñas   f) Malvasia

Sherry is a fortified wine which can be dry or sweet and which is aged in wood. Rioja is a red wine; Valdepeñas, a white wine; and Malaga, Muscatel, and Malvasia are sweet wines.

PORTUGUESE WINES

a) Port
b) Madeira

Port is an after-dinner wine and Madeira is dry and sweet.

LIQUEURS

Liqueurs are an alcoholic beverage made of distilled alcoholic spirits combined with sugar and aromatics. They contain 27 to 80 per cent alcohol. They are sweet, aromatized, sometimes perfumed alcoholic beverages. The best known of these are:

a) Chartreuse ⎱ French
b) Bénèdictine ⎰
c) Curaçao — Dutch
d) Annisette
e) Kirsch

f) Kümmel
g) Cointreau
h) Grand Marnier
i) Crème de Menthe
j) Fruit liqueurs

These are seldom the cause of alcoholism.

CORDIAL

A cordial is a sweetened, alcoholic, fruit-flavored liquid. It differs from liqueur in that aromatic flavors are added to this.

MEASURING TERMS

The following terms are frequently used in describing alcoholic drinks:

Dash — three drops
Pony — one fluid ounce
Jigger — one and one half to two fluid ounces
Split — one-half pint

BEER

Beer is made from grain by fermentation. In the United States its alcoholic content is usually about 4½ per cent. Ale, stout, and porter are heavier and stronger forms of beer.

Most of those who are meticulous drinkers prefer draft beer because bottled or canned beer contains a preservative which affects its flavor.

Many people are heard expressing the idea that one cannot get drunk on beer. This is an error. It can be done. Some alcoholics fortify beer by adding alcohol.

CLASSIFICATION OF DRINKERS

No completely satisfactory classification of alcoholism has been devised. There is a large group of social drinkers to whom alcohol is not a problem. There is another large group, the four million persons previously mentioned, to whom the drinking of alcohol is a problem. On this basis we could, therefore, say that there are two large groups, the social drinker and the problem drinker. It is in breaking down further the group of problem drinkers that the difficulties of classification arise. I find the following classification satisfactory:

1. Social drinkers
2. Reactive drinkers
3. Compulsive drinkers
   a) Primary
   b) Secondary

Concerning the **social drinker**, there is not much more to be said. He drinks for the sake of sociability, for pleasure, to ease tension, because it serves as a social lubricant, to relax after a day's work or perhaps because he likes the flavor. He may occasionally drink too much, but usually knows when to stop, and seldom gets into difficulty because of his drinking.

The **reactive drinker** is one who uses alcohol because of some environmental circumstance and may temporarily overindulge. If the situation recurs, he may again drink to excess. He is conscious of the reason because of which he is drinking, and in this respect differs from the compulsive drinker, who is usually unconscious (in marginal consciousness) of the cause of his drinking.

The **reactive drinker** is not likely to show the gradual deterioration of personality evidenced by the compulsive drinker. He is a good subject for therapy and can be approached with logic.

The **compulsive drinker** is usually unaware or only remotely aware of his reason for drinking. The primary compulsive drinker is the one who was neurotic before he began to drink, and the drinking is a secondary manifestation. The secondary compulsive drinker is one in whom the overindulgence in alcohol is a primary manifestation.[13]

Hereafter, when we speak of chronic alcoholism, the reference is to the compulsive drinker.

DEFINITION

The alcoholic is the compulsive drinker. He is the one who, as a result of forming a habit of using alcohol as an escape from unpleasant situations, is no longer able to control his ingestion of alcohol. **In simple terms, an alcoholic is an individual who, having begun to drink, cannot tell when he is going to stop.**

The alcoholic is a person who "cannot take it or leave it." For him one drink is too many and a dozen not enough. He has lost his ability to control his appetite for alcohol. Various authors are in substantial agreement as to what constitutes an alcoholic. The following is a representative sample of these definitions:

> The explanation that seems to make sense to most A.A. members is that alcoholism is an illness, a *progressive* illness, which can never be cured but which, like some other illnesses, *can* be arrested. Going one step further, many A.A.'s feel that the illness represents the combination of a physical sensitivity to alcohol, plus a mental obsession to drink which, regardless of consequences, cannot be broken by will power alone.
>
> Before they are exposed to A.A., many alcoholics who are unable to stop drinking think of themselves as morally weak, or, possibly, mentally unbalanced. The A.A. concept is that alcoholics are sick people who can recover if they will follow a simple program that has proved successful for thousands of other men and women.[14]

Yahraes defines an alcoholic as

> "one whose drinking interferes with normal living." He further qualifies this broad definition by adding that such a person after taking the first drink cannot stop.[15]

Strecker defines an alcoholic as a person who cannot face reality

---

[13] Bacon, *op. cit.*

[14] *A.A., 44 Questions and Answers About the Program of Recovery From Alcoholism,* issued by Alcoholics Anonymous Publishing, Inc., copyright December, 1952, by Works Publishing, Inc., Grand Central Annex, Post Box 459, New York 17, N. Y., p. 5.

[15] Herbert Yahraes, *Alcoholism Is a Sickness* (New York: Public Affairs Committee, Inc., 1950), p. 2.

without alcohol, and yet whose adequate adjustment to reality is impossible so long as he uses alcohol.[16]

Shepherd defines alcoholism as follows:

> Alcoholism is a progressive, complex illness which passes through recognizable stages and is usually accompanied by psychological physiological, and social symptoms. As the urge to drink becomes uncontrollable and the person becomes dependent on the perpetuation of alcoholic states through repeated intoxication, for whatever reason, alcoholism can be said to be present.[17]

Father Ford gives this definition:

> The alcoholic is the excessive drinker who gets into serious difficulty with his drinking and who generally cannot stop drinking even if he wants to, without outside help.[18]

ETIOLOGY

"Why do people drink?" It would be perhaps more accurate to ask, "Why do people start drinking?" because once the habit is established, the alcoholic loses control; he drinks because he is compelled to. He feels compelled, even though he knows it will eventually cause his ruin.

Alcoholism is of psychogenic origin. Until recently no satisfactory concept of the etiology of overindulgence in alcohol had been formulated. It was ascribed to a number of vague factors, among which were such terms as "constitutional predisposition." The popular concept of the alcoholic was a boisterous, cheerful, "hail fellow, well met," who, when under the influence of alcohol, although at times belligerent, was on the whole a good-natured fool. Much of this previous misinformation came about as a result of a failure to regard alcoholism as a psychic disorder.

The problem at hand is to explain how this disorder, this psychoneurosis, alcoholism, takes possession of the personality of the individual. The answer to this question would account for the etiology of alcoholic psychoses. There is probably no explanation which would fit all cases of chronic alcoholism. The most frequent common denomi-

---

[16] E. A. Strecker, *Fundamentals of Psychiatry* (Philadelphia: J. B. Lippincott and Co., 1947), p. 150; now in its fifth edition.

[17] Earnest A. Shepherd, *Social Work Yearbook* (New York: National Association of Social Workers, 1954), p. 42.

[18] John C. Ford, S.J., *Depth Psychology, Morality and Alcoholism* (Weston, Mass.: Weston College Press, 1951), p. 45.

nator is a strong sense of inferiority especially in social contacts. There may be no single basic conflict but more likely a series of deflating experiences.[19]

In addition to escape from feelings of inferiority, alcohol is also an escape from feelings of inadequacy, from sexual conflicts, from frustration, from anxiety, from an inability to compete with the world on equal terms, from a decreased sense of self-importance, and from feelings of guilt and remorse. It may also be a manifestation of emotional immaturity. Among excessive drinkers are mental defectives and some psychotic individuals, but these should probably not be included in the discussion of the chronic alcoholic. Alcoholism may have causes arising as an outgrowth of social drinking, but this is not usual.

The following are representative opinions from literature concerning the etiology of alcoholism. Doctor R. V. Seliger, M.D., enumerated the following "reasons" for the excessive use of alcohol:

1. As an escape from situations of life which the drinker cannot face.
2. As a result of a personality insufficiently adjusted to the normal course of life.
3. As a development from controlled social drinking to pathological drinking.
4. As an escape from incurable physical pain.
5. As a symptom of an inferior intellectual and/or totally immature emotional make-up.[20]

Strecker states that clinical study leaves him convinced that

alcohol is utilized as psychoneurotic symptoms are utilized — in order to screen effectively unsatisfactory external and inner realities.

He writes further:

The psychoneurotic drinking of the introvert asserts itself as a neurosis of emotional immaturity. . . . True chronic alcoholism is a psychoneurosis, defensive in character, with the object of shutting out reality inimical to emotional immaturity.[21]

Doctor Yahraes, in a pamphlet referring to the findings at the Yale Clinic, states that he considers a large percentage of alcoholism

---

[19] John R. Cavanagh, M.D., and James B. McGoldrick, S.J., *Fundamental Psychiatry* (Milwaukee: The Bruce Publishing Co., 1953), pp. 391–392.

[20] Robert V. Seliger, M.D., *Alcoholics Are Sick People* (New York: William Frederick Press, 1945), pp. 19–24.

[21] Strecker, *op. cit.*, pp. 148, 150.

a neurotic reaction in which a person takes refuge because he cannot face reality.[22]

McCarthy writes:

The experience at the Yale Plan Clinic with more than fifteen hundred alcoholics has confirmed what psychiatrists have long known, that alcoholism is an expression of emotional maladjustment of the individual.[23]

Earl S. Schaefer describes an isolation of personality types which he identifies as:

a) a schizoid personality; b) a relatively normal personality; c) an uncontrolled personality with an anxiety reaction to stress and frustration; d) an emotionally unstable personality; e) a psychoneurotic personality with pronounced sexual conflict and feelings of inadequacy.

Some of these emotional-mental disturbances or conflicts may take the form of:

1) infantilism; 2) an over-sensitive nervous system which is extremely susceptible to the action of alcohol; 3) feelings of inferiority, fear, or guilt; 4) feelings of exuberance or hilarity; and 5) the feeling that life has no meaning.[24]

Phelps says:

Alcoholics are generally of better than average intelligence but are often immature, dependent, and unable to tolerate failure. They are usually handicapped by marked feelings of inferiority, inadequacy and insecurity. Associated conditions are anxieties, over-sensitiveness, psychosexual guilt reactions and an evasion of responsibilities.[25]

And Noyes:

While by no means the only psychological factor that prompts the use of alcohol, there is much to suggest that in many instances the alcoholic is one whose personality has failed to develop beyond the homosexual stage of its evolution and that alcohol is taken to alleviate the resulting conflict.[26]

---

[22] Yahraes, *op. cit.*, pp. 9–10.

[23] Raymond G. McCarthy and Edgar M. Douglass, *Alcohol and Social Responsibility* (New York: Thomas Y. Crowell Co. and Yale Plan Clinic, 1947), p. 240.

[24] Earl S. Schaefer, *The Alcohol Problem Visualized* (Chicago: National Forum, Inc., 1950), pp. 20–21.

[25] Harold A. Phelps and David Henderson, *Contemporary Social Problems* (New York: Prentice-Hall, Inc., 1952), p. 86.

[26] Arthur P. Noyes, M.D., *Modern Clinical Psychiatry* (Philadelphia: W. B. Saunders Co., 1939), pp. 219–220.

Noyes comments further as follows:

McCurdy's comment is doubtless correct: "The alcoholist is, before he touches a drop, an abnormal person." The personality factors that predispose to chronic alcoholism are not fully understood. It would seem, however, that many of them are those mentioned by Carver. "The alcoholist is a highly sensitive, self-indulgent individual with an extremely easily wounded *amour propre*. Self-criticism, no less than the adverse opinion of others, is peculiarly irritating to him. He seeks to evade all responsibility for his maladjustment and blames any circumstance rather than himself. He suffers from a feeling of inferiority and desires excessively the society, sympathy and love of his fellows. Boastfulness and confabulation conspicuously cover ·his inferiority complex, whilst conviviality and intimate contact with his fellows afford occasion for the release of obscene wit and homosexual trends. Alcohol, by producing euphoria, blunting the critical power and progressively relaxing inhibitions, permits of a flight from reality, which up to a certain point is pleasurable, but when it is pushed too far regression proceeds to lower psychological developmental levels, and the return of the repressed from these levels causes great anxiety and antisocial behavior, thus in the long run alcohol is liable to defeat the ends for which it is taken.[27]

Alcoholism is an immature and an inadequate escape from a conflict. Unlike the manic-depressive psychotic who in the presence of his conflict becomes alternately excited and depressed, and unlike the schizophrene who regresses to images when life's cares oppress him and weight him down, the alcoholic in the presence of his unbearable conflict renders himself dazed, insensible, narcotized, and paralyzed. Alcoholism is, therefore, psychogenic in etiology, and is the end result of an ill-conceived and ineffectual attempt to escape life's conflicts. . . . In short, we say that **alcoholism is a psychoneurosis.** . . . The present concept is that chronic alcoholism is a psychoneurosis. The chronic alcoholic is much more likely to be an introvert than an extrovert. His boisterousness and his good-fellowship appear only when he has enough alcohol in his system to elevate him above his feelings of inferiority. He drinks to escape either from his problems or from his feeling of inferiority. Although the individual drinks at first to escape from the dull monotony of the daily routine, he later develops the habit of drinking more and more as he discovers that under the influence of alcohol he is able to escape from his responsibilities.[28]

---

[27] *Ibid.*, pp. 218–219.   [28] Cavanagh and McGoldrick, *op. cit.*, pp. 393–395.

Chronic alcoholism differs from being drunk. This is clear from the definition of drunkenness by Purves-Stewart:

A drunken person is one who has taken alcohol in sufficient quantities to poison the central nervous system, producing a temporary disorder of the faculties so as to render him unable to execute the occupation in which he was engaged at the time, thereby causing danger to himself or to others. This is very similar to the definition advanced by the Committee on Tests for Drunkenness of the British Medical Association, which is as follows: "The word 'drunk' should always be taken to mean that the person concerned was so much under the influence of alcohol as to have lost control of his faculties to such an extent as to render him unable to execute safely the occupation on which he was engaged at the material time."[29]

HEREDITY

There is frequently repeated the idea that alcoholism is inherited. There is no substantial basis for this belief. That social heredity occurs there is no doubt. By social heredity is meant that a child exposed to parental use of alcohol as an escape may find it easy to follow in his footsteps. This, however, is following the example of the parent rather than any physical heredity. Alcoholism is an acquired psychogenic trait and is, therefore, not transmittable in the genes.[30]

EFFECTS OF ALCOHOL

Contrary to the usual opinion, **alcohol is not a stimulant. It is a depressive.** It lowers the inhibitory level so that most individuals will do things and say things under the influence of alcohol which they would not do or say if they were sober.

The expression of basic emotions such as aggression, timidity, feelings of superiority or inadequacy, the sexual drive, emotions which are normally controlled through inhibitions, may be released in proportion to the loss of control resulting from the depressant action of alcohol.[31]

The effect of alcohol on the brain is generally one of slowing the psychological functions. For example, alcohol lowers sensitivity, tactile discrimination, self-control, and efficiency. The response to stimuli is less adequate. The inhibitions are lowered. Memory, ability

[29] Ralph W. Webster, M.D., *Legal Medicine and Toxicology* (Philadelphia: W. B. Saunders Co., 1930), p. 735.
[30] Cavanagh and McGoldrick, *op. cit.,* p. 149 ff.
[31] McCarthy and Douglass, *op. cit.,* p. 103.

to concentrate, and skill, for example, in typing and rifle shooting are decreased.

> Wine does not help us to do a thing well, but makes us less ashamed of doing it badly.[32]

Alcohol, by lowering inhibitions, causes impulsive speech, over-confidence, expansiveness, emotional outbursts, and mood swings.

> The psychic phenomena which follow the ingestion of alcohol arise from an inhibition or depression of higher mental processes, especially those depending on training and previous experience, and which usually make for sobriety and self-restraint. The finer grades of discrimination, memory, concentration and insight are dulled and then lost. Impulsive speech and actions result, and inhibitions are removed. Confidence abounds, and personality becomes expansive and vivacious, and speech may become elequent and occasionally brilliant. Mood swings are un-controlled and emotional outbursts frequent. The individual may be-lieve himself powerful enough to whip several strong men even when it takes this number to hold him upon his feet. The particular type of behavior manifested under the influence of alcohol is the resultant of three factors, the personality of the individual, tolerance for the drug, and extraneous stimuli including those provided by the presence of others. Drinking is usually done in company and much of the hilarity, joviality and excitement is dependent upon mutual stimulation.[33]

Alcohol is not stored as a food. Its absorption after ingestion is usually complete in two and one-half hours, 20 per cent of this absorption taking place in the stomach, and 80 per cent in the small bowel.

There is a popular belief that **alcohol may act as an aphrodisiac.** This belief undoubtedly arises in the greater sexual enjoyment which many inhibited people have after taking a few drinks. It has been recognized, however, that anything more than a small amount is likely to induce impotence. Shakespeare describes this in **Macbeth,** Act II, Scene III:

> Macduff: What three things does drink especially provoke?
> Porter: Marry, sir, nose-painting, sleep and urine. Lechery, sir, it
>   provokes and unprovokes; it provokes the desire, but it takes
>   away the performance. . . .

[32] Anonymous.
[33] Goodman and Gilman, *op. cit.,* p. 109.

Loss of inhibition and restraint is the cause of the less inhibited sexual behavior seen after indulgence in alcohol.

Rosenau summarizes the effects of alcohol quite well in the following comment. It must be remembered that this quote is not from an anti-prohibitionist, but from a serious student of preventive medicine and hygiene:

> The student of preventive medicine still regards the alcohol question as a public health problem. Alcohol is a habit-forming drug; it lowers resistance and shortens life, impairs efficiency, promotes poverty, increases crime, favors accidents, excites passion and diminishes self-control; it leads to immorality and tempts venereal infections. Alcohol increases economic waste and retards social progress. It is a narcotic rather than a stimulant. Its nutritional value is strictly limited. Its habitual use as an aid to work is physiologically unsound. Its local irritation action and its toxic effects upon nerve tissue account for a certain amount of harm; but the greatest harm perhaps results from the fact that alcohol, even in small amounts, clouds judgment, depresses will power, and takes the check off self-restraint. In short, it stupefies the highest and noblest functions of the mind.[34]

WILL POWER

As mentioned above, there is a belief that alcoholism is due to a lack of will power. There is certainly a defective use of the will but the will is there and ready to be used. In developing the habit of drinking the individual drinks with decreasing use of his will to temperance. He is merely making a faulty use of his will. However, will plays an important part in the habit of drinking, and in its correction. It is perhaps in order to define what is meant by a habit. A habit is defined as a facility and a readiness of acting in a certain manner acquired by repeated acts. Since the will is free it can form habits inclining it either to good or to evil. In the former case the habits are called virtues; in the latter, vices. Virtue then is the perfection by which the will is constantly inclined to do good acts, and a vice is an imperfection of the will constantly inclining it to bad acts. No one is born an alcoholic. It is the frequent repetition of the act of drinking which gives rise to the formation of the habit of drinking. Each act of drinking and being drunk depends upon an act of the will. It is not denied that some may have a greater propensity or

---

[34] From Rosenau, Milton J., *Preventive Medicine and Hygiene*, p. 521. Courtesy of Appleton-Century-Crofts, Inc., New York. Copyright, 1927.

ALCOHOLIC INTOXICATION[35]

Stage of Intoxication	Symptoms	Blood Level of Alcohol
Subclinical (Dry and decent)	No detectable symptoms except on very careful examination.	0.0 to 0.1%
Stimulation (Delightful and devilish)	Self-satisfied; feels warm; flushed; light-headed; excited; overtalkative; gestures; increased self-confidence; sense of well-being; "Hail fellow well met"; less inhibited; boisterous; sings; speech more brilliant; acts more freely and with less self-restraint; emotionally unstable; less interested in physical appearance; more agreeable than usual alternating with quick irritability; clumsy in movements due to increasing muscular in-co-ordination.	0.10 to 0.20%
Confusion (Dizzy and delirious)	Slurred speech; loses sense of proportion; less persevering; irresponsible; no regard for feelings of others; euphoric with marked lability of affect; movements uncertain; loud and talkative; takes personal and social liberties; "Sitting on top of world"; glib and flippant; expresses himself more freely; long-winded; rich and vivid memories; staggers; undignified; outbursts of anger and unreasonableness; amorous; unconcerned over problems which had previously been a source of concern; "can lick anyone"; unembarrassed by mistakes; marked blunting of self-criticism; does not notice passage of time; speech difficult and stammering; ataxic gait; disoriented; needs help to perform even familiar tasks; disturbance of sensation; accentuation of personality traits such as jealousy, paranoid tendencies; a psychosis may be unmasked.	0.20 to 0.30%
Stupor (Dazed and dejected)	Sleeps; spurts of energy; stuporous; muscular in-co-ordination marked; decreased response to stimuli.	0.30 to 0.40%
Coma (Dead drunk)	Unconscious; reflexes abolished; death may occur.	0.40 to 0.50%

[35] Bogan, *J. Am. Med. Assn.*, 89, 1508, 1927; *Calif. and West. Med.*, 26, 778, 1927; and 44, 262, 1936; *Am. J. Med. Sci.*, 176, 153, 1938. Modified by Muehlberger; Publications of the National Safety Council; Oscar B. Hunter, M.D., Transactions American Therapeutic Society, Vol. XLI, 1941; Annals of the Medical Society of the District of Columbia; breath tests also used with the Harger Drunkometer, 2000 cc. of breath being comparable to 1 cc. of blood, *J. Am. Med. Assn.*, Vol. 110, p. 779 (March, 1938).

inclination to alcohol, as others are inclined to other vices. However, we cannot say that the weakness is so great that it takes away the freedom of the will. Unfortunately, there are some professional people who make no distinction between the will and the instincts.

SYMPTOMS OF ACUTE ALCOHOLISM

The effects of the ingestion of alcohol are progressive. They depend on the amount of alcohol ingested, the amount of food in the stomach, the speed of ingestion, and the strength of the alcoholic beverage. Temperature also plays a part in that the effects are likely to occur more quickly in a warm room than in a cold one. The individual's desire to feel the effects of the alcohol are also important. If he goes "out on the town" to have a good time and wants to "feel his drinks," he is quite likely to do so very quickly. If, however, he is depressed or indifferent, much larger quantities of alcohol will be ineffective in producing symptoms. The table on page 456 describes this progression of symptoms.

DIAGNOSIS OF CHRONIC ALCOHOLISM

This is an important area with which the marriage counselor should become fully cognizant.

The average chronic alcoholic is an emotionally immature but frequently intellectually brilliant individual. This individual may be either male or female, but is more frequently a male. By the very nature of his disorder he is selfish, thinking first of his own feelings, and giving but little consideration to those near and supposedly dear to him. Without too much struggle, he relinquishes the honor and respect which he owes himself as a person and accepts the narcotic influence of alcohol as an escape from his feelings of inferiority, which so frequently haunt him. His introverted personality welcomes escape into imagery in which it indulges with increasing frequency. His strong feelings of inadequacy and inferiority continue to create conflict and each new social contact calls for further narcosis. He retains sufficient insight, and so his own recognition of the inadequate method of solving his conflicts drives him more deeply under the narcotic influence of alcohol which is his only escape.

Under the influence of alcohol there is for him no introversion, no bashfulness, no inferiority complex, and no critical sense. He feels no social strain and acts as though he had from all quarters secured the most cordial social acceptance. He has daring, courage, and strength. While under the influence of liquor, his approach to life is but semirational and his insight and judgment are practically nil.[36]

The counselor should advise the prospective bride or groom to carefully observe his partner for the manifestations of developing alcoholism. He should advise them that if their partner shows progression down the following steps to alcoholism their courtship or engagement should be canceled or at least prolonged until they are sure that he is able to heed the warning signs and stop. Life with a chronic alcoholic is likely to be very unhappy.

STEPS TO ALCOHOLISM[37]

Step No. 1: **Social drinking increases in amount.**
           There is frequent excessive drinking. Booster shots before and after a party become routine, "one for the road."

Step No. 2: **Amnesia (black-out) for the period of drinking occurs.**

Step No. 3: **Liquor begins to have greater significance.**
           He begins to "sneak a drink." He does not like to talk about his drinking habits. He is defensive and expresses his guilty feelings in irritability when questioned about his drinking habits. He tipples.

First Warning

Step No. 4: **More drinking occurs than was intended.**
           In spite of resolutions to the contrary the drinking keeps on past the intended point of stopping. Behavior becomes more uncontrolled, and extravagant acts are increasingly common as evidenced in long-distance phone calls and other unusual conduct. Quarrels occur with the family and insulting remarks in public become increasingly common.

Step No. 5: **Rationalization of his drinking begins.**
           He offers increasingly frequent excuses for drink-

---

[36] Cavanagh and McGoldrick, *op. cit.,* pp. 392–393.

[37] This section is modeled after: E. M. Jellinek, *Phases in the Drinking History of Alcoholics* (New Haven, Conn.: Hillhouse Press, 1946); John C. Ford, S.J., *Man Takes a Drink* (New York: P. J. Kenedy and Sons, 1954); Morris T. Weeks, Jr., *13 Steps to Alcoholism,* distributed by the Minnesota Department of Health, Minneapolis 14, Minn.

ing. He had a bad day at the office, he has been unable to sleep. He expresses ideas of reference, that people are talking about him, criticizing him. He apologizes for his drinking.

Step No. 6: **An "eye opener" becomes necessary.**

He begins to lose time from work. His need for liquor increases, he develops insomnia, begins to develop problems on the job. His moral sense becomes impaired. His appetite decreases and as his whisky intake increases he cares less about its quality.

SECOND WARNING

Step No. 7: **Solitary drinking begins.**

About this time he begins to hide the bottle. He conceals the amount of his drinking and lies about it.

Step No. 8: **"Antisocial" conduct occurs with drinking.**

He gets angry, he picks fights. He gets into rages and destroys property. There is further deterioration of his moral sense.

DANGER

Step No. 9: **"Benders" occur with increasing frequency.**

A "bender" is a period of several days during which the individual drinks "blindly and helplessly" just to drink. Sobering up may require hospitalization. He becomes increasingly more self-pitying and constantly bemoans his fate and frequently resolves never to drink again.

Step No. 10: **Remorse occurs but without insight.**

He accuses himself of being a failure, but accepts no responsibility. He projects the blame to others. He expresses resentment toward those whom he feels are responsible. He walks out on friends. He becomes tremulous. Anxiety is common. Less liquor is necessary to make him drunk. Drunk driving is not uncommon and he may fall into the hands of the police. During this phase alcoholic hallucinosis and delirium tremors are not uncommon.

Step No. 11: **Depression and discouragement are manifested.**
Suicidal attempts are not uncommon. Loss of sexual potency associated with pathological jealousy occurs. Loss of faith may occur. His drinking continues.

Step No. 12: **The realization that drinking has him licked comes to him.**

Step No. 13: **Help is sought or he sinks finally into the gutter.**

This list is obviously subject to variations because no two people are alike. The progression toward alcoholism does not, however, differ widely. These steps are a useful guide for the early detection of the alcoholic. The complete cycle may take twenty years to run its course. The counselor by careful study of these steps can offer very helpful advice to his client.

TREATMENT

The treatment of alcoholism is not usually considered to be a problem for the marriage counselor. And problem it is. Although such treatment is usually considered to fall within the scope of psychotherapy, most psychiatrists are reluctant to treat alcoholics unless they are completely "dry." Being "dry" means that they are completely over their drunk and are free of withdrawal symptoms. Under these circumstances, referral to a psychiatrist may be useful. Because of the severity of the problem psychotherapy must be long and intensive in most cases. This is expensive even at clinic prices and most alcoholics cannot afford such treatment.

In general, the best recommendation to the alcoholic is to suggest that he go to Alcoholics Anonymous. This organization, since its foundation in 1935, claims to have helped 150,000 problem drinkers. This is probably a conservative figure. In its twenty years of existence, A.A., as it is usually known, has developed a "tradition" which serves as a constitution and bylaws for the organization:

THE TWELVE TRADITIONS OF ALCOHOLICS ANONYMOUS

1 — Our common welfare should come first; personal recovery depends upon A.A. unity.

2 — For our group purpose there is but one ultimate authority — a loving God as He may express Himself in our group conscience. Our leaders are but trusted servants — they do not govern.

3 — The only requirement for A.A. membership is a desire to stop drinking.

4 — Each group should be autonomous, except in matters affecting other groups or A.A. as a whole.

5 — Each group has but one primary purpose — to carry its message to the alcoholic who still suffers.

6 — An A.A. group ought never endorse, finance or lend the A.A. name to any related facility or outside enterprise lest problems of money, property and prestige divert us from our primary spiritual aim.

7 — Every A.A. group ought to be fully self-supporting, declining outside contributions.

8 — Alcoholics Anonymous should remain forever non-professional, but our service centers may employ special workers.

9 — A.A., as such, ought never be organized; but we may create service boards or committees directly responsible to those they serve.

10 — Alcoholics Anonymous has no opinion on outside issues; hence the A.A. name ought never be drawn into public controversy.

11 — Our public relations policy is based on attraction rather than promotion; we need always maintain personal anonymity at the level of press, radio and films.

12 — Anonymity is the spiritual foundation of all our Traditions, ever reminding us to place principles above personalities.[38]

The program of the organization is contained in the "Twelve Steps" which an individual is urged to follow as the road to sobriety:

TWELVE SUGGESTED STEPS OF ALCOHOLICS ANONYMOUS

1 — We admitted we were powerless over alcohol — that our lives had become unmanageable.

2 — Came to believe that a Power greater than ourselves could restore us to sanity.

3 — Made a decision to turn our will and our lives over to the care of God *as we understood Him.*

4 — Made a searching and fearless moral inventory of ourselves.

5 — Admitted to God, to ourselves and to another human being the exact nature of our wrongs.

6 — Were entirely ready to have God remove all these defects of character.

---

[38] *A.A., 44 Questions and Answers About the Program of Recovery From Alcoholism,* back cover.

7 — Humbly asked Him to remove our short-comings.

8 — Made a list of all persons we had harmed, and became willing to make amends to them all.

9 — Made direct amends to such people wherever possible, except when to do so would injure them or others.

10 — Continued to take personal inventory and when we were wrong, promptly admitted it.

11 — Sought through prayer and meditation to improve our conscious contact with God *as we understood Him,* praying only for knowledge of His will for us and the power to carry that out.

12 — Having had a spiritual awakening as the result of these steps, we tried to carry this message to alcoholics and practice these principles in all our affairs.[39]

How does this program work? Suppose we permit a member of the organization to describe this in her own words. Her name may not be given. In accordance with the rules of the organization, she must remain anonymous:

Alcoholics Anonymous is a fellowship of men and women who meet together for the sole purpose of obtaining and maintaining their sobriety. The price of admission is a straightforward acknowledgment that the individual is "powerless" over alcohol — the word powerless cannot be emphasized too strongly. Its importance is that quite probably it is the first time that this individual has said *out loud* to man or to God that he is helpless. "Let go, let God" is the key to rehabilitation. (Psychiatrists are always telling their patients to "let go" or "give in," and there is nothing the poor disturbed patient would rather do, but he rarely has the vaguest idea of what to let go of or give in to.) From the instant that the patient accepts his "powerlessness" over alcohol, it is not too long before he becomes aware of a "Higher Power." Some do this reluctantly, some shamefacedly, but the majority are grateful. This "Higher Power" takes over with the individual's cooperation and willingness to have this happen. Alcoholics Anonymous is a spiritual program. It started as an offshoot of the Oxford Movement through several individuals with severe alcoholic problems. At least one of these had a tremendous spiritual awakening as the result of a small miracle. It is true, however, that members of A.A. will not insist that a new member accept any organized religion. The feeling is that if the individual "stays dry" long enough his thinking will clear up and other benefits will follow.

The main stress in the beginning is on sobriety, on a 24-hour basis.

---

[39] *Ibid.,* front cover.

A.A. is a 24-hour program; "anybody can stay sober for 24 hours." If that period seems too long to start with, and it has for many, "stay sober on an hourly basis, or even less," is the recommendation. The program emphasizes that life is constructed only on a 24-hour basis. Yesterday is gone forever and is completely irretrievable. Tomorrow has not come, and everybody is powerless over what is going to happen tomorrow. (Even the most hard-headed can seem to accept this as sound common sense.) Life consists of doing one thing at a time and first things first; the most important thing is the individual's sobriety. (Later, of course, when new habit patterns are being formed, this has many ramifications.) The new member is told that being a member of A.A. is an entirely selfish thing. One's own sobriety comes before anything else in the world, and this is a novel way of thinking or feeling for many consumed with guilt and regret.

New members are taught the A.A. serenity prayer: "God grant me the serenity to accept the things I cannot change, the courage to change the things I can, and the wisdom to know the difference." And it is amazing the number of atheists, agnostics and the generally unorthodox who quickly learn to rely on this little prayer, although it may be their only spiritual act for months and years to come.

The importance of frequent attendance at A.A. meetings and the constant association with other A.A. members are impressed on the newcomer. It is at meetings that, often for the first time in his life, the individual feels a sense of identification, a feeling of belonging, of being accepted for what he is. One is cautioned to "let the program rub off on you." "If you don't like any of the speakers you happen to hear at a particular meeting, stay around and come again, and sooner or later you will find someone with whom you have an affinity. And you do."

As soon as the individual begins to grasp with some degree of eagerness or willingness the idea of Alcoholics Anonymous, he is promptly introduced to the Twelve Steps, with the caution that they are an outline of general behavior — a way of life — to be interpreted and accepted (or rejected) according to individual needs. The emphasis is on the importance of taking and working it in your own way, at your own tempo. Such slogans as "Walk, don't run," and "Take it easy" very often go hand in hand with the introduction to the Twelve Steps, because the alcoholic is usually quite eager to take them on all at once, if he doesn't temporarily plan to reject all but the first.

In addition to the "Open Meetings" which are available to anyone, there are closed meetings, available to alcoholics only. It is here, in general, that the Twelve Steps are introduced for group discussion. These meetings are invaluable to any alcoholic who wants to maintain his sobriety and discover the causes of the tensions and feelings of depression that compelled him to drink. Joining A.A. does not necessarily mean that one's drinking is removed overnight. A.A. members are constantly being cautioned that they must not give in to feelings of resentment or self-pity. Either of these feelings can lead to a drink faster than anything else. "It is the first drink that makes you drunk." One may get frightfully tired of hearing that last little remark, but it is very true. In the closed meetings, the reasons for resentments, self-pity, rejection and other feelings come to light and are discussed openly and honestly. By comparing his experiences with others, by listening to ideas from others and by being willing to want to change, one certainly cannot help but derive a great deal of insight into his past behavior and some of the reasons for it, as well as ways to avoid repeating the pattern in the future.

It is always mentioned that resentment and self-pity or feelings of rejection are the most frequent reasons for drinking. They are signposts for the new member to watch out for so that he will not get involved in a "dry drunk" or indulge in "stinking thinking." However, there is another area which should be considered. For want of a better expression, I call it "cumulative energy" which, over a period of time, becomes neither an emotion nor an action, because it cannot find an outlet and thus causes great tension.

There is much emphasis placed on various aspects of the "alcoholic personality," especially on his great egotism. To counteract this, the idea of humility and the value of achieving it is ever being stressed. Constant association with other people, awareness of a Higher Power, and helping others are some of the methods an A.A. member uses to keep himself in balance so that his ego will not run away with him. It is quite truly said by A.A. that "to keep it you have to give it away," and thus, man's humanity to man is constantly in evidence by way of helping other alcoholics or A.A. members of good standing who are having temporary "dry drunks" and general emotional upsets.

It is true, too, that wherever an A.A. member goes, he is not alone. He can always find A.A. groups, and his new-found trust in the Higher Power eliminates complete loneliness.

The average A.A. member has an extreme impatience with psychiatry. He will point out that most psychiatrists do not recognize when the symptom of emotional distress takes over as a disease in itself — which it most surely is — whether one believes in allergies or not. Inherent in the new-found thinking of the A.A. member and his new way of behaving is that "yesterday is gone." Regret it as you will, there is nothing you can do about it. "So forget it and concentrate on today." It may be perfectly true that both parents rejected you as a child, but that isn't going to keep you sober today, nor is discussion of it. It is good to be aware that this is part of one's pattern, but it is the way one lives and acts today which counts. "Keep it simple," the A.A. member will say to any person trying to grasp an idea or thought beyond his scope. And he will also quite rightly point out that too many modern psychiatrists have completely ignored the relationship between man and his God. And he will not hesitate either to remind you that many members of the clergy (of all denominations) have a habit of looking at some problems backwards — from the outside rather than from the inside.

Remember these rules:

1. First things first.
2. Easy does it.
3. Live and let live.
4. It is the first drink that gets you drunk.

SECTION V

RELIGIOUS ASPECTS OF MARRIAGE

The beginning of miracles did Jesus in Cana of Galilee, and manifested His glory. Jn. 2:11.

CHAPTER XXX

Catholic Family Movements

Various popes in recent pronouncements have urged the laity to participate in Catholic Action. In spite of apprehension on the part of some members of the clergy that this would lead to difficulty, Catholic Action has become an integral part of our daily living. Nowhere has such lay participation been as vigorous as in the area of marriage and family living.

Throughout history thinking men, both religious and lay, have always been interested in the fundamental unit of society, namely, the family. Studies have been made. New approaches to the concerns of the home, the sanctification of husband and wife relationships, better knowledge of good parent-child relationship have been developed. In history, too, wherever the home was truly Christian, that is, a place where Christ was always a welcome member, society and state flourished. The home means everything to the child who is the man of tomorrow. When homes reflect the teachings of Jesus Christ, there is where one will find peace and happiness such as was found in the Holy Family of Nazareth.

There are three Catholic organizations which are devoted to improving the conditions of marriage and family living:

1. The Family Life Bureau of the National Catholic Welfare Conference;
2. The Christian Family Movement;
3. The Cana Conference Movement.

THE FAMILY LIFE BUREAU

The Family Life Bureau of the National Catholic Welfare Conference was founded in 1931 by the bishops of the United States in response to the encyclicals of Pope Pius XI on **Christian Marriage** (1930) and **Christian Education of Youth** (1930). The Bureau states its own purpose in these words: It "fosters . . . forward moving and constructive activities that give promise of benefiting family life, while it promotes . . . activities that serve to counteract things in our civilization that are inimical to family life."[1]

In its quarterly magazine, **The Family Apostolate,** in the fall of 1951 issue, the Bureau lists the ten major activities in which it is engaged:

1. The teaching of correct principles and ideals of marriage and the family;

2. Promotion of a Christian parent education program;

3. Revival of religious practices within the family circle with emphasis on the spiritual aspects of marriage;

4. Preparation of young folks for marriage;

5. Inspiring of youth with a high regard for sex and the virtue of chastity;

6. The encouragement of common family interests in the home;

7. Urging the correction of economic and moral evils harmful to family life;

8. Promotion of inspirational activities in the family field (such as: selecting the Catholic Mother of the Year, presentation of awards to persons who have helped family life, conduct of the National Family Holy Hour, dissemination of articles promoting its purposes);

9. Emphasizing the father's role in the family (as head of the home);

10. Organization of the family apostolate on a parish basis.[2]

Other activities in which the organization has been engaged are:

11. Renewing consciousness of the value of the family as a social unit; of the honor of parenthood;

12. Development of leaders in the field of marriage and parent education;

13. Establishment of an Information Center where questions of any kind concerning the family will be answered;

14. Working to bring about family security both materially and spiritually. Efforts in the material sphere of activity have been relief in housing and unemployment, correcting the lack of food and suitable medical care for mothers at the time of childbirth, securing

---

[1] *The Family Life Bureau, The Activities It Promotes and The Channels It Utilizes,* The National Catholic Welfare Conference, Washington, D. C., p. 7.

[2] *The Family Apostolate,* The National Catholic Welfare Conference, Washington, D. C., Fall, 1951, pp. 3, 11.

aid for mothers who are driven by poverty to seek work outside the home.[3]

The Bureau co-operates with other social agencies, secular and religious, whose ends are similar to its own. The organization is affiliated with groups not only in the United States but also in foreign countries.

A large number of media are employed for disseminating its information, such as lecture series, discussion clubs, public forums, conventions, little theater groups, newspapers, pamphlets, and books.[4] Within the Bureau are a number of subordinate organizations:

1. The Family Institute;
2. The Family Service Program;
3. The Committee for the Christian Home and Family;
4. The Maternity Guild.

Members of the Bureau write pamphlets and books as well as feature columns for a number of diocesan papers.

Publications of the Bureau are increasing as time goes on. Information concerning the organization and its publications may be obtained by writing to: The Family Life Bureau, National Catholic Welfare Conference, 1312 Massachusetts Avenue, N.W., Washington, D. C.

THE CHRISTIAN FAMILY MOVEMENT

This movement had its origin in 1942. In that year a group of eight Chicago men met to discuss what they could do in a practical way in the lay apostolate. They decided that family life was the area in which their help was most needed. Their wives formed a similar group. It soon became clear that they could work more effectively if they combined their efforts and confined their work to their own parishes. Therefore, they combined and organized along parish lines. With this reorganization, which took place in 1947, the Christian Family Movement had its origin. The first convention of this group took place in 1949 in Wheeling, Illinois. Twenty-five groups representing ten cities were present. The rapid growth of the organization may be seen by the fact that in 1951 at a meeting in South Bend it was reported that there were approximately 119 groups in 39 cities. In 1956 this group reports 20,000 couples in 130 dioceses in the United States, Canada, England, India, Japan, the Philippines, Malta, Den-

---

[3] *The Family Life Bureau . . . Activities . . . and . . . Channels*, pp. 11–17.
[4] *The Family Apostolate*, Spring, 1953.

mark, Australia, New Zealand, and in many dioceses of South America and of Africa.

The working unit of the Christian Family Movement is a group made up of five or six couples from a parish. These couples meet every two weeks in each other's homes. The groups are kept small so that everyone has a chance to speak. They talk about things they have in common that affect their family life and others.

A typical meeting starts with prayer, followed by the reading of a few lines from the Bible. This is discussed in its practical applications for about fifteen minutes. The next fifteen minutes are spent discussing the Mass, the sacraments, and other aspects of being a Christian. Then for about forty-five minutes actual local situations affecting the everyday life of the family are discussed. The group decided how closely their daily lives conform with Christ's teachings and whether or not a change is needed.

The Christian Family Movement has many notable accomplishments to its credit. The most notable of these was its early assistance in the promotion of the Cana Conference in Chicago. In Chicago Cana and Christian Family Movement still work in very close co-operation. It should be remembered that the aim of the two groups is different. The Cana Conference is a day of recollection for married couples aiming at making each home more content and more Christian. On the other hand, the aim of the Christian Family Movement is a couple's movement of the lay apostolate aimed at creating a community which will be a help to families in living a Christian life.

The Pre-Cana Conference was started by groups of the Christian Family Movement.

For those who are interested in learning more of this movement, the Christian Family Movement has the following publications which may be obtained by writing to: The Christian Family Movement, Room 2010, 100 West Monroe Street, Chicago 3, Illinois:

For Happier Families — How to Start a CFM Section containing twelve introductory meetings. An explanation of the Movement and suggestions on how to start.

Annual Inquiry Program — Published each year on the first of July.

ACT — A paper published every month.

A Chaplain's Manual.

A quarterly magazine for priests and interested people.

Marriage Laws of the Catholic Church.

THE CANA CONFERENCE[5]

By Rt. Rev. Monsignor Louis F. Miltenberger, Archdiocesan Director, Cana Conference, Archdiocese of Washington

In 1944 the Reverend John Delaney, S.J., was conducting a series of lectures in New York called "Family Renewal Days." To those days were invited couples interested in making their homes more Christlike or couples who had ambition to renew the fervor of their wedding day. Through assistance at Mass together, sitting side by side listening to the inspiring talks of Father Delaney on what would make their homes better, getting advice on the social, spiritual, psychological problems that must be met in the home, and finally by renewing their marriage vows together, these couples gained much. They were putting Christ into their homes in the proper way. Father Delaney was putting into action the "strong reassertions of the sacred character and divine institution of marriage" from the encyclicals and addresses of Popes Leo XIII, Pius XI, and Pius XII. His purpose was to recall to couples the "full vision of the Christian home" emphasized by the meeting of bishops shortly after the encyclical on **Christian Marriage** by Pope Pius XI.

During the year 1944 the Reverend Edward Dowling, S.J., held a gathering similar to that of Father Delaney in St. Louis, Missouri. He, too, emphasized the restoration of the principles on which the Christian home must be founded. In a particular way he showed the twenty-five or more couples gathered around him that Christ must be injected more and more into their lives if they were to attain the full realization of the vocation of marriage.

If one were to ask what is the Cana Conference Movement we would suggest that it is a "couple movement" which injects Christian principles into the lives and homes of married couples as well as into those couples contemplating marriage. Its purpose in the words of Father Dowling is to consider "not so much spiritual things, as things spiritually." "Holier and happier homes" might well be taken as the motto of this movement which, since 1944, has reached into a large percentage of the dioceses of the United States and is now carried on by several hundred priests as well as a larger group of

[5] The Cana Conference is treated at greater length than the other family movements because it applies more directly to the problems which concern the marriage counselor. Monsignor Miltenberger, as an Archdiocesan Director, is peculiarly qualified to discuss this subject because of his personal experience in the field.

married couples who are interested in the home form of Catholic Action.

Before going into the organization and content of Cana we might say that Cana has succeeded most where an active group of lay couples have assumed the responsibility of the gathering of married couples for conferences. Bishops and priests might furnish the inspiration for Cana. Once its spirit, though, has penetrated into the lives of married couples, it is better carried on by them. The joy, the happiness, the peace, the solution to their problems in domestic life obtained at a conference is contagious. As heat it cannot be contained within itself, it must reach out to others. So thrilled with what Cana has meant to them, these parents gladly make many sacrifices to spread their new-found happiness to others. It is not uncommon in Cana to discover couples having as many as ten children devoting one or two nights a month to finding out more about all that concerns the home and the Christian family living.

Cana seems to have a spirit that is all its own. Couples at first come to a conference wondering just what a director can give them. Expressions such as "What can a priest tell us about husband-wife relationship? He has not lived it"; "I guess this will be just another one of those afternoons or evenings I shall spend following the fancy of my wife," etc. As the conference progresses, though, these same couples change. They come in with good will. They are willing to be shown how to better their relationships by understanding the rights and duties of each other, the way a husband can compliment the wife psychologically, and vice versa, and the great value of the sacramental grace of matrimony, etc. Gradually these couples in attendance come to realize that they are all alike, that they all have problems in common and can help each other. Barriers break down. The couples become more and more composed as they learn how they can make their homes happier. The talks, the discussions, the questions answered seem to give all a new life in their vocation of marriage. Materially they help each other. The spirit one couple catches seems to reflect itself in that of their neighbor until before the conference ends either with the renewal of marriage vows or Benediction of the Blessed Sacrament, a new life, a new spirit permeates all present. They are renewed and refreshed. They go away with a determination to put into action the hopes and ideals of their wedding day.

While the spirit of Cana is contagious as far as couples are concerned, we might say it is more so for the priest conductors. Once a priest begins to read about the concerns of the home and makes a study of the needs of couples today, his enthusiasm grows. More and more he realizes the full meaning of the vocation of marriage and is anxious to share his new-found knowledge and enthusiasm with couples at a conference. Fortunate is the priest who has a chance to sit in on family discussions or to visit homes at various times of the day or evening. Here he sees the theory he has been taught in action. Perhaps he wonders at times; but, after a few visits and listening to what fathers and mothers have to say, besides observing the actions of children in the home, he knows what to talk about. He grows with enthusiasm to share and help. The more a priest gets into the working of a truly Christian home, the more he listens to the problems, hopes and aspirations of married couples, the more he develops a willingness to sacrifice time and sleep to help put Christ into the modern home of today.

Divisions of Cana Work

Cana work falls into three easy divisions in a number of dioceses. **Pre-Cana Conferences** are to prepare young people for the great sacrament of marriage. **Cana Conferences** take up the development of proper attitudes for married couples after marriage. **Follow-up Cana** is carried on in the clubs consisting of from five to seven couples who discuss in more detail, under the direction of a priest chaplain, the virtues necessary in the home, finance, training of children in purity, etc. In a number of dioceses **the follow-up work of Cana is carried on by Christian Family Movement groups.**

Washington, D. C., Cana Conferences

That a **general cross section** of how Cana operates might be presented, the following cross section of its organization in Washington is presented.

In the archdiocese of Washington, Cana Conferences were first begun on a city-wide basis. These conferences were always held in the afternoon. They began at two o'clock and closed at five with renewal of marriage vows and Benediction of the Blessed Sacrament. Because of the working conditions of the people and the problem of baby sitters, most of the conferences since 1954 have been held in the evening on a parish basis from eight until eleven o'clock. Since this change took place the attendance has more than doubled. It is not uncommon to have a hundred or more couples at a conference now and all from one parish. This has created a better parish spirit and parish solidarity. Generally the people of a given neighborhood are interested in the same things. The priest, knowing this and the general social life of the people he is talking to, is able to do a better job of Christianizing and supernaturalizing the problems of their homes.

These evening conferences begin promptly at eight and the topics vary according to the number and type of conferences that were given there before or the need of the parish as is made known by the parish lay committee who make all the arrangements. These lay groups have given the priest conductors invaluable aid especially where they have been active in club work. Generally they know what the people of the parish are talking about or the needs of both parents and children. Whenever possible the priest giving the conference calls on or phones the parish chairman and arranges his talks according to the need. In this way much more satisfactory conferences are given and the couples go away with a new determination to put Christ into every act of the day. After the first talk of about 50 minutes, a brief break is allowed to relax, take a smoke, etc., for about 10 minutes. This is followed by another shorter talk further developing the first one or on some stated subject. After this a 20-minute break is allowed for simple refreshments of cake, cookies, and a beverage (usually coffee, tea, milk, or Coca-Cola).

Following the refreshments comes the questions and discussion period. Cards are always handed out before the second talk. The priest conductor invites questions in writing. These are turned in after the refreshment period. Much valuable information is picked up both by the audience and the priest during this time. Such questions as how to handle study problems, allowances for children from the first grade through high school, how to develop vocations in the home, how to better train children in habits of obedience, respect for authority, attitudes toward Sisters and the clergy, etc., are asked. Often a lively discussion follows if the priest is clever in drawing his listeners out. It is not uncommon for the entire third period to be given over to animated discussion. The couples like it and say they gain much from it.

The climax of the evening comes with the renewal of marriage vows. Generally an explanation of the meaning of the marriage vows is read along with an exhortation to renew the ideals and plans the couples had on their wedding day. Following this the couples face each other, join hands, and repeat the vows they made on their wedding day. The men in unison repeat it to their wives and the women to their husbands. While they stand with hands joined the priest gives his blessing asking the good God to help them capture and further develop the spirit of their wedding day. All seem to agree that this blessing means so much to them, especially if the values of the sacramental graces of marriage have been explained some time during the evening.

Among the topics that have been discussed by the Cana directors of the archdiocese are: "Husband and Wife Relationship," "Parent and Child Relationship," "Parents, the Best Educators in all Fields," "Money in the Home," "The Sacramental Grace of Matrimony," "Training of Children in Purity," "Respect for Authority Taught by the Way Parents Show Respect for Authority," "Teens and Their Problems," etc. Many variations of the above and other topics are given depending on the local needs, the wish of the pastor, or the lay committee.

Cana Clubs are a natural outgrowth of a Cana Conference. At every conference a talk is given by an experienced club member on the value of clubs for the couples themselves, their families, and for Cana family action. Cards are signed by those interested in forming small groups of from five to eight couples to discuss in more detail the topics of the conference or some subject of common interest to the couples. Among the many proven themes that have been discussed are: "Prayer in the Home," "Advent With Christ," "Lent and the Spirit of Penance," "The Liturgy of the Season," "The Family Budget," "Family Recreation," "Easter With Christ," "Christmas With Christ," "Religious Vocations in the Home," "Patience," "Humility," "Christian Love," etc., etc. Two volumes of outlines have been prepared and used successfully; a third is now in preparation.

Clubs operate in different ways. The following is typical. At the previous meeting the subject for the next get-together is decided upon and a leader couple is chosen. This couple gathers books, pamphlets, clippings on the topic and is prepared to lead the discussion of the evening. The meeting time is always decided on and they try to get started promptly. If the chaplain is present he leads them in the Cana prayer. All recite it together. Then the topic of the evening is presented by the leader couple. This is followed by discussion of the matter covered with all couples joining in. Their impressions and experiences are given, what they have found from reading or observation is shared with all. It is most heartening to sit in on a few of these discussions and see how enthusiastic these fathers and mothers are to restore all things to Christ through the home. As they know each other better they are more free in expressing themselves. Others may not agree with them but they want to learn the how of the home and will go to any limits to get the best. Truthfulness and a spirit of humility seem to dominate all club meetings. The discussion continues for about an hour. Then the chaplain (we try to have a chaplain at most meetings) summarizes the meetings and makes some practical application for those present. Each is encouraged to extend in a Catholic Action way all they learn to their neighbors. If a chaplain is not present this is done by the leader couple. These meetings rotate from home to home and generally in alphabetical order on a monthly basis. This plan avoids all confusion.

In brief, the club work of Cana makes the couples more conscious of their obligations and puts Catholic Action into action where it is most needed. These same couples, too, have an enormous influence on their neighbors and children of the neighborhood. From a small beginning of a few clubs the number has gradually grown until in June, 1955, there were about 75 active clubs in the archdiocese of Washington. The total adult membership is 500 couples with approximately 2000 children in these families. A splendid outgrowth of the clubs has been the celebration of Holy Family Day with a special service in one of the city churches. In 1955, the families were invited to St. Martin's Church, in Washington, D. C., for a Family Holy Hour. It consisted of a sermon, procession of the children past the Crib where they were blessed by two monsignori, dedication of the families to the Sacred Heart, and Benediction of the Most Blessed Sacrament. At the end of the service each child received a small religious gift in Christmas wrapping. Over 900 parents and children were present. Through the clubs, parents have learned the value of family groups getting together; in particular, they know the value of the dedication of the family to the Sacred Heart each year. The enthusiasm for the Family Holy Hour clearly indicates the desire of couples to become more Christlike themselves that their love and enthusiasm might overflow into their families and the community.

Pre-Cana Conferences have grown in number and attendance in recent years. Their purpose is to prepare couples better for the sacred and serious obligations of married life. Priests and couples who have made a study of the needs of newlyweds share their knowledge with couples who are to be married within the next six months. Here again the couple program is emphasized. In a city like Washington, it cannot always be carried out; but, wherever possible, it is insisted upon.

Pre-Cana series are held about ten times a year in the city and at least once in the outlying counties. In the city they are conducted in the evening and generally are held one evening a week for three weeks. Two topics of about one hour each are presented each evening. They are held in a central place and begin promptly at eight o'clock. The first evening the meaning of Christian marriage and Christian love is given by a priest. This is followed by a talk on money for newlyweds. Generally an experienced layman gives this lecture. Questions are invited after each speaker finishes. The second evening a husband and wife team talk on marriage adjustments in the early days of marriage and the first child. For the second talk the young men and women are separated. A Catholic woman doctor speaks to the women on the psychology and physiology of marriage. The third evening two priests again conduct the conference. The talk at eight o'clock is on the morality of all acts of husband and wife. At nine marriage as a vocation, the sacramental graces of marriage, etc., are discussed. Many married couples have sat in on these lectures to help the speakers. All have said, "Why didn't we have something like this when we got married? It would have helped so much."

All the affairs of Cana are arranged on the **committee plan.** Three committees are doing an excellent job at present. The **Conference Committee** makes all the arrangements for conferences on a parish basis after the spiritual director has obtained the consent of the pastor to have a conference. This group works very closely with the parish club members who do most of the work. The **Club Committee** helps new clubs get started, keeps all records of club activities, and helps supply discussion material. The **Pre-Cana Committee** cares for all that is necessary for the smooth running of a "Preparation for Marriage" series.

The parish representative couples meet four times a year to formulate plans and to discuss the reports of the committees. Each parish has one couple as its representative. They handle all three phases of Cana in their respective parishes. At the present time there are about thirty parishes organized or in the process of being organized on this basis.

Enthusiastic reports come from other cities where Cana is in action.

From Chicago comes the following report from the Rev. John J. Egan, who has done much to spread the Cana Conference Movement in the United States:

> Cana started in Chicago in 1944; Pre Cana in 1946. From its very humble beginnings it has been slowly growing until this year when we had 140 Cana Conferences and 64 Pre-Cana Conferences. To date .(1953) 31,165 married couples have attended Cana here — in the past seven years 28,248 engaged couples have attended Pre-Cana.
>
> We are working hand in glove with Christian Family Movement now in Chicago — we promote Christian Family Movement and they promote Cana wherever possible. We also develop lecture courses, Mr. and Mrs. Clubs, etc., but usually through Christian Family Movement because we know it is more stable and will organize the activity better over the long haul. Their work is so much broader in scope than ours. In a diocese as large as ours we have a tremendous task in bringing the message of Cana and Pre-Cana to as many as possible. Pre-Cana is held on a Sunday afternoon followed by three evenings, Monday, Wednesday and Friday, at which time a married couple, two doctors and a priest speak and have a discussion. Session concludes with Benediction and dedication ceremony in church on Friday.

Another cross section of what Cana is doing is contained in the following report of the Rev. John C. Knott, Archdiocesan Director of Cana for Hartford, Connecticut:

> Its possibilities are limitless in the hands of qualified leaders. Our homes need such understanding. Our fathers and mothers are willing learners. Most of them want to be the best possible parents. They only need to be shown the way. Cana is the one such compass through the turbulent sea of family unrest the world has today. It does not give the remedy for all problems. It does, however, give all courage to go on. Its enlightened groups can in time meet society with good wholesome family living.

From the diocese of Peoria, Monsignor W. V. Haas wrote in a letter recently:

> We gain much inspiration from the side-lights in the home given by the attending couples. These conferences have helped us in many ways in the training and developing of our children.

It is not the purpose of this brief section to explain how Cana works in all places. What might be practical in one diocese may not be in another. The important thing is that wherever Cana has been introduced, it is doing something. There is a need for help and information in all classes of homes. With the clergy and lay couples co-operating, what is most needed is better understanding. Once a priest really appreciates what goes on in the average home, the problems that must be met day after day in all levels by father and mother, a real desire develops within himself to meet these needs in a Christlike or Marylike way. Cana, really understood, shows couples that they must not necessarily sanctify the day, but let the things of the day sanctify them.[6]

---

[6] Publications in regard to the *Cana Conference Movement:* (1) *The Cana Conference Proceedings,* Vol. I (1949), Cana Conference, 21 W. Superior St., Chicago, Ill.; (2) *The Cana Conference Proceedings,* Vol. II (1950), same address; (3) *Marriage Education and Counseling,* ed. A. H. Clemens, Catholic University of America Press, Washington, D. C.; (4) *Marriage and Family Relationships,* ed. A. H. Clemens, Catholic University of America Press, Washington, D. C.; (5) Dr. A. H. Clemens, *The Cana Movement in the United States* (Washington, D. C.: Catholic University of America Press, 1953).

CHAPTER XXXI

Marriage and the Liturgy

JOHN J. O'SULLIVAN

MARRIAGE AND HOLINESS

Religious conversion and human love are alike in this: each calls for the reorganization of one's whole life and all its aspects around a new center. Love impels one to make another person the center of his life while religious conversion moves the one under its influence to order his life in terms of God known anew or known for the first time.

It is the intention of the author in the present chapter, "Marriage and the Liturgy," to show how the Catholic Church uses the reality of religious worship to support and to secure the couple's pledge of lifelong married love.

The chapter in the beginning will have an account of the ideal proposed to its members by the Church and a record of the achievement resulting from the response to this proposal.

Catholic belief relates marriage to the bond that unites Christ and the Church. In holding for the sacramentality of Matrimony the Church has censured any of its members who would condemn the love of husband and wife.

TERTULLIAN ON MARRIAGE

Even today a reader finds inspiration and understanding in the account of Matrimony to be found, for example, in the second-century writer, Tertullian. He was representative of a tradition which held that "This union is most sacred and most solemn." For his generation as for this one, he had something true to say on the beauty of Christian marriage:

How shall we ever be able adequately to describe the happiness of that marriage which the Church arranges, the Sacrifice strengthens, upon which the blessing sets a seal, at which angels are present as witnesses, and to which the Father gives His consent? For not even on earth do children marry properly and legally without their fathers' permission.

How beautiful, then, the marriage of two Christians, two who are one in hope, one in desire, one in the way of life they follow, one in the religion they practice. They are as brother and sister, both servants of the same Master. Nothing divides them, either in flesh or in spirit. They pray together, they worship together, they fast together; instructing one another, encouraging one another, strengthening one another. Side by side they visit God's church and partake of God's Banquet; side by side they face difficulties and persecution, share their consolations. They have no secrets from one another; they never shun each other's company; they never bring sorrow to each other's hearts. Unembarrassed they visit the sick and assist the needy. They give alms without anxiety; they attend the Sacrifice without difficulty; they perform their daily exercises of piety without hindrance. They need not be furtive about making the Sign of the Cross, nor timorous in greeting the brethren, nor silent in asking a blessing of God. Psalms and hymns they sing to one another, striving to see which one of them will chant more beautifully the praises of their Lord. Hearing and seeing this, Christ rejoices. To such as these He gives His peace. Where there are two together, there also He is present.[1]

Tertullian lived in a time when persecution was a constant challenge to the union of a man and woman. He realized how important it was for their union to be rooted in oneness of religious faith. Our time is not too different from that of the second century and our enemy is certainly more subtle. Tertullian's beauty of thought and his account of the unity which a man and woman can create are a part of that continuing tradition which has always attended holy wedlock. In practice it is almost true to say that no defense of a moral position is adequate which does not involve the beauty of the thing defended.

From Tertullian to the Reverend Raoul Plus, S.J., has been a long time, a slow unfolding of almost all the centuries of the Christian era. Father Plus describes the traditional Christian teaching on marriage:

The Church has transformed the most hazardous of contracts into a divine institution, and strengthened with heavenly help a pact which nature tends to dissolve as soon as it is made; she has blessed and

---

[1] Tertullian, *Treatises on Marriage and Remarriage,* trans. William P. Le Saint, S.J., S.T.D. (Westminster: The Newman Press, 1951), pp. 35–36.

consecrated the passing attraction which draws one sex to the other; she has sanctified the act of generation, she has given God a place in the conservation of society by endowing the married pair and their offspring with virtues.

Society would never be able to ensure the permanence of the married union by a rational proof of its necessity. Only Christian marriage, which claims divine origin, can wean bride and bridegroom from a deeply-rooted egotism, to unite them in the quest of a higher good; only Christian marriage can dare to speak with assurance of the future of the most fragile of bonds. . . .

The sacrament remedies these weaknesses. The physical joys of marriage take the second place, and the moral purpose of the contract is emphasized.[2]

Once this is grasped, it becomes easier to understand why an increasing number of Christians regard marriage as a vocation. Traditionally, the great enemies of spiritual progress have been described as "the world," "the flesh," and "the devil." The Church has formally opposed these foes to personal spiritual perfection with the three vows of poverty, chastity, and obedience. Those who live in the religious state take these three vows and promise to observe them fully. For monks and others there are rules which interpret what their vows mean in detail.

CHRISTIAN MARRIAGE

Those who live in Christian Marriage may aspire to live on a higher level, to adapt to family living certain virtues properly belonging to the regular clergy. Nor does this in any way lessen the nobility of the religious state or involve a distortion of what religious living imposes on its members. Even a passing glance at the incidents proper to married life reveal the many occasions for the practice of habits akin to the virtues of poverty, chastity, and obedience.

The married state will impose the duty of using more carefully the material resources of the couple than was necessary previously. It is a spirit of poverty, of religious detachment, which helps the couple to control desires and to determine true needs.

Married couples will ordinarily have the need of limiting some expressions of their love. This is a reference to the conjugal chastity

---

[2] Père Raoul Plus, *Marriage* (London and Dublin: Burns, Oates and Washbourne, Ltd., 1945), pp. 71–72.

which they may observe. This virtue, where it is present, provides the occasion for their being constantly selfless in their common life — for "love seeks not its own."

The place of obedience in the life of persons committed to religious living is quite apparent. In married life, duty is as real for husband and wife as the superior for the monk. The response of children to their parents, of wives to their husbands, and of husbands to their Lord constitute the docile obedience which marks the truly Christian home. The absence of such obedience may result in extreme instances of the family being only a chaotic group in constant conflict.

All family practices, if the relationship is to be according to God's plan, call for a triumph over self, for a consideration of others and of God. Hence the conclusion emerges that marriage too has its poverty, chastity, and obedience.

THE CEREMONIES OF MARRIAGE

Marriage has been surrounded by sacred rites among almost all peoples. It has been the tradition for centuries for Catholic partners to make their exchange of vows in association with the offering of the nuptial Mass. Thus Matrimony is linked to Calvary and to the Sacrifice renewed there. Since every sacrament points to the great Sacrifice of Christ, it is helpful to Christians to note the deeply religious nature of their union. It is almost true to say that every Mass is a nuptial Mass since it is a pledge of the continuing love of God for His people. That love is a reality. It is meaningful that the couple pledge their lives at His altar. Again and again when they return to their Church for the renewal of Christ's eternal Sacrifice, they are given the occasion for renewing and deepening their love of each other. For Boylan, "only the perfect Christian can be the perfect lover."

Liturgy

The fact of Christian practice in connection with marriage ceremonies raises the deeper meaning of liturgy. Ordinarily **liturgy in the highest sense is the Holy Sacrifice of the Mass, the Divine Office, and the administration of the sacraments and sacramentals.**

Liturgy is the sum of all the religious actions by which man from his first days on this earth has surrounded his essential relationships. Whether he was expressing his fear of, or his dependence on, the great God whom he might have known dimly, or pledging loyalty to his fellows, man has used the ceremonies of religion to give expression to reality.

Liturgy has always answered a very fundamental need or hunger in the being of man — the need to surround the most meaningful things in life with forms of beauty. The great meanings that man has conceived since the Creation, he has sought to embody in symbolic form. He has even sought to capture meanings which transcend his power of understanding and fill him with awe and wonder; he has sought to bring into a closer and more permanent contact with himself by expressing these meanings in forms connatural to his nature, that is, in sensible forms. The concept of God is man's most important source of meaning and has been from the beginning of time. He has expressed it, in an almost infinite variety of symbolic forms from the incarnations of the Hindu Vishnu, through the whole Greek family of gods and goddesses, to the totems of the American Indian.

The liturgy of the Church is a continuation of traditional ceremonies and ritual; but with a far greater reality added — that of the supernatural life of grace — a gift beyond natural attainment. But like traditional ritual, the liturgy is a system of forms that appeal to man's senses — to his eye through art, his hearing through song — stimulating his spiritual powers to communication with God in adoration, praise, and thanksgiving.

Nor is this view on the role of the liturgy an unsupported opinion. Pope Pius XI in instituting a new feast (Christ the King — 1925) explained the advantage of the liturgy for the formation of the faithful. At that time he wrote:

> For people are instructed in the truths of faith and brought to appreciate the inner joys of religion far more effectually by the annual *celebration of our sacred mysteries* than by any official pronouncements of the teaching of the Church . . . her Feasts affect both mind and heart and have a salutary effect upon the whole of man's nature. Man is composed of body and soul and he needs these external festivities so that the sacred rites, in all their beauty and variety, may stimulate him in the religion of Jesus Christ.[3]

Life is demanding, hard, and exacting for the two persons who take each other "for better or for worse, for richer or for poorer, in sickness and in health, until death." A natural question is how liturgy can

---

[3] Joseph Husslein, S.J., *Social Wellsprings*, II (Milwaukee: The Bruce Publishing Co., 1943), p. 39.

make any contribution to the permanence of their pledge and the joy of their love.

Christianity respects all of the primitive awe and wonder for the mystery of human procreation. The Church, recognizing the beauty of traditional symbolism and the natural need it satisfies, has drawn upon ancient sources for the formation of her liturgical system in general. The ceremonies of Matrimony are particularly rich in symbols that have been understood and respected by the most ancient societies. Their meanings are perhaps more important today for the welfare of society and civilization than ever before in the history of the world. Civilization today is in urgent need of meanings because our whole way of life is directed away from the spiritual. Every phase of modern living has its end in the sensual, the temporal. But the individual human being has not lost, cannot lose his hunger for meaning; he must reach for it because of his very nature. He will look for it first in those things that appeal to him through the senses; he will look for it in beauty.

Beauty is not, strictly speaking, a good. Good is sought by the appetite, by the will which seeks to possess it. Beauty, on the other hand, calls forth contemplation. Desire for possession is stilled while we enjoy and admire. But beautiful forms may embody great meanings, and for these meanings man hungers in a manner analogous to his desire for good.

It is precisely because of the contemporary overemphasis upon the practical, the useful, and the ladder-to-success, that the concept of beauty has become antique, nonexistent, or, at best, confused in the minds of the majority of people today.

The real beauty of the symbols and ceremonies of the marriage rite cannot be overemphasized because it is by being drawn to their beauty that their great meanings are discovered, then penetrated and understood.

On the other hand, those born and reared in the midst of the liturgy may tend to take symbols too much for granted and forget that the meaning came first, in that the symbol exists only to facilitate the grasp of the meaning and to deepen the realization of its significance.

BETROTHAL

Because the marriage contract creates an indissoluble bond, the Church has always recognized, as men and women have for centuries before her, that such an act should be preceded by serious preparation. The period of the betrothal was in the first generations of Christianity probably more akin in both celebration and binding force to the Roman practice than to the Jewish. When the Church fully emerged from the catacombs in the early fourth century, and spread over the Western world, the ceremonies of marriage still varied with each diocese. This became more and more the case as the Middle Ages with its passion for allegory advanced and every aspect of the tremendous meaning of marriage was cast into some symbolic form. The Council of Trent in the sixteenth century attempted to bring about uniformity of ritual and succeeding popes followed this example. But the old rites of the Sacramentaries and Agenda were never abolished, and to this day many local customs prevail in the celebration of the marriage ceremonies which are the least uniform of any in the Church.[4]

There is disagreement among historians as to whether the Church has always taken part in the ceremony of betrothal, but there are old rituals to prove that from the very early Middle Ages this was certainly true in some places at least.

It is most probable that up to the time of the Reformation the Church took a passive part in the betrothal by what the Fathers refer to as "approval," and an active part in the nuptials by blessings and the celebration of Mass. The Renaissance emphasis upon intellectual culture and the advance of modern sophistication helped to form the Protestant attitude of "pure" religion and the hostility toward external forms. It was probably during this spiritual upheaval that the ancient and medieval ceremonies became childish or meaningless for many. But the important fact is that the meanings themselves never ceased to exist.

In the ninth century we find Pope Nicholas I describing the ceremonies of betrothal which, as he tells us, ". . . the holy Roman Church received from antiquity." In this ninth-century account, the betrothal consists of the mutual consent of the parties, the placing of the ring, the presentation of the dowry before witnesses, and a signed document. Nicolas then says, ". . . immediately, or rather at a fitting time . . . both come to the actual marriage, which took place in the Church."[5]

---

[4] Cf. Donald Attwater, ed., *A Catholic Dictionary,* 2 rev. ed. (New York: The Macmillan Co., 1953), "Marriage," "Sarum Rite," "Ring."

[5] "Responsa Nicolai ad consulta Bulgarorum," *Patrologia Latina,* J. P. Migne, ed., Paris, Vol. 119, pp. 978–1017.

We may conclude from this and the writings of the Fathers in general that up to the Renaissance the betrothal was a serious step toward marriage and was marked most frequently by the essential consent; the Church's blessing and the consummation were delayed for a time unstated. In monarchical countries betrothal was a form of solemn promise made by the parents to link the houses of ruling families; the practice was carried over onto the other levels of hierarchial societies.

The absolute freedom of Americans in choosing marriage partners is a phenomenon peculiar to a democratic society and until our century unfamiliar to the majority of European nations. Such freedom necessarily brings with it added responsibility. The need for adequate preparation is graver than ever before. To assist the individuals in the work of preparation and to give it deeper meaning, the Church has provided a special form of blessing and prayer for the engagement promise.

There are numerous supporters of a more formal engagement for those approaching Christian marriage. Clearly, the renewal of a practice which has been inactive deserves unhesitating support for the contribution it may make in the lives of young couples. The pledge need not have binding canonical effects, but its solemnity has meaning and inspiration for a generation that needs both. The Church law regarding the betrothal ceremony is contained in Canon 1017:

> The contract of betrothal consists of a fully voluntary and mutual promise of future marriage between a definite man and a definite woman both qualified to fulfill the contract. . . .

Effects of betrothal:

> Even though it is valid and no sound reason exists for the non-fufillment of it, from the promise of marriage no action accrues for its enforcement through the celebration of marriage . . . the present law does not impose censures to compel the parties to honor their promise of marriage as was done in times past.[6]

The strictness of the marriage bond for people committed to the Catholic religion is one of the facts about the Church known to almost everyone. Less well known by far is the basis for the belief and the meaning of the practice. For many people it is quite an

---

[6] John A. Abbo and Jerome D. Hannan, *The Sacred Canons* (St. Louis: B. Herder Book Co., 1952), pp. 172, 174.

arbitrary matter, arrived at under circumstances long since obscured. The permanence of the marriage relation has been a tradition from the very beginning. It has rested, as a reality, on eleven little words: "What therefore God has joined together, let no man put asunder" (Mt. 19:6).

Permanence of Marriage Bond

Now the essence of marriage is in the free and full consent of the people who are giving and receiving certain bodily rights which are proper to the married state. That consent, once it is exchanged, produces a new reality with this result: what has been given cannot be claimed or taken back. The giving of this voluntary consent produces a new entity, the **una caro.** The result of the exchange of the marriage consent is greater than either husband or wife. Moreover, this new reality is stronger than their power to destroy it. Marriage cannot be what two persons say it is: it must be what God says it is. Hence the result follows, not that divorce is merely wrong, but that it is impossible. Regardless of what the couple may feel about it, marriage vows **cannot** be broken. It seems that some ceremonies, at one time in the Church, revealed this more vividly.

Although the marriage ceremonies as we know them today are beautiful and moving, they lack very much of the dramatization and intimate familiarity with ceremonial that was so characteristic of older times. Moreover, ceremonies formerly apart from the nuptial Mass itself — the solemn preliminaries (the betrothal) and the elaborately symbolic processions that followed the marriage have all been more or less amalgamated into one ceremony at the church. The essence of the marriage contract — the mutual consent — has never been confused with any of the ceremonies that surrounded it, but was rather traditionally looked upon with greater reverence through the ceremonial embellishments. There is real need today, not so much for additional ceremonies, as for a deeper understanding of the meanings that our present rites embody.

For a long time, probably from the very beginning up to the seventh or eighth century, the betrothal took place sometime before the nuptials and was characterized by the mutual consent, the giving of the ring, the presentation of the dowry secured by some legal document delivered in the presence of witnesses. During the time between the betrothal and the nuptials all communication between the bride and groom was carried on through friends.[7]

THE MARRIAGE RITUAL

The nuptial day itself was one of great joy and festivity. Tertullian tells us that the bride walked to the church attended by her maids and veiled.[8] The blessing in the church and the celebration of Mass were looked upon as the "crowning" ceremonies, and both bride and groom wore wreaths of flowers to symbolize their great joy, their youth, purity, and triumph over passion. The ceremony of the crowning is still one of the most important in the Eastern Church.[9]

By the time of Pope Nicholas I in the ninth century there is indication that the nuptials followed very soon after the betrothal, for he says in his **Replies to the Bulgarians,** A.D. 866:

> We are going to show you the usages which the Holy Roman Church has received from antiquity and still observes today in these marriages. Our believers, whether men or women, when they contract marriage, do not wear on their heads a crown of gold or silver, or any other metal. But after the betrothal, which is the promise of the future union, and is celebrated with the consent of both parties and of those who have authority over them, after the groom has placed a ring as a pledge on the bride's finger, and has given her in the presence of witnesses brought by both parties the dowry agreed upon with a document which sets forth what has been agreed, immediately, or rather at a fitting time, so that it may not be supposed that these arrangements have been made before the time legally fixed, both come to the actual marriage. First of all they are led into the church with the offerings which they are to present to God by the hands of the priest, and they receive the blessing and the heavenly veil, as it took place in the beginning, when God placed the first pair in the earthly paradise, and blessed them saying: Increase and multiply. . . . But this veil is not received by such as are celebrating their second marriage. Then, on leaving the church, they wear on their heads crowns which are generally

---

[7] Cf. Clement of Alexandria, *Pedagogue*, III, 2; Ambrose, *de lapsu Virginis*, ch. 5; OT Ruth, ch. IV, 2; Augustine, *Sermons*, I, 21; XXXVII, 6; CCXCIII; Tertullian, *de Pudicitia*, ch. IV; *de Monog.*, ch. XI.

[8] Tertullian, *de Cor. Mil.*, ch. IV; *de Veland Virg.*, ch. XI.

[9] Cf. Nicholas I, *Replies to the Bulgarians;* Justin, *Apologies*, ch. IX; Tertullian, *Apologies*, I, 42; Clement of Alexandria, *Pedagogue*, II, 8; Coar, *Euchologium*, pp. 396–400.

kept in the church. And after these nuptial festivities they are permitted to begin living together.[10]

By the early Middle Ages we know that the ceremonies formerly attached to the betrothal were performed at the church door and in some European localities this is still the case.[11] This bringing together of the two formerly separate ceremonies undoubtedly came about in order that the actual forming of the contract by mutual consent (which was at one time a part of the betrothal) might take place in the presence of the priest and through him receive the Church's blessing.

Among the Romans of pre-Christian times, the entire marriage ceremony was almost identical with that described by Pope Nicholas except that the sacrifices were pagan and took place in a temple or sacred grove. In the Roman ceremony, the mutual consent was made at the betrothal and the legalized payment of the dowry was considered the sealing of the contract. The remaining ceremonies were performed as a matter of solemn religious duty.

Because the early Christians were for the most part of Roman or Greek origin, and those Jews who were converted no longer identified themselves with their race,[12] it was natural that the Christians should continue to use those ceremonies with which they were familiar. Therefore we find the betrothal ceremony marked by the legal contract and mutual consent just as among the Romans. Siricius in the fourth century declares the benediction of betrothal to be of so solemn a nature that to break it and marry another constitutes a sacrilege.[13] With the bringing together of the two ceremonies, the difficulty was in large measure solved. It was simply a matter of time needed for the work of systematization and delineation of doctrinal truths that always existed but needed defining.

However, the significant matter is that the Church wished to raise the marriage contract from a purely legal level in order to surround it with her most beautiful prayers and blessings, but above all, to have its performance either closely preceded or followed by the holy Sacrifice of the Mass.

In the oldest Sacramentaries and Agenda, especially those of France, Spain, and the Eastern Churches, we find the richest and most sym-

---

[10] "Responsa Nicolai ad consulta Bulgarorum," *op. cit.*

[11] Cf. Sarum (Salisbury) Rite, formulated by St. Osmond in 1099. See also Chaucer, "Wife of Bath's Tale."

[12] Cf. Msgr. Pierre Battifoll, Litt. D., *Primitive Catholicism*, trans. Henri L. Briancean (New York: Longmans, Green and Co., 1911).

[13] Siricius, Letter to the Bishops of Spain, *First Decretal*, A.D. 385.

bolic ceremonies surrounding the sacrament of Matrimony. It would be impossible even briefly to mention them all here, but their forms and meanings are full of inspiration, and the loss of their usage perhaps to be lamented. We have today only the verbal traces, rich as these may be, of rites that were in older times performed as symbolic dramas.

The beautiful prayer after the **Pater Noster** of the nuptial Mass recited today over the kneeling couple was formerly called the **velatio nuptialis** and was recited over the bride and groom as they lay prone covered by the "heavenly veil."[14] This custom, which still prevails in parts of France and Spain, was in all likelihood an early Christian merger of the Roman bride's **flammeum** and the later Jewish groom's hood and cloak with which he and his bride were covered.[15] Aside from the meanings embodied in the prayer itself, the covering with the veil symbolized the unity of faith in the bride and groom, and their mutual fidelity. The prone position was especially significant of humility and submission on the part of the united couple before the Divine Mystery of Christ and His Church. The veil worn by the bride today is also of ancient and universal origin, a symbol testifying that the woman's whole being belongs to her husband.

Because the marital union is modeled after that of Christ and the Church, a special point of emphasis is placed upon the reception of the Eucharist by the bride and groom at the nuptial Mass. It is, in fact, interesting to note that in the Roman Missal it directs the celebrant to give Holy Communion to the spouses.[16]

THE RING

The blessing of the ring is the oldest marriage rite outside the Mass, and the first known instance of such a blessing took place in the ninth century in France.[17] The wedding ring itself is of ancient origin and was used among the Hindus, Egyptians, and Romans. It was, however, usually given at betrothal as a token or a pledge of future union. Among the Romans it was one of the group of gifts, or **arrhae,** presented by the groom as purchase money for his bride. Because of its symbolism, it became the most important pledge among

---

[14] Nicholas I, *op. cit.;* Tertullian, *de Veland Virg.,* ch. XI; Ambrose, *Epist.* XIX, 7; *de Virginitate,* ch. XVI; *de Inst. Virg.,* ch. XVII; *de Abrah.,* I, IX, 93.

[15] Cf. *Jewish Encyclopedia.*

[16] Plus, *op. cit.,* p. 70.

[17] Cf. A. Villien, *The History and Liturgy of the Sacraments* (New York: Benziger Bros., 1932), pp. 276–334.

the Christians. In many of the oldest rites, the ring was blessed before the Mass along with coins—traces of the Roman **arrhae.** When gold coinage was abandoned in the ninth century, medals were struck for the sole and specific purpose of use in the matrimonial service.[18] Their significance grew almost as important as that of the ring, and the words of the groom as he presented them to his bride with the ring are worth reviving:

> With this ring I thee wed; this *gold and silver I thee give;* with my body I thee worship; and *with all my worldly good I thee endow* (Sarum Rite).

The concept embodied in the symbol of the coins has vanished from the minds of most people today, except perhaps in some small, isolated localities. Such a symbol would be hollow to the many modern wives whose intention of working after marriage involves a meaning directly opposed to such confident dependence of a wife on her partner.

Happily, however, the ring remains, and its symbolism is exceedingly rich. Pope Nicholas and the Fathers before him called it the "ring of fidelity."[19] Its form is the perfect symbol of unity and permanence. In older practices the ring was placed upon the bride's finger in a variety of ways; most frequently, the groom placed it first on the thumb, index finger, middle, and then fourth fingers while saying: "In the name of the Father, the Son, and the Holy Ghost. Amen."[20] The fourth finger was found by ancient Egyptian surgeons to possess a "nerve" that ran to the heart, as Aulus Gellius tells us in his **Attic Nights** (ca. A.D. 180), and Isidore of Seville in the sixth century, following Pliny and Macrobius, says that the reason for placing the ring on the fourth finger is because it contains a "vein" that runs to the heart. The ring, therefore, has long been intimately associated with the source of love.

Primitive peoples attributed such binding force to rings that they were removed from women in labor with child, or persons believed to be possessed by evil spirits.[21] The concept of binding force is

---

[18] Cf. *Paderborn Agenda* of 1602; *Ritual of Rheims* of 1585; "Marriage Ceremonies," Herbert Thurston, *Catholic Encyclopedia.*

[19] Nicholas I, *op. cit.;* cf. Clement of Alexandria, *Pedagogue,* III, 2; Tertullian, *Apologies,* ch. VI; Alexander III, *Decretal,* ch. X; Isidore of Seville, *De Divinis Officiis,* II, 20.

[20] *Sarum Ritual.*

[21] Cf. Sir James Frazer, *The Golden Bough,* 1 vol. ed. (New York: The Macmillan Co., 1944), pp. 234–235.

closely associated with permanency and union. A nineteenth-century French dictionary carefully explains that the ring is placed on the hand of the bride so that it might be always before her eyes to remind her of the indissolubility of the marriage promises and to activate in her the strengthening graces received in the sacrament.[22]

Such are the principal meanings to be found in the symbol of the ring which deserves great reverence and respect both because of its antiquity and because the Church recognized it as the first symbol to be singled out and blessed by a special ceremony. Today we use both the engagement and the wedding rings, and, as we said before, there is a present movement to bring back the formal engagement.[23] It should certainly receive encouragement for the betrothal ceremony, its meanings, and the period of preparation that it initiates can do much to insure a happier and holier marriage union.

THE MARRIAGE KISS

Former ages generally held the kiss as a sacred act; the conventional kiss of today, after the placing of the ring, was formerly given at the betrothal and was considered in such a serious manner that the Codes of Theodosius and of Justin, in the fifth and sixth centuries, specifically state that the kiss makes the betrothal more binding. If a betrothed couple had kissed, and the groom happened to die before the nuptials, half of the arrhae went to his betrothed; if they had not kissed, all of the arrhae was to be returned to his own relatives. In the Middle Ages the kiss of peace (**pax**) was given by the celebrant at the nuptial Mass to the groom who gave it to the bride. In some European countries this custom still prevails.

THE BLESSING OF THE HOME

In the ancient Jewish ceremony of marriage, the bridal pair were conducted after the marriage to the marriage chamber. Among the Romans, the procession in which the groom led his bride to his home, and lifted her over the threshold, was the most important part of the ceremony. The Christians adopted the Roman procession which received both praise and condemnation from the early Fathers.[24] Just when the Church began to bless the house of the newly married

---

[22] *Dictionnaire des Ceremonies et des Rites Sacres*, Redige M. L'Abbe Boissonet (Barrierre D'Enfer de Paris: Ateliers Catholiques du Petit-Montrough, 1847).

[23] *Promised in Christ* (Loveland, Ohio: Grailville, 1955).

[24] Cf. Arnobius, *Against the Heathen*, Book 2, 67; John Chrysostom, *Homily 12 on the First Corinthians; Homily 48 on Genesis;* Basil the Great, *Letter to a Fallen Virgin.*

couple is not at all certain, but it seems most probably that the present blessing of the home evolved from the more ancient custom of blessing the nuptial couch. A late fifteenth-century Agenda contains the blessing of a house. Earlier rituals, however, contain the blessing of the bed. The **Evreux Pontifical** of the eleventh century directs the priest to bless bread and wine after the nuptial Mass and give to the bride and groom to taste; this ceremony is a little symbolic drama that re-enacts the events at Cana; then when evening comes, the rubrics direct the priest to lead the couple to the marriage bed with prayers and blessings. In some of the later rituals, the **benedictio thalmi** is combined with the blessing of bread and wine; the Parisian ritual of the fourteenth century is one of these in which the priest is directed to bless the bread and wine at the door of the home, give it to the bride and groom, and from thence proceed to the blessing of the bed. Still other Pontificals add to the blessing of the bed one of the entire house.[25] This latter blessing is the only one widely used today and is certainly not lacking in significant meaning particularly for our time.

CONCLUSION

It is essential that family life be ordered according to the plan of God. This chapter has intended to show the importance of liturgical observance at the time of the wedding and in the life of the family. Christ said, "My house is a house of prayer." Every Christian father stands to the family in the place of Christ: in an analogous sense he is priest, prophet, and ruler. Augustine described homes as little churches and addressed fathers as "Fellow Bishops." The continuing well-being of the family will depend on the view of this society taken by those who are members of it. One must always be chary of simple answers to the more than ever complex problems of this day. Yet, it would be hard to overestimate the contribution which a recognition of the liturgy can make to the well-being of the family. This is not theory unrelated to facts as two historical instances can suggest.

Urban society has demonstrated its ability to destroy peoples who long reside there. The Jews have been city dwellers since before the time of Christ. The state was seldom their support, and after the destruction of Jerusalem, it became their adversary. The stern exigencies of their unhappy history forced them to turn to the family as

---

[25] Cf. *Manuale Curatorum* of Roeskilde, 1513, ed. J. Freisen (Paderborn, 1898); *Evreux Pontifical,* eleventh century; *Jewish Encyclopedia.*

the focus of their lives. They had the religious leadership of a married rabbinate and their religious feasts were often family-centered. Because of this, their family life has had a religious character second to none. It is a fact that living in a hostile environment they have not only survived, they have increased. To infer that some part of their strength and of their survival can be credited to their observance of family liturgy seems altogether valid.[26]

An incident in the history of the Japanese suggests a similar strength founded on the religious life of the family. In the sixteenth century St. Francis Xavier preached the Christian religion to the Japanese and baptized many. For a limited time after St. Francis, other priests were allowed freedom for missionary activity, but persecution came and all visible traces of the Christian Faith were removed from the public life of the Japanese people. Nearly ten generations of the nation lived under this restriction before Japan was opened to the rest of the world in the past century. When missionaries came again to the islands, they learned to their amazement that a number of families had kept the faith. It was in a shriveled form to be sure, but it was a true and genuine belief with lay people administering Baptism and faithfully saying **in their homes** the prayers that had been handed down through the years.

Since it is generally conceded that the survival of everything depends on the health of the family, there should be a corresponding demand for the program of actions that will assure this survival. These pages have attempted to point out the important place of the liturgy in a program dedicated to building a stronger and holier family life in America. It is evident from all that has been said that unity of faith is generally the greatest guarantee of real marital happiness. The Church seems to look upon "union" as a synonym for the marriage relationship, and that she considers faith the focal point of that union is evident from the fact that only those enjoying such unity of faith share in the fullness of the liturgical drama.[27]

---

[26] Lynn White, Jr., *Educating our Daughters* (New York: Harper and Brothers, 1950), p. 102.

[27] For further treatment of marriage and the liturgy see: Fernand Cabrol, O.S.B., *Liturgical Prayer, Its History and Spirit* (London: Burns, Oates and Washbourne, Ltd., 1925); George Hayward Joyce, S.J., *Christian Marriage* (London: Sheed and Ward, 1948). For treatment of ancient and primitive ceremonies see: Edward Westermarck, *The History of Human Marriage*, Vol. II (New York: Allerton Book Co., 1922); Ernest Crawley, *The Mystic Rose*, A Study of Primitive Marriage, Vol. I (New York: Boni and Liveright, 1927).

The liturgy can only find its real place in the program for survival where the love of a man and woman is fulfilled in their united love for God. There the Church through her liturgy strengthens, gives joy, and assures not only survival but increase and perpetuity.

CHAPTER XXXII

Marriage as a Sacrament

WILLIAM E. MC VEAGH

At the Council of Trent in 1563 the Church officially defined that matrimony is truly one of the seven sacraments of the New Law instituted by Christ.[1] Like every other sacrament, matrimony is the symbol of a sacred thing and the visible form of an invisible grace which not only signifies grace but contains and confers grace automatically on those who place no obstacle in its way.[2] It is doctrinally certain that Christ immediately, that is, directly and personally, instituted all the seven sacraments though He may have left the question of the determination of the elements of some of them to His Church.

The reason for this dogmatic definition by the Council of Trent that marriage is a sacrament was due to the denial of this teaching by the sixteenth-century reformers.

Calvin in his **Institutions** (IV, 19, 34) says:

> Lastly, there is Matrimony, which all admit was instituted by God, though no one before Gregory regarded it as a Sacrament. What man in his sober senses could so regard it? God's ordinance is good and holy; so also are agriculture, architecture, shoemaking, haircutting legitimate ordinances of God, but they are not Sacraments.

Luther in his **Babylonian Captivity** denied that marriage was a divinely instituted sacrament and claimed that the sacramental aspect of marriage was the invention of men in the Church arising from ignorance of the subject. In a German work on marriage, **Von den Ehesachen,** Luther wrote that marriage is an external worldly thing, like clothes and food, house and home, subject to worldly authority, as shown by so many imperial laws governing it.

---

[1] Session XXIV, Canon 1; *Canons and Decrees of the Council of Trent*, trans. H. J. Schroeder (St. Louis: Herder, 1941), p. 181.

[2] *Ibid.*, Session VII, Canon 6, p. 52.

With this denial of the sacramental nature of marriage the high ideals regarding the union of man and wife soon disappear. Little dignity is attributed to marriage when it is considered merely a human contract capable of dissolution by a secular authority. For as soon as men deny the sacredness of marriage, losing sight of its supernatural nature, their view of it becomes material and gross.

MARRIAGE IN THE NEW TESTAMENT

It is freely admitted by theologians that there is no explicit record of Christ instituting marriage as a sacrament in the New Testament. But this doctrine is implied in Christ's explicit teaching on the unity and indissolubility of marriage.

When our Lord was asked by the Pharisees (Mt. 19:1–10) whether it was lawful for a man to put away his wife for any cause, He recalled to their minds the words of the Book of Genesis (2:24). When they protested that Moses commanded that a bill of divorce be given and the wife dismissed, Christ answered, "Because Moses by reason of the hardness of your hearts permitted you to put away your wives; but from the beginning it was not so." Then Christ, speaking as the Divine Legislator, promulgated the New Law concerning the indissolubility of marriage:

> And I say to you, that whosoever shall put away his wife, except it be for fornication, and shall marry another, committeth adultery: and he that shall marry her that is put away, committeth adultery (Mt. 19:9).

By restoring marriage to its primitive indissolubility, Christ made it harder to be faithful to the marriage bond. The Apostles themselves, conservative fishermen, expressed amazement at the difficulty of this doctrine. "If the case of a man with his wife be so, it is not expedient to marry." Therefore Christ would not have taught a doctrine so difficult and onerous to human nature without giving the special help needed to observe this law. And such help or grace is given in the economy of the New Law through a sacrament. Therefore Christ must have instituted marriage as a sacrament of the New Law.

St. Paul, writing on the mutual duties of the Christian husband and wife, offers the example of the union of Christ and the Church to inspire the married couple more efficaciously to fulfill their marital duties.

Let women be subject to their husbands, as to the Lord: Because the husband is the head of the wife, as Christ is the head of the Church. He is the savior of his body. Therefore as the Church is subject to Christ, so also let the wives be to their husbands in all things. Husbands, love your wives, as Christ also loved the Church, and delivered himself up for it; that he might sanctify it . . . that it should be holy and without blemish. So also ought men to love their wives as their own bodies. He that loveth his wife, loveth himself. For no one ever hated his own flesh; but nourisheth and cherisheth it, as also Christ doth the Church: Because we are members of his body, of his flesh, and of his bones. For this cause shall a man leave his father and mother, and shall cleave to his wife, and they shall be two in one flesh. This is a great sacrament; but I speak in Christ and in the Church (Eph. 5:22–32).

From this beautiful exhortation to Christian married couples it is not claimed that St. Paul directly teaches that marriage was instituted as a sacrament of the New Law. But from these words to the Ephesians it can be deduced that Christian marriage is (a) a sacred sign; (b) a sign of grace; (c) and very probably produces grace, so that it is truly a sacrament.

a) Christian marriage signifies something sacred, namely, the union of Christ with the Church. For St. Paul says, "This is a great sacrament; but I speak in Christ and in the Church." St. Paul uses the word "sacrament" in a broad sense meaning mystery, secret, a symbol, and not in our technical sense. But from the entire passage it is clearly seen that the love of Christian spouses for each other should be modeled on the love between Christ and the Church because Christian marriage is a copy, a token, and a symbol of the union of Christ with the Church.

b) Christian marriage is a sign of sanctifying grace because it signifies the union of Christ with the Church. This latter union is one whereby the Church receives grace, as St. Paul says, "Christ loved the Church and delivered himself up for it; that he might **sanctify** it." It is also evident that the union of Christ with the Church brings forth fruits of sanctity which take concrete form in the individual members of the Church.

c) Finally, Christian marriage produces the grace that it signifies. The Council of Trent says in Session XXIV:

The grace which was to perfect that natural love, and confirm that indissoluble union, and sanctify the persons married . . . St. Paul hints at when he says, "Husbands, love your wives, as Christ also loved the Church, and delivered himself up for it," adding immediately, "This is a great sacrament, but I speak in Christ and in the Church."[3]

Christian marriage is shown by St. Paul to be a supernatural and permanent union. It is supernatural because the mutual duties of the spouses, such as St. Paul describes, are supernatural from the model proposed, namely, the love of Christ for the Church and the devoted subjection of the Church toward Christ.

Marriage is portrayed as a permanent union because the love and obedience prescribed for Christian spouses must imitate the love of Christ and the subjection of the Church which are enduring and constant. But the marital union cannot be supernatural without grace; nor can it be permanently supernatural without habitual grace to which actual divine aids are connected, especially when the inconstant human heart tires of such a permanent union. Therefore Christian marriage requires habitual grace together with the right to actual graces. In the economy of the New Law, sanctifying grace with a right to actual grace is wont to be conferred by a special sacramental rite which not only signifies grace but produces it. Therefore, Christian marriage it would seem produces sanctifying habitual grace. Hence it is a sacrament.

Although it is freely admitted that there is no express record of Christ instituting the sacrament of marriage in the New Testament, theologians conjecture about the precise time of its institution. Some urge that Christ added the sacramental dignity to marriage when He attended the wedding feast at Cana and by working His first miracle there. Others say marriage was raised to its sacred role as a sacrament on the occasion when Christ promulgated the indissolubility of marriage (Mt. 19:1–10). Some say that our Lord made marriage a sacrament after His resurrection, when for forty days He appeared to the Apostles and spoke of the kingdom of God (Acts 1:3).

THE FATHERS OF THE CHURCH ON THE SACRAMENT OF MATRIMONY

The doctrine that marriage is a sacrament instituted by Christ for the production of grace is contained in tradition corroborated by the infallible authority of the Church. The living teaching authority

---

[3] *Ibid.,* Session XXIV, p. 181.

is paramount in Christian Revelation. It is in the unanimous and constant tradition of the Church that we find the surest argument that marriage is a sacrament.

In order to prove the continuity of a doctrine throughout the ages, it is not necessary that we possess an uninterrupted chain of explicit testimonies linking our times with the Apostolic period. The reason is this: since the custody and infallible interpretation of the deposit of faith has been entrusted to a living organism which is the Church, and since the Church of today is the same moral person it was in the first and second centuries, it follows logically that whatever the Church holds and teaches today as pertaining to the original deposit of Revelation was also held and taught, at least implicitly, by the Church of the first centuries.

Before we develop the argument from the Fathers of the Church, who are one of the principal instruments by which divine tradition has been preserved, it will be well to consider what kind of evidence the Fathers may be expected to furnish in support of the doctrine that marriage is a sacrament of the New Law.

The name "sacrament" cannot be used as satisfactory evidence. It would be vain to look for the term "sacrament" in the ancient writings since it did not acquire until a later period the exclusively technical meaning it has today. Further, it should be remembered that the Church made use of her sacraments long before she wrought out her Sacramentary; she lived her dogma before she formulated it. Sacramental practice antedates by centuries the systematic elaboration of a sacramental theology. Hence it will suffice to show that the Church has in fact always taught concerning marriage what belongs to the essence of the sacrament, by statements in the Fathers which attribute to marriage the properties expressed in the theological definition of a sacrament.

In the first four centuries, up to the time of St. Augustine, the doctrine of the sanctity, honesty, and indissolubility of Christian marriage was developed in the instructions given by the Fathers to married Christians, and on the occasion of errors put forth on this subject by false teachers, the Gnostics and Manichaeans. The Fathers assert that marriage is a sacred and religious sign, and they enunciate principles which suppose the conferral of grace.

St. Ignatius of Antioch, who died in A.D. 117, shows the influence of St. Paul. He refers to matrimony as a sign of the eternal bond between Christ and His bride, the Church, in these words:

Tell my sisters to love the Lord and to be content with their husbands in body and soul. In like manner, exhort my brethren in the name of Jesus Christ to love their wives as the Lord loves the Church.[4]

Marriage is placed under the supervision of the bishop as something sacred.

For those of both sexes who contemplate marriage it is proper to enter the union with the sanction of the Bishop; thus their marriage will be acceptable to the Lord and not just gratify lust.[5]

Athenagoras of Athens, in defense of Christian morality, wrote on the purpose of marriage in his **A Plea for Christians** about the year 177.

Having the hope of eternal life, we despise the things of this life, even the pleasures of the soul, each of us reckoning her his wife whom he has married according to the laws laid down by us, and that only for the purpose of having children. For as the husbandman throwing seed into the ground awaits the harvest, not sowing more upon it, so to us the procreation of children is the measure of our indulgence.[6]

Clement of Alexandria, writing before the year 200, defends Christian marriage against the Gnostic sects who attempted to discredit and reject it. His lofty concept of marriage presupposes grace.

Who are the two or three gathered together in the name of Christ, in whose midst is the Lord? Are they not man, wife and child because man and wife are joined by God.[7]

Tertullian, born about the year 155, wrote a treatise on marriage addressed to his wife. In it he beautifully extols the dignity of Christian marriage as a sacred thing. Love and harmony such as this are out of reach of man's natural faculties. It supposes that elevation of one's natural faculties and their acts which grace alone can confer.

How shall we ever be able adequately to describe the happiness of that Marriage which the Church arranges, the Sacrifice strengthens, upon which a blessing sets a seal, at which angels are present as witnesses, and to which the Father gives his consent? . . .

[4] Ignatius of Antioch, *Epistle to Polycarp,* 5, Ancient Christian Writers, trans. by J. A. Kleist (Westminster, Md.: Newman, 1946), p. 97.

[5] *Ibid.,* p. 98.

[6] Athenagoras of Athens, *A Plea for Christians,* 33, Ante-Nicean Fathers, Vol. II (Buffalo: The Christian Literature Publishing Co., 1887), p. 146.

[7] Clement of Alexandria, *Stromata,* Bk. III, ch. 10, Ante-Nicean Fathers, Vol. II (Buffalo: The Christian Literature Publishing Co., 1887), p. 393.

How beautiful, then, the Marriage of two Christians, two who are one in hope, one in desire, one in the way of life they follow, one in the religion they practice. They are as brother and sister, both servants of the same master. Nothing divides them, either in flesh or in spirit. They are, in very truth, two in one flesh. And where there is but one flesh there is also but one spirit. They pray together, they worship together, they fast together; instructing one another, strengthening one another. Side by side they visit God's Church and partake of God's banquet; side by side they face difficulties and persecutions, share their consolations. They have no secrets from one another; they never shun each other's company; they never bring sorrow to each other's heart . . . Psalms and hymns they sing to one another, striving to see which one of them will chant more beautifully the praises of their Lord. Hearing and seeing this, Christ rejoices. To such as these He gives His Peace. Where there are two together, there also is He present, and where He is, there evil is not.[8]

Origen, who died about the year 253, expressly teaches that Christian marriage is a source of grace.

It is God who united the two into one, so that from the time the woman is joined to her husband, they are two no longer. And since God united them, therefore those who have been united by God have received a grace.[9]

St. Ambrose, about the year 385, declared that God has sanctified marriage and this grace is lost by sins against the sacrament.

We know that God is as it were the head and protector of Marriage, who does not permit that another's Marriage bed be defiled; and further that one guilty of such a crime sins against God, whose law he violates and whose bond of grace he loosens. Therefore since he sins against God, he loses his participation in the heavenly Sacrament.[10]

Some of the Fathers of the Church thought that our Lord at the marriage feast of Cana elevated marriage to a dignity it did not possess before and conferred on it a supernatural worth. Thus Cyril of Alexandria, writing about the year 415, speaks as follows:

Christ when invited went with His disciples to the wedding not so much to share the feast as to work a miracle, and furthermore to sanctify that which is the source of generation.[11]

---

[8] Tertullian, *Ad Uxorem*, 2, 8, Ancient Christian Writers 13, trans. by William P. Le-Saint, S.J. (Westminster, Md., 1951), p. 35.

[9] *Commentarius in Matthaeum*, t. 14, c. 16 (J. P. Migne, *Patrologiae Cursus Completus*, Series Graeca, Vol. 13, 1229) (Parisiis, 1864–1884).

[10] *De Abraham*, I, 7, 59 (Migne, Series Latina, Vol. XIV, 465).

[11] *Commentarius in Joannem*, II, 3 (Migne, Series Graeca, Vol. 73, 223).

From St. Augustine we obtain more explicit testimony. From his time the divine institution of marriage as a sacrament, that is, as a holy symbol of the union of Christ and His Church, will be universally acknowledged. St. Augustine's contributions to sacramental theology were immense. For him a sacrament is a sign of a sacred thing instituted by Christ; that in a sacrament there is a very close relationship between the sacramental rite and its effects, between the baptismal pouring of water, for example, and the cleansing of the soul; that the sign is connected to the spiritual gift which is signified and destined to sanctify man. Yet St. Augustine does not enunciate the precise definition of a sacrament as an efficacious sign, which produces what it signifies.[12]

Christian marriage, according to St. Augustine, has for its effect the unique and indissoluble bond which typifies the union of Christ with His Church. That bond is undoubtedly holy because of its symbolism, which places the married couple in a state of holiness; the bond, therefore, ought never to be broken. The indissolubility consequent on the symbolism of marriage is comparable, he holds, to the indelible effect produced by baptism and ordination.[13]

Later tradition will make more precise the sacramental efficacy of this divine symbol, and will show that marriage is holy as being the cause of holiness.

It was the work of the medieval theologians to give the precise definition of a sacrament as an efficacious sign of grace. Peter Lombard in his **Book of Sentences** (1147–1150) defined a sacrament as a sign of grace of such sort that it both symbolized the invisible gift of grace and caused what it symbolized. Then, with this definition, he distinguished the seven sacraments of the Church from all her other ceremonies. From this time on we find the doctrine that marriage is a sacrament, in the precise technical meaning of a sign and cause of grace, in the official pronouncements of the Church: the Council of Verona in 1184; the Council of Lyons, 1274; the Council of Florence, 1439; the Council of Trent, 1546–1563.

Reason itself suggests how fitting it is that marriage is a sacrament that signifies and causes grace in the bridal couple. It is through this sacrament that the wedded pair are dedicated to the very noble and useful work for society and the Church, namely, the procreation

---

12 P. Pourrat, *Theology of the Sacraments,* 23 (St. Louis: B. Herder Book Co., 1910).

13 St. Augustine, *De Bono Conjugali,* ch. 24 (J. P. Migne, *Patrologiae Cursus Completus,* Series Latina, Vol. 178, 1745) (Parisiis, 1864–1884).

and education of children. It is by this sacrament that the couple are joined by an indissoluble bond so that they cannot attempt another marriage until one of them dies. The obligations of this life are so serious that it requires not ordinary but heroic virtue at times.

Further, the sacraments were instituted for this very reason that they might confer grace at those different stages of life that are so important and on which the salvation of one's soul depends, especially when from those occasions there arise onerous duties that can hardly be fulfilled without special divine help. Therefore it is fitting and proper that sacramental grace be connected with marriage by means of which the procreation and education of children are sanctified and the Christian couple can more easily carry the burdens imposed on them.[14]

THE NATURE OF THE SACRAMENT OF MARRIAGE

What is the external sign which constitutes the sacrament of marriage? Our Lord could have instituted the sacrament in two ways, either by adding to the natural contract some external sign which would signify and cause grace, for instance, the priestly blessing, or by raising the natural contract itself to the dignity and rank of a sacrament of the New Law.

In the sixteenth century, a Dominican priest, Melchior Canus, taught that the priestly blessing together with the contract constituted the sacrament of marriage. Canus' view was gladly accepted by those who desired to limit the rights of the Church in favor of royal authority. It is clear that if marriage can be validly contracted apart from the sacrament, the rights of the Church extend only to sacramental marriages, and where the parties are content to forego the benefits of the sacrament, the marriage falls under civil, not ecclesiastical, law. The Royalists said that the authority hitherto exercised by the Church in matrimonial affairs was mere usurpation. When toward the end of the eighteenth century Joseph II of Austria began his campaign against the Holy See, his matrimonial legislation was based on this principle.

Canus' opinion is contrary to the traditional teaching of the Church, which holds that the sacrament of marriage is not something superadded to the natural contract of marriage; **it is identical with it.** It is doctrinally certain that the matrimonial contract itself was

[14] Cf. A. Tanquerey, *Synopsis Theologiae Dogmaticae* (Parisiis: Desclée et Socii, 1935), Vol. III, 177.

raised to the dignity of a sacrament, so that between baptized parties there cannot be a true marriage without it being at the same time a true sacrament. Pope Leo XIII, in his great encyclical on marriage, is most explicit on the point:

> For certain it is that in Christian Marriage the contract is inseparable from the Sacrament; and that for this reason the contract cannot be true and legitimate without being a Sacrament as well. For Christ Our Lord added to Marriage the dignity of a Sacrament; but Marriage is the contract itself whenever that contract is lawfully concluded. Marriage is, moreover, a Sacrament, because it is a holy sign which gives grace, showing forth an image of the mystical nuptials of Christ with His Church . . . Hence it is clear that among Christians every true Marriage is in itself and by itself a Sacrament; and nothing can be further from the truth than to say that the Sacrament is a certain ornament or outward endowment which can be torn away from the contract at the caprice of man.[15]

Can the marriage contract between baptized persons ever be separated from the sacrament? It was held by some theologians that if two baptized Christians, while taking each other for husband and wife, nevertheless had the deliberate intention not to form a sacramental marriage, the marriage would be a valid contract, but not a sacrament. But today theologians are agreed that if a couple should resolve that their marital union should not be a sacrament, question would arise as to which was their dominant intention — the intention to contract a true marriage or to avoid the sacrament. If the former, they were married with a sacrament, though the sacrament had been received in mortal sin; if the latter intention prevailed, there was no sacrament, but neither was there a marriage.[16]

It matters not as far as this question is concerned whether the baptized parties consider marriage a sacrament or not or whether they intend to effect a sacrament or not. Provided only that they intend to contract a true marriage and express the requisite consent, their intention and consent are sufficient to constitute a sacrament. But if they are absolutely determined not to effect a sacrament, then, of course, the production of a sacrament would be excluded but the marriage contract also would be null and void. By divine ordinance

---

15 Pope Leo XIII, *Arcanum Divinae Sapientiae,* February 10, 1880, Textus et Documenta Series Theologica 25 (Romae: Apud Aedes Pontificiae Universitatis Gregorianae, 1942), p. 20.

16 G. H. Joyce, S.J., *Christian Marriage* (London: Sheed and Ward, 1933), p. 204.

it is essential to Christian marriage that it should be a sacrament; it is not in the power of the contracting parties to eliminate anything from its nature, and a couple who have the intention of doing this invalidate the whole contract.

The same principle applies to the marriages of baptized non-Catholics. Since the contract and the sacrament are inseparable for the baptized, their marriages are truly sacramental unions. But in the case of a nonbaptized couple, their marriage is not a sacrament. This means that their marriage is not a sign and cause of grace. It is simply the natural contract of marriage. It is interesting to note that in the event that the couple receive baptism their marriage is, by that very fact, raised to the rank and value of a sacrament.

In the case of a Catholic marrying a **nonbaptized** person with a dispensation from the impediment of difference of worship, their marriage is not a sacrament. The reason is that the contract between the Catholic partner and the nonbaptized spouse is one and indivisible. The nonbaptized spouse is incapable of receiving a sacrament because baptism is the requisite condition for receiving the other sacraments. It is quite impossible that the contract be one-sided, partly sacramental and partly natural. Therefore it is now commonly held that their marriage remains a mere natural and nonsacramental contract for both parties.

THE MINISTERS OF THE SACRAMENT OF MARRIAGE — THE COUPLE THEMSELVES

The sacrament is conferred by a minister. Christ is the Author and principal Minister of all the sacraments. He has deputed men to administer them in His name. The person who administers a sacrament in Christ's name contributes to its effect as a secondary efficient cause or agent.

The Decree for the Armenians issued by the Council of Florence in 1439 explicitly says that the efficient cause of matrimony is the mutual consent of the parties.[17] Hence their mutual consent is productive at the same time of the contract and the sacrament which are identical. Therefore those who make the contract, the bride and groom, are also the ministers of the sacrament. They administer the sacrament to each other; the priest does not confer the sacrament by means of his blessing. The priest's role in the marriage ceremony is

---

[17] H. Denzinger and C. Bannwart, *Enchiridion Symbolorum* (St. Louis: B. Herder Book Co., 1937), n. 702.

that of an official witness required by ecclesiastical law for the validity of the marriage when Catholics (or even one Catholic) are concerned.

THE MATTER AND FORM OF MARRIAGE

It was during the thirteenth century that greater precision with regards to the composition of the sacramental rite was obtained. In analyzing the external sign of each of the seven sacraments, the Aristotelian theory about the composition of bodies into matter and form was applied to the sacraments. Like a physical body, a sacrament is a compound resulting from the union of two constitutive elements, one of which is undetermined and corresponds to matter, the other is determining and corresponds to form. The form of the sacraments is supplied by the words used in the administration of the rite; the matter is the material element, determined to its sacramental purpose by the utterance of the form or words. Thus in baptism, the matter is the ablution with water and the form is the Trinitarian formula, "I baptize thee in the name of the Father, and of the Son, and of the Holy Ghost." In Extreme Unction the matter is the anointing with oil, the form is the accompanying prayer of the priest.

So completely did this concept take over that matter and form were considered essential and necessary elements in every sacrament. It became the measure by which a sacred rite was considered to be a sacrament or not. For example, St. Thomas Aquinas, in his article in the **Summa Theologica**, "Whether Matrimony Is a Sacrament?" has an objection that since marriage has neither matter nor form it is not a sacrament. St. Thomas answers the objection by giving the matter and form of marriage.[18]

The sacrament is identical with the contract of marriage. The sacramental sign of marriage is the mutual consent of the parties expressed in words when they take each other for man and wife. In every contract there are two elements — an offer of a right and an acceptance, and the offer is not determined as a contract until it has been accepted. The common teaching applies this to the sacramental contract of marriage. The matter of the sacrament of marriage is the consent, inasmuch as it expresses the mutual offering or surrender of their bodies for marriage purposes, and the form is the consent, inasmuch as it signifies the mutual acceptance of this surrender. Thus each of the parties administers the sacrament to the other.

---

[18] *Summa Theologica* (Romae: Marietti, 1950), III Supplementum, 42, 1, ad 1, 2.

THE GRACE OF THE SACRAMENT OF MARRIAGE

Matrimony, as one of the sacraments of the New Law, produces habitual sanctifying grace automatically on those who place no obstacle in the way. Matrimony, supposing the possession of sanctifying grace by the recipient, confers an **increase** of this grace and is therefore a sacrament of the living, because it was instituted primarily not to remove sin but to sanctify the married couple.

This principal effect of sanctifying grace is common to all the sacraments, making the recipient a son of God and a sharer in the divine nature. It is this quality infused into our souls which is the very principle of the supernatural life and which increases our growth in holiness.

The entire communication of grace comes from the union of Christ with the Church. By their sacramental contract the couple enter into a closer union with the God-Man as Bridegroom of the Church who abounds in grace. Christ Himself consecrates them as active organs of His Mystical Body. Thus by reason of their new dignity new grace and new life must flow into them from the source of the Head, Christ.

Besides the effect of sanctifying grace common to all the sacraments, there is a special grace given by each sacrament which is accommodated to the purpose of each sacrament. This sacramental grace is directly conferred for some special effect necessary in the Christian life to which common sanctifying grace is not directly ordained. For example, the special sacramental grace of baptism is spiritual regeneration, that of Holy Eucharist is spiritual nourishment. In matrimony, sanctifying grace, besides sanctifying the parties, has this special function, that it perfects their natural love and confirms their indissoluble oneness. This sanctifying grace as it is specially modified for the purpose of the sacrament of marriage is called sacramental grace.

Pope Pius XI in his encyclical on marriage implies this real modification between sanctifying grace and sacramental grace in marriage when he says that this sacrament not only increases sanctifying grace, the permanent principle of the supernatural life, but gives a supernatural power for the fulfilling of the rights and duties faithfully, holily, and perseveringly even unto death.[19]

Further, it is through this sacramental grace that there is conferred

---

[19] "*Casti Connubii,*" *Acta Apostolicae Sedis,* XXII, p. 554.

a right to all the actual graces corresponding to the purpose of marriage and necessary for the faithful performance of the marital duties. Pope Pius XI mentions this special effect of the sacrament, saying that matrimony also gives particular gifts; dispositions, and seeds of grace by elevating and perfecting the natural powers. Matrimony bestows the right to the actual assistance of grace whensoever the couple need it for fulfilling the duties of their state.[20]

These duties are: the procreation and education of children; the fostering of mutual love; and the moderation of concupiscence.

Sacramental and actual graces are given for the primary purpose of marriage, the procreation and the education of children. The child holds the first place among the blessings of matrimony — the child, "who should be begotten of love, tenderly cared for and educated in a religious atmosphere." Divine help is assured the married couple in begetting children and raising them in the fear and love of God so that this duty becomes not a burden but a joy. Christian parents must love and honor, educate and rear their children as the future citizens of the kingdom of God. They must take the place of Christ and the Church with regard to their children as their teachers, guardians, and models. This is a lofty, supernatural vocation which demands all the greater graces in proportion as the job is difficult and the parents weak. But the sacrament has bestowed a right to all the actual graces the parents need for the fulfillment of their sublime duties.

Another and secondary purpose of the married life is to foster mutual love. This mutual love of husband and wife is paramount in Christian marriage. Pope Pius XI clearly states that this love is not based on the passing lust of the moment nor does it consist in pleasing words only, but in the deep attachment of the heart which is expressed in action, since love is proved by deed. Its primary purpose is that man and wife help each other day by day in forming themselves in the interior life, advancing more and more in virtue and growing in true love of God and neighbor. This mutual inward molding of husband and wife, this determined effort to perfect each other, is supernatural in character and is only accomplished by the graces of the sacrament.[21]

The secondary purpose of marriage is the easing of concupiscence. It sets the limits within which these sex impulses may receive legitimate

---

[20] *Ibid.*, p. 555.
[21] *Ibid.*, p. 548.

satisfaction. The graces of the sacrament are in evidence here for they give to the husband and wife that spiritual view of things and that power of self-control which enable them so to use their liberty as in no way to offend God. Apart from grace the legitimate satisfaction afforded by marriage would be unavailing as a check on human passion.

In spite of the wealth of grace conferred through the sacrament of marriage it is very common to hear of Catholic marriages that lack happiness and joy and where strain, tension, and dissatisfaction prevail. If in these conditions marriage proves a failure, this should not be taken to mean that the sacrament is a failure. It shows rather man's extreme need of such supernatural assistance, the grace of God.

Supernatural grace always demands the fullest human co-operation. In a plea for such co-operation Pope Pius XI says:

> It is a law of divine Providence in the supernatural order that men do not reap the full fruit of the Sacraments which they receive . . . unless they cooperate with grace. The grace of Matrimony will remain for the most part an unused talent hidden in the field unless the parties exercise these supernatural powers and cultivate and develop the seeds of grace they have received. If, however, doing all that lies within their power, they cooperate diligently, they will be able with ease to bear the burdens of their state and to fulfill their duties. By such a Sacrament they will be strengthened, sanctified and in a manner consecrated.[22]

---

[22] *Ibid.*, p. 554.

CHAPTER XXXIII

Moral Aspects of Marriage

FRANCIS J. CONNELL

Far more important than the physical aspects of marriage are its moral aspects, the norms of moral or ethical right and wrong pertinent to the conjugal union. The purpose of this chapter is to propound and briefly explain the most fundamental principles of Catholic teaching relative to morality in marriage and in the function of marriage counseling. It must be premised that our main concern is the moral law established by God rather than the rulings of Church or State, which will be treated in other chapters. Moreover, a more detailed treatment of some phases of the divine law in reference to marriage will be left to other sections of this book.

THE NATURAL LAW

Experience and observation make us aware that throughout the entire universe there is a wondrous order, an harmonious correlation of the myriads of created beings that come under our perception, a well-planned adaptation of means to ends. Such phenomena as the regular cycles of the planets and the complicated yet orderly processes by which plants and animals come into being and grow and multiply offer a clear proof that there is an all-wise and all-powerful God who created the universe and directs all the activities of creatures to definite ends. The uniform procedures by which the many and varied works of the Creator fulfill their assigned tasks are known as the **laws of nature.**

The concern of the Creator for His creatures shows itself especially in regard to man, the noblest of earth's living beings. However, there is a vast difference between the way in which other creatures function and that in which man acts in fulfilling his destiny. They are bound by the laws of nature to act in a certain definite way, given certain conditions; but man is endowed with free will, which empowers him to act as he should or to act differently. A plant has no choice as to whether it shall grow or not, if the conditions required for its growth are present. An animal has no freedom of action when its instinct directs it to a certain object. But a man has the power to act according to his own choice. If he wishes, he can be gentle and honest, or he can be a murderer and a thief. Furthermore, the destiny of all other creatures is confined to earth, whereas man is endowed with a spiritual and immortal soul which is destined to live forever, receiving from the Creator in the future life either reward or punishment in accordance with the good or evil deeds he has performed in the present life.

In man's very nature there are implanted certain norms of conduct which he must obey if he would act as a human being, in accordance with the characteristics and destiny accorded him by his Creator. Thus, man is by nature a social being, adapted to live in society with his fellow men, and accordingly his nature requires him to practice those virtues which promote the welfare of society, such as justice and honesty. Again, man's very nature demands that he subordinate the cravings of the body to the direction of the higher element of his being, the soul. Hence, he acts contrary to his nature when he indulges excessively in intoxicating liquor and thus allows the desires of the body to reduce the soul to a form of slavery. Man's status as an intelligent creature requires that he adore his Creator. This law of right and wrong which is based on human nature is called the **natural law,** and is the fundamental rule of conduct for every human being. It is God's law, inasmuch as He created man with a particular form of nature to which certain actions are conformable and others opposed. The former actions are morally good, the latter are morally bad.[1]

THE PURPOSE OF SEX AND MARRIAGE

It must be evident to every intelligent person that the primary purpose of the sex power is the generation of new life. To hold that the principal purpose of this faculty is the gratification of the individual is absurd, at least to anyone who admits the wise designs of God in the formation of human nature. The pleasure attached to the use of the sexual organs manifests the wisdom of the Creator,

---

[1] Cf. Heinrich A. Rommen, *The Natural Law,* trans. J. R. Hanley (St. Louis: B. Herder Book Co., 1947).

who thus draws men and women to employ these organs in accordance with their purpose, and thus to propagate and preserve the human race. There is an analogy between the digestive organs and the sexual organs. Pleasure is consequent on the use of both; but the pleasure is not the principal end of their functioning but is rather the divinely constituted allurement to human beings to use these powers and thus to maintain life — in the former instance the life of the individual, in the latter case the life of the human race.

It follows logically that only those human beings act in accordance with the natural law who, in using these faculties, employ them in a manner adapted to the attainment of their primary purpose. In the case of the digestive organs this means that the individual must be temperate in the use of food and drink, taking enough, but not too much, so that his body will be sustained in health and vigor. In the case of the sexual organs it means that a person may use them only in a manner that will tend toward their primary purpose, the procreation of new life. This does not imply that a married couple may have sexual intercourse only when there is hope of effecting pregnancy, for nature itself often renders conception impossible, as in advanced age and at the sterile time of the menstrual cycle. But it means that the use of the sexual faculties is in accordance with the natural law only when there is a normal coitus between a man and a woman, an act which by its nature is adapted to produce new life, even though in the particular circumstances conception is actually impossible. Any other use of the sexual faculty, such as masturbation or sodomy or contraception, is against the natural law and consequently is an offense against God, the Author of nature.

Furthermore, since it is surely nature's plan that any child brought into the world shall be cared for by its parents until it can make its own way in the world, the natural law demands that only those may generate children who are agreed that they will abide together and share in the work of rearing the offspring that may result from their sexual activities. In other words, only those may perform the sex act who are united to each other by the permanent bond of marriage. All extramarital relations are immoral because they tend to bring children into the world who will not be properly cared for because their parents are not permanently united, and consequently are not properly prepared to give their offspring the necessary attention and care that every human being needs in childhood and adolescence. Even though in a particular case the unmarried couple are resolved to give proper parental care to any child that may be born or are sure that no child can be conceived, their act of sexual union is still immoral. For law must be based on conditions as they ordinarily exist (**ex ordine rerum**), not on exceptional cases. Hence, the law of God forbidding sexual intercourse to every couple not united to each other by the stable bond of marriage holds even in those cases when conception is impossible or when any child born of the act would be assured of a proper rearing.[2] More serious than the act of sexual union between two unmarried persons (fornication) is the coition of a married person with one who is single (simple adultery); and still more serious is the act of intercourse when both have other married partners (double adultery). The sin of adultery involves not only evil effects to society as a whole, but also grave injustice to the spouse of the sinful married person.

The primary purpose of marriage is the procreation and proper rearing of children. There are indeed other ends of the conjugal state, such as the love and assistance mutually rendered and received by the married couple and the lawful relief of the strong inclination to sexual gratification that is in every normal human being.[3] But these are to be regarded as secondary purposes, always subordinate to the primary end, the welfare of society through the preservation and propagation of the human race.[4] On this account a person may not marry if he is permanently impotent — that is, if this person is physically unable to perform his or her part in the act of intercourse, and there is no hope that sexual potency will ever be gained. For one who is permanently impotent cannot transfer to the other party the right which forms the chief object of the marriage contract, the right to sexual union. Similarly, one who is not sufficiently intelligent or mature to understand at least in a general way the rights and duties of married life cannot make a valid marriage contract.[5]

---

[2] Cf. Ryan, *The Norm of Morality* (Washington, D. C.: N.C.W.C., 1946), p. 37.

[3] "The primary end of matrimony is the procreation and the rearing of children; the secondary end is the mutual assistance and the remedy of concupiscence" (Canon 1013, 1, *Code of Canon Law*).

[4] On April 1, 1944, the Holy Office issued a decree declaring that the primary end of marriage is the generation and education of children, and condemning the view that the secondary ends are not essentially subordinate to the primary end but are equally principal and independent (*Acta Apostolicae Sedis*, 1944, p. 103).

[5] Canons 1068 and 1082.

THE RIGHT TO MARRY

The right to marry and to raise a family is one of the most important personal rights of every human being. A person can freely renounce this right, as is done by Catholic priests and members of religious orders on their voluntary acceptance of the ecclesiastical or religious state. Moreover, some natural defect, such as permanent physical impotence or lack of sufficient intelligence to make the marriage contract, may render an individual incapable of using his right to marry. But when a person is mentally and physically capable of entering marriage, no individual or civil society is entitled to prevent him permanently and absolutely from exercising his right to marry.

From this it follows that a civil government is acting unjustly if it prohibits marriage to those who are somewhat retarded mentally, but have sufficient understanding to make a marriage contract. Similarly, a civil government is exceeding its authority if it permanently debars from marriage those who are afflicted with certain forms of sickness (such as tuberculosis or epilepsy), as long as they possess the physical and intellectual capacity for the conjugal state.[6] A civil ordinance requiring that a prospective married couple have a physical examination, with the results shown to both before the marriage, is fully reasonable. But certainly, those civil laws which forbid marriage because of racial or national differences are an unjust exercise of civil authority.[7]

The right to marry is so sacred that it may be exercised even when the couple have reason to fear that the offspring will be defective because of the transmission of some hereditary disease or because of the presence of the Rh factor. In such cases celibacy may be advisable, but it is not obligatory. Even a child born with a physical defect

---

[6] In an address to the participants in a genetic symposium on September 7, 1953, Pope Pius XII stated: "A ban on marriage, namely making marriage physically impossible through segregation of those whose heredity is defective, must also be rejected. The purpose intended is good in itself, but the means of attaining it violate a person's right to contract and to use marriage. When a person with an hereditary defect is unable to behave like a human being, or, in consequence, is unfit to contract marriage, or when later he becomes incapable of claiming by an act of free will the right he has acquired through valid marriage, then he can be prevented by lawful means from procreating a new life. Outside these cases the banning of marriage or of marital intercourse for biological, genetical or eugenical reasons is an injustice, no matter who it is that issues that prohibition, whether a private individual or a public authority."

[7] Cf. Joseph F. Doherty, *Moral Problems of Interracial Marriage* (Washington, D. C.: Catholic University of America, 1949).

can attain to everlasting happiness, which is the final goal of every human being.[8]

Since marriage is primarily directed toward the welfare of society, the right to marry can be limited to some degree by public authority, which may regulate such matters as the minimum age for marriage, the degrees of kinship within which a couple may not contract a valid marriage, etc. The Catholic Church claims the exclusive right to legislate on these matters for the marriages of baptized persons, who are subject to the Church's authority in sacred matters — and marriage is a sacred matter (a sacrament, when both parties are baptized).[9] The civil authority possesses a similar right of restriction and regulation in regard to the marriages of unbaptized persons.[10]

STERILIZATION

According to the natural law as interpreted by the Catholic Church human beings do not possess full dominion over themselves. That belongs to the Creator. Consequently, a person has no right to take his own life. Neither is he permitted to mutilate his body unless this is needed to promote the welfare of the whole body (or, according to some theologians, the bodily welfare of a fellow man, to whom one could give the cornea of an eye, an ovary, etc.). This principle has an intimate relation with marriage, inasmuch as sterilizing operations for the sole purpose of rendering a person incapable of parenthood — eugenic sterilizations, as they are called — are frequently performed at the present day.

According to the teaching of the Catholic Church, particularly the statement of Pope Pius XI in his encyclical **Casti Connubii,** "eugenic sterilization is forbidden by the law of God, and hence may never be inflicted on a man or a woman, either by the individual's own wish or against it, either by private or by public authority."[11]

Hence, the Catholic Church teaches that the State may not sterilize the mentally defective so that they may not propagate, though such persons can be segregated if they are so lacking in intelligence that they cannot make a marriage contract.[12] Moreover, eugenic steriliza-

[8] Cf. Francis J. Connell, C.SS.R., "May the State Forbid Marriage Because of a Social Disease?" *American Ecclesiastical Review,* December, 1938, p. 507 ff.

[9] Canon 1038.

[10] Cf. John A. Abbo and Jerome D. Hannan, *The Sacred Canons* (St. Louis: B. Herder Book Co., 1952), II, p. 214.

[11] Cf. *Five Great Encyclicals* (New York: Paulist Press, 1939), p. 96.

[12] Cf. Lehane, *The Morality of American Civil Legislation Concerning Eugenical Sterilization* (Washington, D. C.: Catholic University of America, 1944).

tion is illicit in the case of a married woman whose life might be endangered if she conceived. Abstinence, either total or periodic, is the only lawful way in which she can avoid future pregnancy.

Catholic theologians are not in agreement as to whether sterilization as a punishment for serious crime (punitive sterilization) may be inflicted lawfully by civil authority. But all agree that therapeutic sterilization can be allowed when serious reasons are present. In other words, an operation primarily intended to cure a grave pathological condition is permissible, even though sterility follows. For example, if a woman is suffering from a cancerous condition of the womb she may have the diseased organ excised, even though sterility necessarily follows. In that event the direct effect of the operation is the removal of a dangerous growth, while the sterility is the indirect effect.

THE PRINCIPLE OF THE DOUBLE EFFECT

This example illustrates what is known in Catholic theology as the principle of the double effect, and is frequently used to solve cases of conscience. It means that when certain conditions are fulfilled a person may lawfully perform an action from which a bad effect as well as a good effect will follow. The conditions that must be present to justify such an action are these:

1. The action must be in itself morally good.

2. The bad effect may not be willed positively by the agent as something desirable in itself, but may only be tolerated.

3. The good effect must be produced by the action that is performed, not by the evil effect. In other words, it is never permitted to achieve a good effect through the instrumentality of a bad means. This latter would be an exemplification of the false axiom that "the end justifies the means."

4. The good effect must be sufficiently beneficial to compensate for the toleration of the bad effect.

In the case of a therapeutic sterilization for the healing of a serious pathological condition we find these requirements realized. The cutting out of a diseased organ is a good action; the sterility consequent on the operation is presumably only tolerated, not directly willed, by the agents; the good effect (restoration of health) is produced by the operation itself, not by the sterilization; the great benefit of the preservation of the patient's life, or the curing of a serious pathological condition, is sufficient to compensate for the toleration of the resultant sterility. As is evident, this case differs radically from the case of a sterilization effected for the benefit of a woman who will probably be in danger of death if she becomes pregnant. In this latter case the third condition described above is lacking; the good effect (the protection of the woman's life) is procured **through** the sterilizing operation; a bad means is used for a good end.

CONTRACEPTION

Since the primary purpose of sexual intercourse is to produce new life, it is a grave distortion of the generative faculty on the part of a married couple to use positive means of avoiding conception while enjoying sexual relations. From the moral standpoint it makes no difference whether the means employed is the "natural method" of onanism (the withdrawal of the man immediately before orgasm and the spilling of the seed) or a chemical or mechanical device, employed either by the man or by the woman. In all of these methods there is a positive frustration of the divinely established purpose of the conjugal act and consequently a grave offense against the natural law of God. The Catholic Church has always taught this doctrine, the most clear and forceful authoritative statement being found in the encyclical **Casti Connubii** of Pope Pius XI.[13]

However, in the same encyclical the Pope made it clear that it is possible for one of the married couple to be guilty of contraception while the other remains innocent. According to the unanimous teaching of Catholic theologians, this can take place when a husband uses the "natural method" mentioned above. If the wife sincerely protests without success, she can lawfully undertake the act of coition, as long as there is sufficient reason for her to tolerate her husband's sin, which reason would be present if otherwise he would be angry and embittered. Furthermore, she may take an active part in the sexual union, obtaining the full degree of gratification, up to the time of his withdrawal, since up to that moment the action is in itself a normal and good act of conjugal union. However, if the husband uses a condom, there is no true act of conjugal intercourse. Hence, it is ordinarily the duty of a wife to refuse the petition of her husband, even to the extent of employing physical resistance. Only when it is truly probable that some grave injury will be inflicted on her by her husband if she resists (such as a severe beating) may the wife in such a case passively allow him to perform the act,

---

[13] Cf. *Five Great Encyclicals,* pp. 92–94.

just as a girl who is being raped may abstain from physical resistance if she fears that it will only stimulate the attacker to injure or to kill her. She may not consent to the pleasure of the act.[14]

If a wife uses a douche immediately after intercourse for the purpose of avoiding conception, the husband will be guiltless, as long as he protests sincerely and forcefully. For, in this supposition, the sin is entirely on the part of the wife, and the husband may ask for his marriage rights (even foreseeing her sinful act) as long as there is sufficient reason for his material co-operation toward her sin, such as the difficulty of observing total abstinence. Some theologians hold, on the same principle, that a husband may have intercourse when his wife is using a diaphragm, as long as he protests. For the diaphragm produces its contraceptive effect after coition; hence the wife alone sins in this case.[15]

From the fact that the Catholic Church condemns contraception as a violation of the natural law it does not follow that the Church teaches that married couples are required to have as many children as is physically possible. There are times when it is advisable for a couple not to have more children, at least for the time being. This can happen when they are in financial difficulties, or when there are already several small children to keep the mother busy. The wife may be so weak and sickly that her life would be endangered by another pregnancy; or the couple may realize that because of the Rh factor they cannot bring healthy children into the world.

On such occasions a married couple have no obligation to generate offspring, at least as long as the excusing circumstances remain. But this does not mean that they are allowed to practice contraception. The only means of avoiding conception in harmony with the law of God is abstinence from conjugal relations, either total or periodic (the Rhythm). According to a statement of Pope Pius XII made in October, 1951, this latter method — the use of conjugal rights during the period of sterility and abstinence during the period of fertility — is licit provided the couple have grave reasons for not having more children, at least at the present time. The Pope added, however, that if a couple used Rhythm without a sufficient reason they would be failing "against the very meaning of marriage." On entering marriage, they accepted a state of life ordained to promote the welfare of society through the generation and proper rearing of children. Hence, a

---

[14] Cf. Connell, *American Ecclesiastical Review*, April, 1945, pp. 276–286.
[15] Cf. *ibid.*, December, 1950, p. 460.

couple act in a manner contrary to the plan of the Creator if they take the privileges of married life while avoiding its burdens and obligations, unless they have very good reasons for not having children at the present time.[16]

However, it must be evident to every intelligent person that Rhythm is very different from contraception. For contraception involves some form of positive distortion or frustration of the conjugal act, whereas Rhythm means merely abstention from conjugal relations at certain times in the month, while sexual intercourse is had in the proper way at other times which nature itself has rendered sterile.[17]

ABORTION

According to the natural law every human being has a right to life, and no other human being may directly deprive him of this right unless he has forfeited it by some act of wrongdoing. There are three cases in which a person may forfeit his right to life because of wrongdoing. The first is the case of the criminal, sentenced to death because of some grave offense, whom the civil authority may lawfully kill. The second occurs when a nation has justly gone to war. The government may authorize the soldiers to kill the soldiers of the enemy who are fighting for an unjust cause. The third case is present when a person unjustly attacks another for the purpose of injuring or killing him or seizing some valuable possession. The one attacked may kill the unjust aggressor, if this is necessary to protect himself or his possessions. In these instances the right to inflict death on a fellow man ultimately proceeds from God, the Author and Lord of human life.

Apart from these cases, all human beings must be regarded as innocent persons, who may not be directly put to death, either by individuals or by public authority. Thus, what is known as "mercy killing" is simply murder.[18] Furthermore, under no circumstances may a child in its mother's womb, not yet viable, be slain by direct abortion. For a living fetus, however immature it may be, has all the rights of any human being. Hence, a direct abortion, even to

---

[16] Cf. Bouscaren, *Canon Law Digest* (Milwaukee: The Bruce Publishing Co., 1953), III, p. 440 ff.

[17] Cf. Rev. Orville N. Griese, S.T.L., *The Morality of Periodic Continence* (Washington, D. C.: Catholic University of America, 1942).

[18] Cf. Sullivan, *Catholic Teaching on the Morality of Euthanasia* (Washington, D. C.: Catholic University of America, 1949).

save the life of a mother who is in grave danger because of heart or kidney disease, eclampsia, pernicious vomiting, etc., is never allowed by the law of God. A bad means may not be used to procure a good end.

On the other hand, an operation necessary to save the life of a pregnant woman because of the presence of a pathological condition, such as cancer of the womb, may be performed, even though the nonviable fetus is killed or expelled as a concomitant result. This is an application of the principle of the double effect, explained above (p. 520 f.). Similarly, when a pregnancy is in progress in a Fallopian tube, without any reasonable prospect that the fetus will descend to the womb, the tube may be excised because it is affected by a pathological condition. In this event the removal of the diseased tube is the direct effect of the operation, the death of the fetus is the indirect effect.[19]

UNITY AND INDISSOLUBILITY OF MARRIAGE

By the natural law marriage is endowed with two properties — unity and indissolubility. The former means that marriage by its very nature is the union of one man and one woman, to the exclusion of polygamy. This property belongs to the married state because marriage is intended to be a bond of complete, undivided love, and when a man has more than one wife or a woman more than one husband at the same time, it is impossible for the mutual love to be complete and undivided. "They shall be **two** in one flesh" is the fundamental principle of marriage laid down by the Almighty when He created the first husband and wife.[20]

Indissolubility means that marriage by its very nature is intended to last until the death of one of the partners separates them, so that the natural law forbids divorce involving the right to contract another marriage as long as the first spouse is still living. The primary reason why divorce is sinful is that it is destructive of the proper rearing of children. A home broken by divorce, or a household in which there is a new "parent" in place of the real father or mother, affords a most unfavorable atmosphere for the upbringing of a child.

This chief reason for the immorality of divorce — its evil effect on the rearing of the offspring — is a valid argument even in the

---

[19] Cf. Henry Davis, S.J., *Moral and Pastoral Theology* (New York, 1946), II, pp. 168–186.

[20] Gen. 2:24.

case of marriages where there are no children, because, as was stated above, a law must be based on conditions as they normally occur and not be modified to suit exceptional circumstances. Moreover, other arguments against divorce can be given, such as the undeniable fact that even the prospect that the marriage will end in divorce surely diminishes the ardor of the love that should bind husband and wife, and is very likely to engender suspicion and insincerity.

According to Catholic belief, Almighty God has made certain exceptions to the laws of unity and indissolubility. In the Old Testament, before the establishment of the Christian law, both polygamy and divorce were allowed, under certain circumstances. Under the Christian law God has granted no dispensation for polygamy, but there have been exceptions to the law of indissolubility, subject to the authority of the Catholic Church, the Church established by Jesus Christ, as was explained more fully in another chapter (see Chapter XXV).

The Catholic Church teaches that under no circumstances may the civil law dissolve a valid marriage, whether the parties are baptized or unbaptized. This poses a problem for the Catholic judge and lawyer approached by a person seeking a civil divorce. The chief difficulty lies not in the divorce itself (which is not intrinsically wrong, since it merely means that a couple are no longer regarded as husband and wife by civil law) but in the subsequent attempted remarriage by a divorced person, which is not a true marriage in the eyes of God. The judge who grants a divorce, and the lawyer who promotes the case are co-operators toward a future invalid union, unless they have good reason to believe that neither of the parties will attempt a future remarriage. However, they are **material,** not **formal,** co-operators. (A formal co-operator is one who takes part in the bad action of another. A material co-operator is one who performs an action that is not bad in itself, though it offers the occasion for a sinful action by another. The judge or lawyer who promotes a divorce case does not participate in an intrinsically evil action but usually affords the occasion for a future invalid marriage.) Hence, for a sufficiently grave reason a Catholic judge may be justified in pronouncing a decree of divorce and a Catholic lawyer in promoting a divorce case, even when it is evident that the marriage is valid and that there is a probability of a future (invalid) marriage. Pope Pius XII made a declaration to this effect as regards judges in an address to jurists in 1949,[21] and theologians commonly apply the same principle to lawyers requested to plead a divorce case. However, it is quite evident that there is generally greater reason for a judge to pronounce a decree of divorce when the conditions required by civil law are present (since this is the obligation of the judge by civil law) than there is for a lawyer to undertake a divorce suit, since he has no obligation to take the case. Only when the lawyer would otherwise have to endure some very grave inconvenience or loss would he be allowed to promote a divorce suit for a person who is validly married.[22]

As far as Catholic judges in the United States are concerned, this doctrine offers no difficulty. When a divorce suit comes to an American judge in the course of his official duties and he cannot avoid accepting the case (as usually happens), he may, without any violation of conscience, grant the divorce if the conditions required by law are fulfilled. If, however, there is some hope that the parties can be reconciled, the judge should try to solve the case in this manner, in preference to a civil dissolution of the bond, when the marriage is valid.

Since the Catholic Church upholds the doctrine of the indissolubility of the marriage bond (with the exceptions noted elsewhere), the Church logically regards those persons who contract another marriage after a civil divorce as living in sin. Toward those who are living in such a situation Catholics must logically manifest a different attitude than they do toward persons living in honorable and sacred matrimony. Thus, a Catholic cannot be expected to attend the marriage ceremony of a person who already has a living spouse, even though there has been a civil divorce. When a divorced person has remarried, a Catholic cannot regard him and his present spouse as a truly married couple, and hence must limit his social relations with persons in this situation. This does not mean that the Catholic Church looks on one who is thus entangled in a "bad marriage" as involved in a hopeless situation or as unable to return to God's grace. A separation is often possible, and when this has taken place a Catholic who has made the unfortunate step can return to the sacraments. Indeed, there can be cases in which the Church will

---

[21] Cf. T. Lincoln Bouscaren, *Canon Law Digest,* III, 3–10; Davis, *The Moral Obligation of Catholic Civil Judges* (Washington, D. C.: Catholic University of America, 1953).

[22] Cf. Francis J. Connell, C.SS.R., *Morals in Politics and Professions* (Westminster, Md.: Newman Bookshop, 1951), p. 110.

allow a Catholic involved in an invalid marriage to continue to abide in the same home with the partner in the invalid marriage, but without the right of sexual intercourse. This "brother and sister" cohabitation may be allowed especially when there are children of the union, who need the care of both parents.[23]

MARRIAGE COUNSELING

The function of the marriage counselor is a most important one. On his advice and decisions depend the success or failure of many marriages, the happiness or unhappiness of many individuals. Hence, he must ever uphold the highest ideals of matrimony and family life. He may not compromise on moral principles; he must strive to solve the problems submitted to him according to the laws of God.

The Catholic counselor must not depart from the teachings of the Catholic Church regarding the holiness of the state of marriage and its grave obligations. Thus, he may never recommend birth control or remarriage after a divorce. Those who seek his help should receive advice and encouragement in harmony with the teachings of the Church for the past twenty centuries, which remind married couples that they must be willing to make sacrifices and endure hardships for the sake of each other and for the benefit of the children whom God may send them. The Catholic counselor must guard himself against the materialistic principles of the modern world which would advise people to reject the divine law rather than sacrifice their comfort and convenience.

However, at times the counselor may refrain from correcting or reproving those who come to him, even though he knows they are committing grave sin in their married life. Thus, if a couple who are habitually committing the sin of contraception seek advice only with reference to the bringing up of their children, he may give the guidance which they seek without referring to their sinful habit, if he feels that a correction would not be heeded.

PROFESSIONAL SECRECY

According to Catholic moral principles, a person is sometimes obliged to keep certain information secret, so that it would be a sin for him to divulge it, apart from special excusing circumstances.

---

[23] Cf. Francis J. Connell, C.SS.R., "More About the Bad-Marriage Dilemma," *Catholic Digest*, June, 1954, pp. 112–117.

There are three classes of secrets — natural, promised, and committed
(or entrusted). The first embraces information which by its very
nature calls for secrecy, such as the knowledge that a fellow man
committed a sinful deed in his former life, which has not become
public and which is in no way harmful to anyone nowadays. It would
be a sin of detraction to divulge this fact. A promised secret is one
that must be kept because of a promise explicitly made after one
has acquired the knowledge in question. Such, for example, is the
knowledge that a girl is planning to marry soon, which she communicates to a dear friend, exacting at the same time a promise
that it will be kept secret. Such a secret binds in fidelity. The third
type, the committed or entrusted secret, binds because of a contract,
either explicit or implicit, between the one who communicates the
confidential information and the one who receives it. The most
frequent form of the committed secret is the professional secret, which
binds a professional person with respect to his clients — for example,
a doctor with respect to his patients. Such a secret is obligatory on
the marriage counselor in relation to those who seek his advice and
direction.

This means that the counselor is bound in justice to keep secret
what he learns about his clients when they seek his professional
advice — their problems and difficulties, and particularly their moral
lapses. The counselor would ordinarily commit a grave sin if he
spoke of these matters to another person — even to the client's spouse.
He may at times seek advice from an expert in some particular
phase of a problem — a theologian, for example — but in that case
he should not divulge the client's name or otherwise identify him.
To reveal even matters that seem in themselves unimportant would
usually be a serious sin, because the breaking of secrecy in a matter
that seems trivial may create a general distrust of those engaged in
counseling service — a very unfortunate repercussion.

Exceptional circumstances can arise in which the revelation of a
professional secret is justifiable — for example, when the strict observance of secrecy would result in grave harm to the community or
to the client or to a third party. Thus, if a client informs the counselor
that he is contemplating suicide or a murder, the counselor may and
should reveal this dangerous situation to someone capable of preventing a tragedy. But the counselor should not accept the erroneous
notion that he may tell anything he learns about the client to a
physician or a psychiatrist or a clergyman. Only in extraordinary cases

is this permissible — namely, when some urgent reason justifies the divulging of secret information to avert some grave evil.[24]

CONCLUSION

The principles of the natural law concerning the obligations and the rights of married life, as the Catholic Church proposes them, are not acceptable to many persons outside the Catholic Church. Indeed, at the present day there are some who condemn and ridicule the Church's teachings on the moral aspects of marriage as antiquated and unrealistic. But anyone who admits an all-wise Creator who has ordained that His human children shall live as befits those destined to everlasting life, and not merely in accordance with their selfish and sensual desires, must perceive that the Catholic interpretation of the natural law on marriage is adapted, not only to promote the welfare of society, but also to bring the greatest happiness into the lives of married couples.

Sometimes the charge is made that the rules for marriage promulgated by the Catholic Church are too difficult for the average human being to observe. To this we answer that every human being is endowed with free will, enabling him to choose the right course, even when it is difficult. And when a person finds difficulty in fulfilling his obligations, he should have recourse to prayer, with the assurance that God will give him the help he needs to be faithful to his duties. Those who counsel their fellow men in regard to the problems and obligations of married life should bear these truths in mind and should endeavor to direct those who seek their advice toward the observance of God's law, however difficult it may seem at times. For men are not animals, led necessarily by instinct and passion; they are the children of God who, with the aid of His grace, can serve Him faithfully if they will to do so.

---

[24] Cf. Robert E. Regan, *Professional Secrecy* (Washington, D. C.: Catholic University of America, 1943).

Bibliography

The counselor will find listed here most of the books and articles upon which this book is based. All of the books listed here would not be suitable for use by a nonprofessional person. Many of them contain material which needs interpretation and might be misunderstood by the untrained individual. Because it is often desirable to have material to which a client can be referred, there is appended to the bibliography a list of selected Catholic pamphlets on the subject of sex and marriage (p. 556 ff.).

Abortion

Barnes, Harry L., and Lena, R., "Pregnancy and Tuberculosis," *Am. J. Obst. & Gynec.,* Vol. 44 (August, 1942), p. 183, quoted by Roy J. Heffernan and William A. Lynch, "Is Therapeutic Abortion Scientifically Justified?" *The Linacre Quarterly,* Vol. 19 (1952), p. 13.

Clement, George, M.D., *Thou Shalt Not Kill,* 4 French ed. (Philadelphia: Peter Reilly Co., 1930).

Cox, Ignatius, S.J., *Liberty: Its Use and Abuse* (New York: Fordham University Press, 1946).

Dickinson, Robert L., *Control of Conception,* 2 ed. (Baltimore: The Williams and Wilkins Co., 1938).

Goldstein, David, *Suicide Bent* (St. Paul: Radio Replies Press, 1945).

Guttmacher, Alan F., *Abortions and Miscarriages in Successful Marriage,* ed. Morris Fishbein and Ernest W. Burgess (Garden City, N. Y.: Garden City Books, 1951).

Heffernan, Roy J., and Lynch, William A., "Is Therapeutic Abortion Scientifically Justified?" *The Linacre Quarterly,* Vol. 19 (1952), pp. 11–27.

Huser, Roger J., *The Crime of Abortion in Canon Law* (Washington, D. C.: Catholic University of America Press, 1942).

Kelly, Gerald, S.J., "Direct and Indirect Abortion," *Hospital Progress* (October, 1948).

McCarthy, J., "Censure and the Crime of Abortion," *The Irish Ecclesiastical Record* (November, 1947), pp. 1007–1010.

McHugh, J., "Canonical Penalties for Abortion," *Homiletic and Pastoral Review* (February, 1934), pp. 552–554.

Mahoney, E., "Therapeutic Abortion," *The Clergy Review,* Vol. 14 (June, 1938), pp. 497–507.

Malpas, P., "A Study of Abortion Sequences," *J. Obst. & Gynec. of Brit. Emp.*, Vol. 45 (1938), pp. 932–949.

Mears, J. Gerard, "In Fear and In Secret They Do Damnable Deeds," *America*, Vol. 67 (1942), pp. 96–97.

O'Malley, Austin, M.D., *The Ethics of Medical Homicide and Mutilation* (New York: Devin-Adair Co., 1919).

O'Sullivan, Richard, "The Committee's Report on Abortion," *The Clergy Review*, Vol. 17 (1939), p. 395.

Ruland, Rev. Ludwig, D.D., *Pastoral Medicine* (St. Louis: B. Herder Book Co., 1934).

Schaaf, V., "Canon Law and Abortion," *American Ecclesiastical Review*, Vol. 93, no. 6 (December, 1935), pp. 623–624.

Taussig, Frank J., *Abortion, Spontaneous and Induced — Medical and Social Aspects* (St. Louis: C. V. Mosby Co., 1936).

Treub, Hector, M.D., van Oppenraay, R., S.J., and Vlaming, T., M.D., *The Right to Life of the Unborn Child* (New York: Joseph Wagner Co., 1903).

Woywod, Stanislaus, O.F.M., "Excommunication in Cases of Abortion," *Homiletic and Pastoral Review* (December, 1935), pp. 294–295.

———— *The Casuist* (New York: Joseph F. Wagner, 1925).

Alcoholism

Alcoholics Anonymous, *The Story of How More Than One Hundred Men Recovered From Alcoholism* (New York: The Works Publishing Co., 1939).

Alcohol and Society, A Study of Some Socio-Economic Implications, published at Des Moines, State of Iowa, 1953.

Angluin, Edward F., *The Use and Control of Alcoholic Drink* (Washington, D. C.: Catholic University of America Press, 1953).

Bacon, Selden D., Ph.D., "Alcoholism: Nature of the Problem," *Congressional Record* (Wednesday, September 28, 1949), pp. 3–13.

———— "Inebriety, Social Integration, and Marriage," *Quarterly Journal of Studies of Alcohol,* Vol. 5, no. 2 (1944), pp. 303–339.

Blocker, Hyacinth, O.F.M., *Don't Kid Yourself About Drink* (Huntington, Ind.: Our Sunday Visitor Press, 1954).

Bogen, Emil, M.D., *What About Alcohol?* (Los Angeles: Angelus Press, 1946).

Cushny, Arthur R., M.D., *A Textbook of Pharmacology and Therapeutics on the Action of Drugs in Health and Disease* (New York: Lea and Febiger, 1924).

D'Angelo, J. I., *A Comparative Study of the Socio-Economic Backgrounds of Repeatedly Incarcerated Alcoholics With Those Voluntarily Seeking*

Rehabilitation, unpublished M.A. dissertation (Washington, D. C.: Catholic University of America, 1953).

Emerson, Haven, M.D., *Alcohol, Its Effects On Man* (New York: D. Appleton-Century Co., 1934).

Ford, John C., S.J., "Alcohol Education in the Seminary," *Bulletin,* National Catholic Educational Association, Vol. 1, no. 1 (August, 1953), pp. 98–106.

———— *Depth Psychology, Morality and Alcoholism* (Weston, Mass.: Weston College, 1951).

———— *Man Takes a Drink* (New York: P. J. Kenedy and Sons, 1954).

Forty-Four Questions and Answers About the Program of Recovery from Alcoholism, The Alcoholic Foundation, Box 459, Grand Central Annex, New York 17, N. Y., issued by Alcoholics Anonymous Publishing, Inc., 1952.

Genug, E., "Medical and Ethical Aspects of Alcoholism," *The Catholic World,* Vol. CLXXVII, no. 1059 (June, 1953), pp. 182–186.

Goodman, Louis, M.D., and Gilman, Alfred, Ph.D., *The Pharmacological Basis of Therapeutics* (New York: The Macmillan Co., 1941).

Hesse, Erich, M.D., *Narcotics and Drug Addiction* (New York: Philosophical Library, 1946).

Hirsh, Joseph, *The Problem Drinker* (New York: Duell, Sloan and Pearce, 1949).

Jellinek, E. M., *Memoirs of the Section of Studies on Alcohol* (New Haven, Conn.: Hillhouse Press, 1946).

Kelly, Gerald, S.J., *The Good Confessor* (New York: The Sentinel Press, 1951).

Lerner, Arthur, "Considerations of Content Material of Group Counseling Sessions with Jailed Alcoholics," *Quar. J. of Studies on Alcohol,* Vol. 15, no. 3 (September, 1954), pp. 432–452.

———— *The Blue Book,* Vol. 5 (The Proceedings of the Fifth National Clergy Conference on Alcoholism) (Jamaica: Bishop Malloy Retreat House, 1953).

———— *The Blue Book,* Vol. 6 (The Proceedings of the Sixth National Clergy Conference on Alcoholism) (N.C.C.A., 1954).

McCarthy, Raymond G., and Douglass, Edgar M., *Alcohol and Social Responsibility* (New York: Thomas Y. Crowell Co. and Yale Plan Clinic, 1949).

Moynihan, Msgr. James H., *Life of Archbishop John Ireland* (New York: Harper and Brothers, 1953).

The National Catholic Almanac — 1954, ed. Felician A. Foy, O.F.M., compiled by the Franciscan Clerics of Holy Name College (Washington, D. C.: St. Anthony's Guild, 1954).

O'Brien, Patricia, *Casework Treatment with Alcoholics* (Washington, D. C.: Catholic University of America Press, 1950).

Patrick, Clarence H., *Alcohol, Culture, and Society* (Durham, N. C.: Duke University Press, 1952).

Pfau, Rev. Ralph S., *Alcoholism, Sin or Disease?* (New York: The Catholic Information Society, 1952).

Schaefer, Earl S., *Fundamental Personality Structures of Chronic Alcoholics in Outpatient Psychotherapy,* unpublished Ph.D. dissertation (Washington, D. C.: Catholic University of America, 1954).

Seliger, Robert V., M.D., *A Guide on Alcoholism for Social Workers* (New York: William Frederick Press, 1945).

Seliger, Robert V., M.D., and Cranford, Victoria, *Alcoholics Are Sick People* (New York: William Frederick Press, 1945).

Social Work Year Book — 1954, Russel Kurtz, ed. (New York: National Association of Social Workers, 1954).

Straus, Robert, and Bacon, Selden D., *Drinking in College* (New Haven, Conn.: Yale University Press, 1953).

Strecker, E. A., and Chambers, F. F., Jr., *Alcohol One Man's Meat* (New York: The Macmillan Co., 1949).

Yahraes, Herbert, *Alcoholism Is a Sickness* (New York: Public Affairs Commitee, Inc., 1950).

Canon and Civil Law

Abbo, John A., and Hannan, Jerome D., *The Sacred Canons,* 2 vols. (St. Louis: B. Herder Book Co., 1952).

Aryrinhac, H. A., and Lydon, P. J., *Matrimonial Legislation in the New Code of Canon Law,* rev. ed. (New York: Benziger Brothers, 1938).

Bouscaren, T. Lincoln, S.J., *The Canon Law Digest,* 3 vols. (Milwaukee: The Bruce Publishing Co., 1934, 1943, 1953).

Bouscaren, T. Lincoln, S.J., and Ellis, A. C., S.J., *Canon Law* (Milwaukee: The Bruce Publishing Co., 1946).

Bradway, John S., "Some Domestic Relations Laws That Counselors in Marital Difficulties Need to Know," *Social Forces,* Vol. 17 (October, 1938), pp. 83–89.

Codex Iuris Canonici (Rome: Vatican Press, 1918).

Doheny, W. J., C.S.C., *Canonical Procedure in Matrimonial Cases,* 2 vols. (Milwaukee: The Bruce Publishing Co., 1938, 1944).

Gulovich, Stephen, "Matrimonial Laws of the Catholic Eastern Churches," *The Jurist,* Vol. 4, No. 2 (April, 1944), pp. 200–245.

——— "The Motu Proprio Crebrae Allatae," *The Jurist,* Vol. 10, No. 3 (July, 1950), pp. 334–356.

Joyce, G. H., S.J., *Christian Marriage* (London and New York: Sheed and Ward, 1933).

Julien, Alfred, "Proof of Death Cases Involving Military Personnel Killed or Missing as the Result of War Action," *The Jurist*, Vol. 6, No. 1 (January, 1946).

Keezer, F. H., *On the Law of Marriage and Divorce* (Indianapolis, Ind.: Bobbs-Merrill Co., 1946).

Król, John, "Permission to Parties Invalidly Married to Live as Brother and Sister," *The Jurist*, Vol. 11, No. 1 (January, 1951), pp. 7–32.

Lehane, Joseph B., *The Morality of American Civil Legislation Concerning Eugenical Sterilization* (Washington, D. C.: Catholic University of America Press, 1944).

Long, J. R., *A Treatise on the Law of Domestic Relations*, 3 ed. (Indianapolis, Ind.: Bobbs-Merrill Co., 1923).

Madden, J. W., *Handbook of the Law of Person and Domestic Relations* (St. Paul, Minn.: West Publishing Co., 1931).

Marbach, J., *Marriage Legislation for the Catholic of the Oriental Rites in the United States and Canada* (Washington, D. C.: Catholic University of America Press, 1946).

Nelson, W. T., *Divorce and Annulment*, 2 ed. (Chicago: Callaghan and Co., 1945).

Peck, E., *The Law of Persons and of Domestic Relations*, 3 ed. (Chicago: Callaghan and Co., 1930).

Rice, Patrick William, *Proof of Death in the Prenuptial Investigation*, Canon Law Studies, No. 123 (Washington, D. C.: Catholic University of America Press, 1940).

Rommen, Heinrich A., *The Natural Law*, trans. Thomas R. Hanley (St. Louis: B. Herder Book Co., 1947).

Schouler, J., *A Treatise on the Law of Marriage, Divorce, Separation and Domestic Relations*, 6 ed. (Albany, N. Y.: Mathew Bender Co., 1921).

Vernier, C. G., *American Family Laws*, 5 vols. (Stanford University, Calif.: Stanford University Press, 1931).

Counseling

Bingham, W. V., and Moore, B. B., *How to Interview* (New York: Harper and Brothers, 1941).

Blum, Milton L., and Balinsky, Benjamin, *Counseling and Psychology* (New York: Prentice-Hall, Inc., 1951).

Brewer, J. M., *History of Vocational Guidance* (New York: Harper and Brothers, 1942).

Connell, F. J., C.SS.R., *Some Moral Problems in Marriage Education and Counseling* (Washington, D. C.: Catholic University of America Workshop Papers, 1952).

Cox, R. D., *Counselors and Their Work* (Philadelphia: Archives Publishing Co. of Pennsylvania, 1945).

Cuber, John F., *Marriage Counseling Practice* (New York: Appleton-Century-Crofts, Inc., 1948).

Curran, Charles A., *Counseling in Catholic Life and Education* (New York: The Macmillan Co., 1952).

―――― *Personality Factors in Counseling* (New York: Grune and Stratton, 1945).

Darley, John G., *The Interview in Counseling* (Washington, D. C.: U. S. Department of Labor, Government Printing Office, 1946).

Garrett, Annett, *Interviewing, Its Principles and Methods* (New York: Family Welfare Association of America, 1942).

Goldstein, Sidney E., *Marriage and Family Counseling* (New York: McGraw-Hill Book Co., Inc., 1945).

Greenleaf, Walter J., *Guide to Occupational Choice and Training* (Washington, D. C.: Superintendent of Documents, Government Printing Office, 1947).

Hahn, Milton E., and MacLean, Malcolm S., *General Clinical Counseling* (New York: McGraw-Hill Book Co., Inc., 1950).

Jager, Harry A., "The Guidance Program Broadens Its Base," *Occupations,* Vol. 27 (April, 1949), pp. 469–473.

Kraines, S. H., *Live and Help Live* (New York: The Macmillan Co., 1950).

Mace, David, *Marriage Counseling:* the first full account of the remedial work of the marriage guidance councils (London: J. & A. Churchill, 1948).

Magner, Rev. James A., *The Art of Happy Marriage* (Milwaukee: The Bruce Publishing Co., 1947).

Marriage Education and Counseling, ed. A. H. Clemens (Washington, D. C.: Catholic University of America Press, 1951).

Mudd, Emily H., "Analysis of 100 Consecutive Cases in Marriage Council of Philadelphia," *Mental Hygiene,* Vol. 2, no. 2 (April, 1939), pp. 198–217.

―――― "Marriage Counseling," *The Cyclopedia of Medicine, Surgery and Specialties,* Vol. 11 (Philadelphia: F. A. Davis Co., 1955), pp. 601–611.

―――― "Marriage Counseling as Afforded by Recently Developed Marriage and Family Counseling Clinics," *The Family,* Vol. 18, no. 9 (January, 1938), p. 310.

―――― *The Practice of Marriage Counseling* (New York: Association Press, 1951).

National Marriage Guidance Council, *Syllabus for the Training of Marriage Counselors* (London, 1949).

Roethlisberger, F. J., and Dickson, W. J., *Management and the Worker* (Cambridge, Mass.: Harvard University Press, 1946).

Rogers, Carl R., *Client Centered Therapy* (Boston: Houghton Mifflin Co., 1951).

——— *Counseling and Psychotherapy* (Boston: Houghton Mifflin Co., 1942).

Shostrom, E. L., and Brammer, L. M., *The Dynamics of the Counseling Process* (New York: McGraw-Hill Book Co., Inc., 1952).

Stafford, John W., C.S.V., "The Equipment of the Marriage Counselor," *Marriage Counseling* (Family Life Bureau, N.C.W.C., Washington, D. C.), pp. 39–43.

Stone, Abraham, "Marriage Education and Marriage Counseling in the United States," *Marriage and Family Living,* Vol. 11, no. 2 (Spring, 1949), pp. 38–39.

Super, Donald, *Appraising Vocational Fitness* (New York: Harper and Brothers, 1949).

Courtship and Marriage

Adams, Clifford R., *Looking Ahead to Marriage* (Chicago: Science Research Associates, 1949).

Bergler, Edmund, *Unhappy Marriage and Divorce* (New York: International Universities Press, 1946).

Bigelow, William F., *The Good Housekeeping Marriage Book* (New York: Prentice-Hall, Inc., 1938).

Bowdern, William S., S.J., *Problems of Courtship and Marriage* (St. Louis: The Queen's Work, 1939).

Bowman, Henry A., *Marriage for Moderns* (New York: McGraw-Hill Book Co., Inc., 1942).

Brown, Fred, and Kempton, Rudolf T., *Sex Questions and Answers: A Guide to Happy Marriage* (New York: McGraw-Hill Book Co., Inc., 1950).

Burgess, Ernest W., and Cottrell, Leonard S., Jr., *Predicting Success or Failure in Marriage* (New York: Prentice-Hall, Inc., 1939).

Burgess, Ernest W., and Wallin, Paul, *Engagement and Marriage* (Chicago: J. B. Lippincott Co., 1953).

The Cana Conference Proceedings, Vols. 1 and 2 (1949–1950), Cana Conference, 21 W. Superior St., Chicago, Ill.

Clemens, Alphonse H., *The Cana Movement in the United States* (Washington, D. C.: Catholic University of America Press, 1953).

Connell, F. J., C.SS.R., "Juvenile Courtships," *American Ecclesiastical Review,* March, 1955, pp. 181–190.

Cuber, John F., "Changing Courtship and Marriage Customs," *The Annals of the American Academy of Political and Social Science,* Vol. 229 (September, 1943), pp. 30–38.

Dooley, Lester M., S.V.D., *Happy Married Life* (Island Creek, Mass.: Miramar Book Department, 1955).

Doyle, Rev. Charles Hugo, *Blame No One But Yourself* (Tarrytown, N. Y.: The Nugent Press, 1955).

—— *Cana Is Forever, Counsels for Before and After Marriage* (Tarrytown, N. Y.: Nugent Press, 1949).

—— *Sins of Parents, Counsels on Marriage and Youth Guidance* (Tarrytown, N. Y.: Nugent Press, 1951).

Duval, Evelyn M., *Building Your Marriage,* Public Affairs Pamphlet, No. 113 (New York: Public Affairs Committee, 1946).

Duval, Evelyn M., and Hill, Reuben, *When You Marry* (New York: Association Press, 1953).

Eckert, Ralph G., *So You Think It's Love* (New York: Public Affairs Committee, 1950).

Edson, Newell W., *Choosing a Home Partner* (New York: American Social Hygiene Association, 1951).

The Family Apostolate (Washington, D. C.: The National Catholic Welfare Conference, 1951).

The Family Life Bureau, The Activities It Promotes and the Channels It Utilizes (Washington, D. C.: The National Catholic Welfare Conference, n.d.).

Farrell, Mr. and Mrs. John J., *This Is Cana* (St. Meinrad, Ind.: The Grail Office, 1952).

Fishbein, Morris, and Burgess, Ernest W., *Successful Marriage* (New York: Doubleday and Co., 1947).

Gallaway, T. W., *Qualifications of a Mate* (New York: The Macmillan Co., 1945).

Grant, Dorothy, *So! You Want to Get Married!* (Milwaukee: The Bruce Publishing Co., 1947).

Groupe Lyonnais D'Études Médicales Philosophiques et Biologiques, *Médicine et Mariage* (Paris: Convergences Spes, 1952).

A Handbook of Cana Family Action, prepared by the Cana Committee of the Archdiocese of Newark (Staten Island, N. Y.: Society of St. Paul, 2187 Victory Blvd., 1954).

For Happier Families (Chicago: The Christian Family Movement, 1952).

Harrington, Edward, *Cana Catechism* (St. Louis: The Queen's Work, 1950).

Healy, Edwin F., S.J., *Marriage Guidance* (Chicago: Loyola University Press, 1948).

Hull, Ernest R., *Love, Courtship and Marriage* (St. Louis: B. Herder Book Co., 1934).

Hutton, L., *The Single Woman and Her Problems* (Baltimore: Williams and Wilkins Co., 1937).

Kelly, Gerald L., S.J., *Modern Youth and Chastity* (St. Louis: The Queen's Work, 1941).

Kirkendall, Lester A., and Osborne, Ruth F., *Dating Days* (Chicago: Science Research Associates, 1949).

Landis, Judson T. and Mary G., *Building a Successful Marriage* (New York: Prentice-Hall, Inc., 1948).

Landis, Paul H., *Making the Most of Marriage* (New York: Appleton-Century-Crofts, Inc., 1955).

Locke, Harvey J., "Predicting Marital Adjustment by Comparing a Divorced and Happily Married Group," *American Sociological Review,* Vol 12, no. 2 (April, 1947), pp. 187–191.

Locke, Harvey J., and Klausner, W. J., "Marital Adjustment of Divorced Persons in Subsequent Marriages," *Sociology and Social Research,* Vol. 33, no. 2 (November-December, 1948).

Lord, Daniel A., S.J., *About Divorce* (St. Louis: The Queen's Work, 1946).

―――― *Some Questions I'm Asked About Marriage* (St. Louis: The Queen's Work, 1938).

―――― *The Questions They Always Ask* (St. Louis: The Queen's Work, 1943).

Lover, James F., C.SS.R., *Is Your Marriage on the Rocks?* (New York: The Paulist Press, 1952).

Marriage Preparation Service, *Correspondence Course for Preparation for Marriage,* 1 Stewart St., Ottawa, Canada.

Messenger, Rev. E. C., *Two in One Flesh* (Westminster: Md.: The Newman Press, 1950).

Mihanovich, Clement S., Schnepp, Gerald J., and Thomas, John L., *A Guide to Catholic Marriage* (Milwaukee: The Bruce Publishing Co., 1955).

Mudd, Emily H., "How Women Adjust to Marriage," Part 5, Chap. 6, in *Successful Marriage,* M. Fishbein and E. Burgess, eds. (New York: Doubleday and Co., 1947).

O'Brien, Rev. John A., *Choosing a Partner for Marriage* (Notre Dame, Ind.: Ave Maria Press, 1948).

O'Connor, John J., S.J., *Preparation for Marriage and Family Life* (New York: The Paulist Press, 1947).

Popenoe, Paul, *I Married a Stingy Husband* (Los Angeles: Kingsway Press, 1945).

―――― *Marriage Before and After* (New York: Wilfred Funk, Inc., 1943).

―――― *Modern Marriage* (Los Angeles: American Institute of Family Relations, 1945).

—— "Study of 738 Elopements," *American Sociological Rev.,* Vol. 3 (1938), pp. 47–53.

Ryan, John, *Medical Aspects of Marriage* (London: Burns, Oates and Washbourne, Ltd., 1951).

Scott, Martin J., S.J., *Courtship and Marriage* (Dublin: The Irish Messenger, 1936).

—— *Marriage* (New York: The Paulist Press, 1940).

Steiner, Richard M., *A Guide to a Good Marriage* (Boston: The Beacon Press, 1955).

Stone, Doctors Hannah and Abraham, *A Marriage Manual* (New York: Simon and Schuster, 1935).

Terman, Lewis M., *Psychological Factors in Marital Happiness* (assisted by Paul Buttenwieser, Leonard W. Ferguson, Winifred B. Johnson, and Donald P. Wilson) (New York: McGraw-Hill Book Co., Inc., 1938).

Thorman, George, *Broken Homes,* Public Affairs Pamphlet, No. 135 (New York: Public Affairs Committee, 1947).

Toward Happiness and Holiness in Marriage (Washington, D. C.: Family Life Bureau, N.C.W.C.).

Weber, Rev. Gerard P., *Chaplain's Manual* (Chicago: The Chicago Federation of the Christian Family Movement, 1952).

Economic Aspects

Book, Dorothy L., *Family Budget Counseling* (New York: The Family Welfare Association of America, 1944).

Callaghan, Hubert C., S.J., *The Family Allowance Procedure* (Washington, D. C.: The Catholic University of America Press, 1947).

Cissell, Robert and Helen, *Stretching the Family Income* (New York: J. F. Wagner, 1953).

Clemens, Alphonse, "Values in Family Living," *Social Order,* Vol. 3, No. 3 (March, 1953), pp. 123–127.

Corley, Francis J., S.J., *Family Allowances* (St. Louis: The Queen's Work, 1947).

—— *Family Allowances, U.S. Plan* (St. Louis: Institute of Social Order, 1951).

Dewhurst, J. Frederic, and Associates, *America's Needs and Resources* (New York: 20th Century Fund, 1947).

Harwood, E. C., and Fowle, H., *How to Make Your Budget Balance* (Great Barrington, Mass.: American Institute of Economic Research, 1947).

"How Much to Raise a Child?" *Changing Times,* The Kiplinger Magazine (December, 1950), pp. 14–17.

Jordan, D. F., and Willett, E. F., *Managing Personal Finances* (New York: Prentice-Hall, 1945).

Masteller, K. C., *How to Avoid Financial Tangles* (Great Barrington, Mass.: Amer. Inst. for Economic Research, 1947).

Shields, H. G., and Wilson, W. H., *Consumer Economic Problems* (New York: Southwestern Publishing Co., 1945).

Upchurch, G. R., and Harwood, E. C., *Life Insurance and Annuities from the Buyer's Point of View* (Great Barrington, Mass.: Amer. Inst. for Economic Research, 1947).

Vaile, Roland S., and Canoyer, Helen G., *Income and Consumption* (New York: Henry Holt and Co., 1938).

PERIODICALS:

American Economic Review, 450 Ahniap Street, Menasha, Wis.

Amer. J. of Econ. & Socio., North Queen Street and McGovern Avenue, Lancaster, Pa.

Consumer Reports, Consumers Union of the United States, Inc., Mount Vernon, N. Y.

Federal Reserve Bulletin, Federal Reserve Board, Washington, D. C.

J. of Home Economics, American Home Econ. Assoc., Washington, D. C.

Survey of Current Business, U. S. Dept. of Commerce, Government Printing Office, Washington, D. C.

Ethics and Morals

Bonnar, A., *The Catholic Doctor,* 2 ed. (New York: P. J. Kenedy & Sons, 1939).

Brosnahan, Timothy J., *Prolegomena to Ethics* (New York: Fordham University Press, 1941).

Burke, E., *Acute Cases in Moral Medicine* (New York: The Macmillan Co., 1929).

Connell, Francis J., C.SS.R., *Marriage, Human or Divine?* (New York: The Paulist Press, 1940).

―――― "May the State Forbid Marriage Because of a Social Disease?" *Amer. Eccles. Review* (December, 1938).

―――― *Morals in Politics and Professions* (Westminster, Md.: The Newman Press, 1951).

―――― "More About the Bad-Marriage Dilemma," *Catholic Digest* (June, 1954), pp. 112–117.

―――― *Outlines of Moral Theology* (Milwaukee: The Bruce Publishing Co., 1953).

Coppens, Charles, S.J., *Moral Principles and Medical Practices,* new ed. (New York: Benziger Bros., 1921).

Davis, Henry, S.J., *Moral and Pastoral Theology,* 4 vols. (New York: Sheed and Ward, Inc., 1946).

Doyle, Rev. Charles H., *Cana is Forever* (Tarrytown, N. Y.: Nugent Press, 1949).

——— *Sins of Parents* (Tarrytown, N. Y.: Nugent Press, 1949).

Ethical and Religious Directives for Catholic Hospitals, 2 ed. (St. Louis: The Catholic Hospital Association of the U. S. and Canada, 1955).

Ficarra, Bernard J., *Newer Ethical Problems in Medicine and Surgery* (Westminster, Md.: The Newman Press, 1951).

Fink, C. T., C.M., and LaRochelle, S. A., O.M.I., *Handbook of Medical Ethics,* 8 ed. (Westminster, Md.: The Newman Press, 1947).

Finney, Patrick A., C.M., *Moral Problems in Hospital Practice,* 4 ed. (St. Louis: B. Herder Book Co., 1930).

Flood, Dom Peter, O.S.B., *New Problems in Medical Ethics* (Westminster, Md.: The Newman Press, 1953).

Flynn, Vincent S., *The Norm of Morality* (Washington, D. C.: The Catholic University of America Press, 1928).

Griese, Rev. Orville N., S.T.L., *The Morality of Periodic Continence,* Studies in Sacred Theology No. 69 (Washington, D. C.: The Catholic University Press, 1942).

Handren, Walter J., S.J., *No Longer Two* (Westminster, Md.: The Newman Press, 1955).

Häring, Bernard, C.SS.R., *Das Gesetz Christi, Moraltheologie* (Freiburg im Breisgau: Erich Wewel Verlag, 1954).

Harvey, J. F., *The Moral Theology of the Confessions of St. Augustine* (Washington, D. C.: The Catholic University of America Press, 1951).

Healy, Edwin F., S.J., *Moral Guidance* (Chicago: Loyola University Press, 1943).

Jone, Heribert, O.F.M.Cap., and Adelman, Urban, O.F.M.Cap., *Moral Theology* (Westminster, Md.: The Newman Press, 1953).

Joyce, G. H., S.J., *Christian Marriage* (New York: Sheed and Ward, Inc., 1933).

Kelly, Gerald, S.J., *Medico-Moral Problems* (St. Louis: The Catholic Hospital Association of the U. S. and Canada, 1951).

Kenny, John, O.P., *Principles of Medical Ethics* (Westminster, Md.: The Newman Press, 1952).

LaRochelle, Stanislas A., and Fink, C. T., C.M., *Handbook of Medical Ethics,* trans. M. E. Poupore with the collaboration of A. Carter and R. M. H. Power (Westminster, Md., The Newman Press, 1949).

Leclercq, Jacques, *Marriage and the Family,* trans. Thomas R. Hanley (New York: Pustet, 1947).

McAllister, Joseph, S.S., *Ethics* (Philadelphia: W. B. Saunders Co., 1947).

McFadden, Charles J., O.S.A., *Medical Ethics,* 4 ed. (Philadelphia: F. A. Davis Co., 1956).

Macksey, Charles, "Society," *Readings in Ethics,* ed. J. F. Leibell (Chicago: Loyola University Press, 1926).

Merkelbach, B., O.P., *Summa Theologiae Moralis,* 8 ed. (Brussels: Desclée, 1949).

Messenger, Ernest C., *Two in One Flesh,* 3 vols. (Westminster, Md.: Newman Press, 1949).

Meyer, Fulgence, O.F.M., *Plain Talks on Marriage* (Cincinnati: St. Francis Bookshop, 1927).

Moore, Dom Thomas V., O.S.B., *Principles of Ethics* (Philadelphia: J. B. Lippincott Co., 1945).

Noldin, Hieronymus, *Summa Theologiae Moralis* (New York: Pustet, 1941).

—————— *Moral Theology* (Westminster, Md.: The Newman Press, 1952).

O'Brien, P., *Emotions and Morals* (New York: Grune and Stratton, 1950).

Regan, Robert E., *Professional Secrecy* (Washington, D. C.: The Catholic University of America, 1943).

Rommen, Heinrich, *The Natural Law,* trans. Thomas R. Hanley (St. Louis: B. Herder Book Co., 1949).

Natural Childbirth

Baker, Maggie, "Natural Childbirth," *Coronet,* Vol. 36 (May, 1954), pp. 45–52.

Brindel, Mrs. June, "I'll Take Hypnosis," *The American Weekly* (February 20, 1955).

Davenport, Charles, "A Mother is Creative," *Our Sunday Visitor* (September 27, 1953).

Doyle, Rev. Charles H., *Cana Is Forever* (Tarrytown, N. Y.: The Nugent Press, 1949).

Gelb, Barbara, *The ABC of Natural Childbirth* (New York: W. W. Norton and Co., 1954).

Good, Frederick L., M.D., and Kelly, Father Otis, M.D., *Marriage, Morals and Medical Ethics* (New York: P. J. Kenedy and Sons, 1951).

Gray, Coleen, "Why I Had My Baby Nature's Way," *Mirror* (New York *Mirror's* Sunday Magazine Section, September 26, 1954).

Healy, Edwin F., S.J., *Marriage Guidance* (Chicago: Loyola University Press, 1948).

Heardman, Helen, *A Way to Natural Childbirth* (Baltimore: The Williams and Wilkins Co., 1950).

Hogan, Aileen, "Natural Childbirth," *The Grail Magazine* (December, 1950).

Read, Grantly Dick, M.D., *Childbirth Without Fear* (New York: Harper and Bros., 1944).

Scadron, Eugene, M.D., "Myths About Pregnancy," *This Week Magazine* (February 6, 1955).

Thomas, Herbert, M.D., *Training for Childbirth* (New York: McGraw-Hill Book Co., 1950).

von Gagern, Baron Frederick, M.D., *The Meaning of Life and Marriage* (Westminster, Md.: The Newman Press, 1954).

Papal Talks

Five Great Encyclicals (New York: The Paulist Press, 1939).

Leo XIII, *Arcanum Divinae Sapientiae,* trans. Gerald C. Treacy, S.J. (New York: The Paulist Press, 1942).

Pius XI, *On the Christian Education of Youth* (New York: The Paulist Press, n.d.).

────── *Encyclical Letter on Christian Marriage (Casti Connubii)* (New York: The America Press, 1936).

────── *Quadragesimo Anno* (Washington, D. C.: National Catholic Welfare Conference, 1942).

Pius XII, "Allocution to Catholic Mothers," *Acta Apostolicae Sedis,* Vol. 33 (November 26, 1941), pp. 450–458.

────── *Humani Generis* (New York: The Paulist Press, 1953).

────── *Moral Questions Affecting Married Life,* address to Italian Catholic Union of Midwives, October 21, 1951 (Washington, D. C.: National Catholic Welfare Conference, n.d.).

────── *On Psychotherapy and Religion,* address to the Fifth International Congress on Psychotherapy and Clinical Psychology, April 13, 1953 (Washington, D. C.: National Catholic Welfare Conference, n.d.).

────── *The Moral Limits of Medical Research and Treatment,* discourse to the Fourth International Congress of the Histopathology of the Nervous System, Rome, September 29, 1949.

────── *Woman's Duties in Social and Political Life,* allocution to working mothers, Rome, October 21, 1945 (Washington, D. C.: National Catholic Welfare Conference, n.d.).

Treacy, Gerald C., S.J., *Love Undying,* simplified edition of the encyclical *Casti Connubii* (New York: The Paulist Press, 1944).

Vermeersch, A., S.J., *What is Marriage?* a catechism arranged according to the encyclical *Casti Connubii,* trans. T. Lincoln Bouscaren, S.J. (New York: The America Press, 1932).

Werth, Alvin, O.F.M.Cap., and Mihanovich, Clement S., *Papal Pronouncements on Marriage and the Family* (Milwaukee: The Bruce Publishing Company, 1955).

Physical Aspects

Assyrian Prescriptions for Diseases of the Urine, quoted by Henry E. Sigerist, M.D., *A History of Medicine,* Vol. 1 (London: Oxford University Press, 1951).

Best, Charles H., and Taylor, Norman B., *The Living Body,* rev. ed. (New York: Henry Holt and Co., 1944).

Calkins, H., O.S.M., "Rhythm, the Unhappy Compromise," *Integrity* (June, 1948).

Causey, Davis, *Uninvited Guests* (New York: Alfred A. Knopf, 1932).

Charny, C. W., M.D., "Treatment of Male Infertility with Large Doses of Testosterone," *The Journal of the American Medical Association,* Vol. 160, No. 2 (January 14, 1956).

Clendening, Logan, M.D., *The Human Body* (New York: Alfred A. Knopf, 1941).

Connell, Francis J., C.SS.R., "The Lawful Use of Rhythm," *The American Ecclesiastical Review,* Vol. 127 (August, 1952), pp. 136–141.

———— "The Use of Rhythm," *The American Ecclesiastical Review,* Vol. 126, No. 1 (January, 1952), pp. 64–67.

Davidson, Henry A., M.D., *Forensic Psychiatry* (New York: The Ronald Press Co., 1952).

DeLee, Joseph B., *The Principles and Practice of Obstetrics,* 2 ed. (Philadelphia: W. B. Saunders Co., 1915).

Diagnostic and Statistical Manual of Mental Disorders, American Psychiatric Association, Mental Hospital Service, 1952.

Dublin, Louis I., "Women Are Different," *The Reader's Digest,* Vol. 57 (December, 1950), pp. 58–60; *Your Life,* Vol. 27 (December, 1950), pp. 23–27, The Kingsway Press, Inc., New York, N. Y.

Dugdale, R. L., *The Jukes, A Study in Crime, Pauperism, Disease and Heredity, also Further Studies of Criminals* (New York: G. P. Putnam's Sons, 1877).

Gemelli, A., *Artificial Insemination* (Milan, Italy: Catholic University of the Sacred Heart, n.d.).

Gilbert, Margaret S., *Biography of the Unborn* (Baltimore: The Williams and Wilkins Co., 1938).

Goldzieher, Max A. and Joseph W., "The Male Climacteric and Post-climacteric State," *Geriatrics,* Vol. 8, No. 1 (January, 1953), pp. 1–11.

Good, Frederick L., and Kelly, Otis F., *Marriage, Morals and Medical Ethics* (New York: P. J. Kenedy & Sons, 1951).

Goodall, J. R., *Puerperal Infection,* quoted by R. L. Dickinson in *Control of Conception* (Baltimore: The Williams and Wilkins Co., 1938).

Greenblatt, R., "Trichomoniasis," *West. J. Surg. Obst. and Gynec.* (May, 1945).

Greenhill, J. P., *Office Gynecology* (Chicago: The Year Book Publishers, Inc., 1940).

Griese, Rev. Orville N., S.T.L., *The Morality of Periodic Continence* (Washington, D. C.: The Catholic University of America Press, 1942).

——— *The Rhythm in Marriage and Christian Morality* (Westminster, Md.: The Newman Press, 1946).

Guilford, J. P., *Fields of Psychology* (New York: D. Van Nostrand Co., Inc., 1950).

Hamblen, E. C., *Facts for Childless Couples* (Springfield, Ill.: Charles C. Thomas, 1950).

Harvey, B. C. H., M.D., *Simple Lessons in Human Anatomy* (Chicago: The American Medical Association, 1931).

Huhner, Max, *The Diagnosis and Treatment of Sexual Disorders in the Male and Female* (Philadelphia: F. A. Davis Co., 1937).

Jacobi, Mary P., *The Question of Rest for Women During Menstruation*, Harvard University (The Boylston Prize, 1876) (New York: G. P. Putnam's Sons, 1877).

Jenkinson, Bruce L., *Marriage and Divorce in the United States: 1937–1945* (Washington, D. C.: National Office of Vital Statistics, 1946).

Kaufman, S. A., "What is Normal Semen," *Human Fertility*, Vol. 2, no. 1 (March, 1946).

Kaump, Donald H., "The Rh Factor in Hemolytic Disease of the New Born," *The Linacre Quarterly*, Vol. 14 (1947), pp. 1–8.

Keenan, Alan, O.F.M., and Ryan, John, M.D., *Marriage, A Medical and Sacramental Study* (New York: Sheed and Ward, 1955).

Keettel, W. C., M.D., Bunge, R. G., M.D., Bradbury, J. T., Sc.D., Nelson, W. O., Ph.D., "Report of Pregnancies in Infertile Couples," *The Journal of the American Medical Association*, Vol. 160, No. 2 (January 14, 1946).

Kelly, Gerald, S.J., *Medico-Moral Problems*, Vol. 2 (St. Louis: The Catholic Hospital Association, 1950).

——— "Moral Aspects of Sterilizing Tests and Artificial Insemination," *The Linacre Quarterly*, Vol. 16, no. 1 (January–April, 1949), p. 31.

——— "Rhythm in Marriage: Duty and Idealism," *America*, Vol. 87 (May 3, 1952), pp. 128–131.

Knaus, Hermann, *Periodische Fruchtbarkeit und Unfruchtbarkeit Des Weibes, Der Weg Zur Naturlichen Geburtenregelung* (Wein: Wilhelm Maudrich, 1934).

Kopeloff, Nicholas, *Man Versus Microbes* (New York: Alfred A. Knopf, 1936).

Latz, Leo J., *The Rhythm* (Chicago: Latz Foundation, 1939).

Lord, Daniel A., S.J., *Speaking of Birth Control* (St. Louis: The Queen's Work, 1930).

McNally, H. B., M.D., and Fitzpatrick, Vincent de P., "Patients with Four or More Cesarean Sections," *The Journal of the American Medical Association,* Vol. 160, No. 12 (March 24, 1956).

Meaker, Samuel R., M.D., *Preparing for Motherhood* (Chicago: The Year Book Publishers, 1956).

Montagu, Ashley, F. M., *Adolescent Sterility* (Springfield, Ill.: Charles C. Thomas, 1946).

Moore, Edward, *The Case Against Birth Control* (New York: The Century Co., 1931).

Ochsner, Alton, *Smoking and Cancer* (New York: Julian Messner, Inc., 1954).

Ogino, Kyusaku, "Ovulationstermin und Konzeptionstermin," *Zentralblatt Für Gynakologie,* Vol. 54 (February 22, 1930), pp. 464–479.

Oliven, John F., M.D., *Sexual Hygiene and Pathology,* "A Manual for the Physician" (Philadelphia: J. B. Lippincott Co., 1955).

Planned Parenthood (New York: Planned Parenthood Federation of America, Inc., n.d.).

Ploss, Hermann Heinrich, *et al., Woman — An Historical Gynaecological and Anthropological Compendium* (London: William Heinemann Medical Books, Ltd., 1935).

Popenoe, Paul, *The Child's Heredity* (Baltimore: The Williams and Wilkins Co., 1929).

Rongy, A. J., "Birth Control," *The Universal Jewish Encyclopedia,* Vol. 2, 1940, pp. 380–381.

Rosenau, Milton J., *Preventive Medicine and Hygiene* (New York: D. Appleton and Co., 1927).

Rubinstein, B. B., "Emotional Factors in Female Sterility," *Am. Soc. for the Study of Sterility* (June 7, 1949).

Ruland, Ludwig, *Pastoral Medicine,* trans. T. Rattler (St. Louis: B. Herder Book Co., 1947).

Sanford, Alexander E., M.D., *Pastoral Medicine* (New York: Joseph F. Wagner, 1905).

Scheinfeld, Amram, *You and Heredity* (New York: Frederick A. Stokes Co., 1939).

Titus, Paul, and Willson, J. Robert, *Management of Obstetric Difficulties,* 5 ed. (St. Louis: C. V. Mosby Co., 1955).

Tyler, E. T., M.D., and Singher, H. O., Ph.D., "Male Infertility — Status of Treatment, Prevention, and Current Research," *The Journal of the American Medical Association,* Vol. 160, No. 2 (January 14, 1956).

U. S. Department of Health, Education and Welfare, National Office of Vital Statistics, *Vital Statistics of the United States: 1950* (Washington, D. C., 1954), Vol. 1, p. 73, fig. 5C.

Webster, Ralph W., M.D., *Legal Medicine and Toxicology* (Philadelphia: W. B. Saunders Co., 1930).

"Wedding Plans," U. S. Department of Health, Education and Welfare, Public Health Service Publication No. 431, Public Health Service Series, No. 86, 1950 Revision.

Williams, J. Whitridge, *Obstetrics* (New York: D. Appleton and Co., 1927).

Psychology and Psychiatry

Alexander, Leo, M.D., *Treatment of Mental Disorder* (Philadelphia: W. B. Saunders Co., 1953).

Anastasi, Anne, *Psychological Testing* (New York: The Macmillan Co., 1954).

Anastasi, Anne, and Foley, John P., Jr., *Differential Psychology* (New York: The Macmillan Co., 1949).

Brennan, Robert E., *General Psychology* (New York: The Macmillan Co., 1952).

Cavanagh, John R., M.D., and McGoldrick, James B., S.J., *Fundamental Psychiatry* (Milwaukee: The Bruce Publishing Co., 1953).

de Beauvoir, Simone, *The Second Sex* (New York: Alfred A. Knopf, 1953).

Dobbelstein, H., *Psychiatry for Priests,* trans. from the German (New York: P. J. Kenedy and Sons, 1953).

Dollard, J., and Miller, N., *Personality and Psychotherapy* (New York: McGraw-Hill Book Co., 1950).

Doob, Leonard W., *Social Psychology* (New York: Henry Holt and Co., 1952).

Hurlock, Elizabeth B., *Developmental Psychology* (New York: McGraw-Hill Book Co., 1953).

Jersild, Arthur T., *Child Psychology* (New York: Prentice-Hall, Inc., 1947).

Kanner, Leo, M.D., *Child Psychiatry* (Springfield, Ill.: Charles C. Thomas Press, 1948).

Kroger, William S., and Freed, S. Charles, *Psychosomatic Gynecology* (Philadelphia: W. B. Saunders Co., 1951).

McCarthy, Raphael C., S.J., *Safeguarding Mental Health* (Milwaukee: The Bruce Publishing Co., 1937).

McGovern, J. Leo., and Laverty, R. H. D., *Happiness in Marriage* (London: Sands and Co., 1940).

McKinney, Fred, *Psychology of Personal Adjustment* (New York: John Wiley and Sons, Inc., 1949).

Magner, Rev. James A., *Mental Health in a Mad World* (Milwaukee: The Bruce Publishing Co., 1953).

—— *Personality and Successful Living* (Milwaukee: The Bruce Publishing Co., 1944).

Moore, Thomas V., *The Driving Forces of Human Nature* (New York: Grune and Stratton, 1948).

Noyes, Arthur, P., M.D., *Modern Clinical Psychiatry* (Philadelphia: W. B. Saunders Co., 1939).

Overholser, Winfred, and Richmond, Winfred, *Handbook of Psychiatry* (Philadelphia: J. B. Lippincott Co., 1947).

Powers, Francis F.; McConnell, T. R.; Trow, William C.; Moore, Bruce V.; and Skinner, Charles E., *Psychology in Everyday Living* (Boston: D. C. Heath Co., 1938).

Rosanoff, A. J., *Manual of Psychiatry* (New York: John Wiley and Sons, 1927).

Ruch, Floyd L., *Psychology and Life* (New York: Scott, Foresman and Co., 1941).

Sapirstein, M. R., *Emotional Security* (New York: Crown Publishing Co., 1948).

Schaffer, Laurance F., *The Psychology of Adjustment* (Boston: Houghton Mifflin Co., 1936).

Sheed, Frank J., *Theology and Sanity* (New York: Sheed and Ward, 1948).

Stern, Karl, *The Third Revolution* (New York: Harcourt, Brace and Co., 1954).

Strecker, Edward, *Their Mothers' Sons* (Philadelphia: J. B. Lippincott Co., 1946).

Terman, L. M., *Psychological Factors in Marital Happiness* (New York: McGraw-Hill Book Co., Inc., 1938).

Thorpe, Louis P., *Personality and Life* (New York: Longmans, Green and Co., 1941).

VanderVeldt, Rev. James H., and Odenwald, Robert P., M.D., *Psychiatry and Catholicism* (New York: McGraw-Hill Book Co., Inc., 1952).

Woodworth, Robert S., and Marquis, Donald, *Psychology* (New York: Henry Holt and Co., 1947).

Sacramental and Liturgical Aspects

Athenagoras of Athens, *A Plea for Christians, 33* (Ante-Nicean Fathers, Vol. II, p. 146) (Buffalo: The Christian Literature Publishing Co., 1887).

Battifoll, Msgr. Pierre, *Primitive Catholicism,* trans. Henri L. Briancean (New York: Longmans, Green and Co., 1911).

Cabrol, Fernand, O.S.B., *Liturgical Prayer, Its History and Spirit* (London: Burns, Oates and Washbourne, Ltd., 1925).

Canons and Decrees of the Council of Trent (St. Louis: B. Herder Book Co., 1941).

Clement of Alexandria, *Stromata,* Book III (Ante-Nicean Fathers, Vol. II,

p. 393) (Buffalo: The Christian Literature Publishing Co., 1887).

Commentarius in Joannem, II, 3 (Migne, Series Graeca, Vol. 73, 223).

Commentarius in Matteum, t. 14, c. 16, *Patrologiae Cursus Completus,* Series Graeca, Vol. 13, 1229 (Parisiis: J. P. Migne, 1884).

Connell, Francis J., C.SS.R., *The Seven Sacraments* (New York: The Paulist Press, 1939).

Denzinger, H., and Bannwart, C., *Enchiridion Symbolorum* (St. Louis: B. Herder Book Co., 1932).

Doms, Herbert, *The Meaning of Marriage,* trans. George Sayer (New York: Sheed and Ward, 1939).

Gerrard, Thomas J., *Marriage and Parenthood, the Catholic Ideal* (New York: J. F. Wagner), revised by Edgar Schmiedler, 1937.

Husslein, Joseph, S.J., *Social Wellsprings,* II (Milwaukee: The Bruce Publishing Co., 1943).

Ignatius of Antioch, *Epistle to Polycarp 5,* trans. J. A. Kleist (Westminster, Md.: The Newman Book Shop, 1946).

Joyce, George H., S.J., *Christian Marriage* (London: Sheed and Ward, 1948).

Martindale, Cyril C., *Wedlock* (New York: Sheed and Ward, 1938).

Parente, Pietro, *Dictionary of Dogmatic Theology,* trans. E. Doronzo (Milwaukee: The Bruce Publishing Co., 1951).

Plus, Père Raoul, *Marriage* (London and Dublin: Burns, Oates and Washbourne, Ltd., 1945).

Pourrat, P., *Theology of the Sacraments* (St. Louis: B. Herder Book Co., 1910).

St. Augustine, *De Bono Conjugali* (Parisiis: J. P. Migne, 1884).

Schroeder, H. J., O.P., *Canons and Decrees of the Council of Trent,* original text with English translation (St. Louis: B. Herder Book Co., 1941).

Tanquerey, A., *Synopsis Theologiae Dogmaticae* (Parisiis: Desclée et Socii, 1935).

The Teachings of the Catholic Church, ed. George Smith (New York: The Macmillan Co., 1949).

Tertullian, *Ad Uxorem,* trans. William P. LeSaint, S.J. (Westminster, Md.: The Newman Press, 1951).

―――― *Treatises on Marriage and Remarriage,* trans. William P. LeSaint, S.J. (Westminster, Md.: The Newman Press, 1951).

Toth, Tihamer, *The Christian Family,* trans. V. G. Agotai (St. Louis: B. Herder Book Co., 1943).

Villien, A., *The History and Liturgy of the Sacraments* (New York: Benziger Bros., 1932).

White, Lynn, Jr., *Educating Our Daughters* (New York: Harper and Brothers, 1950).

Sex

Allers, Rudolph, "Sex and Morals," *Commonweal,* Vol. 53 (December, 1950), pp. 276–277.

Allers, Rudolph, and Raemers, Sidney, *Sex Psychology in Education* (St. Louis: B. Herder Book Co., 1937).

Boutin, Louis-Napoleon, O.M.I., *Penance: Most Human of the Sacraments* (Ottawa: University of Ottawa Press, 1954).

Cory, Donald W., *The Homosexual in America* (New York: Greenberg, 1951).

Darke, Roy, "Heredity as an Etiological Factor in Homosexuality," *J. of Nervous and Mental Disease,* Vol. 107, No. 3 (March, 1948), pp. 251–268.

"Depravity and Unbelief," from a legal correspondent, *The Tablet,* Vol. 202 (December 19, 1953), p. 606.

Encyclopedia of Aberrations, ed. Edward Podolsky, M.D. (New York: Philosophical Library, Inc., 1953).

Foerster, F. W., M.D., *Marriage and the Sex Problem* (Philadelphia: J. B. Lippincott Co., 1936).

Ford, Clelland S., and Beach, Frank A., *Patterns of Sexual Behaviour* (London: Eyre and Spottiswoode, 1952).

Geis, Rudolph, M.D., *Principles of Catholic Sex Morality* (New York: Joseph F. Wagner, 1930).

Glass, H. J., S.J., and Wright, C. A., "Sex Hormone Studies in Male Homosexuals," *Endocrinology,* Vol. 26 (1940), pp. 590–594.

Graf, Ernest, O.S.B., "A Survey of the Reviews," *Homiletic and Pastoral Review,* Vol. 39, No. 4 (January, 1939), pp. 400–404.

Hamilton, Gilbert V., *On the Cause of Homosexuality* (New York: G. Legman, 1950).

Harvey, John F., O.S.F.S., "Homosexuality as a Pastoral Problem," *Theological Studies* (March, 1955), pp. 86–108.

Higgins, Thomas J., S.J., *Man as Man* (Milwaukee: The Bruce Publishing Co., 1950).

Kelly, Gerald, S.J., *The Good Confessor* (New York: The Sentinel Press, 1951).

King, J. L., S.J., *Sex Enlightenment and the Catholic* (London: Burns, Oates and Washbourne, Ltd., 1947).

Kirkendall, Lester A., *Sex Adjustments of Young Men* (New York: Harper and Brothers, 1940).

Moore, Thomas V., O.S.B., "The Pathogenesis and Treatment of Homosexual Disorders," *J. of Personality,* Vol. 14, no. 1 (September, 1945), pp. 47–83.

Odenwald, Robert P., M.D., "Counseling the Homosexual," *Priest,* Vol. 9 (December, 1953), pp. 940–944.

—— "The Problem of Masturbation, I & II," *Priest,* Vol. II, nos. 1 and 2 (January and February, 1955).

Schofield, Michael G., *Society and the Homosexual* (London: Gollancz, 1952).

Vann, Gerald, O.P., "Moral Dilemmas," *Blackfriars,* Vol. 35 (January, 1954), pp. 6–7.

Sex Education

Blake, Florence G., R.N., *The Child, His Parents, and the Nurse* (Philadelphia: J. B. Lippincott Co., 1954).

Bradford, Elizabeth, *Let's Talk About Children* (New York: Prentice-Hall, Inc., 1947).

Breckenridge, Marian E., M.S., and Vincent, E. Lee, Ph.D., *Child Development* (Philadelphia: W. B. Saunders Co., 1943).

DeSchweinitz, Karl, *Growing Up* (New York: The Macmillan Co., 1935).

Fleege, Urban H., S.M., *Self-Revelation of the Adolescent Boy* (Milwaukee: The Bruce Publishing Co., 1945).

Gruenberg, Benjamin C., *How Can We Teach About Sex,* Public Affairs Pamphlet No. 122 (New York: Public Affairs Committee, Inc., 1946).

Hennrich, Kilian J., O.F.M.Cap., *Watchful Elders* (Milwaukee: The Bruce Publishing Co., 1947).

Hurlock, Elizabeth B., Ph.D., *Child Development* (New York: McGraw-Hill Book Co., Inc., 1950).

—— "Timetable for Sex Education," *Today's Health* (August, 1954), pp. 68–69.

Jean Patrice, Sister, *Your Family Circle* (Milwaukee: The Bruce Publishing Co., 1952).

Jenkins, G. D., Shacter, Helen, and Bauer, W. W., *These are Your Children* (Chicago: Scott, Foresman and Co., 1949).

Kempf, Rev. Joseph G., *Helping Youth to Grow* (Milwaukee: The Bruce Publishing Co., 1941).

Kieffer, F. J., S.M., *The Child and You* (Milwaukee: The Bruce Publishing Co., 1941).

Kirsch, Felix M., O.F.M.Cap., *In Defense of Chastity* (Huntington, Ind.: Our Sunday Visitor Press, 1938).

—— *Sex Education and Training in Chastity* (New York: Benziger Bros., 1930).

—— *Training in Chastity* (Huntington, Ind.: Our Sunday Visitor Press, 1947).

Knoebber, Sister Mary Mildred, O.S.B., *Self-Revelation of the Adolescent Girl* (Milwaukee: The Bruce Publishing Co., 1936).

Lerrigo, Marion O., and Southard, Helen, *Finding Yourself* (Chicago: American Medical Association, 1955).

——— *Learning About Love* (Chicago: American Medical Association, 1955).

——— *Parents Privilege* (Chicago: American Medical Association, 1955).

——— *A Story About You* (Chicago: American Medical Association, 1955).

Lord, Daniel A., S.J., *Some Notes for the Guidance of Parents* (St. Louis: The Queen's Work, 1944).

Moodie, W., *The Doctor and the Difficult Child* (New York: Commonwealth Fund, 1940).

Mudd, Emily H., "Sex Education for the Married Couple," *Hygeia,* Vol. 19 (August, 1941).

Neumeyer, Martin H., *Juvenile Delinquency in Modern Society* (New York: D. Van Nostrand Co., Inc., 1949).

Rice, Thurman B., M.D., *How Life Goes On and On* (Chicago: The American Medical Association, 1933).

Sattler, Henry V., *Parents, Children and the Facts of Life* (Paterson, N. J.: St. Anthony Guild Press, 1952).

Spock, Benjamin, M.D., *The Common Sense Book of Baby and Child Care* (New York: Duell, Sloan and Pearce, 1946).

U. S. Department of Labor, Children's Bureau, *Understanding Juvenile Delinquency* (Washington, D. C.: U. S. Government Printing Office, 1943).

When Children Ask About Sex (New York: Child Study Association of America, 1946).

Your Child from 6 to 12, Federal Security Agency, Social Security Administration, Children's Bureau, 1949.

Society and the Family

American Hierarchy, Statement, "The Christian Family," *The Catholic Mind,* Vol. 43 (February, 1950).

Baber, Ray E., *Marriage and the Family* (New York: McGraw-Hill Book Co., Inc., 1939).

Bebel, August, *Woman in the Past, Present and Future,* trans. (San Francisco: A. B. Benham, 1897).

Breen, W., "Neo-Malthusianism," *Irish Eccles. Review* (November, 1931), pp. 467–481.

Briffault, Robert, *The Mothers,* 3 vols. (New York: The Macmillan Co., 1927).

Burgess, Ernest W., "The Family in a Changing Society," *Amer. J. of Sociology,* Vol. 53 (May, 1948).

Burgess, Ernest W., and Locke, Harvey, *The Family from Institution to Companionship* (New York: American Book Co., 1945).

Calhoun, Arthur W., *A Social History of the American Family* (New York: Barnes and Noble, 1945).

Crawley, Ernest, *The Mystic Rose, a Study of Primitive Marriage,* 2 vols. (New York: Boni and Liveright, 1927).

Cuber, John F., and Harper, Robert A., *Problems of American Society: Values in Conflict* (New York: Henry Holt and Co., 1948).

Cuber, John F., and Kenkel, William F., *Social Stratification in the United States* (New York: Appleton-Century-Crofts, Inc., 1954).

Elliott, Mabel A., and Merrill, Francis E., *Social Disorganization* (New York: Harper and Brothers, 1941).

Elmer, Manuel C., *The Sociology of the Family* (Boston: Ginn and Co., 1945).

Godwin, William, *Thoughts on Man, His Nature, Productions and Discoveries Interspersed With Some Particulars Respecting the Author* (London: E. Wilson, 1831).

Groves, Ernest R., *Conserving Marriage and the Family* (New York: The Macmillan Co., 1945).

———— *The Family and Its Social Functions* (Chicago: J. B. Lippincott Co., 1940).

———— *Marriage* (New York: Henry Holt and Co., 1933).

Haas, Most Rev. Francis J., *Man and Society* (New York: Appleton-Century-Crofts, 1952).

Hall, Calvin, "The Instability of Post-War Marriages," *J. of Social Psychology,* Vol. 5 (November, 1934), pp. 523–530.

Higgins, Thomas J., S.J., *Man as Man* (Milwaukee: The Bruce Publishing Co., 1951).

Hughes, R. O., *Today's Problems* (Boston: Allyn and Bacon, 1951).

James, E. O., *Marriage and Society* (New York: Hutchinson's University Library, 1952).

Kane, John J., *Marriage and the Family, a Catholic Approach* (New York: Dryden Press, 1952).

———— *The Modern Family* (New York: William Sloane Associates, 1952).

Kidger, Horace, *Problems Facing American Democracy* (Boston: Ginn and Co., 1953).

Koos, E. L., *Families in Trouble* (New York: King's Crown Press, 1946).

Lange, F., *Degeneration in Families,* trans. C. C. Sonne (London: Kimpton, 1907).

Malthus, Thomas R., *An Essay on the Principles of Population or a View of its Past and Present Effects on Human Happiness, with an Inquiry into our Prospects Respecting the Future Removal or Mitigation of the Evils which it Occasions* (London: J. Murray, 1826).

Marriage and the Family, Howard Becker and Reuben Hill, eds. (Boston: D. C. Heath and Co., 1942).

Marriage and Family Relationships, A. H. Clemens, ed. (Washington, D. C.: Catholic University of America Press, 1950).

Mihanovich, Clement S., Schnepp, Gerald J., S.M., and Thomas, John L., S.J., *Marriage and the Family* (Milwaukee: The Bruce Publishing Co., 1952).

Modean, Erik W., "Augustana Left to 'Go It Alone,'" *The Christian Century,* Vol. 71, no. 27 (July 7, 1954), pp. 828–830.

Odegard, O., "Marriage and Mental Disease — A Study in Social Psychopathology," *J. of Mental Science,* Vol. 92 (1946), pp. 35–59.

Popenoe, Paul, *The Conservation of the Family* (Baltimore: The Williams and Wilkins Co., 1926).

———— "The First Ten Years of the American Institute of Family Relations," *Mental Hygiene,* Vol. 21 (1937), pp. 218–223.

Rienow, Robert, *American Problems Today* (Boston: D. C. Heath, 1953).

Ross, Eva J., *Basic Sociology* (Milwaukee: The Bruce Publishing Co., 1953).

Schmiedeler, Edgar, O.S.B., *The Family, a School of the Virtues* (Washington, D. C.: National Catholic Welfare Conference, 1949).

———— *An Introductory Study of the Family* (New York: D. Appleton-Century Co., Inc., 1947).

———— *The Industrial Revolution and the Home* (Washington, D. C.: The Catholic University of America Press, 1927).

Westermarck, Edward A., *The History of Human Marriage,* 3 vols. (New York: Allerton Book Co., 1922).

Zimmerman, Carle C., *Family and Civilization* (New York: Harper and Brothers, 1947).

Miscellaneous

Barron, Milton L., *People Who Intermarry* (Syracuse, N. Y.: Syracuse University Press, 1946).

Bishop's Committee on Mixed Marriages, *A Factual Study of Mixed Marriages* (Washington, D. C.: National Catholic Welfare Conference, 1943).

Bonzelet, Honoratus, O.F.M., *Mixed Marriages and Prenuptial Instructions* (Milwaukee: The Bruce Publishing Co., 1942).

Chesterton, Gilbert K., *The Superstition of Divorce* (London: Chatto and Windus, 1920).

Connell, Francis J., C.SS.R., "Problem of Mixed Marriage," *Ecclesiastical Review,* Vol. 115 (November, 1946), p. 386.

Doherty, Joseph F., *Moral Problems of Interracial Marriage* (Washington, D. C.: Catholic University of America Press, 1949).

DuBois, W. E., *The Negro American Family* (Atlanta, Ga.: The Atlanta University Press, 1908).

Ellard, Gerald, S.J., *Christian Life and Worship,* rev. ed. (Milwaukee: The Bruce Publishing Co., 1956).

Frazier, E. Franklin, *The Negro Family in Chicago* (Chicago: The University of Chicago Press, 1932).

Glogger, Placidus, O.S.B., *The Beauties of Motherhood* (New York: P. J. Kenedy and Sons, 1932).

Joyce, G. H., S.J., *Christian Marriage* (London: Sheed and Ward, 1933).

Lerner, Arthur, *A Catholic Commentary on Holy Scripture* (London: Thomas Nelson and Sons, 1953).

Miller, Ernest F., C.SS.R., "Mixed Company-Keeping," *The Homiletic and Pastoral Review,* Vol. 41 (August, 1941), pp. 1073–1079.

Scupoli, Laurence, *The Spiritual Combat* (New York: Catholic Book Publishing Co., 1948).

Tanquerey, Adolphe, *The Spiritual Life,* trans. Herman Brandeis, S.S. (Westminster, Md.: The Newman Press, 1930).

Thomas, J., *The American Catholic Family* (New York: Prentice-Hall, Inc., 1956).

Wertham, Frederic, M.D., *The Seduction of the Innocent* (New York: Rinehart and Co., Inc., 1954).

CATHOLIC PAMPHLET LITERATURE ON SEX AND MARRIAGE

*This list is not complete, but we believe that it contains a sufficient number of titles to adequately cover the field. Those pamphlets marked ** are recommended wholeheartedly. Those marked * are recommended with some reservation, either because they inadequately cover the subject or because of some other defect. We have omitted those pamphlets which we read which seemed inadequate.*

Birth Control

* Cox, Ignatius W., S.J., *American Medicine, American Morals and Birth Control* (New York: Paulist Press).

* Dolan, Albert H., O.Carm., *All the Answers About Marriage and Birth Control* (Chicago: Carmelite Press).

** Donovan, Joseph P., C.M., *Horse and Mule Marriages vs. Sacramental Achievement* (New York: Paulist Press).

** Lord, Daniel A., S.J., *A Mother Looks at Birth Control* (St. Louis: The Queen's Work).

** —— *Speaking of Birth Control* (St. Louis: The Queen's Work).

** —— *What of Lawful Birth Control?* (St. Louis: The Queen's Work).

* Mercier, Cardinal, *The Duties of Married Life* (London: International Catholic Truth Society).

* Mihanovich, Clement S., *Whither Birth Control?* (St. Louis: The Queen's Work).

** Miller, D. F., *What's Your Reason for Birth Control?* (Liguori, Mo.: Liguorian Pamphlet Office).

* Pruemmer, Dominic, O.P., *Birth Control* (New York: Paulist Press).

** Rumble and Carty, Revs., *Birth Prevention Quizzes* (St. Paul: Radio Replies Press).

Courtship and Marriage

** Connell, Rev. Francis J., *Christian Marriage* (Washington, D. C.: National Council of Catholic Men, 1955).

** Gartland, Frank E., C.S.C., *Boy Meets Girl the Christian Way* (Huntington, Ind.: Our Sunday Visitor Press).

** Hall, Winfield Scott, M.D., *Steering the Girl to a Happy Marriage* (Huntington, Ind.: Our Sunday Visitor Press).

* Knights of Columbus, *The Real Secret of Successful Marriage* (St. Louis: Religious Information Bureau).

** Lord, Daniel A., S.J., *I Was Going Steady* (St. Louis: The Queen's Work).

** —— *Love Is Like That* (St. Louis: The Queen's Work).

** —— *Love's All That Matters* (St. Louis: The Queen's Work).

** —— *M — Is For Marriage* (St. Louis: The Queen's Work).

** —— *Planning Your Happy Marriage* (St. Louis: The Queen's Work).

** —— *Questions I'm Asked About Marriage* (St. Louis: The Queen's Work).

** —— *The Girl Worth Choosing* (St. Louis: The Queen's Work).

** —— *The Man of Your Choice* (St. Louis: The Queen's Work).

** —— *What To Do On a Date* (St. Louis: The Queen's Work).

** Lovasik, Lawrence G., S.V.D., *Clean Love in Courtship* (St. Paul: Radio Replies Press).

** McCarthy, Rev. John M., *Charity Begins At Home* (Huntington, Ind.: Our Sunday Visitor Press).

** McCarthy, Raphael C., S.J., *Grow Up and Marry* (St. Louis: The Queen's Work).

* Mann, Fred, C.SS.R., *The Spirit of Marriage* (Huntington, Ind.: Our Sunday Visitor Press).

** A Medical Woman, A Girl, and A Wife, *Into Their Company* (New York: P. J. Kenedy and Sons).

** O'Brien, Rev. John A., *Achieving Happiness in Marriage* (Notre Dame, Ind.: Ave Maria Press).

** ———— *Choosing a Partner for Marriage* (Notre Dame, Ind.: Ave Maria Press).

** ———— *Preparing for Marriage* (Notre Dame, Ind.: Ave Maria Press).

** ———— *So You'd Like to Get Married* (Huntington, Ind.: Our Sunday Visitor Press).

** ———— *The Way of Love* (New York: Paulist Press).

** ———— *Whom Shall I Marry?* (New York: Paulist Press).

** Poage, Godfrey, C.P., *What You Ought to Know Before Marriage* (St. Louis: The Queen's Work).

** ———— *When the Honeymoon's Over* (St. Louis: The Queen's Work).

** Rumble and Carty, Revs., *Six Pre-Marriage Instructions for Catholics and Non-Catholics* (St. Paul: Radio Replies Press).

** Semmler, Nerius, O.F.M.Cap., *For Bride and Groom* (Huntington, Ind.: Our Sunday Visitor Press).

Divorce

* Handly, John, C.S.P., *Dorothy's Divorce* (New York: Paulist Press).

** Lord, Daniel A., S.J., *About Divorce* (St. Louis: The Queen's Work).

** ———— *Divorce — A Picture from the Headlines* (St. Louis: The Queen's Work).

** ———— *Forever and Forever* (St. Louis: The Queen's Work).

* Lydon, Rev. P. J., D.D., *Catholic Teaching on Marriage and Divorce* (New York: Catholic Information Society).

** O'Brien, Rev. John A., *Love For Keeps* (Huntington, Ind.: Our Sunday Visitor Press).

** ———— *Making Marriage Stick* (Notre Dame, Ind.: Ave Maria Press).

** Scott, Rev. Martin J., *Divorce A Disease Which Destroys Marriage* (New York: America Press).

Family Life

* * Arnold, Oren, *Love Enough to Go Around* (Notre Dame, Ind.: Ave Maria Press).

* Barry, Rev. David, P.P., *Happiness in the Home* (Dublin: Irish Messenger Office).

** Corley, Francis J., S.J., *Family Allowances* (St. Louis: Institute of Social Order).

** Dunn, Margaret Mary, *Mothers Are Important People* (New York: Catholic Information Society).

** Filas, Francis L., S.J., *The Family for Families* (Chicago: J. S. Paluch Co.).

* Hurley, Wilfred G., C.S.P., *Home and Happiness* (New York: Paulist Press).

** Lord, Daniel A., S.J., *In-Laws Aren't Funny* (St. Louis: The Queen's Work).

** —————— *In Praise of Father* (St. Louis: The Queen's Work).

** —————— *Parenthood* (St. Louis: The Queen's Work).

* —————— *Questions People Ask About Their Children With Answers* (St. Louis: The Queen's Work).

* Lynch, Ella Frances, *The Renegade Home* (New York: Paulist Press).

** Lyons, J. Roger, S.J., *Our Place in the Christian Family* (St. Louis: The Queen's Work).

** McCormack, Owen F., O.F.M., *The Catholic Family* (Paterson, N. J.: St. Anthony's Guild).

** Miller, D. F., *How to Be a Good Father* (Liguori, Mo.: Liguorian Pamphlet Office).

** —————— *How to Be a Good Husband* (Liguori, Mo.: Liguorian Pamphlet Office).

** —————— *How to Be a Good Wife* (Liguori, Mo.: Liguorian Pamphlet Office).

** Murphy, Eugene P., *The Catholic Mother — Her Glory* (Huntington, Ind.: Our Sunday Visitor Press).

* National Council of Catholic Men, *The Christian in Action in the Home* (Huntington, Ind.: Our Sunday Visitor Press).

** O'Brien, Rev. John A., *God in the Home* (New York: Paulist Press).

** —————— *The Christian Home* (Paterson, N. J.: St. Anthony's Guild).

* —————— *The Christian Mother* (Huntington, Ind.: Our Sunday Visitor Press).

** Schmiedeler, Edgar, O.S.B., *Concerning Parents* (Paterson, N. J.: St. Anthony's Guild Press).

** —————— *Concerning Your Children* (Paterson, N. J.: St. Anthony's Guild Press).

* Sherman, James E., S.T.D., *Litany for Catholic Parents* (New York: Paulist Press).

** Wolfe, Msgr. J. M., *Juvenile Delinquency* (Huntington, Ind.: Our Sunday Visitor Press).

Marriage as a Contract and a Sacrament

** Anonymous, *Marriage Legislation of the Catholic Church* (Paterson, N. J.: St. Anthony's Guild Press).

* Anonymous, *United In Christ* (Clyde, Mo.: Benedictine Convent of Perpetual Adoration).

* Berger, Valerian, O.S.B., *The Eve of Marriage* (New York: Paulist Press).

** Coakley, Rev. Thomas F., *How Catholics Get Married* (Brooklyn, N. Y.: International Catholic Truth Society).

** Connell, Rev. Francis J., *Marriage — Human or Divine?* (New York: Paulist Press).

** Fides Album, *Marriage* (Chicago: Fides Publishers Association).

* Griffin, John, *The Dignity of Christian Marriage* (Boston: John Griffin).

* Hallett, Msgr. P. E., *Nullity of Marriage* (London: Catholic Truth Society).

* Hurley, Wilfred G., C.S.P., *Marriage Is a Sacrament* (New York: Paulist Press).

** Lord, Daniel A., S.J., *They're Married!* (St. Louis: The Queen's Work).

** ———— *Your Partner in Marriage* (St. Louis: The Queen's Work).

** Lovasik, Lawrence G., S.V.D., *Making Marriage Click* (St. Paul: Radio Replies Press).

* Lover, James F., C.SS.R., *Is Your Marriage on the Rocks?* (New York: Paulist Press).

* McCown, James H., S.J., *Man, Woman and God* (St. Louis: The Queen's Work).

* Miller, D. F., *Can the Catholic Church Annul Any Marriages?* (Liguori, Mo.: Liguorian Pamphlet Office).

** Murphy, Msgr. James H., *Matrimony* (Paterson, N. J.: St. Anthony's Guild Press).

* O'Brien, Rev. John A., *The Church and Marriage* (New York: Paulist Press).

** Pope Leo XIII, *Christian Marriage* (New York: Paulist Press).

** Power, Rev. Richard E., *Marriage in Christ* (Collegeville, Minn.: Liturgical Press).

* Ross, Rev. J. Elliot, *Whom God Hath Joined* (New York: Paulist Press).

** Rumble and Carty, Revs., *Marriage Quizzes to a Street Preacher* (St. Paul: Radio Replies Press).

** Scott, Martin J., S.J., *Marriage Problems* (New York: Paulist Press).

** Vermeersch, A., S.J., and Bouscaren, T. Lincoln, S.J., *What Is Marriage?* (New York: The America Press).

Mixed Marriage

** Bampfield, Rev. G., *Mixed Marriages* (Brooklyn, N. Y.: International Catholic Truth Society).

* Lord, Daniel A., S.J., *Don't Marry a Catholic* (St. Louis: The Queen's Work).

* —— *Marry Your Own* (St. Louis: The Queen's Work).

** Magner, Rev. James A., *Shall I Marry a Non-Catholic?* (Huntington, Ind.: Our Sunday Visitor Press).

**Noll, Most Rev. J. F., D.D., *Seven Instructions Before Marriage* (Huntington, Ind.: Our Sunday Visitor Press).

** O'Brien, Rev. John A., *Catholic Marriage: How Achieve It?* (Huntington, Ind.: Our Sunday Visitor Press).

** —— *Marriage: Catholic or Mixed?* (Huntington, Ind.: Our Sunday Visitor Press).

* —— *The Ideal Marriage — How Achieve It?* (New York: Paulist Press).

** —— *Why Not a "Mixed" Marriage?* (New York: Paulist Press).

** Schlarman, Most Rev. Joseph, *Why Six Instructions?* (St. Louis: B. Herder Book Co.).

Morality

** Cox, Ignatius W., S.J., *Is Sexual Abstinence Harmful?* (New York: Paulist Press).

* —— *The Divine Romance of Marriage* (New York: Paulist Press).

** Ginder, Rev. Richard, S.T.L., *Getting Married?* (Huntington, Ind.: Our Sunday Visitor Press).

** Griffin, Rev. Leo F., *The Catholic Girl Examines Her Conscience* (Huntington, Ind.: Our Sunday Visitor Press).

** Haungs, Edwin C., S.J., *An Examination of Conscience for Married Couples* (St. Louis: The Queen's Work).

* Jarrett, Bede, O.P., *Purity* (London: Catholic Truth Society).

* Juergens, Sylvester, S.M., *Fundamental Talks on Purity* (Milwaukee: The Bruce Publishing Co.).

** Kelly, Gerald, S.J., *Modern Youth and Chastity* (St. Louis: The Queen's Work).

** Kirsch, Felix M., O.F.M.Cap., *Training in Chastity* (Huntington, Ind.: Our Sunday Visitor Press).

* Lord, Daniel A., S.J., *Why Be Decent?* (St. Louis: The Queen's Work).

* Mahoney, Rev. E. J., *Training in Purity* (London: Catholic Truth Society).

** O'Brien, Rev. James J., *Sex, Alcohol and Young Folks* (New York: Paulist Press).

* A Redemptorist Father, *Aids to Purity* (Huntington, Ind.: Our Sunday Visitor Press).

** Schmiedeler, Edgar, O.S.B., *They're Growing Up* (Huntington, Ind.: Our Sunday Visitor Press).

** Southard, R. E., S.J., *Problems of Decency* (St. Louis: The Queen's Work).

* Tanner, Rev. Paul, *Youth and Chastity* (Huntington, Ind.: Our Sunday Visitor Press).

Sex Instruction

** Barclay Street Institute of Catholic Action, *The Toddler and Sex* (New York: Paulist Press).

** A Catholic Woman Doctor, *Growing Up — A Book For Girls* (New York: Benziger Bros.).

* Edwards, Paul, *Sex and the Teenage* (New York: Paulist Press).

** Hall, Winfield, M.D., *Steering the Boy to a Happy Marriage* (Huntington, Ind.: Our Sunday Visitor Press).

* Kirsch, Felix M., O.F.M.Cap., *The Sex Problem* (New York: Paulist Press).

** Rumble, Rev. Dr. L., *What Parents Should Tell Their Little Ones on Sex* (St. Paul: Radio Replies Press).

Miscellaneous

* Cox, Ignatius W., S.J., *The Folly of Human Sterilization* (New York: Paulist Press).

* Croarkin, Rev. Walter E., *This Thing Called Love* (Techny, Ill.: Society of the Divine Word, The Mission Press).

** Dowling, Edward, S.J., *Cana Catechism* (St. Louis: The Queen's Work).

** Lord, Daniel A., S.J., *Do You Love Your Children?* (St. Louis: The Queen's Work).

** ———— *So We Abolished the Chaperone* (St. Louis: The Queen's Work).

** ———— *Spinsters Are Wonderful People* (St. Louis: The Queen's Work).

** O'Brien, Rev. John A., *How Love Helps You* (Huntington, Ind.: Our Sunday Visitor Press).

** ———— *Is the Church Woman's Enemy?* (Huntington, Ind.: Our Sunday Visitor Press).

** ———— *Love's Ministry* (St. Louis: The Queen's Work).

Glossary

No attempt has been made to include all terms in the glossary. If a word is not found here, reference should be made to the Index.

Abortion. Interruption of pregnancy before twenty-eighth week. It may be spontaneous or induced.

Abrasion. Superficial loss of tissue.

Adolescent. Growing or advancing from childhood to maturity.

Adultery. Sexual relationship in which at least one partner is married to someone else.

Afferent Impulses. Nervous impulses directed from the periphery to the central nervous system.

Affinity. Relationship by marriage.

Afterbirth. The placenta and membranes with which the fetus is connected, and which are expelled after delivery of the fetus.

Alienage. The status of an alien; the state of being alienated or transferred to another.

Amenorrhea. Failure of a menstrual period to occur.

Anaphrodisiac. A substance which decreases sexual desire.

Anatomy. The art or science which deals with the structure of animals and humans.

Anterior Hypophysis. Anterior lobe of pituitary gland.

Antibody. Any of various bodies or substances in the tissues or fluids, as blood or serum of an organism, which act in antagonism to specific foreign bodies, as toxins, or the bacteria producing the toxins.

Aphrodisiac. A sexually stimulating substance.

Artificial Onanism. Masturbation.

Autoerotism. Self-sexual stimulation.

Azoospermia. Absence of spermatozoa from the semen.

Bartholin's Glands. Glands near the vaginal orifice which supply lubricant for the sex act.

Bimanual Examination. A pelvic examination in the female in which one hand examines through the abdominal wall and the other is in the vagina or rectum.

Biopsy. Removal of a small section of living tissue for microscopic examination.

Bisexuality. A condition of being erotically stimulated by both sexes.

Carcinoma. A malignant growth of epithelial cells.

Castrate. The act of removing both testicles or ovaries. In psychoanalytical terminology, refers to the removal of the penis.

Caul. The amniotic membrane; in the past a child born with unruptured membranes was considered to have special powers.

Cauterization. The removal of diseased tissue by burning — usually by an electric cautery.

Celibate. Unmarried. An individual who has given up sexual contacts.

Cervical Spoon. A plastic spoon inserted into the vagina to assist spermigration or to collect a specimen of sperm for examination.

Cervix. The lower portion of the uterus which is projected into the vagina and through which the cavity of the uterus communicates with the vagina.

Chancre. Characteristic initial lesion of syphilis which usually occurs at the site of contact.

Chromosome. One of the small bodies, ordinarily definite in number, in the cells of a given species, into which the chromatin of a cell nucleus resolves itself previous to the mitotic division of the cell.

Circumcision. The removal of the prepuce (foreskin) of the penis by surgical means.

Climacteric. The period of life during which the involutional endocrine changes take place.

Climax. The peak of sexual excitement associated with the ejaculation in the male and the orgasm in the female.

Coitus. Sexual relations; sexual intercourse.

Coitus Interruptus. Sexual intercourse in which the penis is withdrawn from the vagina before ejaculation; natural onanism.

Coitus Reservatus. Prolonged intromission without ejaculation. This may or may not be associated with orgasm in the female.

Communicable Disease. A disease transmittable from one person to another by any means.

Conception. The union of the spermatozoon and ovum to form a new life.

Concupiscence. Ardent desire, hence sexual lust; any longing of the soul for what will give it delight.

Congenital Syphilis. Syphilis transmitted through the placenta to the child from the mother.

Consanguinity. Related by blood.

Copulation. Sexual union; sexual intercourse.

Corpus Hemorrhagicum. The cavity left after rupture of the Graafian follicle fills with blood. This later becomes the corpus luteum.

Corpus Luteum. If pregnancy occurs, the corpus hemorrhagicum gradually turns yellow in color and becomes an important source of hormones.

Cowper's Glands. Two small glands discharging into the male urethra named for William Cowper, the English surgeon who discovered them.

Cryptorchidism. Undescended testicles.

Cunnilinctus. A form of sexual relations in which the male applies his mouth to the genital region of the female.

Cutaneous. Applying to the skin.

Cyst. A pouch or sac without an opening containing fluid or semifluid morbid material. It is an abnormal development.

Divorce. *A menso et thoro:* a separation from bed and board; separate maintenance.

Dorsal. Referring to the back; posterior.

Douche. A stream of water, usually medicated, used to clean a body cavity; usually when not modified means a vaginal douche.

Dowry. The money, goods, or estate which a woman brings to her husband in marriage.

Dysmenorrhea. Painful or difficult menstrual periods.

Dyspareunia. Painful or difficult sexual intercourse.

Eastern Church. Any body of Christians following an Eastern rite as distinguished from the Roman rite.

Ectopic. Outside of its usual place, usually, when not modified, refers to a pregnancy outside the cavity of the uterus.

Efferent Impulses. Nervous impulses going outward to the periphery.

Egocentric. Self-centered.

Ejaculation. The climax of the sex act in the male during which the semen is ejected in spurts through the urethra.

Embryo. The developing fetus, especially during the early months when it is not fully formed.

Emission. See **Ejaculation.**

Emotion. The physical expression of an inner feeling.

Empathy. Projection of one's own personality into the personality of another in order to understand him better.

Encyclical. A formal statement of the Pope on a matter of interest and importance to the whole Church.

Endometrium. The lining of the uterine cavity.

Erectile Tissues. A spongy form of tissue found in erectile tissues. When the interstices of this tissue fill with blood it enlarges and hardens, e.g., the penis during erection.

Erection. The hardening of the penis caused by filling with blood resulting from sexual stimulation.

Erogenous. Productive of sexual desire.

Erotic. Sexually stimulating.

Estrogen. Ovarian hormone.

Estrus (Heat). Period of fertility in higher animals.

Etiology. The science of studying the causes of disease.

Exhibitionism. A sexual perversion in which the individual derives sexual satisfaction from exhibiting parts of the body usually covered, usually the sex organs in the male.

Fellatio. Sexual act in which the penis is inserted into the mouth.

Fetishism. A sexual deviation in which satisfaction is obtained by the sight of some part of the person or clothing of the sexual object.

Fetus. The unborn child.

Fornication. Sexual relations between two unmarried persons.

Gene. An entity concerned with the transmission and development or determination of hereditary characters; a small part of a chromosome.

Genital Corpuscle. Type of nerve endings found in the glans penis and clitoris.

Genotype. A type determined by the genetic characters common to a group.

Germ Cell. A cell which is capable of contributing to a new life. The sperm cell in the male and the ovum in the female are germ cells.

Gestation. The period of development of the fetus *in utero;* in the human, this period of gestation is nine months.

Gonadotrophin. Pituitary hormone which reacts on Graafian follicle to cause ovulation.

Gonads. The testicles or ovaries.

Gumma. Characteristic lesion of tertiary or late syphilis; a granulomatous lesion which may occur in any system of the body.

Gynecologist. A doctor of medicine who specializes in the treatment of diseases peculiar to women.

Hemophilia. A blood disease characterized by abnormal bleeding tendencies transmitted through the female but affecting only the male.

Hereditary. Transmitted from one generation to the next through the genes.

Hermaphroditism. A condition in which the organs of both sexes are present in the same individual.

Heterosexual. Referring to an individual whose sexual interest is in members of the opposite sex.

Heterozygous Chromosome. A chromosome possessing genes for both members of at least one pair of allelomorphic Mendelian characters.

Homologous Chromosome. A chromosome corresponding in type or structure.

Homozygous Chromosome. A chromosome possessing genes for only one member of at least one pair of allelomorphic Mendelian characters.

Hormone. A chemical substance found in an endocrine gland which is liberated directly into the blood stream and affects distant organs or tissues.

Hostility. State of being hostile, hating, ill will, antagonistic, angry.

Huhner Test. Post-coital examination of spermatozoa removed from vagina.

Hydatidiform Mole. A tumor composed of numerous small cysts.

Hymen. A membrane surrounding the vaginal orifice and partially closing it in the virgin.

Hysterectomy. An operation for removal of the uterus.

Illicit Marriage. Mixed marriage without proper dispensation.

Impediment. A condition or circumstance which, under natural, or divine, or Church Law, renders a marriage unlawful or invalid.

Impotentia Coeundi. Inability to perform the sex act.

Impotentia Erigendi. Impotence due to failure to get an erection.

Impotentia Generandi. Sterility.

Impregnation. The act of fertilization.

Infancy (Legal). A state of being a minor; at common law, any person under the age of 21.

Inguinale Region. The groin.

Insemination. The act of depositing semen into the vagina.

Instinct. Inborn tendencies to act.

Introitus. The vaginal orifice.

Intromission. The act of inserting the penis into the vagina.

Invalid Marriage. There is no marriage because it failed in some respect to meet all the requirements of a true marriage.

Involutional Melancholia. An agitated depression usually, but not always, occurring during the involutional period.

Irradiation. The act of applying radium or X rays to tissue.

Labor. The process of expelling the fetus from the uterus to the external world.

Lactation. The process of secretion of milk in the breast; usually post-natal.

Leydig Cells. Cells in testicles which produce testosterone.

Libido. Unnatural sexual desire. In psychoanalysis, the psychic energy associated with the instincts.

Ligation. The act of tying, e.g., the tying of a blood vessel to prevent bleeding.

Liturgy. The sum of all the religious actions by which man from his first days has surrounded his essential relationships.

Lust. Sexual desire.

Maidenhead. Hymen.

Masturbation. Self-abuse; the act of self-sexual stimulation to ejaculation.

Meatus. An opening, e.g., the urinary meatus is the opening of the urethra to the outside.

Mendelian Law.   Discovered by Gregor J. Mendel (Austrian Augustinian abbot, 1822–1884). He showed that the height, color, and other characters depend on the presence of determining factors (genes) which behave as units.

Menopause.   Cessation of the menses in the female.

Metastatic Effect.   An effect which takes place at some distance from the cause from which it results.

Miscarriage.   Premature delivery of the fetus before it is viable.

Miscegenation.   Marriage between persons of different races.

Mitosis.   Cell division in which division of chromosomes takes place before separation of the cells.

Mixed Marriage.   Marriage between two persons of different religions.

Mucous Membrane.   The surface lining of internal organs.

Mucous Patches.   Characteristic lesions of secondary syphilis consisting of slightly raised patches on the mucous membranes, usually seen in the mouth.

Mutation.   A chemical change which alters the gene in such a way that it causes the expression of other characteristics.

Naegele Rule.   A rule to determine the estimated date of confinement, i.e., add nine days to the first day of the last menstrual period which took place and count back three months.

Narcissistic.   Erotic feeling aroused by one's own body and personality; self-centered.

Natural Childbirth.   Childbirth without anesthesia or analgesic.

Natural Law.   That part of the divine law which is not directly revealed but which is discernible by reason.

Natural Onanism.   Coitus interruptus.

Nature, Law of.   The uniformity which exists in nature in the production of phenomena.

Necrophilia.   Sexual stimulation from contact with the dead.

Neoplasm.   A new growth; it may be either malignant or benign.

Nidation.   Nesting; the process by which the fertilized ovum is buried in the endometrium of the uterus.

Nocturnal Emission.   A spontaneous ejaculation, usually associated with a sex dream, occurring during sleep.

Nymphomania.   A morbid, insatiable impulse to heterosexuality in women.

Onanism.   Coitus interruptus.

Orchidectomy.   Removal of the testicles.

Orgasm.   The peak of sexual excitement characterized by ejaculation in the male and pleasurable muscle contractions in the female.

Ovum.   The egg; the female contribution to new life.

Paresis. Weakness, usually in the sense of limitation of motion. **General Paresis:** syphilis of the central nervous system involving the parenchymatous structure of the brain.

Parturition. The process of giving birth; labor.

Passion. A violent emotion; in scholastic philosophy, a synonym for emotion.

Pederasty. Sodomy with a male child.

Pelvic Examination. A manual examination of the female pelvic organs.

Pernicious Vomiting of Pregnancy (Hyperemesis Gravidarum). Severe vomiting of undetermined origin occurring early in pregnancy.

Personality. The aggregate of the physical and mental qualities which enable the individual to respond in characteristic fashion to different situations and distinguish him from others and give him his own peculiar individuality.

Perversion. A maladjustment of the sexual life, such that satisfaction is sought in deviant ways, e.g., sadism, exhibitionism, homosexuality, etc. The deviation is not sought as a sexual stimulant, but as an end in itself.

Pessary. An implement inserted into the vagina to support the uterus.

Phallus. The penis.

Phantasy (Fantasy). Daydreaming.

Phenotype. A type determined by the visible characters common to a group as distinguished from their hereditary characters.

Placenta. See **Afterbirth.**

Polyandrous. Refers to marriage in which one woman has many husbands.

Polygamous. Refers to marriage of one man to many wives.

Precocious Pregnancy. Pregnancy occurring before the usual age.

Premature Ejaculation. Ejaculation before or simultaneous with intromission.

Prepuce. The skin covering the glans penis.

Priapism. Persistent, sustained erection of the penis.

Progesterone. Hormone from the corpus luteum.

Prognosis. Forecast or estimation of the course, outcome, and duration of an illness.

Prostatectomy. Surgical removal of the prostate gland.

Prostatic Smear. A thin preparation for microscopic examination after the manual expression of the secretion from the prostate gland.

Psychogenic. Produced by the mind and its mechanisms, but not due to an organic condition or anatomical injury.

Psychopathic Personality. Individuals with deficient personalities due to defective character organization with lack of insight.

Psychosomatic. The process by which a mental conflict gains outlet through somatic agencies.

Puberty. Sexual maturity characterized by the onset of the menses in the female and by ability to fertilize in the male.

Purulent Discharge. Discharge of pus from a wound or organ.

Pustule. A small cutaneous lesion containing pus.

Rapport. Confidence of the subject in the therapist with willingness to co-operate.

Rational Will. That spiritual or supraorganic rational appetitive power which tends to possess an object intellectually presented to it as good or desirable. The rational will is free to choose or not to choose.

Reagin. An antibody or substance acting like an antibody in the complement-fixation reaction and similar reactions.

Repression. The unconscious process whereby a conflict is removed from consciousness.

Resistance. A psychoanalytic term meaning the instinctive opposition displayed toward any attempt to lay bare the unconscious (a manifestation of the repressing forces).

Revelation. Act of revealing or communicating divine truth; disclosure or manifestation of Himself or of His will by God to man.

Rhythm, The. A term usually employed to denote a method of birth prevention based on the periodicity of ovulation.

Rubin Test. Injection of air into the Fallopian tubes; a test for sterility in the female.

Sacrament. "An outward sign instituted by Christ to give grace."

Salpingectomy. A surgical procedure for removal of the Fallopian tubes.

Sanctifying Grace. "That grace which confers on our souls a new life, that is, a sharing in the life of God Himself."

Satyriasis. Pathological excessive heterosexuality in the male.

Secret. A fact, matter, or purpose kept from the knowledge of others, or disclosed confidentially to but one or a few; what is not, or is not to be, revealed.

Semen. The viscid, whitish fluid produced in the male reproductive organs, which contains the spermatozoa.

Seminal Pool. Collection of semen in the vault of the vagina after ejaculation.

Serology. The study of the blood serum, usually used in reference to the diagnosis of syphilis.

Sexual Anhedonia (Anesthesia, Anaphrodism). Frigidity.

Smegma. A secretion which forms under the prepuce.

Sodomy. Sexual intercourse through the anus.

Somatic Cell. A cell contributing to a bodily organ as distinguished from a germ cell.

Spermatogenesis. The process of development of the spermatozoa.

Spermigration. The movement of the spermatozoa from the vagina to the Fallopian tube.

Spirocheta Pallida. The organism causing syphilis.

Spontaneous Orgasm. Sexual reaction occurring without physical stimulation.

"Spotting." Small amounts of bleeding between menstrual periods.

Sterility. Inability to conceive.

Sterilization. A procedure designed to permanently produce sterility.

Stillbirth. A child born dead.

Tabes Dorsalis. A syphilitic disease of the posterior columns of the spinal cord.

Tampon. A plug of cotton or like material introduced into a natural or artificial cavity to arrest hemorrhage or to absorb secretion.

Tertullian of Carthage. A pioneer Latin theologian, violent opponent of paganism and heresy (circa 203).

Testosterone. The male sex hormone.

Toxemia. A pathological state characterized by the circulation of toxic substances in the blood stream.

Transvestitism. A sexual perversion characterized by obtaining sexual satisfaction from wearing the clothes of the opposite sex.

Turgescent. Becoming turgid, distended, or inflated; swelling; growing big.

Urethral Smear. Preparation for microscopic examination of material, usually pus, obtained from the urethra.

Vaginal Smear. Preparation for microscopic examination of material obtained from the vagina.

Vaginismus. A painful spasm of the vagina.

Vasectomy. Surgical removal of a portion of the vasa deferentia, usually to produce sterility.

Vasotomy. Surgical severance of the vasa deferentia, usually to produce sterility.

Viable. Capable of living.

Voyeurism. "A sexual perversion characterized by obtaining sexual satisfaction from peeping"; a desire to see members of the opposite sex undressing.

Index